P9-CRO-149

HARCOURT MATHEMATICS 12

Advanced Functions and Introductory Calculus

Editors

Ronald Dunkley
Enzo Carli
Ronald Scoins

Authors

Ruth Malinowski
Dean Murray
Jeffrey Shifrin
Loraine Wilson

Performance Assessment Consultant

Richard Long
Hastings and Prince Edward District School Board

Technology Consultant

Atul Kotecha
Limestone District School Board

Contributors

Ray MacDonald
Bluewater District School Board

Gordon Nicholls

Frank Rachich

C. Gary Reid
York Region District School Board

Anita Santin

Dan Schnabel
York Region District School Board

Canadian Cataloguing in Publication Data

Main entry under title:

Harcourt advanced functions and introductory calculus

Includes index.
ISBN 0-7747-1454-9

1. Calculus. 2. Functions. I. Dunkley, Ronald G. II. Carli, E. G. III. Scoins, Ronald G.

QA303.H37 2002 515 C2002-900446-2

Nelson
1120 Birchmount Road
Toronto, Ontario M1K 5G4
1-800-668-0671
www.nelson.com

ISBN-13: 978-0-7747-1454-9
ISBN-10: 0-7747-1454-9

Project Manager: Deborah Davidson
Editor: Sasha Patton
Production Manager: Cheryl Tiongson
Production Editors: Sharon Dzubinsky, Jane A. Clark
Photo Researcher: Karen Becker
Cover and Interior Design: Sonya V. Thursby/Opus House Incorporated
Page Composition, Technical Art, and Illustrations: Brian Lehen • Graphic Design Ltd.

Photo credits: **Cover photo:** Getty Images/Eyewire; **Chapter 1** Chapter Opener: COMSTOCK IMAGES/Mike & Carol Werner; Career Link: CP Picture Archive; **Chapter 2** Chapter Opener: COMSTOCK IMAGES; Career Link: COMSTOCK IMAGES; **Chapter 3** Chapter Opener: Geostock/Getty Images Photodisc; Career Link: Superstock/ J. Silver; **Chapter 4** Chapter Opener: Ivy Images; Career Link: Corbis/Magma; **Chapter 5** Chapter Opener: Getty Images Photodisc; Career Link: CP Picture Archive/Aaron Harris; **Chapter 6** Chapter Opener: COMSTOCK IMAGES; Career Link: COMSTOCK IMAGES/Bruce Hands; **Chapter 7** Chapter Opener: Superstock/Ron Brown; Career Link: Corbis/Magma; **Chapter 8** Chapter Opener: CP Picture Archive/Scott Macdonald; Career Link: Getty Images Photodisc/Ryan McVay; **Chapter 9** Chapter Opener: Superstock; Career Link: CP Picture Archive.

This book is printed in Canada.
3 4 5 ITIB 08 07 06

Acknowledgements

A special thanks to the reviewers listed below for their helpful observations and recommendations. Feedback from reviewers has been extremely valuable in creating a text that fulfills the requirements of both teachers and students in Ontario.

Michael Cafferata
Head of Mathematics
Agincourt Collegiate Institute
Toronto District School Board

Atul Kotecha
Mathematics Teacher
Frontenac Secondary School
Limestone District School Board

David McKay
Mathematics Teacher
Westdale Secondary School
Hamilton-Wentworth District School Board

David Nicholson
Mathematics Teacher
St. Mary's College
Huron-Superior Catholic District
School Board

Marjorie Tellis
Mathematics Teacher
Norwood District High School
Kawartha Pine Ridge District School Board

Gene Yawny
Chair of Mathematics
St. Theresa's High School
Simcoe Muskoka Catholic District
School Board

Ed D'Andrea
Head of Mathematics
Father John Redmond Catholic
Secondary School
Toronto Catholic District School Board

Stephanie Leonard
Mathematics Teacher
Napanee District Secondary School
Limestone District School Board

Henry Mengers
Mathematics Teacher
John Diefenbaker Secondary School
Bluewater District School Board

Linda Obermeyer
Department Head of Mathematics
Notre Dame Secondary School
Halton Catholic District School Board

Joan Tomiuk
Mathematics Teacher
Glebe Collegiate Institute
Ottawa-Carleton District School Board

Elizabeth Fraser
Mathematics Department Head
Glebe Collegiate Institute
Ottawa-Carleton District School Board

Mike McGibbon
Head of Mathematics
Aurora High School
York Region District School Board

Colleen Morgulis
Curriculum Chair of Mathematics
All Saints Catholic Secondary School
Durham Catholic District School Board

Susan Smith
Mathematics Teacher
Bramalea Secondary School
Peel District School Board

Paul Wren
Mathematics and Computer Teacher
Georgetown District High School
Halton District School Board

We gratefully acknowledge the following educators for participating in our mathematics discussion group meetings throughout Ontario.

Jeff Anderson
Head of Mathematics
Forest Heights Collegiate Institute
Waterloo Region District School Board

Lorenzo Ciapanna
Head of Mathematics
St. Jean de Brebeuf Catholic Secondary
School
Hamilton-Wentworth Catholic District
School Board

Ken Billey
Head of Mathematics
Holy Names High School
Windsor-Essex Catholic District
School Board

W.K. Dutton
Mathematics Teacher
Lester B. Pearson High School
Halton District School Board

Chris Brady
Mathematics Teacher
Sherwood Secondary School
Hamilton-Wentworth District School Board

Wendy Fitzsimmons
Mathematics Teacher
Milton District Secondary School
Halton District School Board

continued

Michele Goveia
Head of Mathematics
Father Henry Carr
Toronto Catholic District School Board

Garry Kiziak
Head of Mathematics and Science
Burlington Central High School
Halton District School Board

Darren Luoma
Mathematics Teacher
Bear Creek Secondary School
Simcoe County District School Board

Cheryl McQueen
Head of Mathematics
Central Elgin Collegiate Institute
Thames Valley District School Board

Mark Pankratz
Math Teacher
Hillcrest High School
Ottawa-Carleton District School Board

John Santarelli
Head of Mathematics
Cathedral High School
Hamilton-Wentworth Catholic District
School Board

Scott Taylor
Head of Mathematics
Bell High School
Ottawa-Carleton District School Board

Peter Wei
Head of Mathematics
North Toronto Collegiate Institute
Toronto District School Board

Laurie A. Zahnow
Head of Mathematics
Silverthorn Collegiate Institute
Toronto District School Board

Patrick Grew
Head of Mathematics
Frontenac Secondary School
Limestone District School Board

Mike Lawson
Head of Mathematics
Father Michael Goetz Secondary School
Dufferin-Peel Catholic District
School Board

Glenn McDermott
Head of Mathematics
Woodstock Collegiate Institute
Thames Valley District School Board

Chris Monk
Head of Mathematics
Marc Garneau Collegiate
Toronto District School Board

C. Gary Reid
Head of Mathematics
Sutton District High School
York Region District School Board

Dwight Stead
Head of Mathematics
Cardinal Leger Secondary School
Dufferin-Peel Catholic District
School Board

Joan Tomiuk
Mathematics Teacher
Glebe Collegiate Institute
Ottawa-Carleton District School Board

Shelley Wilton
Head of Mathematics
Westminster Secondary School
Thames Valley District School Board

John Yakopich
Head of Mathematics
Sandwich Secondary School
Greater Essex County District
School Board

John C. Holden
Math Teacher
Ridgemont High School
Ottawa-Carleton District School Board

Frank LoForte
Head of Mathematics
Riverdale Collegiate Institute
Toronto District School Board

Bob McRoberts
Head of Mathematics
Dr. G.W. Williams Secondary School
York Region District School Board

Peter O'Hara
Mathematics Teacher
Glendale High School
Thames Valley District School Board

David Rushby
Head of Mathematics
Martingrove Collegiate Institute
Toronto District School Board

Jenny Stillman
Head of Mathematics
Central Secondary School
Thames Valley District School Board

Jane Uloth
Mathematics Teacher
Lester B. Pearson High School
Halton District School Board

Beryl Wong
Mathematics Teacher
Holy Name of Mary Secondary School
Dufferin-Peel Catholic District
School Board

Contents

CHAPTER 4
Derivatives 121

CHAPTER 5
Applications of Derivatives 171

CHAPTER 6
The Exponential Function 225

CHAPTER 7
The Logarithmic Function and Logarithms 257

CHAPTER 8
Derivatives of Exponential and Logarithmic Functions 295

CHAPTER 9
Curve Sketching 335

Using Advanced Functions and Introductory Calculus

A GUIDED TOUR OF YOUR TEXTBOOK

CHAPTER OPENER

You will be introduced to each chapter by reading about some real-life applications of the mathematical concepts that will be presented within the chapter. A colourful image accompanies this introduction.

A list of skills identifies the specific curriculum expectations addressed in the chapter.

References point you to the section in which each expectation is addressed.

Chapter 6

THE EXPONENTIAL FUNCTION

Are you thinking of buying a computer? Moore's Law suggests that the processing power of computers doubles every eighteen months, which means that in a year and a half from today, computers will be twice as powerful as they are now! This is an example of exponential growth. In this chapter, you will study the exponential functions that can be used to describe and make predictions about the growth of biological populations, including human populations and populations of cancerous cells, the growth of financial investments, the growth of the Internet, and the decaying of radioactive substances. Another application of exponential functions occurs in psychology, where it has been noted that, in certain circumstances, there is an exponential relationship between the size of a stimulus and a nerve's response to the stimulus. The common feature in all these situations and many others is that the amount of growth or decline at any point in time is directly proportional to the size of the thing that is growing or declining.

CHAPTER EXPECTATIONS In this chapter, you will

- identify key properties of exponential functions, **Section 6.1, 6.2**
- determine intercepts and positions of the asymptotes to a graph, **Section 6.2, 6.3**
- describe graphical implications of changes in parameters, **Section 6.3**
- describe the significance of exponential growth or decay, **Section 6.4, 6.5**
- pose and solve problems related to models of exponential functions, **Section 6.4, 6.5, Career Link**
- predict future behaviour by extrapolating from a mathematical model, **Section 6.5**

REVIEW OF PREREQUISITE SKILLS

Narrative and exercises allow you to review the knowledge and skills you need in order to proceed successfully to the new concepts introduced in the chapter.

Review of Prerequisite Skills

Before beginning your study of Polynomial Functions, you may wish to review the following factoring methods that you learned in previous courses.

Common Factor

- $4x^2 - 8x = 4x(x - 2)$

Grouping

- By grouping terms together it is often possible to factor the grouped terms.
  Factor fully $ax + cx + ay + cy = (ax + cx) + (ay + cy)$
  $= x(a + c) + y(a + c)$
  $= (a + c)(x + y)$

Trinomial Factoring

- Factor fully $3x^2 - 7x + 4$.

Solution 1 (by decomposition)

$3x^2 - 7x + 4 = 3x^2 - 3x - 4x + 4$
$= 3x(x - 1) - 4(x - 1)$
$= (x - 1)(3x - 4)$

Solution 2 (by inspection)

$3x^2 - 7x + 4 = (x - 1)(3x - 4)$

Factor $12x^2 - x - 20$.

Solution

Create a chart using factors of 12 and –20.

12	6	4	20	−20	10	−10	5	−5	1	−1	2	−2	4	−4
1	2	3	−1	1	−2	2	−4	4	−20	20	−10	10	−5	5

Notice that what looks like a lot of work can be greatly simplified when numbers in the upper right that have common factors with 12, 6, and 4 are crossed out.

The reduced chart is

12	6	4	5	−5	1	−1
1	2	3	−4	4	−20	20

From the numbers that remain, we see that $4 \times (-4) = -16$, an
gives $-16 + 15 = -1$. Therefore, $12x^2 - x - 20 = (4x + 5)(3x$

Difference of Squares

- Because $(a + b)(a - b) = a^2 - b^2$, it is always possible to fac
  between two perfect squares.
  $16x^2 - 81 = (4x + 9)(4x - 9)$

Special Cases

- Sometimes by grouping terms, the difference between squares can be created.
  $a^2 - p^2 + 1 + 2a = (a^2 + 2a + 1) - p^2$
  $= (a + 1)^2 - p^2$
  $= [(a + 1) + p][(a + 1) - p]$
  $= (a + 1 + p)(a + 1 - p)$

Exercise

1. Factor fully.
   a. $p^2 + 2pr + r^2$ b. $16n^2 + 8n + 1$ c. $9u^2 + 30u + 25$
   d. $v^2 + 4v + 3$ e. $2w^2 + 3w + 1$ f. $3k^2 + 7k + 2$
   g. $7y^2 + 15y + 2$ h. $5x^2 - 16x + 3$ i. $3v^2 - 11v - 10$
2. Factor fully.
   a. $25x^2 - y^2$ b. $m^2 - p^2$ c. $1 - 16r^2$
   d. $49m^2 - 64$ e. $p^2r^2 - 100x^2$ f. $3 - 48y^2$
   g. $(x + n)^2 - 9$ h. $49u^2 - (x - y)^2$ i. $x^4 - 16$
3. Factor fully.
   a. $kx + px - ky - py$ b. $fx - gy + gx - fy$ c. $h^3 + h^2 + h + 1$
   d. $x - d + (x - d)^2$ e. $4y^2 + 4yz + z^2 - 1$ f. $x^2 - y^2 + z^2 - 2xz$

LESSONS

Lessons and investigations provide you with opportunities to explore concepts independently or working with others.

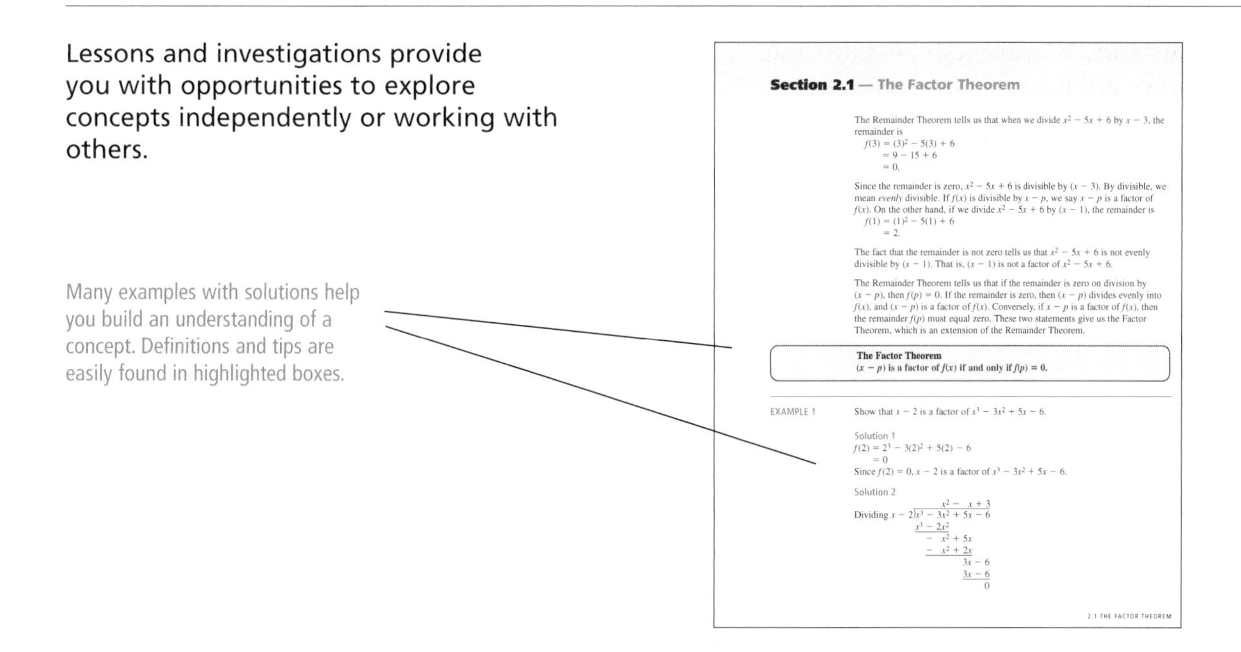

Section 2.1 — The Factor Theorem

The Remainder Theorem tells us that when we divide $x^2 - 5x + 6$ by $x - 3$, the remainder is

$$\begin{aligned} f(3) &= (3)^2 - 5(3) + 6 \\ &= 9 - 15 + 6 \\ &= 0. \end{aligned}$$

Since the remainder is zero, $x^2 - 5x + 6$ is divisible by $(x - 3)$. By divisible, we mean *evenly* divisible. If $f(x)$ is divisible by $x - p$, we say $x - p$ is a factor of $f(x)$. On the other hand, if we divide $x^2 - 5x + 6$ by $(x - 1)$, the remainder is

$$\begin{aligned} f(1) &= (1)^2 - 5(1) + 6 \\ &= 2. \end{aligned}$$

The fact that the remainder is not zero tells us that $x^2 - 5x + 6$ is not evenly divisible by $(x - 1)$. That is, $(x - 1)$ is not a factor of $x^2 - 5x + 6$.

The Remainder Theorem tells us that if the remainder is zero on division by $(x - p)$, then $f(p) = 0$. If the remainder is zero, then $(x - p)$ divides evenly into $f(x)$, and $(x - p)$ is a factor of $f(x)$. Conversely, if $x - p$ is a factor of $f(x)$, then the remainder $f(p)$ must equal zero. These two statements give us the Factor Theorem, which is an extension of the Remainder Theorem.

The Factor Theorem
$(x - p)$ is a factor of $f(x)$ if and only if $f(p) = 0$.

EXAMPLE 1 Show that $x - 2$ is a factor of $x^3 - 3x^2 + 5x - 6$.

Solution 1

$$\begin{aligned} f(2) &= 2^3 - 3(2)^2 + 5(2) - 6 \\ &= 0 \end{aligned}$$

Since $f(2) = 0$, $x - 2$ is a factor of $x^3 - 3x^2 + 5x - 6$.

Solution 2

Dividing $x - 2\overline{)x^3 - 3x^2 + 5x - 6}$ with quotient $x^2 - x + 3$:

$$\begin{array}{r} x^3 - 2x^2 \\ \hline - x^2 + 5x \\ - x^2 + 2x \\ \hline 3x - 6 \\ 3x - 6 \\ \hline 0 \end{array}$$

2.1 THE FACTOR THEOREM

Many examples with solutions help you build an understanding of a concept. Definitions and tips are easily found in highlighted boxes.

EXERCISES

Exercises follow each lesson, and are organized by level of difficulty. Questions allow you to master essential mathematical skills, communicate about mathematics, and attempt more challenging and thought-provoking problems.

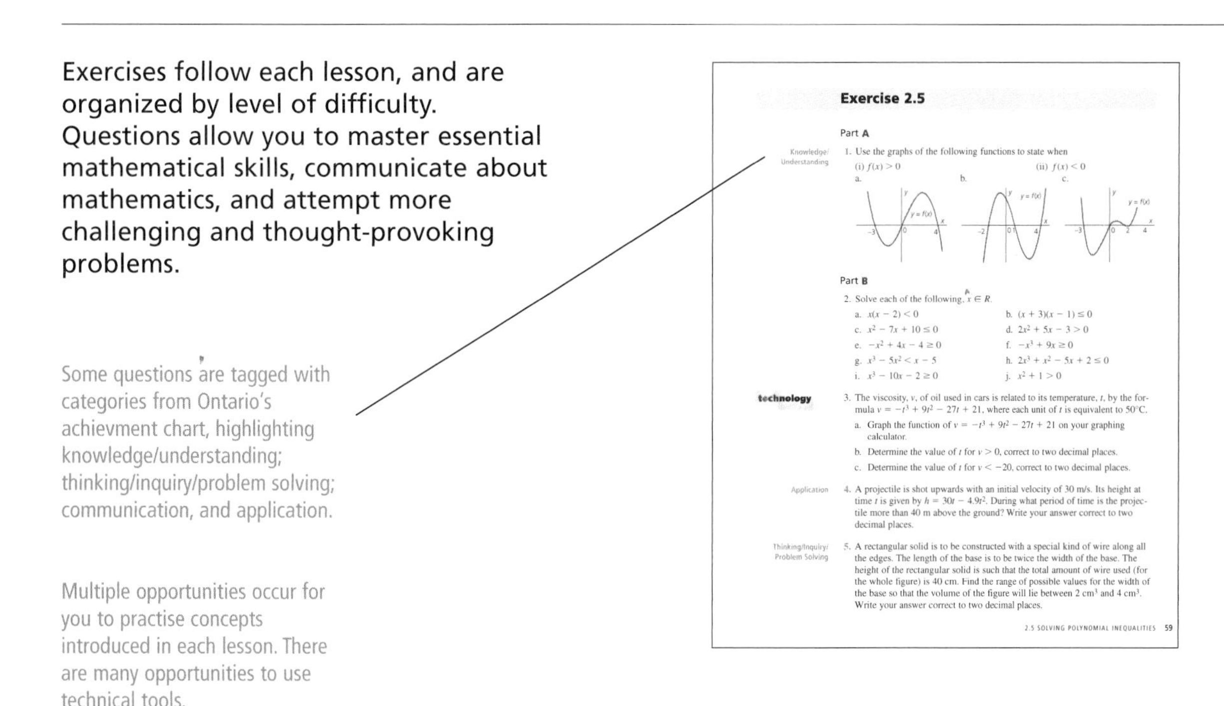

Exercise 2.5

Part **A**

Knowledge/Understanding

1. Use the graphs of the following functions to state when
   (i) $f(x) > 0$ (ii) $f(x) < 0$
   a. b. c.

Part **B**

2. Solve each of the following, $x \in R$.
   a. $x(x - 2) < 0$ b. $(x + 3)(x - 1) \le 0$
   c. $x^2 - 7x + 10 \le 0$ d. $2x^2 + 5x - 3 > 0$
   e. $-x^2 + 4x - 4 \ge 0$ f. $-x^3 + 9x \ge 0$
   g. $x^3 - 5x^2 < x - 5$ h. $2x^3 + x^2 - 5x + 2 \le 0$
   i. $x^3 - 10x - 2 \ge 0$ j. $x^2 + 1 > 0$

technology

3. The viscosity, v, of oil used in cars is related to its temperature, t, by the formula $v = -t^3 + 9t^2 - 27t + 21$, where each unit of t is equivalent to 50°C.
   a. Graph the function of $v = -t^3 + 9t^2 - 27t + 21$ on your graphing calculator.
   b. Determine the value of t for $v > 0$, correct to two decimal places.
   c. Determine the value of t for $v < -20$, correct to two decimal places.

Application

4. A projectile is shot upwards with an initial velocity of 30 m/s. Its height at time t is given by $h = 30t - 4.9t^2$. During what period of time is the projectile more than 40 m above the ground? Write your answer correct to two decimal places.

Thinking/Inquiry/Problem Solving

5. A rectangular solid is to be constructed with a special kind of wire along all the edges. The length of the base is to be twice the width of the base. The height of the rectangular solid is such that the total amount of wire used (for the whole figure) is 40 cm. Find the range of possible values for the width of the base so that the volume of the figure will lie between 2 cm³ and 4 cm³. Write your answer correct to two decimal places.

2.5 SOLVING POLYNOMIAL INEQUALITIES 59

Some questions are tagged with categories from Ontario's achievment chart, highlighting knowledge/understanding; thinking/inquiry/problem solving; communication, and application.

Multiple opportunities occur for you to practise concepts introduced in each lesson. There are many opportunities to use technical tools.

CAREER LINK

The Career Link feature at the beginning of each chapter presents a real-world scenario and allows students the opportunity to apply their learning to real issues.

Discussion questions require students to explain how mathematical principles will be applied. You are encouraged to think about and use prior knowledge in math, and reflect on your own life experiences to guide you through these investigations.

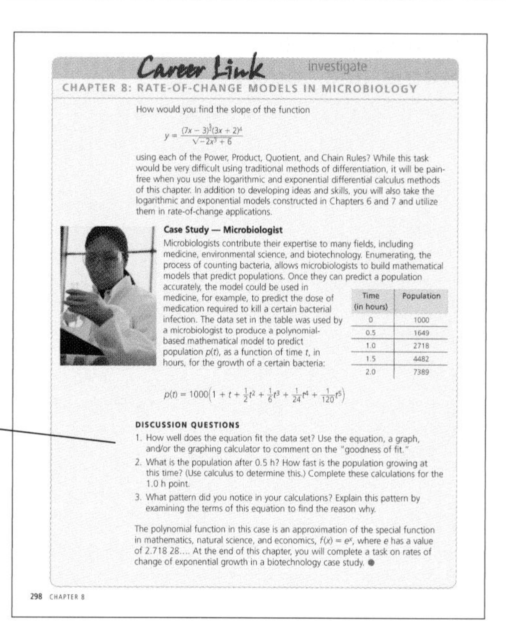

Career Link investigate

CHAPTER 8: RATE-OF-CHANGE MODELS IN MICROBIOLOGY

How would you find the slope of the function

$$y = \frac{(7x-3)^{\frac{2}{3}}(3x+2)^4}{\sqrt{-2x^3+6}}$$

using each of the Power, Product, Quotient, and Chain Rules? While this task would be very difficult using traditional methods of differentiation, it will be pain-free when you use the logarithmic and exponential differential calculus methods of this chapter. In addition to developing ideas and skills, you will also take the logarithmic and exponential models constructed in Chapters 6 and 7 and utilize them in rate-of-change applications.

Case Study — Microbiologist

Microbiologists contribute their expertise to many fields, including medicine, environmental science, and biotechnology. Enumerating, the process of counting bacteria, allows microbiologists to build mathematical models that predict populations. Once they can predict a population accurately, the model could be used in medicine, for example, to predict the dose of medication required to kill a certain bacterial infection. The data set in the table was used by a microbiologist to produce a polynomial-based mathematical model to predict population $p(t)$, as a function of time t, in hours, for the growth of a certain bacteria:

Time (in hours)	Population
0	1000
0.5	1649
1.0	2718
1.5	4482
2.0	7389

$$p(t) = 1000\left(1 + t + \frac{1}{2}t^2 + \frac{1}{6}t^3 + \frac{1}{24}t^4 + \frac{1}{120}t^5\right)$$

DISCUSSION QUESTIONS

1. How well does the equation fit the data set? Use the equation, a graph, and/or the graphing calculator to comment on the "goodness of fit."
2. What is the population after 0.5 h? How fast is the population growing at this time? (Use calculus to determine this.) Complete these calculations for the 1.0 h point.
3. What pattern did you notice in your calculations? Explain this pattern by examining the terms of this equation to find the reason why.

The polynomial function in this case is an approximation of the special function in mathematics, natural science, and economics, $f(x) = e^x$, where e has a value of 2.718 28.... At the end of this chapter, you will complete a task on rates of change of exponential growth in a biotechnology case study.

298 CHAPTER 8

CAREER LINK WRAP-UP

At the conclusion of the chapter, the Career Link Wrap-Up allows you to combine the skills you have learned through the chapter exercises with the challenges of an expanded version of the real-world scenarios introduced earlier.

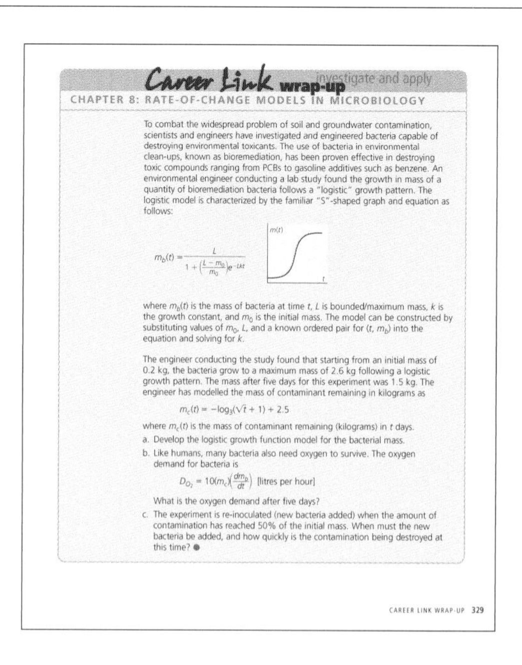

Career Link wrap-up investigate and apply

CHAPTER 8: RATE-OF-CHANGE MODELS IN MICROBIOLOGY

To combat the widespread problem of soil and groundwater contamination, scientists and engineers have investigated and engineered bacteria capable of destroying environmental toxicants. The use of bacteria in environmental clean-ups, known as bioremediation, has been proven effective in destroying toxic compounds ranging from PCBs to gasoline additives such as benzene. An environmental engineer conducting a lab study found the growth in mass of a quantity of bioremediation bacteria follows a "logistic" growth pattern. The logistic model is characterized by the familiar "S"-shaped graph and equation as follows:

$$m_b(t) = \frac{L}{1 + \left(\frac{L - m_0}{m_0}\right)e^{-Lkt}}$$

where $m_b(t)$ is the mass of bacteria at time t, L is bounded/maximum mass, k is the growth constant, and m_0 is the initial mass. The model can be constructed by substituting values of m_0, L, and a known ordered pair for (t, m_b) into the equation and solving for k.

The engineer conducting the study found that starting from an initial mass of 0.2 kg, the bacteria grow to a maximum mass of 2.6 kg following a logistic growth pattern. The mass after five days for this experiment was 1.5 kg. The engineer has modelled the mass of contaminant remaining in kilograms as

$$m_c(t) = -\log_3(\sqrt{t} + 1) + 2.5$$

where $m_c(t)$ is the mass of contaminant remaining (kilograms) in t days.

a. Develop the logistic growth function model for the bacterial mass.

b. Like humans, many bacteria also need oxygen to survive. The oxygen demand for bacteria is

$$D_{O_2} = 10(m_c)\left(\frac{dm_b}{dt}\right) \text{ [litres per hour]}$$

What is the oxygen demand after five days?

c. The experiment is re-inoculated (new bacteria added) when the amount of contamination has reached 50% of the initial mass. When must the new bacteria be added, and how quickly is the contamination being destroyed at this time?

CAREER LINK WRAP-UP 329

TECHNOLOGY

Technology features are integrated throughout in a flexible and optional manner.

Technology icons highlight opportunities for you to choose to use calculators, graphing calculators, and computers.

Some icons have page references that direct you to the technology appendix.

Section 5.4 — Maximum and Minimum on an Interval

INVESTIGATION

The purpose of this investigation is to determine how the derivative can be used in determining the maximum (largest) value or the minimum (smallest) value of a function on a given interval.

1. For each of the following functions, determine, by completing the square, the value of x that produces a maximum or minimum function value on the given interval.
   a. $f(x) = -x^2 + 6x - 3$, interval $0 \leq x \leq 5$
   b. $f(x) = -x^2 - 2x + 11$, interval $-3 \leq x \leq 4$
   c. $f(x) = 4x^2 - 12x + 7$, interval $-1 \leq x \leq 4$
2. For each function, determine the value of c such that $f'(c) = 0$.
3. Compare the values obtained in Questions 1 and 2 for each function.

technology
APPENDIX P. 444

4. Using your calculator, graph each of the following functions and determine all values of x that produce a maximum or minimum function value on the given interval.
   a. $f(x) = x^3 - 3x^2 - 8x + 10$, interval $-2 \leq x \leq 4$
   b. $f(x) = x^3 - 12x + 5$, interval $-3 \leq x \leq 3$
   c. $f(x) = 3x^3 - 15x^2 + 9x + 23$, interval $0 \leq x \leq 4$
   d. $f(x) = -2x^3 + 12x + 7$, interval $-2 \leq x \leq 2$
   e. $f(x) = -x^3 - 2x^2 + 15x + 23$, interval $-4 \leq x \leq 3$
5. For each function in Question 4, determine all values of c such that $f'(c) = 0$.
6. Compare the values obtained in Questions 4 and 5 for each function.

technology

7. From your conclusions in Questions 3 and 6, state a method for using the derivative of a function to determine values of the variable that determine maximum or minimum values of the function.
8. Repeat Question 4 for the following functions, using the indicated intervals.
   a. $f(x) = -x^2 + 6x - 3$, interval $4 \leq x \leq 8$
   b. $f(x) = 4x^2 - 12x + 7$, interval $2 \leq x \leq 6$
   c. $f(x) = x^3 - 3x^2 - 9x + 10$, interval $-2 \leq x \leq 6$
   d. $f(x) = x^3 - 12x + 5$, interval $0 \leq x \leq 5$.
   e. $f(x) = x^3 - 5x^2 + 3x + 7$, interval $-2 \leq x \leq 5$

196 CHAPTER 5

KEY CONCEPTS REVIEW

At the end of each chapter, the principles taught are clearly restated in summary form. You can refer to this summary when you are studying or doing homework.

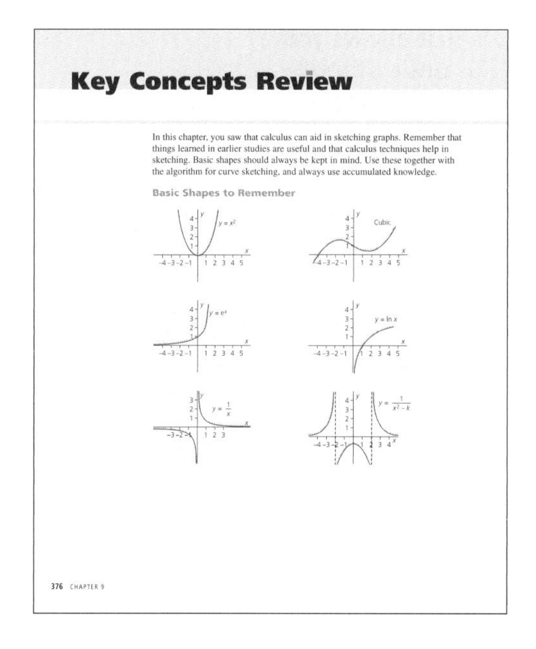

Key Concepts Review

In this chapter, you saw that calculus can aid in sketching graphs. Remember that things learned in earlier studies are useful and that calculus techniques help in sketching. Basic shapes should always be kept in mind. Use these together with the algorithm for curve sketching, and always use accumulated knowledge.

Basic Shapes to Remember

376 CHAPTER 9

REVIEW EXERCISE

The chapter Review Exercise addresses and integrates the principles taught throughout the chapter, allowing you to practise and reinforce your understanding of the concepts and skills you have learned.

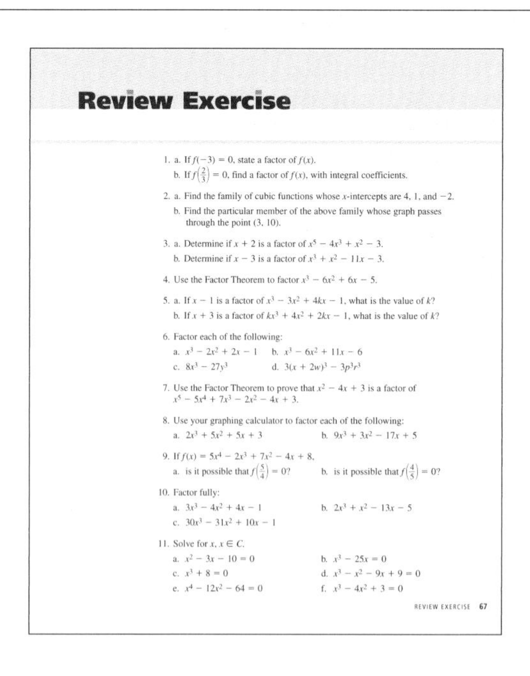

Review Exercise

1. a. If $f(-3) = 0$, state a factor of $f(x)$.
   b. If $f\left(\frac{2}{3}\right) = 0$, find a factor of $f(x)$, with integral coefficients.
2. a. Find the family of cubic functions whose x-intercepts are 4, 1, and -2.
   b. Find the particular member of the above family whose graph passes through the point (3, 10).
3. a. Determine if $x + 2$ is a factor of $x^5 - 4x^3 + x^2 - 3$.
   b. Determine if $x - 3$ is a factor of $x^3 + x^2 - 11x - 3$.
4. Use the Factor Theorem to factor $x^3 - 6x^2 + 6x - 5$.
5. a. If $x - 1$ is a factor of $x^3 - 3x^2 + 4kx - 1$, what is the value of k?
   b. If $x + 3$ is a factor of $kx^3 + 4x^2 + 2kx - 1$, what is the value of k?
6. Factor each of the following:
   a. $x^3 - 2x^2 + 2x - 1$ b. $x^3 - 6x^2 + 11x - 6$
   c. $8x^3 - 27y^3$ d. $3(x + 2w)^3 - 3p^3r^3$
7. Use the Factor Theorem to prove that $x^2 - 4x + 3$ is a factor of $x^5 - 5x^4 + 7x^3 - 2x^2 - 4x + 3$.
8. Use your graphing calculator to factor each of the following:
   a. $2x^3 + 5x^2 + 5x + 3$ b. $9x^3 + 3x^2 - 17x + 5$
9. If $f(x) = 5x^4 - 2x^3 + 7x^2 - 4x + 8$,
   a. is it possible that $f\left(\frac{5}{4}\right) = 0$? b. is it possible that $f\left(\frac{4}{5}\right) = 0$?
10. Factor fully:
    a. $3x^3 - 4x^2 + 4x - 1$ b. $2x^3 + x^2 - 13x - 5$
    c. $30x^3 - 31x^2 + 10x - 1$
11. Solve for x, $x \in C$.
    a. $x^2 - 3x - 10 = 0$ b. $x^3 - 25x = 0$
    c. $x^3 + 8 = 0$ d. $x^3 - x^2 - 9x + 9 = 0$
    e. $x^4 - 12x^2 - 64 = 0$ f. $x^3 - 4x^2 + 3 = 0$

REVIEW EXERCISE 67

CHAPTER TEST

The Chapter Test allows you to measure your understanding and allows you and your teachers to relate results to the curriculum achievement charts.

The achievement chart indicates how questions correlate to the achievement categories in Ontario's Mathematics Curriculum.

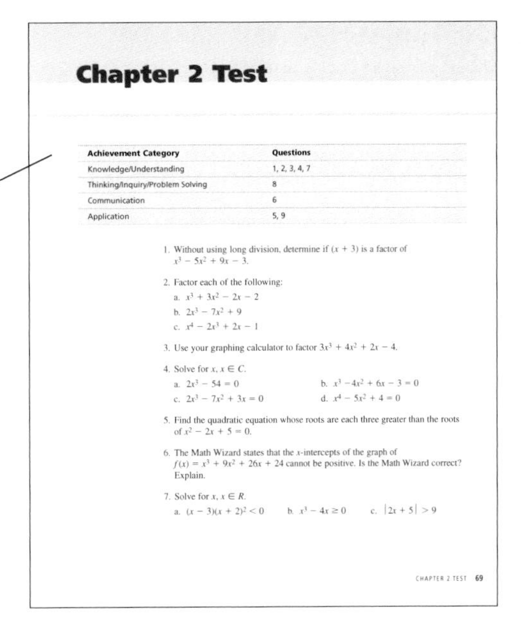

Chapter 2 Test

Achievement Category	Questions
Knowledge/Understanding	1, 2, 3, 4, 7
Thinking/Inquiry/Problem Solving	8
Communication	6
Application	5, 9

1. Without using long division, determine if $(x + 3)$ is a factor of $x^3 - 5x^2 + 9x - 3$.
2. Factor each of the following:
   a. $x^3 + 3x^2 - 2x - 2$
   b. $2x^3 - 7x^2 + 9$
   c. $x^4 - 2x^3 + 2x - 1$
3. Use your graphing calculator to factor $3x^3 + 4x^2 + 2x - 4$.
4. Solve for $x, x \in C$.
   a. $2x^3 - 54 = 0$
   b. $x^3 - 4x^2 + 6x - 3 = 0$
   c. $2x^3 - 7x^2 + 3x = 0$
   d. $x^4 - 5x^2 + 4 = 0$
5. Find the quadratic equation whose roots are each three greater than the roots of $x^2 - 2x + 5 = 0$.
6. The Math Wizard states that the x-intercepts of the graph of $f(x) = x^3 + 9x^2 + 26x + 24$ cannot be positive. Is the Math Wizard correct? Explain.
7. Solve for $x, x \in R$.
   a. $(x - 3)(x + 2)^2 < 0$
   b. $x^3 - 4x \geq 0$
   c. $|2x + 5| > 9$

CHAPTER 2 TEST 69

CUMULATIVE REVIEW

This feature appears at the end of chapters 4, 7, and 9.

Concepts covered in the preceding chapters are further practised through additional exercises and word problems.

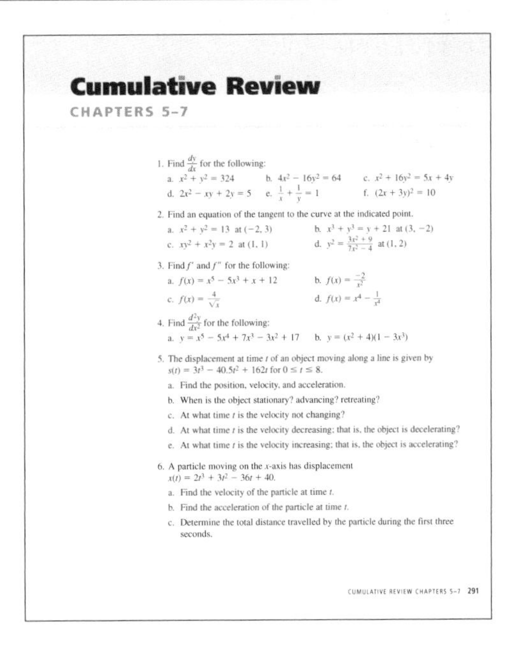

Cumulative Review

CHAPTERS 5–7

1. Find $\frac{dy}{dx}$ for the following:
   a. $x^2 + y^2 = 324$
   b. $4x^2 - 16y^2 = 64$
   c. $x^2 + 16y^2 = 5x + 4y$
   d. $2x^2 - xy + 2y = 5$
   e. $\frac{1}{x} + \frac{1}{y} = 1$
   f. $(2x + 3y)^2 = 10$
2. Find an equation of the tangent to the curve at the indicated point.
   a. $x^2 + y^2 = 13$ at $(-2, 3)$
   b. $x^3 + y^3 = y + 21$ at $(3, -2)$
   c. $xy^2 + x^2y = 2$ at $(1, 1)$
   d. $y^2 = \frac{3x^2 + 9}{7x^2 - 4}$ at $(1, 2)$
3. Find f' and f'' for the following:
   a. $f(x) = x^5 - 5x^3 + x + 12$
   b. $f(x) = \frac{-2}{x^2}$
   c. $f(x) = \frac{4}{\sqrt{x}}$
   d. $f(x) = x^4 - \frac{1}{x^4}$
4. Find $\frac{d^2y}{dx^2}$ for the following:
   a. $y = x^5 - 5x^4 + 7x^3 - 3x^2 + 17$
   b. $y = (x^2 + 4)(1 - 3x^3)$
5. The displacement at time t of an object moving along a line is given by $s(t) = 3t^3 - 40.5t^2 + 162t$ for $0 \leq t \leq 8$.
   a. Find the position, velocity, and acceleration.
   b. When is the object stationary? advancing? retreating?
   c. At what time t is the velocity not changing?
   d. At what time t is the velocity decreasing; that is, the object is decelerating?
   e. At what time t is the velocity increasing; that is, the object is accelerating?
6. A particle moving on the x-axis has displacement $x(t) = 2t^3 + 3t^2 - 36t + 40$.
   a. Find the velocity of the particle at time t.
   b. Find the acceleration of the particle at time t.
   c. Determine the total distance travelled by the particle during the first three seconds.

CUMULATIVE REVIEW CHAPTERS 5–7 291

APPENDICES

The Technical Assistance Appendix teaches techniques for using the graphing calculator.

The Derivatives Appendix takes concepts covered in the text and extends and applies them to the area of trigonometric functions.

The Antiderivatives Appendix gives you the opportunity to "work backward," applying the concepts of derivatives in order to determine the original functions.

The Performance Assessment and Career Link Appendix expands on the real-world applications of the Career Links with a series of "Letterhead Tasks" that present opportunities to apply calculus methodologies to solving problems for government and corporate clients.

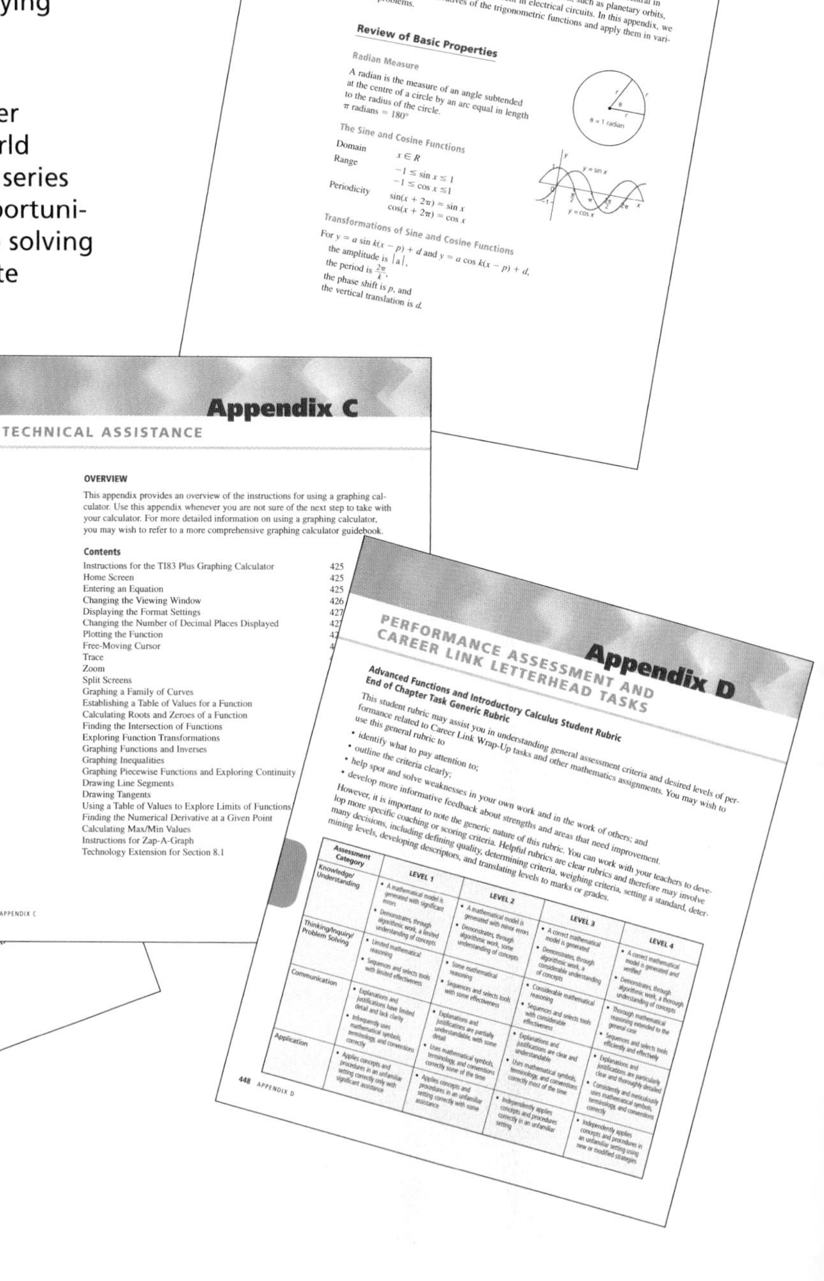

Appendix A

DERIVATIVES OF TRIGONOMETRIC FUNCTIONS

So far in our study of calculus, we have worked with polynomial, rational, power, exponential, and logarithmic functions. Trigonometric functions are central in modelling oscillatory phenomena and periodic motion, such as planetary orbits, the rise and fall of tides, and the current in electrical circuits. In this appendix, we will develop the derivatives of the trigonometric functions and apply them in various problems.

Review of Basic Properties

Radian Measure

A radian is the measure of an angle subtended at the centre of a circle by an arc equal in length to the radius of the circle.
π radians = 180°

The Sine and Cosine Functions

Domain $x \in R$
Range $-1 \le \sin x \le 1$
$-1 \le \cos x \le 1$
Periodicity $\sin(x + 2\pi) = \sin x$
$\cos(x + 2\pi) = \cos x$

Transformations of Sine and Cosine Functions

For $y = a \sin k(x - p) + d$ and $y = a \cos k(x - p) + d$,
the amplitude is $|a|$,
the period is $\frac{2\pi}{k}$,
the phase shift is p, and
the vertical translation is d.

Appendix C

TECHNICAL ASSISTANCE

OVERVIEW

This appendix provides an overview of the instructions for using a graphing calculator. Use this appendix whenever you are not sure of the next step to take with your calculator. For more detailed information on using a graphing calculator, you may wish to refer to a more comprehensive graphing calculator guidebook.

Contents

424 APPENDIX C

Appendix B

ANTIDERIVATIVES

Throughout the text, we have studied the derivatives of functions—how they are defined, their geometric interpretation, how they are calculated, and how they are applied—to help solve different types of problems. In this appendix, we are going to reverse the process. If we were to give an alternative title for this appendix, it could be called "Working Backwards."

SECTION B1 – FINDING ANTIDERIVATIVES

Find a function whose derivative is $f(x) = 3x^2 - 4x$.

Example 1

Solution
If we let F be the name of the function that we are trying to find, then $F'(x) = f(x)$ or $F'(x) = 3x^2 - 4x$. Using the rules that we learned and thinking backwards, we know that the derivative of x^3 is $3x^2$, and the derivative of $2x^2$ is $2(2x) = 4x$. So if $F'(x) = 3x^2 - 4x$, then $F(x) = x^3 \ldots$

Note: We can check our answer by differentiating F to get $F'\ldots$

For a function f, if we can find a function F such that $F'\ldots$ we say that F is an antiderivative of f.

From the example above, $F(x) = x^3 - 2x^2$ is an antideriv… Is $F(x) = x^3 - 2x^2$ the only antiderivative of $f(x) = 3x^2 \ldots$ struct another antiderivative of $f(x) = 3x^2 - 4x$, say $G \ldots$ $G(x) = x^3 - 2x^2 + 1$. We know that the derivative of … $G'(x) = 3x^2 - 4x = f(x)$, and G is another antideriv… there are an infinite number of antiderivatives of $f(\ldots$ found simply by adding (or subtracting) different c…

If F is an antiderivative of f (i.e., $F'(x) = f(x)$), … the general antiderivative of f, where C is any constant.

406 APPENDIX B

Appendix D

PERFORMANCE ASSESSMENT AND CAREER LINK LETTERHEAD TASKS

Advanced Functions and Introductory Calculus Student Rubric
End of Chapter Task Generic Rubric

This student rubric may assist you in understanding general assessment criteria and desired levels of performance related to Career Link Wrap-Up tasks and other mathematics assignments. You may wish to use this general rubric to
- identify what to pay attention to;
- outline the criteria clearly;
- help spot and solve weaknesses in your own work and in the work of others; and
- develop more informative feedback about strengths and areas that need improvement.

However, it is important to note the generic nature of this rubric. You can work with your teachers to develop more specific coaching or scoring criteria. Helpful rubrics are clear rubrics and therefore may involve many decisions, including defining quality, determining criteria, weighing criteria, setting a standard, determining levels, developing descriptors, and translating levels to marks or grades.

Assessment Category	LEVEL 1	LEVEL 2	LEVEL 3	LEVEL 4
Knowledge/ Understanding	• A mathematical model is generated with significant errors • Demonstrates, through algorithmic work, a limited understanding of concepts	• A mathematical model is generated with minor errors • Demonstrates, through algorithmic work, some understanding of concepts	• A correct mathematical model is generated • Demonstrates, through algorithmic work, a considerable understanding of concepts	• A correct mathematical model is generated and verified • Demonstrates, through algorithmic work, a thorough understanding of concepts
Thinking/Inquiry/ Problem Solving	• Limited mathematical reasoning • Sequences and selects tools with limited effectiveness	• Some mathematical reasoning • Sequences and selects tools with some effectiveness	• Considerable mathematical reasoning • Sequences and selects tools with considerable effectiveness	• Thorough mathematical reasoning extended to the general case • Sequences and selects tools efficiently and effectively
Communication	• Explanations and justifications have limited detail and lack clarity • Infrequently uses mathematical symbols, terminology, and conventions correctly	• Explanations and justifications are partially understandable, with some detail • Uses mathematical symbols, terminology, and conventions correctly some of the time	• Explanations and justifications are clear and understandable • Uses mathematical symbols, terminology, and conventions correctly most of the time	• Explanations and justifications are particularly clear and thoroughly detailed • Consistently and meticulously uses mathematical symbols, terminology, and conventions correctly
Application	• Applies concepts and procedures in an unfamiliar setting correctly only with significant assistance	• Applies concepts and procedures in an unfamiliar setting correctly with some assistance	• Independently applies concepts and procedures correctly in an unfamiliar setting	• Independently applies concepts and procedures in an unfamiliar setting using new or modified strategies

448 APPENDIX D

Chapter 1

POLYNOMIAL FUNCTIONS

Have you ever wondered how computer graphics software is able to so quickly draw the smooth, life-like faces that we see in video games and animated movies? Or how in architectural projects builders compensate for the fact that a horizontal beam, fixed in position at both ends, will bend under its own weight? Can you imagine how computers mould automotive body panels? Believe it or not, all three tasks are possible thanks to polynomials! Polynomials are composed by applying addition, subtraction, and multiplication to numbers and variables. The information needed to perform certain tasks like the ones listed above is reduced to the polynomial segments between key points. Much like words in language, polynomials are the vocabulary of algebra, and, as such, they are used in a wide variety of applications by designers, engineers, and others. Calculus, the study of motion and rates of change, requires a clear understanding of polynomials, so we'll begin our study there.

CHAPTER EXPECTATIONS In this chapter, you will

- determine properties of the graphs of polynomial functions, **Section 1.1**
- sketch the graph of a polynomial function, **Section 1.1**
- describe the nature of change in polynomial functions, **Section 1.2**
- determine an equation to represent a given graph of a polynomial function, **Career Link**
- understand the Remainder and Factor Theorems, **Section 1.3, 1.4**

Review of Prerequisite Skills

Before beginning your study of Polynomial Functions, you may wish to review the following factoring methods that you learned in previous courses.

Common Factor

- $4x^2 - 8x = 4x(x - 2)$

Grouping

- By grouping terms together it is often possible to factor the grouped terms.
  Factor fully $\quad ax + cx + ay + cy = (ax + cx) + (ay + cy)$
  $$= x(a + c) + y(a + c)$$
  $$= (a + c)(x + y)$$

Trinomial Factoring

- Factor fully $3x^2 - 7x + 4$.

Solution 1 (by decomposition)

$$\begin{aligned} 3x^2 - 7x + 4 &= 3x^2 - 3x - 4x + 4 \\ &= 3x(x - 1) - 4(x - 1) \\ &= (x - 1)(3x - 4) \end{aligned}$$

Solution 2 (by inspection)

$3x^2 - 7x + 4 = (x - 1)(3x - 4)$

Factor $12x^2 - x - 20$.

Solution

Create a chart using factors of 12 and –20.

12	6	4	~~20~~	~~−20~~	~~10~~	~~−10~~	5	−5	1	−1	~~2~~	~~−2~~	~~4~~	~~−4~~
1	2	3	~~−1~~	~~1~~	~~−2~~	~~2~~	−4	4	−20	20	~~−10~~	~~10~~	~~−5~~	~~5~~

Notice that what looks like a lot of work can be greatly simplified when numbers in the upper right that have common factors with 12, 6, and 4 are crossed out.

The reduced chart is

12	6	4	5	−5	1	−1
1	2	3	−4	4	−20	20

From the numbers that remain, we see that $4 \times (-4) = -16$, and $3 \times 5 = 15$ gives $-16 + 15 = -1$. Therefore, $12x^2 - x - 20 = (4x + 5)(3x - 4)$.

Difference of Squares

- Because $(a + b)(a - b) = a^2 - b^2$, it is always possible to factor the difference between two perfect squares.
  $16x^2 - 81 = (4x + 9)(4x - 9)$

Special Cases

- Sometimes by grouping terms, the difference between squares can be created.

$$\begin{aligned} a^2 - p^2 + 1 + 2a &= (a^2 + 2a + 1) - p^2 \\ &= (a + 1)^2 - p^2 \\ &= [(a + 1) + p][(a + 1) - p] \\ &= (a + 1 + p)(a + 1 - p) \end{aligned}$$

Exercise

1. Factor fully.

   a. $p^2 + 2pr + r^2$ b. $16n^2 + 8n + 1$ c. $9u^2 + 30u + 25$
   d. $v^2 + 4v + 3$ e. $2w^2 + 3w + 1$ f. $3k^2 + 7k + 2$
   g. $7y^2 + 15y + 2$ h. $5x^2 - 16x + 3$ i. $3v^2 - 11v - 10$

2. Factor fully.

   a. $25x^2 - y^2$ b. $m^2 - p^2$ c. $1 - 16r^2$
   d. $49m^2 - 64$ e. $p^2r^2 - 100x^2$ f. $3 - 48y^2$
   g. $(x + n)^2 - 9$ h. $49u^2 - (x - y)^2$ i. $x^4 - 16$

3. Factor fully.

   a. $kx + px - ky - py$ b. $fx - gy + gx - fy$ c. $h^3 + h^2 + h + 1$
   d. $x - d + (x - d)^2$ e. $4y^2 + 4yz + z^2 - 1$ f. $x^2 - y^2 + z^2 - 2xz$

4. Factor fully.

a. $4x^2 + 2x - 6$
b. $28s^2 + 8st - 20t^2$
c. $y^2 - (r - n)^2$
d. $8 + 24m - 80m^2$
e. $6x^2 - 13x + 6$
f. $y^3 + y^2 - 5y - 5$
g. $60y^2 - 10y - 120$
h. $10x^2 + 38x + 20$
i. $27x^2 - 48$

5. Factor fully.

a. $36(2x - y)^2 - 25(u - 2y)^2$
b. $g(1 - x) - gx + gx^2$
c. $y^5 - y^4 + y^3 - y^2 + y - 1$
d. $n^4 + 2n^2w^2 + w^4$
e. $9(x + 2y + z)^2 - 16(x - 2y + z)^2$
f. $8u^2(u + 1) + 2u(u + 1) - 3(u + 1)$
g. $p^2 - 2p + 1 - y^2 - 2yz - z^2$
h. $9y^4 + 12y^2 + 4$
i. $abx^2 + (an + bm)x + mn$
j. $x^2 + 2 + \frac{1}{x^2}$

Career Link investigate

CHAPTER 1: MODELLING WATER DEMAND

Imagine if you woke up one morning looking forward to a shower only to have your mom tell you the local water utility ran out of water because they made a mistake in predicting demand. That does not happen, in part, because water utilities develop reliable mathematical models that accurately predict water demand. Of particular use in mathematical modelling are the polynomial functions that you will investigate in this chapter. You are already familiar with two classes of polynomials: the linear ($y = mx + b$) and the quadratic ($y = ax^2 + bx + c$). You can find polynomial mathematical models in a multitude of places, from computers (e.g., Internet encryption), to business (e.g., the mathematics of investment), to science (e.g., population dynamics of wildlife).

Case Study — Municipal Engineer/Technologist

Civil Engineers and Technologists frequently model the relationship between municipal water demand and time of day to ensure that water supply meets demand plus a factor of safety for fire flows. Water demand data for a city with a population of 150 000 is presented in the table below.

Water Demand for Blueborough, Ontario

Time of Day	t (in hours)	Water Demand (in cubic metres per hour)
13:00	1	5103
14:00	2	4968
15:00	3	5643
16:00	4	7128
17:00	5	8775
18:00	6	9288
19:00	7	6723

DISCUSSION QUESTIONS

1. Plot a rough sketch of the data in the table above. What kind of relationship, if any, does the data show? Remember that you have been investigating linear, quadratic, rational, and periodic functions. Does the hour-to-hour trend in the data make sense? Explain.
2. Sketch the water demand over a 24-h period for your community. Use an average daily demand of 600 L per capita and a peak hourly flow of about 2.5 times the average hourly flow. Explain the peaks and valleys.
3. Find out how much water costs in your community and estimate the cost per hour of operating your community's water distribution system at the peak flow rate determined in Question 1.

At the end of this chapter you will develop and utilize a mathematical model for the data presented in this case study. ●

Section 1.1 — Graphs of Polynomial Functions

The graph of a linear function of the form $f(x) = ax + b$ has either one x-intercept or no x-intercepts.

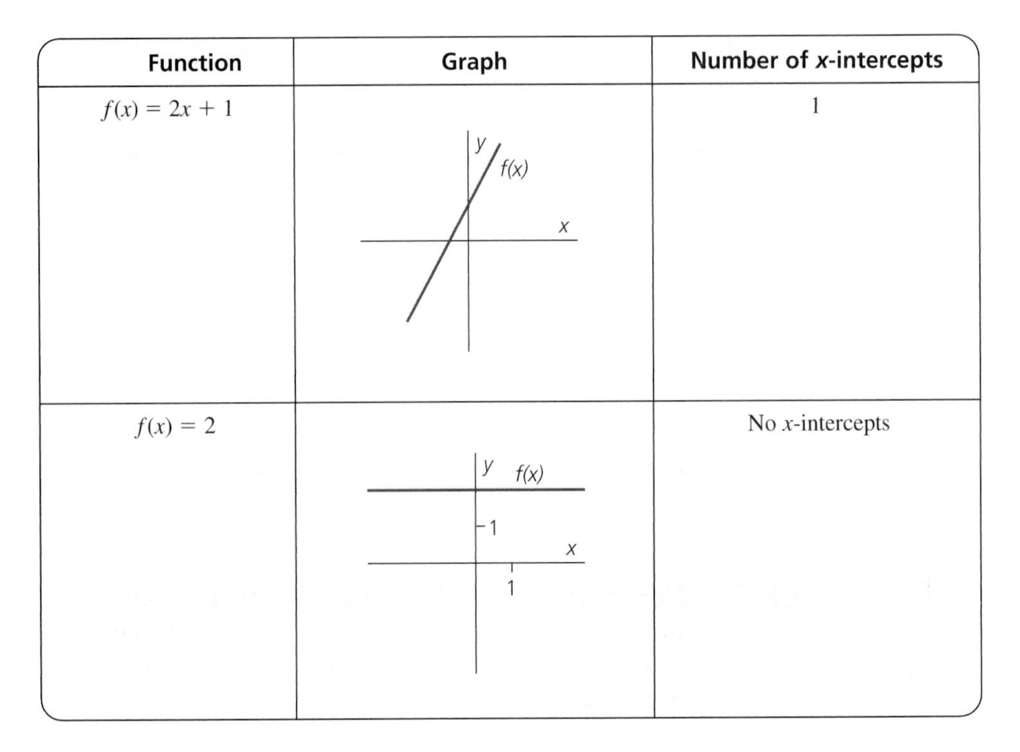

Function	Graph	Number of x-intercepts
$f(x) = 2x + 1$	y, f(x), x	1
$f(x) = 2$	y, f(x), 1, x, 1	No x-intercepts

By graphing a quadratic function of the form $f(x) = ax^2 + bx + c$, $a \neq 0$, we can determine the number of x-intercepts. Each x-intercept indicates a real root of the corresponding quadratic equation.

Function	Graph	Number of x-intercepts
$f(x) = x^2 - 7x + 10$	y, f(x), x	2

chart continued

$f(x) = -x^2 - 6x - 9$	y, x, f(x)	1 When a curve touches the x-axis, there are two equal roots for the corresponding
$f(x) = 2x^2 + 3x + 4$	f(x), y, x	0 There are no real roots.

INVESTIGATION 1: CUBIC FUNCTIONS

technology
APPENDIX P. 427

1. Use a graphing calculator or a computer to graph each of the following cubic functions. Sketch each of the graphs in your notebook so that you can make observations about the shapes of the graphs and list the number of x-intercepts.

   a. $y = x^3$
   b. $y = x^3 + 2x$
   c. $y = x^3 - 2x^2$
   d. $y = 2x^3 - 3$
   e. $y = 2x^3 - 5x^2 - 8x + 12$
   f. $y = x^3 - 3x + 2$
   g. $y = 4x^3 - 16x^2 + 13x - 3$
   h. $y = x^3 - 5x^2 + 2x + 8$
   i. $y = (x - 2)(x + 1)(3x - 1)$

2. From your observations, list the possible numbers of real roots for a cubic equation.

3. a. Explain how you would graph the cubic function $y = (x - 2)(x + 3)(x - 4)$ without using a graphing calculator.

   b. Draw a sketch of the function in part **a.**

4. Sketch two possible general shapes for the graph of a cubic function that has a coefficient of x^3 that is positive.

5. For the functions in Question 1, change the coefficient of x^3 from positive to negative and redraw the graphs. For example, $y = x^3 - 2x^2$ changes to $y = -x^3 - 2x^2$. What observation do you make for the general shape of the graph of a cubic function that has a coefficient of x^3 that is negative?

INVESTIGATION 2: QUARTIC FUNCTIONS

technology

1. Use a graphing calculator or a computer to graph each of the following quartic functions. Sketch each of the graphs in your notebook so that you can make observations about the shapes of the graphs and list the number of x-intercepts.

   a. $y = x^4$
   b. $y = x^4 - 4$
   c. $y = x^4 - 3x^3$
   d. $y = x^4 - 3x^3 - 12x^2$
   e. $y = x^4 - 3x^3 - 6x^2 + 2x - 3$
   f. $y = (x - 1)(x + 2)(x - 3)(2x - 3)$

2. From your observations, list the possible numbers of real roots for a quartic equation.

3. a. Explain how you would graph the quartic function $y = (x + 3)(x - 2)(x + 1)(x + 4)$ without using a graphing calculator.

   b. Draw a sketch of the function in part **a**.

4. Sketch two possible general shapes for the graph of a quartic function that has a coefficient of x^4 that is positive.

5. For the functions in Question 1, change the coefficient of x^4 from positive to negative and redraw the graphs. For example, $y = x^4 - 3x^3$ changes to $y = -x^4 - 3x^3$. What observation do you make for the general shape of the graph of a quartic function that has a coefficient of x^4 that is negative?

INVESTIGATION 3

technology

1. Use your graphing calculator to graph each of the following:

   a. $y = x(x - 3)^2$
   b. $y = (x - 1)(x + 2)(x + 1)^2$
   c. $y = (x + 2)^2(x - 2)^2$

   Based on these graphs, draw a sketch of what you think the graph of $y = (x + 2)(x - 1)^2$ looks like.

2. Use your graphing calculator to graph each of the following:

a. $y = (x - 2)^3$ b. $y = x(x - 3)^3$ c. $y = (x - 1)^2(x + 1)^3$

Based on these graphs, draw a sketch of what you think the graph of $y = (x + 1)(x - 1)^3$ looks like.

Exercise 1.1

Part A

Knowledge/Understanding

technology

1. Check your conclusions about the shape of the graphs of functions by using your graphing calculator to draw each of the following:

a. $y = x^3 - 12x + 16$
b. $y = x^3 - x^2 - 10x + 15$
c. $y = - 2x^3 + 11x + 6$
d. $y = -2x^4 + 3x^3 - 5$
e. $y = (2x + 3)(3x - 1)(x + 2)(x - 3)$
f. $y = (x - 1)(x^2 - 3)(9x^2 - 4)$
g. $y = x^5 - 2x^4 - 4x^3 + 4x^2 - 5x + 6$
h. $y = -x^5 + 4x^3 + x^2 - 3x - 3$

Part B

Application

2. Draw a rough sketch (without using your graphing calculator) of each of the following:

a. $y = (x + 1)(x - 2)$
b. $y = (x + 2)(x - 1)(x + 3)$
c. $y = (x - 2)(x + 3)(x + 1)(x - 4)$
d. $y = (x - 1)(x + 2)^2$

Communication

3. a. Draw as many different shapes as possible of a cubic function.

b. Draw as many different shapes as possible of a quartic function.

Thinking/Inquiry/Problem Solving

4. You have investigated the general shape of the graphs of cubic and quartic functions. Sketch a possible general shape for the graphs of each of the following:

a. A fifth-degree function that has a coefficient of x^5 that is

(i) positive (ii) negative

b. A sixth-degree function that has a coefficient of x^6 that is

(i) positive (ii) negative

Section 1.2 — Polynomial Functions from Data

In earlier courses, you used finite differences as a means of identifying polynomial functions. If we have the right data we can obtain a sequence of first differences, second differences, and so on. The purpose of the investigation in this section is to determine the pattern of finite differences for given polynomials.

The table below lists finite differences for the linear function $f(x) = x$.

x	$f(x)$	$\Delta f(x)$
1	1	$2 - 1 = 1$
2	2	$3 - 2 = 1$
3	3	$4 - 3 = 1$
4	4	⋮
⋮	⋮	⋮
$m - 1$	$m - 1$	$m - (m - 1) = 1$
m	m	$m + 1 - m = 1$
$m + 1$	$m + 1$	

The set of first differences of a linear function is constant.

INVESTIGATION

The purpose of this investigation is to determine the pattern of finite differences for quadratic and cubic functions.

1. For the function $f(x) = x^2$, copy and complete the table below, calculating first differences, second differences, and so on, to determine whether or not the sequence of entries becomes constant.

x	$f(x)$	$\Delta f(x)$ first difference	$\Delta^2 f(x)$* second difference	$\Delta^3 f(x)$ third difference
1				
2				
3				
⋮				
$m - 2$				
$m - 1$				
m				
$m + 1$				
$m + 2$				

*$\Delta^2 f(x)$ means second difference.

2. For the function $f(x) = x^3$, copy and complete the table below, calculating first differences, second differences, and so on, to determine whether or not the sequence of entries becomes constant.

x	$f(x)$	$\Delta f(x)$ first difference	$\Delta^2 f(x)^*$ second difference	$\Delta^3 f(x)$ third difference
1				
2				
3				
⋮				
$m - 2$				
$m - 1$				
m				
$m + 1$				
$m + 2$				

*$\Delta^2 f(x)$ means second difference.

If the set $\{m - 2, m - 1, m, m + 1, m + 2\}$ describes every set of five consecutive x values, can you make a general statement about the pattern of successive finite differences for polynomial functions?

EXAMPLE

technology

Given that the points (1,1), (2, −3), (3, 5), (4, 37), (5, 105), and (6, 221) lie on the graph of a polynomial function, determine a possible expression for the function having integer coefficients.

Solution

Input the data in your graphing calculator as follows:

1. Select the STAT function and press ENTER to select EDIT mode.
2. In the L_1 column, input 1, 2, 3, 4, 5, 6, and for the L_2 column, input 1, −3, 5, 37, 105, 221.
3. Move the cursor to the L_3 column. Select 2nd STAT (LIST) for the LIST function. Move the cursor to OPS and then select option **7:ΔList(**.
4. Enter L_2 in the **ΔList** (L_2) to obtain the first finite differences for L_2.
5. Move the cursor to the L_4 column. Repeat steps 3 and 4 to obtain the second finite differences for L_3. Note: Enter L_3 in the **ΔList** (L_3).
6. Move the cursor to the L_5 column. Repeat steps 3 and 4 to obtain the third finite differences for L_3. *Note*: Enter L_4 in the **ΔList** (L_4).

```
L1    L2    L3     2
1     1     -4
2     -3    8
3     5     32
4     37    68
5     105   116
6     221   ------
------ ------
L2 = {1,-3,5,37...}
```

```
L3    L4    L5     5
-4    12    12
8     24    12
32    36    12
68    48    ------
116   ------
------
L5 = {12, 12, 12}
```

If the first finite difference is constant, then $f(x)$ is a linear function. If the second finite difference is constant, then $f(x)$ is a quadratic function.

The third finite difference in column L_5 is constant. If $f(x)$ is a polynomial function, then it must be cubic, of the form $f(x) = ax^3 + bx^2 + cx + d$. Use the **CubicReg** function to obtain the following result. The **CubicReg** function is located in the CALC mode on the STAT key.

```
CubicReg
 y=ax³+bx²+cx+d
 a=2
 b=-6
 c=-2.4E-11
 d=5
 R²=1
```

Note that $c = -2.4 \times 10^{-11}$ is a very small number, so let $c = 0$ and the required result is $f(x) = 2x^3 - 6x^2 + 5$.

A second method, using algebra, is as follows. Let the function be $f(x)$.

Using differences, we obtain the following:

x	$f(x)$	$\Delta f(x)$	$\Delta^2 f(x)$	$\Delta^3 f(x)$
1	1	−4	12	12
2	−3	8	24	12
3	5	32	36	12
4	37	68	48	
5	105	116		
6	221			

From the data, $\Delta^3 f(x)$ is constant. If $f(x)$ is a polynomial, it must be cubic, therefore $f(x)$ must be of the form $f(x) = ax^3 + bx^2 + cx + d$.

Using the given ordered pairs, we get

$$f(1) = a + b + c + d = 1 \quad ①$$
$$f(2) = 8a + 4b + 2c + d = -3 \quad ②$$
$$f(3) = 27a + 9b + 3c + d = 5 \quad ③$$
$$f(4) = 64a + 16b + 4c + d = 37 \quad ④$$

Solving these equations, we have

② − ① $\quad 7a + 3b + c = -4$ ⑤

③ − ② $\quad 19a + 5b + c = 8$ ⑥

④ − ③ $\quad 37a + 7b + c = 32$ ⑦

⑥ − ⑤ $\quad 12a + 12b = 12$ ⑧

⑦ − ⑥ $\quad 18a + 2b = 24$ ⑨

⑨ − ⑧ $\quad 6a = 12$

$a = 12$

Substituting into ⑧ $\quad 24 + 2b = 12$

$b = -6$

Substituting into ⑤ $\quad 14 - 18 + c = -4$

$c = 0$

Substituting into ① $\quad 2 - 6 + 0 + d = 1$

$d = 5$

Therefore, the function is $f(x) = 2x^3 - 6x^2 + 5$.

Exercise 1.2

Part A

technology

In each of the following, you are given a set of points that lie on the graph of a function. Determine, if possible, the equation of the polynomial function using a graphing calculator or the algebraic method.

Knowledge/Understanding

1. (1, 0), (2, −2), (3, −2), (4, 0), (5, 4), (6, 10)
2. (1, −1), (2, 2), (3, 5), (4, 8), (5, 11), (6, 14)
3. (1, 4), (2, 15), (3, 30), (4, 49), (5, 72), (6, 99)
4. (1, −9), (2, −10), (3, −7), (4, 0), (5, 11), (6, 26)
5. (1, 12), (2, −10), (3, −18), (4, 0), (5, 56), (6, 162)
6. (1, −34), (2, −42), (3, −38), (4, −16), (5, 30), (6, 106)
7. (1, 10), (2, 0), (3, 0), (4, 16), (5, 54), (6, 120), (7, 220)
8. (1, −4), (2, 0), (3, 30), (4, 98), (5, 216), (6, 396)
9. (1, −2), (2, −4), (3, −6), (4, −8), (5, 14), (6, 108), (7, 346)
10. (1, 1), (2, 2), (3, 4), (4, 8), (5, 16), (6, 32), (7, 64)

Part B

Application

11. The volume, V, of air in the lungs during a 5 s respiratory cycle is given by a cubic function (with time t as the independent variable).

a. The following data was recorded:

t (in seconds)	V (in litres)
1	0.2877
2	0.6554
3	0.8787
4	0.7332

technology

Determine the cubic function that satisfies this data.

b. Using your graphing calculator, find the maximum volume of air in the lungs during the cycle, and find when during the cycle this maximum occurs.

Thinking/Inquiry/
Problem Solving

12. a. The population of a town is given by a polynomial function. Let time, t, be the independent variable, $t = 0$ in 1981, and use the data below to determine the function.

Year	Population
1981	4031
1982	4008
1983	3937
1984	3824
1985	3675
1986	3496

b. The town seemed destined to become a "ghost town" until oil was discovered there and the population started to increase. In what year did this happen?

c. If the function continues to describe the population correctly, what will the population be in 2030?

Section 1.3 — Division of Polynomials

Division of polynomials can be done using a method similar to that used to divide whole numbers. Since division of polynomials cannot be done on all calculators, let's first review the division process in arithmetic.

EXAMPLE 1

Divide 579 by 8.

Solution

$$\begin{array}{r} 72 \\ 8\overline{)579} \\ \underline{56} \\ 19 \\ \underline{16} \\ 3 \end{array}$$

Step 1: Divide 8 into 57, obtaining 7.
Step 2: Multiply 8 by 7, obtaining 56.
Step 3: Subtract 56 from 57, obtaining 1.
Step 4: Bring down the next digit after 57.
Step 5: Repeat steps 1–4 using the new number, 19.
Step 6: Stop when the remainder is less than 8.

We can state the results in the form of the division statement $579 = 8 \times 72 + 3$. Division with polynomials follows the same procedure. When you are performing division, you should write both the divisor and dividend in descending powers of the variable.

EXAMPLE 2

Divide $x^2 - 7x - 10$ by $x + 2$.

Solution

$$\begin{array}{r} x - 9 \\ x+2\,\overline{)x^2 - 7x - 10} \\ \underline{x^2 + 2x} \\ -9x - 10 \\ \underline{-9x - 18} \\ 8 \end{array}$$

Step 1: Divide first term of the dividend $(x^2 - 7x - 10)$ by the first term of the divisor [i.e., $x^2 \div x = x$].
Step 2: Multiply $(x(x + 2) = x^2 + 2x)$, placing the terms below those in the dividend of the same power.
Step 3: Subtract and bring down the next term.
Step 4: Repeat steps 1–3.
Step 5: Stop when the degree of the remainder is less than that of the divisor.

We can express the results as $x^2 - 7x - 10 = (x + 2)(x - 9) + 8$.
Note: This is of the form dividend = divisor × quotient + remainder or $f(x) = d(x)q(x) + r(x)$.

EXAMPLE 3

Perform the following divisions and express the answers in the form $f(x) = d(x)q(x) + r(x)$.

a. $(2x^3 + 3x^2 - 4x + 3) \div (x + 3)$ b. $(x^3 - x^2 - 4) \div (x - 2)$

Solution

a.

$$\begin{array}{r} 2x^2 - 3x + 5 \\ x + 3\,\overline{)\,2x^3 + 3x^2 - 4x + 3} \\ \underline{2x^3 + 6x^2} \qquad\quad \\ -3x^2 - 4x \qquad \\ \underline{-3x^2 - 9x} \qquad \\ 5x + 3 \\ \underline{5x + 15} \\ -12 \end{array}$$

Since the remainder, $r(x) = -12$, is of a degree less than that of the divisor, the division is complete.

$2x^3 + 3x^2 - 4x + 3 = (x + 3)(2x^2 - 3x + 5) - 12$

b. Insert $0x$ in the function so that every term is present.

$$\begin{array}{r} x^2 + x + 2 \\ x - 2\,\overline{)\,x^3 - x^2 + \mathbf{0x} - 4} \\ \underline{x^3 - 2x^2} \qquad\qquad \\ x^2 + 0x \qquad \\ \underline{x^2 - 2x} \qquad \\ 2x - 4 \\ \underline{2x - 4} \\ 0 \end{array}$$

Since the remainder is 0, $x - 2$ is a factor of $x^3 - x^2 - 4$. The other factor is $x^2 + x + 2$.

$x^3 - x^2 - 4 = (x-2)(x^2 + x + 2)$

EXAMPLE 4

Perform the following division and express the answer in the form $f(x) = d(x)q(x) + r(x)$.

$(3x^4 - 2x^3 + 4x^2 - 7x + 4) \div (x^2 - 3x + 1)$.

Solution

$$\begin{array}{r} 3x^2 + 7x + 22 \\ x^2 - 3x + 1\,\overline{)\,3x^4 - 2x^3 + 4x^2 - 7x + 4} \\ \underline{3x^4 - 9x^3 + 3x^2} \qquad\qquad\quad \\ 7x^3 + x^2 - 7x \qquad \\ \underline{7x^3 - 21x^2 + 7x} \qquad \\ 22x^2 - 14x + 4 \\ \underline{22x^2 - 66x + 22} \\ 52x - 18 \end{array}$$

Since the remainder, $r(x) = 52x - 18$, is of a lower degree than the divisor, $x^2 - 3x + 1$, the division is complete.

$3x^4 - 2x^3 + 4x^2 - 7x + 4 = (x^2 - 3x + 1)(3x^2 + 7x + 22) + (52x - 18)$

EXAMPLE 5

Determine the remainder when $9x^3 - 3x^2 - 4x + 2$ is divided by:

a. $3x - 2$

b. $x - \frac{2}{3}$

Solution

a.

$$\begin{array}{r} 3x^2 + x - \frac{2}{3} \\ 3x - 2 \overline{)9x^3 - 3x^2 - 4x + 2} \\ \underline{9x^3 - 6x^2} \qquad\qquad \\ 3x^2 - 4x \qquad \\ \underline{3x^2 - 2x} \qquad \\ -2x + 2 \\ \underline{-2x + \frac{4}{3}} \\ \frac{2}{3} \end{array}$$

b.

$$\begin{array}{r} 9x^2 + 3x - 2 \\ x - \frac{2}{3} \overline{)9x^3 - 3x^2 - 4x + 2} \\ \underline{9x^3 - 6x^2} \qquad\qquad \\ 3x^2 - 4x \qquad \\ \underline{3x^2 - 2x} \qquad \\ -2x + 2 \\ \underline{-2x + \frac{4}{3}} \\ \frac{2}{3} \end{array}$$

The remainders are equal. Is this always true if a function is divided by $px + t$ and by $x + \frac{t}{p}$? Suppose that $f(x)$ divided by $d(x) = px + t$ produces quotient $q(x)$ and remainder $r(x)$. We can write $f(x) = (px + t)q(x) + r(x)$.

Now $f(x) = (px + t)q(x) + r(x)$

$$= p\left(x + \frac{t}{p}\right)q(x) + r(x)$$

$$= \left(x + \frac{t}{p}\right)[p \bullet q(x)] + r(x).$$

From this it is clear that division by $\left(x + \frac{t}{p}\right)$ produces a quotient greater by a factor p than that of division by $(px + t)$, but the remainders are the same.

Exercise 1.3

Part A

1. Perform each of the following divisions and express the result in the form **dividend = divisor × quotient + remainder.**

a. $17 \div 5$	b. $42 \div 7$	c. $73 \div 12$
d. $90 \div 6$	e. $103 \div 10$	f. $75 \div 15$

Communication

2. a. In Question 1 **a**, explain why 5 is not a factor of 17.
   b. In Question 1 **b**, explain why 7 is a factor of 42.
   c. In Questions 1 **d** and 1 **f**, what other divisor is a factor of the dividend?

Communication

3. Explain the division statement $f(x) = d(x)q(x) + r(x)$ in words.

Part B

Knowledge/Understanding

4. For $f(x) = (x - 2)(x^2 + 3x - 2) + 5$,
   a. identify the linear divisor $d(x)$.
   b. identify the quotient $q(x)$.
   c. identify the remainder $r(x)$.
   d. determine the dividend $f(x)$.

5. When a certain polynomial is divided by $x - 3$, its quotient is $x^2 - 5x - 7$ and its remainder is 5. What is the polynomial?

Application

6. When a certain polynomial is divided by $x^2 + x + 1$, its quotient is $x^2 - x + 1$ and its remainder is -1. What is the polynomial?

7. In each of the following, divide $f(x)$ by $d(x)$, obtaining quotient $q(x)$ and remainder r. Write your answers in the form $f(x) = d(x)q(x) + r(x)$.
   a. $(x^3 - 3x^2 + x + 2) \div (x + 2)$
   b. $(x^3 + 4x^2 - 3x - 2) \div (x - 1)$
   c. $(2x^3 - 4x^2 - 3x + 5) \div (x - 3)$
   d. $(3x^3 + x^2 - x - 6) \div (x + 1)$
   e. $(3x^2 - 4) \div (x - 4)$
   f. $(x^3 - 2x - 4) \div (x - 2)$
   g. $(4x^3 + 6x^2 - 6x - 9) \div (2x + 3)$
   h. $(3x^3 - 11x^2 + 21x - 7) \div (3x - 2)$
   i. $(6x^3 + 4x^2 - 3x + 9) \div (3x - 2)$
   j. $(3x^3 + 7x^2 + 5x + 1) \div (3x + 1)$

Communication

8. For the pairs of polynomials in Question 7, state whether the second is a factor of the first. If not, compare the degree of the remainder to the degree of the divisor. What do you observe?

Knowledge/Understanding

9. Perform the following divisions:
   a. $(x^4 - x^3 + 2x^2 - 3x + 8) \div (x - 4)$
   b. $(2x^4 - 3x^2 + 1) \div (x + 1)$
   c. $(4x^3 + 32) \div (x + 2)$
   d. $(x^5 - 1) \div (x - 1)$

10. One factor of $x^3 + 3x^2 - 16x + 12$ is $x - 2$. Find all other factors.

11. Divide $f(x) = x^3 + 2x^2 - 4x - 8$ by $x + 3$.

12. Divide $f(x) = x^4 + x^3 - x^2 - x$ by $d(x) = x^2 + 2x + 1$.

13. Divide $f(x) = x^4 - 5x^2 + 4$ by $d(x) = x^2 - 3x + 2$.

Thinking/Inquiry/ Problem Solving

14. In $f(x) = d(x)q(x) + r(x)$, what condition is necessary for $d(x)$ to be a factor of $f(x)$?

15. If $f(x) = d(x)q(x) + r(x)$ and $r(x) \neq 0$, given that the degree of $d(x)$ is 2, what are the possible degrees of $r(x)$?

Part C

Thinking/Inquiry/ Problem Solving

16. If x and y are natural numbers and $y \leq x$, then whole numbers q and r must exist such that $x = yq + r$.

   a. What is the value of r if y is a factor of x?

   b. If y is not a factor of x, what are the possible values of r if $y = 5$, $y = 7$, or $y = n$?

17. a. Divide $f(x) = x^3 + 4x^2 - 5x - 9$ by $x - 2$ and write your answer in the form $f(x) = (x - 2)q(x) + r_1$. Now divide $q(x)$ by $x + 1$ and write your answer in the form $q(x) = (x + 1)Q(x) + r_2$.

   b. If $f(x)$ is divided by $(x - 2)(x + 1) = x^2 - x - 2$, is $Q(x)$ in part **a** the quotient obtained? Justify your answer.

   c. When $f(x)$ is divided by $(x - 2)(x + 1)$, can the remainder be expressed in terms of r_1 and r_2?

Section 1.4 — The Remainder Theorem

With reference to polynomial functions, we can express the division algorithm as follows:

When a function $f(x)$ is divided by a divisor $d(x)$, producing a quotient $q(x)$ and a remainder $r(x)$, then $f(x) = d(x)q(x) + r(x)$, where the degree of $r(x)$ is less than the degree of $d(x)$.

Note that if the divisor is a linear function then the remainder must be a constant.

INVESTIGATION

The following investigation will illustrate an interesting way in which this relationship can be used.

1. a. For the function $f(x) = x^3 + x^2 - 7$, use long division to divide $(x^3 + x^2 - 7)$ by $(x - 2)$.
   b. What is the remainder?
   c. What is the value of $f(2)$?

2. a. Use long division to divide $(x^3 + 3x^2 - 2x + 1)$ by $(x + 1)$.
   b. What is the remainder?
   c. What is the value of $f(-1)$?

3. a. What was the relationship between $f(2)$ and the remainder in the first division?
   b. What was the relationship between $f(-1)$ and the remainder in the second division?
   c. Why do you think we chose the value 2 to use in Question 1 **c**?
   d. Why do you think we chose the value -1 to use in Question 2 **c**?

Based on these examples, complete the following statement:

When $f(x)$ is divided by $(x - 2)$, then the remainder $r(2) = f(\ )$.
When $f(x)$ is divided by $(x + 1)$, then the remainder $r(\ ) = f(\ )$.
When $f(x)$ is divided by $(x - a)$, then the remainder $r(\ ) = f(\ )$.

EXAMPLE 1 Show that for the function $f(x) = x^3 - x^2 - 4x - 2$, the value of $f(-2)$ is equal to the remainder obtained when $f(x)$ is divided by $(x + 2)$.

Solution

$$\begin{aligned} f(-2) &= (-2)^3 - (-2)^2 - 4(-2) - 2 \\ &= -8 - 4 + 8 - 2 \\ &= -6 \end{aligned}$$

$$\begin{array}{r} x^2 - 3x + 2 \\ x + 2 \,\overline{\smash{)}\, x^3 - x^2 - 4x - 2} \\ \underline{x^3 + 2x^2 } \\ -3x^2 - 4x \\ \underline{-3x^2 - 6x} \\ 2x - 2 \\ \underline{2x + 4} \\ -6 \end{array}$$

Since the remainder is -6, then the remainder equals $f(-2)$.

It appears that there is a relationship between the remainder and the value of the function. We now address this in general terms.

If the divisor is the linear expression $x - p$, we can write the division statement as $f(x) = (x - p)q(x) + r$. This equation is satisfied by all values of x. In particular, it is satisfied by $x = p$. Replacing x with p in the equation we get

$$\begin{aligned} f(p) &= (p - p)q(p) + r \\ &= (0)q(p) + r \\ &= r. \end{aligned}$$

This relationship between the dividend and the remainder is called the **Remainder Theorem**.

The Remainder Theorem If $f(x)$ is divided by $(x - p)$, giving a quotient $q(x)$ and a remainder r, then $r = f(p)$.

The Remainder Theorem allows us to determine the remainder in the division of polynomials without performing the actual division, which, as we will see, is a valuable thing to be able to do.

EXAMPLE 2

Find the remainder when $x^3 - 4x^2 + 5x - 1$ is divided by

a. $x - 2$

b. $x + 1$

Solution

Let $f(x) = x^3 - 4x^2 + 5x - 1$; therefore,

a. when $f(x)$ is divided by $x - 2$, the remainder is $f(2)$.

$$\begin{aligned} r &= f(2) \\ &= (2)^3 - 4(2)^2 + 5(2) - 1 \\ &= 1 \end{aligned}$$

b. when $f(x)$ is divided by $x + 1$, the remainder is $f(-1)$.

$$\begin{aligned} r &= f(-1) \\ &= (-1)^3 - 4(-1)^2 + 5(-1) - 1 \\ &= -11 \end{aligned}$$

What do we do if the divisor is not of the form $(x - p)$, but of the form $(kx - p)$? We have already seen that the remainder in dividing by $(kx - p)$ is the same as in dividing by $\left(x - \frac{p}{k}\right)$, so there is no difficulty. In this case, $r = f\left(\frac{p}{k}\right)$.

EXAMPLE 3

Find the remainder when $f(x) = x^3 - 4x^2 + 5x - 1$ is divided by $(2x - 3)$.

Solution

To determine the remainder, we write $2x - 3 = 2\left(x - \frac{3}{2}\right)$ and calculate $f\left(\frac{3}{2}\right)$.

The remainder is $r = f\left(\frac{3}{2}\right) = \left(\frac{3}{2}\right)^3 - 4\left(\frac{3}{2}\right)^2 + 5\left(\frac{3}{2}\right) - 1$

$$= \frac{27}{8} - \frac{4 \times 9}{4} + \frac{15}{2} - 1$$

$$= \frac{7}{8}.$$

EXAMPLE 4

When $x^3 + 3x^2 - kx + 10$ is divided by $x - 5$, the remainder is 15. Find the value of k.

Solution

Since $r = 15$ and $r = f(5)$, where $f(5) = 125 + 75 - 5k + 10$,

then $210 - 5k = 15$ (by the Remainder Theorem)

$$\begin{aligned} -5k &= -195 \\ k &= 39. \end{aligned}$$

We have noted that the remainder is always of a degree lower than that of the divisor. In the examples so far, the divisor was a linear function, so the remainder had to be a constant. In the next example, the divisor is a quadratic expression, so the remainder can be a linear expression.

EXAMPLE 5

Find the remainder when $x^4 + 2x^3 - 5x^2 + x + 3$ is divided by $(x + 2)(x - 1)$.

Solution 1 Using Long Division

Expand $(x + 2)(x - 1) = x^2 + x - 2$.

$$
\begin{array}{r}
x^2 + x - 4 \\
x^2 + x - 2 \overline{) x^4 + 2x^3 - 5x^2 + x + 3} \\
\underline{x^4 + x^3 - 2x^2} \\
x^3 - 3x^2 + x \\
\underline{x^3 + x^2 - 2x} \\
-4x^2 + 3x + 3 \\
\underline{-4x^2 - 4x + 8} \\
7x - 5
\end{array}
$$

The remainder is $7x - 5$.

Solution 2 Using the Remainder Theorem

We have $f(x) = x^4 + 2x^3 - 5x^2 + x + 3$. ①

Then $f(x) = (x + 2)(x - 1)q(x) + r(x)$ where $r(x)$ is at most a linear expression.

Let $r(x) = Ax + B$.

Now $f(x) = (x + 2)(x - 1)q(x) + (Ax + B)$. ②

From ② $f(1) = (3)(0)q(1) + A + B$

$= A + B$.

From ① $f(1) = 1^4 + 2(1)^3 - 5(1)^2 + 1 + 3 = 2$.

So $A + B = 2$. ③

Similarly $f(-2) = (0)(-3)8(x) + (-2A + B) = -2A + B$

and $f(-2) = (-2)^4 + 2(-2)^3 - 5(-2)^2 - 2 + 3 = -19$

so $-2A + B = -19$. ④

We solve equations ③ and ④ for A and B.

$A + B = 2$

$-2A + B = -19$

Subtracting $3A = 21$

$A = 7$ and $B = -5$

Since $r(x) = Ax + B$, the remainder is $7x - 5$.

Exercise 1.4

Part A

Communication

1. Explain how you determine the remainder when $x^3 + 4x^2 - 2x - 5$ is divided by $x - 1$.

2. What is the remainder when $x^3 - 4x^2 + 2x - 6$ is divided by

   a. $x - 2$ b. $x + 1$ c. $2x - 1$ d. $2x + 3$

3. Determine the remainder in each of the following:

   a. $(x^2 + 3) \div (x - 3)$
   b. $(x^3 + x^2 - x + 2) \div (x - 1)$
   c. $(2x^3 + 4x - 1) \div (x + 2)$
   d. $(3x^4 - 2) \div (x + 1)$
   e. $(x^4 - x^2 + 5) \div (x - 2)$
   f. $(-2x^4 + 3x^2 - x + 2) \div (x + 2)$

Part B

Knowledge/Understanding

4. Determine the remainder in each of the following using the Remainder Theorem:

   a. $(x^3 - 2x^2 + 3x + 4) \div (x + 1)$
   b. $(x^4 - x^3 + x^2 - 3x + 4) \div (x - 3)$
   c. $(x^3 + 3x^2 - 7) \div (x - 2)$
   d. $(x^5 - 1) \div (x - 1)$
   e. $(6x^2 - 10x + 7) \div (3x + 1)$
   f. $(4x^3 + 9x - 10) \div (2x - 1)$
   g. $(x^3 + 3x^2 - x - 2) \div (x + 3)$
   h. $(3x^5 - 5x^2 + 4x + 1) \div (x - 1)$

Application

5. Determine the value of k in each of the following:

   a. When $x^3 + kx^2 + 2x - 3$ is divided by $x + 2$, the remainder is 1.
   b. When $x^4 - kx^3 - 2x^2 + x + 4$ is divided by $x - 3$, the remainder is 16.
   c. When $2x^3 - 3x^2 + kx - 1$ is divided by $2x - 1$, the remainder is 1.

Thinking/Inquiry/Problem Solving

6. If $f(x) = mx^3 + gx^2 - x + 3$ is divided by $x + 1$, the remainder is 3. If $f(x)$ is divided by $x + 2$, the remainder is -7. What are the values of m and g?

7. If $f(x) = mx^3 + gx^2 - x + 3$ is divided by $x - 1$, the remainder is 3. If $f(x)$ is divided by $x + 3$, the remainder is -1. What are the values of m and g?

Part C

8. Determine the remainder when $(x^3 + 3x^2 - x - 2)$ is divided by $(x + 3)(x + 5)$.

9. Determine the remainder when $(3x^5 - 5x^2 + 4x + 1)$ is divided by $(x - 1)(x + 2)$.

Thinking/Inquiry/ Problem Solving

10. When $x + 2$ is divided into $f(x)$, the remainder is 3. Determine the remainder when $x + 2$ is divided into each of the following:
    a. $f(x) + 1$
    b. $f(x) + x + 2$
    c. $f(x) + (4x + 7)$
    d. $2f(x) - 7$
    e. $[f(x)]^2$

11. If $f(x) = (x + 5)q(x) + (x + 3)$, what is the first multiple of $(x + 5)$ greater than $f(x)$?

12. The expression $x^4 + x^2 + 1$ cannot be factored using known techniques. However, by adding and subtracting x^2, we obtain $x^4 + 2x^2 + 1 - x^2$.

    Therefore, $x^4 + 2x^2 + 1 - x^2 = (x^2 + 1)^2 - x^2$
    $= (x^2 + x + 1)(x^2 - x + 1)$.

    Use this approach to factor each of the following:
    a. $x^4 + 5x^2 + 9$
    b. $9y^4 + 8y^2 + 4$
    c. $x^4 + 6x^2 + 25$
    d. $4x^4 + 8x^2 + 9$

Key Concepts Review

After your work in this chapter on Polynomial Functions, you should be familiar with the following concepts:

Factoring Types

You should be able to identify and simplify expressions of the following types:

- common
- trinomial
- grouping
- difference of squares

Sketching Polynomial Functions

- Make use of the relationships between x-intercepts and the roots of the corresponding equation to sketch the graph of functions.

Division of Polynomials

Remainder Theorem

- If $f(x)$ is divided by $(x - a)$, giving a quotient $q(x)$ and a remainder r, then $r = f(a)$.

Polynomial Functions from Data

- The first differences of a linear function are constant.
- The second differences of a quadratic function are constant.
- The third differences of a cubic function are constant.

Career Link wrap-up

investigate and apply

CHAPTER 1: MODELS FOR WATER FLOW RATES

1. Using the data presented in the Career Link, develop and utilize a polynomial mathematical model of the flow-rate and time relationship $[Q = f(t)]$ by

   a. determining the degree of the polynomial, then using the graphing calculator to obtain an algebraic model for $Q = f(t)$ with the appropriate polynomial regression function.

   b. using the graphing calculator to determine the peak flow. When does this occur? Is this a reasonable time for a peak daily flow? Explain.

   c. determining an algebraic model for the velocity $[V(t)]$ of the water in the pipe (metres per hour) leaving the water plant if the cross-sectional area $[A(t)]$ of the pipe changes over time with the relationship:

   $$A(t) = 0.1t + 0.4$$

   where $A(t)$ is cross-sectional area in square metres, t is time in hours, and $Q(t) = A(t)\ V(t)$.

   d. verifying that your model in part **c** is correct using the graphing calculator. Explain how you did this.

2. Water travelling at high velocities can cause damage due to excessive forces at bends (elbows) in pipe networks. If the maximum allowable velocity in this specific pipe is 2.5 m/s, will the pipe be damaged at the peak flow rate? ●

Review Exercise

1. Draw a sketch of each of the following without using your graphing calculator.

a. $y = (x - 2)(x + 3)$

b. $y = -(x + 3)^2 + 1$

c. $y = x(x - 1)(x - 3)$

d. $y = (x + 2)(x - 4)(x - 2)$

e. $y = -(x - 2)^3$

f. $y = -(x + 4)(x - 1)(x + 3)$

g. $y = (x + 2)^2 (x - 4)$

h. $y = (x - 2)^2(x + 1)^2$

i. $y = -x^2(x - 3)(x + 2)$

j. $y = (x - 4)(x + 1)(x + 2)(x - 3)$

k. $y = (x - 2)^3(x + 3)$

l. $y = -x(x + 2)(x - 3)$

2. In each of the following, you are given a set of points that lie on the graph of a polynomial function. If possible, determine the equation of the function.

a. $(-1, -27), (0, -11), (1, -5), (2, -3), (3, 1), (4, 13)$

b. $(0, 4), (1, 15), (2, 32), (3, 67), (4, 132), (5, 239)$

c. $(1, -9), (2, -31), (3, -31), (4, 51), (5, 299), (6, 821)$

d. $(1, 1), (2, 2), (3, 5), (4, 16)$

e. $(-2, 75), (-1, -11), (0, -21), (1, -27), (2, -53)$

3. Perform the following divisions:

a. $(x^3 - 2x^2 + 3x - 1) \div (x - 3)$

b. $(2x^3 + 5x + 4) \div (x + 2)$

c. $(4x^3 + 8x^2 - x + 1) \div (2x + 1)$

d. $(x^4 - 4x^3 + 3x^2 - 3) \div (x^2 + x - 2)$

4. Without using long division, determine the remainder when

a. $(x^2 - x + 1)$ is divided by $(x - 2)$.

b. $(x^3 + 4x^2 - 2)$ is divided by $(x + 1)$.

c. $(x^3 - 5x^2 + 2x - 1)$ is divided by $(x + 2)$.

d. $(x^4 - 3x^2 + 2x + 3)$ is divided by $(x + 1)$.

e. $(3x^3 + x + 2)$ is divided by $(3x - 1)$.

5. Divide each polynomial by the factor given, then express each polynomial in factored form.

   a. $x^3 + 2x^2 - x - 2$, given $x - 1$ is a factor.

   b. $x^3 - 3x^2 - x + 3$, given $x - 3$ is a factor.

   c. $6x^3 + 31x^2 + 25x - 12$, given $2x + 3$ is a factor.

6. a. When $x^3 - 3kx^2 + x + 5$ is divided by $x - 2$, the remainder is 9. Find the value of k.

   b. When $rx^3 + gx^2 + 4x + 1$ is divided by $x - 1$, the remainder is 12. When it is divided by $x + 3$, the remainder is -20. Find the values of r and g.

Chapter 1 Test

Achievement Category	Questions
Knowledge/Understanding	1, 3, 5, 7b
Thinking/Inquiry/Problem Solving	8
Communication	4
Application	2, 6, 7a, 9

1. Factor each of the following:
   a. $18x^2 - 50y^2$
   b. $pm^3 + m^2 + pm + 1$
   c. $12x^2 - 26x + 12$
   d. $x^2 + 6y - y^2 - 9$

2. Without using a graphing calculator, sketch the graph of
   a. $y = (x + 2)(x - 1)(x - 3)$
   b. $y = x^2(x - 2)$

3. Find the quotient and remainder when
   a. $x^3 - 5x^2 + 6x - 4$ is divided by $x + 2$.
   b. $(x^3 - 6x + 2)$ is divided by $(x - 3)$.

4. Since $f(1) = 0$ for $f(x) = 4x^3 - 6x + 2$, do you think $(x - 1)$ is a factor of $f(x) = 4x^3 - 6x + 2$? Explain.

5. Without using long division, find the remainder when $(x^3 - 6x^2 + 5x + 2)$ is divided by $(x + 2)$.

6. Find the value of k if there is a remainder of 7 when $x^3 - 3x^2 + 4x + k$ is divided by $(x - 2)$.

7. a. Do $(1, -1)$, $(2, -1)$, $(3, 1)$, $(4, 5)$ lie on the graph of a quadratic function?
   b. Use your graphing calculator to find the simplest polynomial function that contains the following points: $(1, -4)$, $(2, 6)$, $(3, 34)$, $(4, 92)$.

8. When $x^3 + cx + d$ is divided by $x + 1$, the remainder is 3, and when it is divided by $x - 2$, the remainder is -3. Determine the values of c and d.

9. One factor of $x^3 - 2x^2 - 9x + 18$ is $x - 2$. Determine the other factors.

Chapter 2

POLYNOMIAL EQUATIONS AND INEQUALITIES

It's happened to everyone. You've lost your favourite CD, and your room is an unbelievable mess. Rather than attempting to sort through everything, why not consider a few key places where it could be, and examine these areas closely until you find your CD. Similarly, if a manufacturer discovers a flaw in her product, the key intermediate assembly stages are examined individually until the source of the problem is found. These are two examples of a general learning and problem solving strategy: consider a thing in terms of its component parts, without losing sight of the fact that the parts go together. This problem solving strategy is a great way to solve mathematical equations, as well. In this chapter, you will see that polynomial equations can be solved using the same strategy you might use for finding a lost CD. Just examine the key component factors until you solve the problem!

CHAPTER EXPECTATIONS In this chapter, you will

- understand the Remainder and Factor Theorems, **Section 2.1**
- factor polynomial expressions, **Section 2.2**
- compare the nature of change in polynomial functions with that of linear and quadratic functions, **Section 2.3**
- determine the roots of polynomial equations, **Section 2.3**
- determine the real roots of non-factorable polynomial equations, **Section 2.4**
- solve problems involving the abstract extensions of algorithms, **Section 2.4**
- solve factorable and non-factorable polynomial inequalities, **Section 2.5**
- write the equation of a family of polynomial functions, **Section 2.5**
- write the equation of a family of polynomial functions, **Career Link**
- describe intervals and distances, **Section 2.6**

Review of Prerequisite Skills

To begin your study of Polynomial Equations and Inequalities in Chapter 2, you should be familiar with the following skills:

Solving Linear Equations and Inequalities

- $4(2x - 3) - 2x = 9 - x$
  $8x - 12 - 2x = 9 - x$
  $7x = 21$
  $x = 3$
- $2x - 3 \leq 6x + 13$
  $2x - 6x \leq 3 + 13$
  $-4x \leq 16$
  $4x \geq -16$
  $x \geq -4.$

Evaluating Polynomial Functions

- If $f(x) = 2x^3 - 3x + 7$, then $f(2) = 2(2)^3 - 3(2) + 7$
  $= 17.$

Factoring Quadratic Polynomials

- $x^2 - 7x + 12 = (x - 3)(x - 4)$
- $6x^2 - 17x - 14 = (2x - 7)(3x + 2)$

Solving Quadratic Equations by Factoring

- $3x^2 - 5x - 2 = 0$
  $(3x + 1)(x - 2) = 0$
  $3x + 1 = 0$ or $x - 2 = 0$
  $x = -\frac{1}{3}$ or $x = 2$
- $12x^2 + 7x - 10 = 0$
  $(3x - 2)(4x + 5) = 0$
  $3x - 2 = 0$ or $4x + 5 = 0$
  $x = \frac{2}{3}$ or $x = -\frac{5}{4}$

Solving Quadratic Equations Using the Quadratic Formula

- For the equation $ax^2 + bx + c = 0$, $x = \dfrac{-b \pm \sqrt{b^2 - 4ac}}{2a}$.

For $6x^2 - x - 2 = 0$, $a = 6$, $b = -1$, $c = -2$.

$$x = \frac{1 \pm \sqrt{1 - 4(6)(-2)}}{12}$$
$$= \frac{1 \pm 7}{12}$$
$$x = \frac{2}{3} \text{ or } x = -\frac{1}{2}$$

For $6x^2 + 2x - 3 = 0$, $a = 6$, $b = 2$, $c = -3$.

$$x = \frac{-2 \pm \sqrt{4 - 4(6)(-3)}}{12}$$
$$= \frac{-2 \pm \sqrt{76}}{12}$$
$$= \frac{-2 \pm 2\sqrt{19}}{12}$$
$$= \frac{-1 \pm \sqrt{19}}{6}$$

$x = 0.6$ or 0.9 (correct to one decimal)

Exercise

1. Solve.

   a. $3x + 1 = x - 5$
   b. $3(x - 2) + 7 = 3(x - 7)$
   c. $7x - 2(x - 3) = 9x - 5$
   d. $(x + 3)(x - 2) = x^2 - 5x$

2. Solve and graph on the real number line.

   a. $3x - 2 > 2x + 5$
   b. $5x + 4 \geq 7x - 8$
   c. $4x - 5 \leq 2(x - 7)$
   d. $4x + 7 < 9x + 17$

3. Evaluate each of the following for $f(x) = 2x^2 - 3x + 1$.

   a. $f(1)$
   b. $f(-2)$
   c. $f(3)$
   d. $f\left(\frac{1}{2}\right)$

4. Evaluate each of the following for $f(x) = x^3 - 2x^2 + 4x + 5$.

   a. $f(-1)$
   b. $f(2)$
   c. $f(-3)$
   d. $f\left(\frac{1}{2}\right)$

5. Factor each of the following fully.

   a. $x^2 - 14x + 48$
   b. $y^2 - 3y + 2$
   c. $3x^2 - 10x + 7$
   d. $3x^3 - 75x$
   e. $6x^2 + 7x - 3$
   f. $x^3 + x^2 - 56x$
   g. $4x^2 + 20x$
   h. $3x^3 - 12x$
   i. $6x^2 - 14x - 12$

6. Solve.

   a. $x(x + 4) = 0$
   b. $(x - 3)(x + 2) = 0$
   c. $x^2 + 5x + 6 = 0$
   d. $y^2 + 9y + 18 = 0$
   e. $x^2 - 2x - 15 = 0$
   f. $7x^2 + 3x - 4 = 0$
   g. $3x^2 - 10x + 7 = 0$
   h. $x^3 - 9x = 0$
   i. $3x^2 - 13x + 4 = 0$

7. Recall that the quadratic formula to solve the quadratic equation $ax^2 + bx + c = 0, x \in C$ is $x = \frac{-b \pm \sqrt{b^2 - 4ac}}{2a}$.

   Solve correct to one decimal place.

   a. $x^2 + 4x - 8 = 0$
   b. $3y^2 - 5y - 4 = 0$
   c. $3x^2 + x + 3 = 0$
   d. $x^2 - 5x - 4 = 0$
   e. $2x^2 = 3 + 5x$
   f. $6y^2 - 5y = 6$
   g. $2p^2 - 3p + 5 = 0$
   h. $x^2 + 5x - 6 = 0$
   i. $2x(x - 5) = (x + 2)(x - 3)$

Career Link investigate

CHAPTER 2: RESEARCHING DOSE–RESPONSE RELATIONSHIPS

In response to the health concerns of Canada's aging population, the pharmaceutical industry has dramatically increased its investment in research over the past ten years. A key component of the research process is the generation of mathematical models that predict dose-response relationships. "Dose" refers to the quantity of medication administered to a patient, and response refers to the effect on the patient. For example, the dose-response relationship for asthma medication may be in terms of the mass of drug administered versus the percentage increase in lung capacity. Polynomial equations are often used to model the dose-response relationship because they can be fit to a data set that changes slope a number of times and may cross the x-axis multiple times (i.e., it may feature multiple roots). In this chapter, you will develop the algebraic tools to solve polynomial equations and inequalities, then you will investigate the properties of polynomial roots and the absolute-value function.

Case Study — Pharmaceutical Researcher

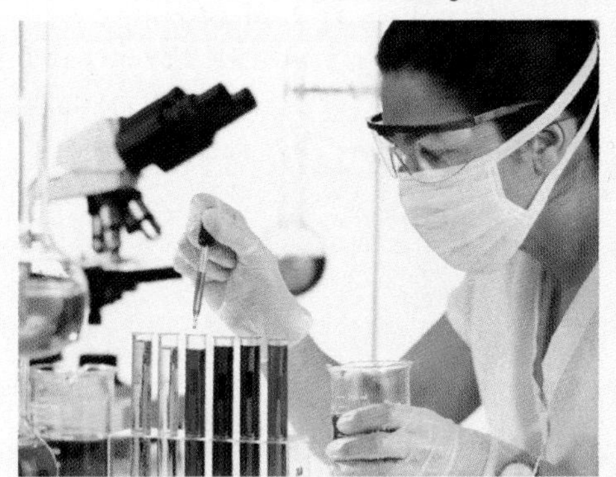

Pharmaceutical companies are, of course, also interested in modelling the side-effect responses of medication. For example, the equation

$$R(t) = 5\left(t^4 - 4t^3 + \frac{19}{4}t^2 - \frac{3}{2}t\right)$$

can be used to model the side-effect response $[R(t)]$ in degrees Celsius above or below the normal body temperature (36.9°C) of an experimental drug t hours after it was administered. The equation is valid for $0 < t < 2.2$ hours. Due to the stress of temperature change on the body, a second drug is administered at the moment the patient's temperature starts to exceed 36.9°C.

DISCUSSION QUESTIONS

1. Within the context of the problem, what happens when $R(t)$ crosses the t-axis?
2. Using your prior knowledge of linear and quadratic functions and your work in Chapter 1, predict how many times the second drug will have to be administered. (*Hint:* Think about the degree of the function.) Explain using a rough sketch. Do not make a table of values or plot the graph.
3. Once again using your prior knowledge of linear and quadratic functions and your work in Chapter 1, predict how many times the patient's temperature can "spike" (i.e., reach a maximum or minimum). Explain using a rough sketch.

At the end of this chapter you will apply the tools of solving polynomial equations and inequalities in assessing the performance of the experimental drug introduced above. ●

Section 2.1 — The Factor Theorem

The Remainder Theorem tells us that when we divide $x^2 - 5x + 6$ by $x - 3$, the remainder is

$$\begin{aligned} f(3) &= (3)^2 - 5(3) + 6 \\ &= 9 - 15 + 6 \\ &= 0. \end{aligned}$$

Since the remainder is zero, $x^2 - 5x + 6$ is divisible by $(x - 3)$. By divisible, we mean *evenly* divisible. If $f(x)$ is divisible by $x - p$, we say $x - p$ is a factor of $f(x)$. On the other hand, if we divide $x^2 - 5x + 6$ by $(x - 1)$, the remainder is

$$\begin{aligned} f(1) &= (1)^2 - 5(1) + 6 \\ &= 2. \end{aligned}$$

The fact that the remainder is not zero tells us that $x^2 - 5x + 6$ is not evenly divisible by $(x - 1)$. That is, $(x - 1)$ is not a factor of $x^2 - 5x + 6$.

The Remainder Theorem tells us that if the remainder is zero on division by $(x - p)$, then $f(p) = 0$. If the remainder is zero, then $(x - p)$ divides evenly into $f(x)$, and $(x - p)$ is a factor of $f(x)$. Conversely, if $x - p$ is a factor of $f(x)$, then the remainder $f(p)$ must equal zero. These two statements give us the Factor Theorem, which is an extension of the Remainder Theorem.

The Factor Theorem
$(x - p)$ is a factor of $f(x)$ if and only if $f(p) = 0$.

EXAMPLE 1

Show that $x - 2$ is a factor of $x^3 - 3x^2 + 5x - 6$.

Solution 1

$$\begin{aligned} f(2) &= 2^3 - 3(2)^2 + 5(2) - 6 \\ &= 0 \end{aligned}$$

Since $f(2) = 0$, $x - 2$ is a factor of $x^3 - 3x^2 + 5x - 6$.

Solution 2

Dividing

$$\begin{array}{r} x^2 - x + 3 \\ x - 2 \overline{\big) x^3 - 3x^2 + 5x - 6} \\ \underline{x^3 - 2x^2} \qquad\qquad \\ -x^2 + 5x \qquad \\ \underline{-x^2 + 2x} \qquad \\ 3x - 6 \\ \underline{3x - 6} \\ 0 \end{array}$$

Since the remainder is zero, $x - 2$ is a factor of $x^3 - 3x^2 + 5x - 6$. Both solutions verify that $x - 2$ is a factor. Note that Solution 2 tells us that the second factor is $x^2 - x + 3$.

EXAMPLE 2 Is $(x + 2)$ a factor of $f(x) = x^3 + 3x^2 + 5x + 4$?

Solution

We test if $x + 2$ is a factor by evaluating $f(-2)$.

$$\begin{aligned} f(-2) &= (-2)^3 + 3(-2)^2 + 5(-2) + 4 \\ &= -8 + 12 - 10 + 4 \\ &= -2 \end{aligned}$$

Since $f(-2) \neq 0$, $(x + 2)$ is not a factor of $x^3 + 3x^2 + 5x + 4$.

In using the Factor Theorem, we must find a value p so that $f(p) = 0$. We can then say that $(x - p)$ is a factor, and by division we can determine the second factor. The question is how to determine the value of p. This is partly a matter of guessing, but we make the guessing easier by noting that there is a limited number of possible values. In the function $f(x) = x^3 - 4x^2 + 3x - 6$, if there is a value for p such that $f(p) = 0$, then $p^3 - 2p^2 + 3p - 6 = 0$. We are, of course, interested in **integer values** for p. Note that $p^3 - 2p^2 + 3p = 6$ means that $p(p^2 - 2p + 3) = 6$. If p is an integer, then $p^2 - 2p + 3$ is an integer, so the only possible values for p are ±1, ±2, ±3, ±6, and we need to consider only these. In other words, **the only possible values for p are divisors of the constant term in $f(x)$.**

EXAMPLE 3 Factor $x^3 - x^2 - 14x + 24$.

Solution

Possible values for p are ±1, ±2, ±3, ±4, ±6, ±12, and ±24.

$$\begin{aligned} f(1) &= 1 - 1 - 14 + 24 \neq 0 \\ f(-1) &= -1 - 1 + 14 + 24 \neq 0 \\ f(2) &= 8 - 4 - 28 + 24 = 0 \end{aligned}$$

Therefore $(x - 2)$ is a factor of $f(x)$.

To find the other factor(s), one method is to use long division and divide $x^3 - x^2 - 14x + 24$ by $x - 2$ as follows:

$$\begin{array}{r} x^2 + x - 12 \\ x - 2 \overline{)\, x^3 - x^2 - 14x + 24} \\ \underline{x^3 - 2x^2} \\ x^2 - 14x \\ \underline{x^2 - 2x} \\ -12x + 24 \\ \underline{-12x + 24} \\ 0 \end{array}$$

Factoring further, $x^2 + x - 12 = (x + 4)(x - 3)$.
Therefore, $x^3 - x^2 - 14x + 24 = (x - 2)(x + 4)(x - 3)$.

An alternative is to use the following method of comparing coefficients:

$$\begin{aligned} x^3 - x^2 - 14x + 24 &= (x - 2)(x^2 + kx - 12) \\ &= x^3 + kx^2 - 12x - 2x^2 - 2kx + 24 \\ &= x^3 + (k - 2)x^2 + (-12 - 2k)\,x + 24 \end{aligned}$$

Comparing the coefficients of x^2, $k - 2 = -1$, so $k = 1$. A check can be obtained by comparing the coefficients of x, which gives $-12 - 2k = -14$ and $k = 1$. Therefore, $x^3 - x^2 - 14x + 24 = (x - 2)(x^2 + x - 12)$, and further factoring gives $x^3 - x^2 - 14x + 24 = (x - 2)(x - 3)(x + 4)$.

EXAMPLE 4

Factor $f(x) = x^3 + 9x^2 + 5x - 18$.

Solution

technology

Possible values of p such that $f(p) = 0$ are ± 1, ± 2, ± 3, ± 6, ± 9, and ± 18. Checking all of these is time-consuming. We can help ourselves by using a calculator to sketch the graph $y = f(x)$. From the graph there are three potential integer values: $p = 1$, $p = -2$, and $p = -8$. But $p = -8$ is impossible, since it is not a divisor of 18.

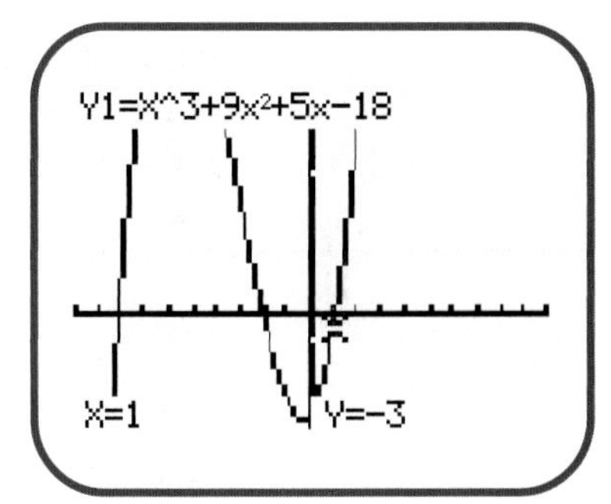

Now $f(1) = 1 + 9 + 5 - 18$
$= -3$

$f(-2) = (-2)^3 + 9(-2)^2 + 5(-2) - 18$
$= 0$.

Therefore $x + 2$ is a factor of $f(x)$. To find the other factor(s), you can use long division or you can compare coefficients.

$$\begin{array}{r} x^2 + 7x - 9 \\ x + 2\overline{)x^3 + 9x^2 + 5x - 18} \\ \underline{x^3 + 2x^2} \qquad\qquad \\ 7x^2 + 5x \qquad \\ \underline{7x^2 + 14x} \qquad \\ -9x - 18 \\ \underline{-9x - 18} \\ 0 \end{array}$$

Since $x^2 + 7x - 9$ cannot be factored further,
$x^3 + 9x^2 + 5x - 18 = (x + 2)(x^2 + 7x - 9)$.

EXAMPLE 5

Factor $f(x) = x^4 - 3x^3 - 13x^2 + 3x + 12$.

Solution

Possible values of p such that $f(p) = 0$ are ± 1, ± 2, ± 3, ± 4, ± 6, and ± 12. From the graph, values to check are $p = 6$, $p = 1$, and $p = -1$. Note that the fourth x-intercept is between -2 and -3 and is not an integer. Graph $y = f(x)$ and use the **1:value** mode under the CALCULATE menu or substitute to evaluate $f(6)$, $f(1)$, and $f(-1)$.

technology

$$f(6) = 6^4 - 3(6)^3 - 13(6)^2 + 3(6) + 12$$
$$= 210$$
$$f(1) = 1 - 3 - 13 + 3 + 12$$
$$= 0$$
$$f(-1) = 1 + 3 - 13 - 3 + 12$$
$$= 0$$

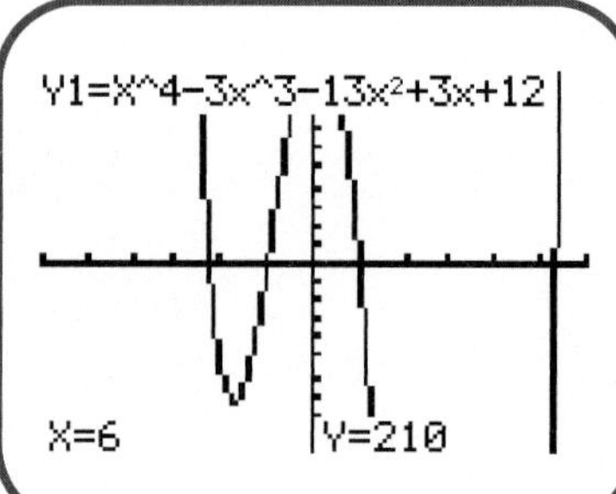

Therefore $x - 1$ and $x + 1$ are factors of $f(x)$.
To determine the other factor(s), use the method of comparing coefficients.

$$x^4 - 3x^3 - 13x^2 + 3x + 12 = (x - 1)(x + 1)(x^2 + kx - 12)$$
$$= (x^2 - 1)(x^2 + kx - 12)$$
$$= x^4 + kx^3 - 12x^2 - x^2 - kx + 12$$
$$= x^4 + kx^3 - 11x^2 - kx + 12$$

Since $kx^3 = -3x^3$, $k = -3$.
Now $x^4 - 3x^3 - 13x^2 + 3x + 12 = (x^2 - 1)(x^2 - 3x - 12)$.

All examples considered here involve monic polynomials. A monic polynomial has one as the coefficient of its highest degree term. In the next section, we will consider the use of the Factor Theorem with polynomials having first-term coefficients other than one.

EXAMPLE 6

Factor $x^3 - y^3$.

Solution

Consider this as a function of x. That is, $f(x) = x^3 - y^3$.
Since $f(y) = y^3 - y^3$
$= 0$,
then, by the Factor Theorem, $(x - y)$ is a factor of $x^3 - y^3$. Divide to obtain the other factor(s).

$$\begin{array}{r} x^2 + \ xy \ + y^2 \\ x - y \overline{)x^3 + 0x^2y + 0xy^2 - y^3} \\ \underline{x^3 - \ x^2y} \qquad\qquad\qquad \\ x^2y + 0xy^2 \qquad\quad \\ \underline{x^2y - \ xy^2} \qquad\quad \\ xy^2 - y^3 \\ \underline{xy^2 - y^3} \\ 0 \end{array}$$

Therefore $x^3 - y^3 = (x - y)(x^2 + xy + y^2)$.

The expression $x^3 - y^3$ is referred to as a **difference of cubes** and it occurs often enough that its factorization is worth memorizing:

$x^3 - y^3 = (x - y)(x^2 + xy + y^2)$.

Since $x^3 + y^3 = x^3 - (-y)^3$,

we have $x^3 + y^3 = (x - (-y))(x^2 + x(-y) + (-y)^2$

$= (x + y)(x^2 - xy + y^2)$.

The expression $x^3 + y^3$ is referred to as a **sum of cubes.** By the same process as above, $x^3 + y^3 = (x + y)(x^2 - xy + y^2)$.

The Sum and Difference of Cubes

$\mathbf{x^3 - y^3 = (x - y)(x^2 + xy + y^2)}$

$\mathbf{x^3 + y^3 = (x + y)(x^2 - xy + y^2)}$

EXAMPLE 7

Factor $27u^3 - 64$.

Solution

Since $27u^3 - 64 = (3u)^3 - (4)^3$

$= (3u - 4)((3u)^2 + (3u)(4) + (4)^2)$

$= (3u - 4)(9u^2 + 12u + 16)$.

Exercise 2.1

Part A

1. If $(x + 8)$ is a factor of $f(x)$, then what is the value of $f(-8)$?

Communication

2. a. If $f(5) = 0$, state a factor of $f(x)$.

   b. Explain how you would find the other factors of $f(x)$.

3. If $f(x) = x^3 + 2x^2 - 5x - 6$ is equal to 0 when $x = -1$ or 2 or -3, what are the factors of $f(x)$? Explain.

4. In each of the following, determine whether the binomial is a factor of $f(x)$.

   a. $x - 1; f(x) = x^2 - 7x + 6$
   b. $x + 2; f(x) = x^2 + 8x + 6$
   c. $x - 2; f(x) = x^3 - 3x^2 - 4x + 12$
   d. $x - 3; f(x) = x^3 + 6x^2 - 2x + 3$
   e. $x + 1; f(x) = x^3 - 5x^2 - 4x + 3$
   f. $2x - 1; f(x) = 4x^3 - 6x^2 + 8x - 3$

Part B

Knowledge/Understanding

5. If $f(x) = x^3 - 2x^2 - 2x - 3$,

   a. show that $f(3) = 0$.

   b. what is a linear factor of $f(x)$?

   c. find the quadratic factor by long division.

6. If $g(x) = x^3 - 2x^2 - 5x + 6$,

   a. show that $g(-2) = 0$.

   b. what is a linear factor of $g(x)$?

   c. find the quadratic factor by the method of comparing coefficients.

Application

7. Completely factor the following:

   a. $x^3 - 4x + 3$
   b. $x^3 + 2x^2 - x - 2$
   c. $y^3 + 19y^2 - 19y - 1$
   d. $x^3 + 2x^2 + 5x + 4$
   e. $y^3 - y^2 - y - 2$
   f. $x^3 - 9x^2 + 22x - 8$
   g. $x^4 - 8x^3 + 3x^2 + 40x - 12$
   h. $x^4 - 6x^3 - 15x^2 - 6x - 16$

Thinking/Inquiry/Problem Solving

8. If $(x - 1)$ is a factor of $x^3 - 2kx^2 + 3x + 1$, what is the value of k?

9. If $x^3 + 4x^2 + kx - 5$ is divisible by $(x + 2)$, what is the value of k?

Knowledge/Understanding

10. Using the formulas for factoring the sum or difference of cubes, factor each of the following:

    a. $x^3 - 27$
    b. $y^3 + 8$
    c. $125u^3 - 64r^3$
    d. $2000w^3 + 2y^3$
    e. $(x + y)^3 - u^3z^3$
    f. $5u^3 - 40(x + y)^3$

Part C

11. Use the Factor Theorem to prove that $x^3 - 6x^2 + 3x + 10$ is divisible by $x^2 - x - 2$.

Thinking/Inquiry/Problem Solving

12. a. Show that $x - y$ is a factor of $x^4 - y^4$.

    b. What is the other factor?

    c. Factor $x^4 - 81$.

13. a. Show that $x - y$ is a factor of $x^5 - y^5$.

    b. What is the other factor?

    c. Factor $x^5 - 32$.

14. a. Show that $x - y$ is a factor of $x^n - y^n$.

    b. What is the other factor?

15. Prove that $(x + a)$ is a factor of $(x + a)^5 + (x + c)^5 + (a - c)^5$.

16. Prove that $(x - a)$ is a factor of $x^3 - (a + b + c)x^2 + (ab + bc + ca)x - abc$.

17. If $n \in N$, under what conditions will $(x + y)$ be a factor of $x^n + y^n$?

18. Factor $x^5 + y^5$.

19. Does the expression $x^3 + 2x^2 + 5x + 12$ have any rational factors? Explain.

Section 2.2 — The Factor Theorem Extended

We have seen that if an expression such as $x^3 - 4x^2 + 5x - 6$ has a factor $(x - k)$, where k is an integer, then k must be a divisor of 6. In order to determine which, if any, of the divisors of 6 could be a value for k, we used a graphing calculator to determine a suitable value. In this example, $k = 3$ and $x^3 - 4x^2 + 5x - 6 = (x - 3)(x^2 - x + 2)$. What happens when the coefficient of the highest-order term is an integer other than 1? Let's consider an example.

EXAMPLE 1

Factor $f(x) = 3x^3 - 19x^2 + 27x - 7$.

Solution

If the factors have integers as coefficients, then the first terms must be $3x$, x, and x, and the second terms must be 7, 1, and 1, with the signs in the factors to be determined. We might have a factor such as $(3x - 1)$ or $(3x + 7)$ or $(x - 7)$. Are there other possibilities?

technology
APPENDIX P. 428

We draw the graph and search for possible values. The graph shown indicates three intercepts, but it is not easy to determine their values. Restricting the domain to $X_{min} = -1$ and $X_{max} = 5$ shows more clearly that there are three possible values for k. They are approximately $k = \frac{1}{3}$, $k = \frac{5}{3}$, and $k = \frac{13}{3}$, since the only denominator we can use is 3 (because 3 and 1 are the only divisors of the coefficient of x^3). Of these, only $\frac{1}{3}$ is a possible value for k, because the numerator must be a divisor of 7. Since $f\left(\frac{1}{3}\right) = 0$, $3x - 1$ is a factor. By long division, or the method of comparing coefficients, $3x^3 - 19x^2 + 27x - 7 = (3x - 1)(x^2 - 6x + 7)$. Since $x^2 - 6x + 7$ has no integer factors, we are done.

Y1=3X^3-19X²+27X-7
X=.33333333 Y=0

A function $f(x) = a_nx^n + a_{n-1}x^{n-1} + \ldots + a_0$ has a factor $(qx - p)$, if $f\left(\frac{p}{q}\right) = 0$, where q divides a_n and p divides a_0.

EXAMPLE 2

Factor $f(x) = 6x^3 - x^2 - 9x - 10$.

Solution

technology

A graph of the function shows that only one value of $k = \frac{p}{q}$ is possible, that it lies between 1 and 2, and that it is close to 2. Since p is a divisor of 10 and q is a divisor of 6, a good guess for k is $\frac{5}{3}$. Evaluating, $f\left(\frac{5}{3}\right) = 0$, so $6x^3 - x^2 - 9x - 10 = (3x - 5)(2x^2 + 3x + 2)$.

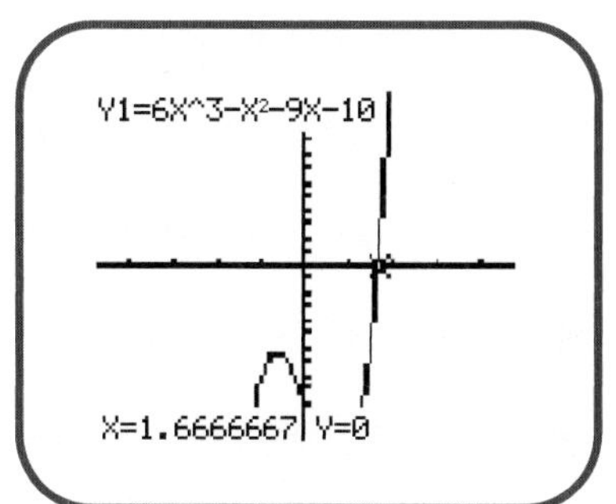

EXAMPLE 3

Factor fully $f(x) = 6x^4 - 17x^3 + 7x^2 - x - 10$.

Solution

technology

A graph of the function shows that $k = \frac{p}{q}$ can be between -1 and 0, or it can be between 2 and 3. Since p divides 10 and q divides 6, we try $k = -\frac{2}{3}$ and $k = \frac{5}{2}$, obtaining $f\left(-\frac{2}{3}\right) = 0$ and $f\left(\frac{5}{2}\right) = 0$. Therefore, two factors are $(3x + 2)$ and $(2x - 5)$. The other factors can be determined by division or by comparison. Then $6x^4 - 17x^3 + 7x^2 - x - 10 = (3x + 2)(2x - 5)(x^2 - x + 1)$, and the third factor cannot be simplified in integers.

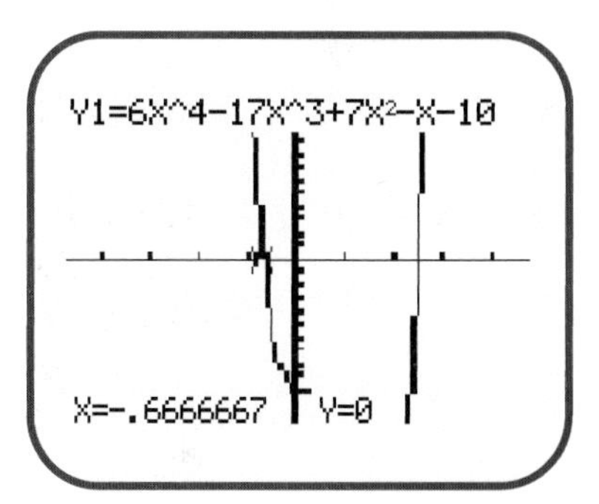

Exercise 2.2

Part A

Communication

1. For each of the following, explain how you could find the values $\frac{p}{q}$ of x that potentially could make the polynomial have a value of zero. State all the possible values of $\frac{p}{q}$.

   a. $2x^2 + 9x - 5$

   b. $3x^3 - 4x^2 + 7x + 8$

   c. $4x^3 + 3x^2 - 11x + 2$

   d. $8x^3 - 7x^2 + 23x - 4$

   e. $6x^3 - 7x^2 + 4x + 3$

   f. $2x^3 - 8x^2 + 5x - 6$

Part B

Application

2. A cubic function $f(x)$ with integral coefficients has the following properties: $f\left(\frac{3}{2}\right) = 0$, $(x - 2)$ is a factor of $f(x)$, and $f(4) = 50$. Determine $f(x)$.

3. A cubic function $g(x)$ with integral coefficients has the following properties: $g(3) = 0$, $g\left(-\frac{3}{4}\right) = 0$, $(x + 2)$ is a factor of $g(x)$, $g(1) = -84$. Determine $g(x)$.

Knowledge/Understanding

4. Factor fully the following polynomials:
   a. $2x^3 + x^2 + x - 1$
   b. $5x^3 + 3x^2 - 12x + 4$
   c. $6x^3 - 17x^2 + 11x - 2$
   d. $6x^3 + x^2 - 46x + 15$
   e. $5x^4 + x^3 - 22x^2 - 4x + 8$
   f. $18x^3 - 15x^2 - x + 2$
   g. $3x^4 - 5x^3 - x^2 - 4x + 4$
   h. $4x^4 - 19x^3 + 16x^2 - 19x + 12$

Part C

5. Factor fully the following expressions:
   a. $px^3 + (p - q)x^2 + (-2p - q)x + 2q$
   b. $abx^3 + (a - 2b - ab)x^2 + (2b - a - 2)x + 2$

Section 2.3 — Solving Polynomial Equations

In earlier grades, you learned to solve linear and quadratic equations. A quadratic equation can be solved by factoring (if possible) or by the quadratic formula $x = \frac{-b \pm \sqrt{b^2 - 4ac}}{2a}$. We now consider solutions to higher-order equations.

There are formulas for solving a general cubic equation and a general quartic equation, but they are quite complicated. The following examples demonstrate strategies that you can use in solving cubic, quartic, and other higher-order equations. Any equation of the form $f(x) = 0$ can be solved if $f(x)$ can be expressed as a combination of linear and quadratic factors. The first strategy, then, is to factor $f(x)$. It may be possible to factor $f(x)$ by familiar methods, such as grouping terms. If not, we can employ the Factor Theorem.

We will assume that unless otherwise stated, we are to solve all equations using the set of complex numbers, C, as the domain.

In general, if the domain is C, a polynomial equation of degree n has n roots.

EXAMPLE 1

Solve $x^3 - x^2 - 9x + 9 = 0$.

technology

Solution

The pattern of coefficients $(1, -1, -9, 9)$ suggests grouping the terms.

$$x^3 - x^2 - 9x + 9 = 0$$
$$x^2(x - 1) - 9(x - 1) = 0$$
$$(x - 1)(x^2 - 9) = 0$$
$$(x - 1)(x - 3)(x + 3) = 0$$

Then $x - 1 = 0$ or $x - 3 = 0$ or $x + 3 = 0$ so $x = 1$ or $x = 3$ or $x = -3$.

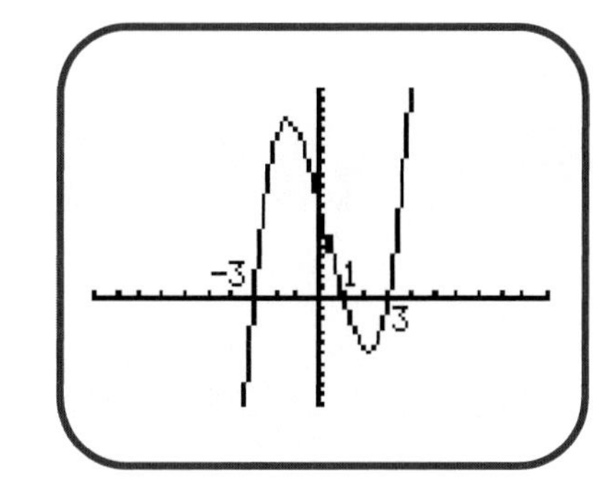

Note that 1, 3, and -3 are the x-intercepts of the graph of the corresponding cubic function $y = x^3 - x^2 - 9x + 9$.

EXAMPLE 2

Solve $x^3 + 4x - 5 = 0$.

Solution

Since there is no obvious way of grouping, the Factor Theorem is employed. The factors of 5 are ± 1, and ± 5.

If $\quad f(x) = x^3 + 4x - 5$,
then $f(1) = 1 + 4 - 5 = 0$,
therefore $(x - 1)$ is a factor.

There are two methods we can use for finding the second factor:

Comparing Coefficients

$$\begin{aligned} x^3 + 4x - 5 &= (x - 1)(x^2 + kx + 5) \\ &= x^3 + kx^2 + 5x - x^2 - kx - 5 \\ &= x^3 + x^2(k - 1) + x(5 - k) - 5 \end{aligned}$$

Therefore $k - 1 = 0$ or $5 - k = 4$

$k = 1$ $\qquad k = 1$

The second factor is

$x^2 + x + 5 = 0.$

Using Long Division

$$\begin{array}{r} x^2 + x + 5 \\ x - 1\overline{)x^3 + 0x^2 + 4x - 5} \\ \underline{x^3 - x^2} \\ x^2 + 4x \\ \underline{x^2 - x} \\ 5x - 5 \\ \underline{5x - 5} \\ 0 \end{array}$$

The second factor is

$x^2 + x + 5 = 0.$

Then $x^3 + 4x - 5 = (x - 1)(x^2 + x + 5)$

The equation $x^3 + 4x - 5 = 0$

becomes $(x - 1)(x^2 + x + 5) = 0$

$$\begin{aligned} \text{Then } x - 1 &= 0 \quad \text{or} \quad x^2 + x + 5 = 0 \\ x &= 1 \quad \text{or} \quad x = \frac{-1 \pm \sqrt{1 - 20}}{2} \\ &\qquad\qquad\quad\;\; = \frac{-1 \pm \sqrt{19}i}{2} \end{aligned}$$

EXAMPLE 3 Solve $x^3 + 9x^2 + 13x + 5 = 0.$

Solution

technology

The graph of $f(x) = x^3 + 9x^2 + 13x + 5$ is shown. If there are integer roots, they must be either ± 1 or ± 5. From the graph, one possible root is -1. Checking, $f(-1) = 0$. Then, by long division or the method of comparison,

$f(x) = (x + 1)(x^2 + 8x + 5).$

Therefore, $x^3 + 9x^2 + 13x + 5 = 0$

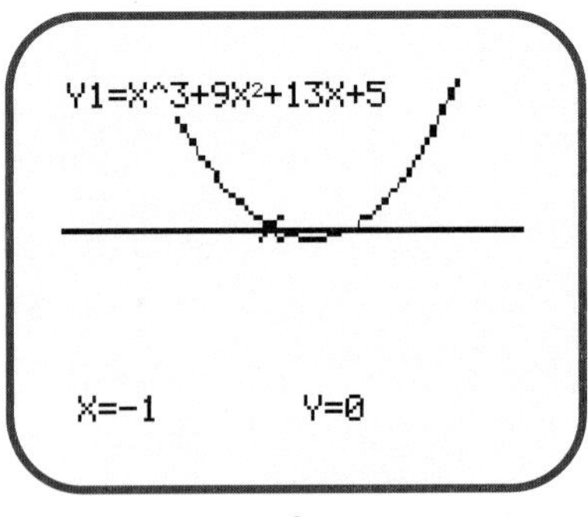

$$\begin{aligned} \text{and} \qquad (x + 1)(x^2 + 8x + 5) &= 0 \\ x = -1 \text{ or } x^2 + 8x + 5 &= 0 \\ x &= \frac{-8 \pm \sqrt{44}}{2} \\ &= \frac{-8 \pm 2\sqrt{11}}{2} \\ &= -4 \pm \sqrt{11} \end{aligned}$$

The solutions are $x = -1$, $x = -4 \pm \sqrt{11}$.

$$\begin{array}{r} x^2 + 8x + 5 \\ x + 1\overline{)x^3 + 9x^2 + 13x + 5} \\ \underline{x^3 + x^2} \\ 8x^2 + 13x \\ \underline{8x^2 + 8x} \\ 5x + 5 \\ \underline{5x + 5} \\ 0 \end{array}$$

EXAMPLE 4 Solve $6x^3 - 13x^2 + x + 2 = 0$.

Solution

technology

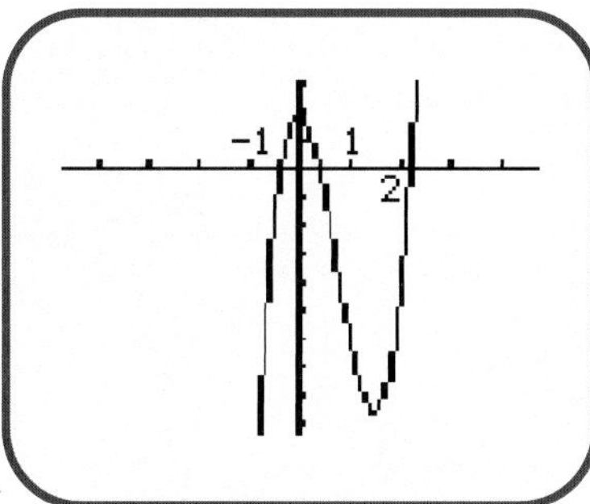

Let $f(x) = 6x^3 - 13x^2 + x + 2$.
Since $f(x)$ is not a monic polynomial, non-integer rational roots are possible for $f(x) = 0$. Since p is a divisor of 6 and q is a divisor of 2, the possible values for $\frac{q}{p}$ are $\pm 1, \pm 2, \pm\frac{1}{2}, \pm\frac{1}{3}, \pm\frac{1}{6}$, and $\pm\frac{2}{3}$.
Graphing $f(x)$ on a graphing calculator using $X_{min} = -2$ and $X_{max} = 2$ as our domain, we find that one root of $f(x) = 0$ lies in the interval $-.34 < x < -.29$, another lies in the interval $.46 < x < .51$, and the third root appears to be 2.

Checking our list of values for $\frac{q}{p}$, we see that the only possible values are $-\frac{1}{3}, \frac{1}{2}$, and 2.
Checking, we find that $f\left(-\frac{1}{3}\right) = f\left(\frac{1}{2}\right) = f(2) = 0$.
Therefore $f(x) = (3x + 1)(2x - 1)(x - 2)$ and the roots of $f(x) = 0$ are $-\frac{1}{3}, \frac{1}{2}$, and 2.

EXAMPLE 5

a. Find the family of cubic functions whose x-intercepts are -2, 1, and 3.

b. Find the particular member of the above family whose graph passes through the point (2, 20).

Solution

a. Since -2, 1, and 3 are x-intercepts, $(x + 2)$, $(x - 1)$, and $(x - 3)$ must be factors of the cubic function. Therefore, $y = k(x + 2)(x - 1)(x - 3)$, where k is a constant, represents the family of cubic functions.
b. If (2, 20) lies on the graph of one member of the above family, then (2, 20) must satisfy its equation. Substituting, we get $20 = k(4)(1)(-1)$ or $k = -5$. Therefore, the particular cubic function is $y = -5(x + 2)(x - 1)(x - 3)$.

We frequently encounter equations that cannot be factored. In such situations, the best we can hope for is to determine approximate values for the roots using a graphing calculator. The following example illustrates this application.

EXAMPLE 6 Solve $x^3 - 5x^2 + 11 = 0$.

Solution

Can the expression be factored?

The only factors of 11 are ± 1 and ± 11, and none is a root of the equation.

Using a graphing calculator, graph $f(x) = x^3 - 5x^2 + 11$. Using the **ZDecimal** instruction in the ZOOM mode, note from the graph that there is a root slightly to the left of -1.

technology

Press [2nd] [TRACE] (CALC) for the CALCULATE menu.
Select **2:zero** and press [ENTER].
Input -2 as the **Left Bound.**
Input -1 as the **Right Bound.**
Input -1 as the **Guess.**
The approximate root is -1.31935.

Referring back to the graph, you will notice that there is another root close to 2.
Use 1 and 3 as the left and right bounds and 2 as your guess.
The second root is approximately 1.87667.
Use a similar procedure for the other root between 4 and 5.
This third root is approximately 4.44268.

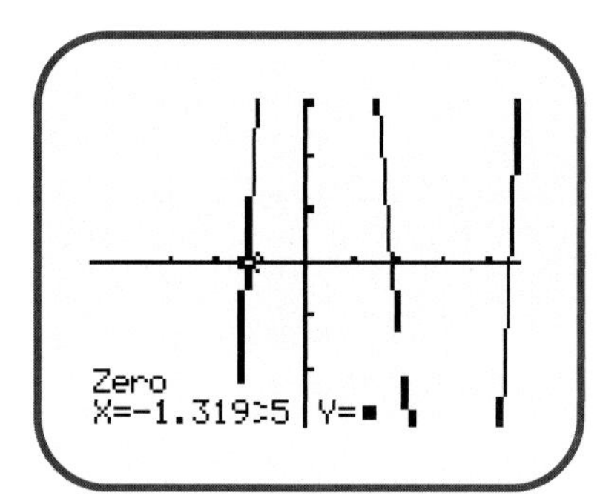

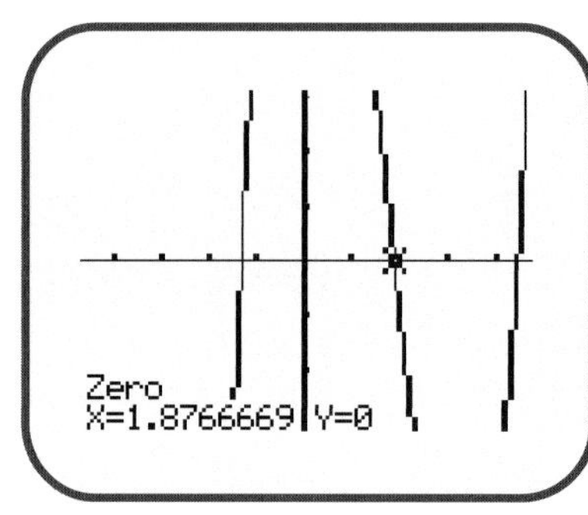

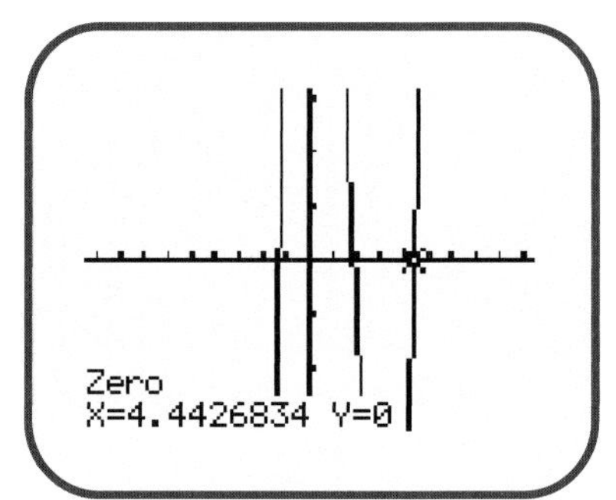

The roots of the equation are -1.3, 1.9, and 4.4, to one decimal place. Note that this procedure will find approximate real roots but will not find the non-real roots (if there are any) of a polynomial equation.

EXAMPLE 7 Solve: $x^4 - 24x^2 - 25 = 0$.

Solution

$(x^2 - 25)(x^2 + 1) = 0$

$x^2 = 25$ or $x^2 = -1$

Then $x = \pm 5$ or $x = \pm i$.

Sometimes making a substitution assists in the solving of higher-order equations. In Example 7, you could let $y = x^2$ to get the equation $y^2 - 24y - 25$. Solve for y and then solve for x. In the next example, the substitution is more subtle.

EXAMPLE 8 Solve $(x^2 - 5x - 5)(x^2 - 5x + 3) = 9$.

Solution

Note the identical $x^2 - 5x$ in the two quadratic factors.
Let $y = x^2 - 5x$, so the equation becomes

$$(y-5)(y+3) = 9$$
$$y^2 - 2y - 24 = 0$$
$$(y - 6)(y + 4) = 0$$
$$y = 6 \text{ or } y = -4.$$

Then $x^2 - 5x = 6$ or $x^2 - 5x = -4$

$$x^2 - 5x - 6 = 0 \text{ or } x^2 - 5x + 4 = 0$$
$$(x - 6)(x + 1) = 0 \text{ or } (x - 4)(x - 1) = 0$$

$x = 6$ or -1 or 4 or 1.

Exercise 2.3

Part A

Communication

1. For the function $f(x) = x^3 + 5x^2 + 2x - 8$, explain how you determine which integral values of x you would use to make $f(x) = 0$.

2. Write a monic polynomial equation with roots 1, -2, and 4.

3. a. Find the family of cubic functions whose x-intercepts are -3, 0, and 2.
   b. Find the particular member of the above family whose graph passes through the point $(-1, 12)$.

4. a. Find the family of cubic functions whose x-intercepts are -2, -1, and 1.
   b. Find the particular member of the above family whose graph passes through the point $(2, -6)$.

5. a. Find the family of quartic functions whose x-intercepts are -2, -1, 1, and 3.
   b. Find the particular member of the above family whose graph passes through the point $(2, -6)$.

6. Write a polynomial equation with integer coefficients that has the roots 1, 2, and $\frac{3}{5}$.

7. If 2 is a root of the equation $2x^3 - 5kx^2 + 7x + 10 = 0$, find the value of k.

Part B

Knowledge/Understanding

8. Solve for x in each of the following, $x \in C$.

a. $x^2 - x - 20 = 0$
b. $x^2 + 2x + 10 = 0$
c. $x(x - 2)(x + 5) = 0$
d. $x(x^2 - 4) = 0$
e. $x^3 = x$
f. $x^4 - 1 = 0$
g. $x^3 - 3x^2 - 4x = 0$
h. $8x^3 - 27 = 0$
i. $x^3 - 3x^2 - 4x + 12 = 0$
j. $x^3 - 9x^2 + 26x = 24$
k. $x^3 - 3x - 2 = 0$
l. $x^3 - 2x^2 - 15x + 36 = 0$
m. $x^3 + 8x + 10 = 7x^2$
n. $x^3 - 3x^2 + 16 = 6x$

9. Solve for x in each of the following, $x \in C$.

a. $2x^3 + 5x^2 - 3x - 4 = 0$
b. $4x^3 + 19x^2 + 11x - 4 = 0$
c. $5x^3 - 8x^2 - 27x + 18 = 0$
d. $4x^4 - 2x^3 - 16x^2 + 8x = 0$
e. $x^4 - 13x^2 + 36 = 0$
f. $x^4 - 7 = 6x^2$
g. $5(x + 1)^3 = -5$
h. $(x + 1)(x + 5)(x + 3) = -3$

10. Solve for x in each of the following, $x \in C$.

a. $x^8 - 10x^4 + 9 = 0$
b. $x^6 - 7x^3 - 8 = 0$
c. $(x^2 - x)^2 - 8(x^2 - x) + 12 = 0$
d. $\left(x - \frac{1}{x}\right)^2 - \frac{77}{12}\left(x - \frac{1}{x}\right) + 10 = 0$
e. $(3x - 5)(3x + 1)^2(3x + 7) + 68 = 0$
f. $(x^2 + 6x + 6)(x^2 + 6x + 8) = 528$

Application

11. A steel cube is uniformly coated with ice. The volume of ice is given by $y = 8x^3 + 36x^2 + 54x$ cm^3, where x is the thickness of ice. Find the thickness of the ice when its volume is 2170 cm^3.

12. Find the approximate roots of the following equations, correct to three decimal places, using a graphing calculator.

a. $x^2 + 7x - 1 = 0$
b. $x^3 - 2x^2 - 8x + 13 = 0$
c. $2x^3 - 6x^2 + 4 = 0$
d. $3x^4 - 20x^2 + 23 = 0$

Application

13. The height, length, and width of a small box are consecutive integers with the height being the smallest of the three dimensions. If the length and width are increased by 1 cm each and the height is doubled, then the volume is increased by 120 cm^3. Find the dimensions of the original small box.

Thinking/Inquiry/
Problem Solving

14. A silo has a cylindrical main section and a hemispherical roof. If the height of the main section is 10 m, what should the radius be in order that the volume of the silo (including the part inside the roof section) is 2000 m^3? (You will need to use your graphing calculator to find the approximate answer correct to two decimal places.)

Part C

15. We start observing a rocket at time $t = 0$, when it has a velocity of 4 km/s (and its displacement is considered to be zero). Its acceleration is 2 km/s^2, and this acceleration is increasing at a rate of 0.6 km/s^2. The displacement of the rocket at time t ($t > 0$) is represented by $s = 0.1t^3 + t^2 + 4t$. At what time has the rocket travelled 25 km?

Section 2.4 — Properties of the Roots of Quadratic Equations

Suppose you are asked to verify that 2 and 7 are the roots of the quadratic equation $x^2 - 9x + 14 = 0$. How would you do it? One way is to substitute each of these values into the left side of the equation and show that the resulting value is zero (the value of the right side). That will certainly work, but is there any other way?

Suppose you are asked to find the quadratic equation whose roots are each five more than the roots of the equation $2x^2 - 17x + 2 = 0$. How could you do that? One way would be to first solve this equation and find its roots. (In this particular case, the roots are not very pretty. They are $\frac{17 \pm \sqrt{273}}{4}$.) Then you would add 5 to each of these numbers (giving you $\frac{37 \pm \sqrt{273}}{4}$, which one still wouldn't describe as pretty) to get the roots of the required new equation. Then you could write the new equation as $\left(x - \frac{37 + \sqrt{273}}{4}\right)\left(x - \frac{37 - \sqrt{273}}{4}\right) = 0$, and finally you could multiply this out and simplify the result, ending with $2x^2 - 37x + 137 = 0$. But here's the good news: there is another way to handle problems such as these, because the roots of a quadratic equation $ax^2 + bx + c = 0$ are related to the coefficients a, b, and c. The investigation below helps us to identify the relationships.

INVESTIGATION

For each equation, complete the table, then answer the questions below.

Equation	a	b	c	Roots	Sum of Roots	Product of Roots
$x^2 - 5x + 6 = 0$	1	−5	6			
$x^2 + 3x - 28 = 0$	1	3	−28			
$3x^2 + 19x + 6 = 0$	3	19	6			
$x^2 - 4x + 1 = 0$	1	−4	1			
$2x^2 - 17x + 2 = 0$	2	−17	2			
$5x^2 + x + 2 = 0$	5	1	2			

1. State a relationship between the sum of the roots of a quadratic equation and the coefficients of the equation.
2. State a relationship between the product of the roots of a quadratic equation and the coefficients of the equation.

The results you have noted are easy to prove in general. The quadratic equation $ax^2 + bx + c = 0$ has roots $x_1 = \frac{-b + \sqrt{b^2 - 4ac}}{2a}$ and $x_2 = \frac{-b - \sqrt{b^2 - 4ac}}{2a}$.

$$x_1 + x_2 = \frac{-b + \sqrt{b^2 - 4ac}}{2a} + \frac{-b - \sqrt{b^2 - 4ac}}{2a}$$

$$= \frac{-2b + \sqrt{b^2 - 4ac} - \sqrt{b^2 - 4ac}}{2a}$$

$$= -\frac{b}{a}$$

and $x_1 x_2 = \left(\frac{-b + \sqrt{b^2 - 4ac}}{2a}\right)\left(\frac{-b - \sqrt{b^2 - 4ac}}{2a}\right)$

$$= \frac{b^2 - (b^2 - 4ac)}{4a^2}$$

$$= \frac{4ac}{4a^2}$$

$$= \frac{c}{a}$$

Also, if x_1 and x_2 are the roots of $ax^2 + bx + c = 0$, then this equation can be written as $(x - x_1)(x - x_2) = 0$, which, when simplified, becomes $x^2 - (x_1 + x_2)x + x_1x_2 = 0$. However, $ax^2 + bx + c = 0$ can also be written as $x^2 + \frac{b}{a}x + \frac{c}{a} = 0$.
Then $x^2 - (x_1 + x_2)x + x_1x_2 = x^2 + \frac{b}{a}x + \frac{c}{a}$, and we can conclude that $-(x_1 + x_2) = \frac{b}{a}$ or $(x_1 + x_2) = -\frac{b}{a}$ and $x_1x_2 = \frac{c}{a}$.

The sum of the roots of $ax^2 + bx + c = 0$ is $-\frac{b}{a}$.

The product of the roots of $ax^2 + bx + c = 0$ is $\frac{c}{a}$ and any quadratic equation can be written as $x^2 - (\text{sum of the roots})x + (\text{product of the roots}) = 0$.

EXAMPLE 1

Find the sum and product of the roots of $3x^2 + 5x + 8 = 0$.

Solution

In this case, $a = 3$, $b = 5$, and $c = 8$.
Therefore, the sum of the roots is $-\frac{b}{a} = -\frac{5}{3}$, and the product of the roots is $\frac{c}{a} = \frac{8}{3}$.

EXAMPLE 2

Find the quadratic equation whose roots are $\frac{1}{2}$ and 2.

Solution

The sum of the roots is $\frac{1}{2} + 2 = \frac{5}{2}$ and the product of the roots is $\left(\frac{1}{2}\right)(2) = 1$.
The quadratic equation is $x^2 - (\text{sum of the roots})\, x + (\text{product of the roots}) = 0$.
Therefore, the equation is $x^2 - \frac{5}{2}x + 1 = 0$ or $2x^2 - 5x + 2 = 0$. It is customary to express the equation with integral coefficients.

EXAMPLE 3 If 4 is one root of the equation $x^2 + kx - 24 = 0$, determine the value of k.

Solution 1

Since 4 is a root, substitute $x = 4$.

$$\begin{aligned} 4^2 + 4k - 24 &= 0 \\ 16 + 4k - 24 &= 0 \\ 4k &= 8 \\ k &= 2 \end{aligned}$$

Solution 2

Let h represent the second root. The product of the roots is $4h$.

Then $4h = \frac{c}{a} = -24$

so $h = -6$,

and the sum of the roots is $-6 + 4 = -\frac{b}{a} = -k$.

Therefore, $k = 2$.

EXAMPLE 4 Find the equation whose roots are each three more than the roots of $x^2 + 7x + 2 = 0$.

Solution

Let x_1 and x_2 represent the roots of the given equation.

Then $x_1 + x_2 = -7$ and $x_1x_2 = 2$.

The roots of the required equation will be $(x_1 + 3)$ and $(x_2 + 3)$.

For the new equation, the sum of the roots is
$$\begin{aligned}(x_1 + 3) + (x_2 + 3) &= (x_1 + x_2) + 6 \\ &= -7 + 6 \\ &= -1\end{aligned}$$

and the product of the roots is
$$\begin{aligned}(x_1 + 3)(x_2 + 3) &= x_1x_2 + 3x_1 + 3x_2 + 9 \\ &= x_1x_2 + 3(x_1 + x_2) + 9 \\ &= 2 + 3(-7) + 9 \\ &= -10.\end{aligned}$$

Therefore, the required equation is $x^2 - (-1)x + (-10) = 0$ or $x^2 + x - 10 = 0$.

EXAMPLE 5 Find the equation whose roots are the squares of the roots of $3x^2 - 9x + 4 = 0$.

Solution

Let x_1 and x_2 represent the roots of the given equation.

Then $x_1 + x_2 = 3$ and $x_1x_2 = \frac{4}{3}$.

The roots of the required equation are x_1^2 and x_2^2.

The sum of these roots is
$$\begin{aligned}(x_1^2 + x_2^2) &= (x_1^2 + 2x_1x_2 + x_2^2) - 2x_1x_2 \\ &= (x_1 + x_2)^2 - 2x_1x_2 \\ &= (3)^2 - 2\left(\frac{4}{3}\right)\end{aligned}$$

$$= 9 - \frac{8}{3}$$
$$= \frac{19}{3}$$

and the product of these roots is $(x_1^2)(x_2^2) = (x_1x_2)^2$

$$= \left(\frac{4}{3}\right)^2$$
$$= \frac{16}{9}.$$

The required equation is $x^2 - \frac{19}{3}x + \frac{16}{9} = 0$ or $9x^2 - 57x + 16 = 0$.

Exercise 2.4

Part A

Knowledge/ Understanding

1. State the sum and product of the roots of the following equations:

   a. $x^2 + 5x + 11 = 0$ b. $2x^2 - 5x + 9 = 0$ c. $3x^2 - 7x - 8 = 0$

Application

2. Find a quadratic equation (with integral coefficients) whose roots have the given sum and product.

   a. sum is 3; product is 7
   b. sum is -6; product is 4
   c. sum is $\frac{1}{5}$; product is $-\frac{2}{25}$
   d. sum is $-\frac{13}{12}$; product is $\frac{1}{4}$
   e. sum is -11; product is $-\frac{2}{3}$

Knowledge/ Understanding

3. Find a quadratic equation (with integral coefficients) having the given roots:

   a. 3, 7
   b. -5, 8
   c. 3, $\frac{1}{3}$
   d. $\frac{1}{2}$, $\frac{3}{4}$
   e. $-\frac{4}{5}$, $\frac{3}{25}$
   f. $2+i$, $2-i$

Communication

4. If 5 is one root of the equation $2x^2 + kx - 20 = 0$, explain two methods that you would use to find the value of k. Determine k.

Part B

5. If -7 is one root of the equation $x^2 + x - 2k = 0$, determine the other root and the value of k.

6. Find the equation whose roots are each six more than the roots of $x^2 + 8x - 1 = 0$.

7. Find the equation whose roots are each five more than the roots of $2x^2 - 17x + 2 = 0$.

Application

8. Find the equation whose roots are each three times the roots of $3x^2 + 7x + 3 = 0$.

9. Find the equation whose roots are the squares of the roots of $4x^2 - 9x - 2 = 0$.

10. Find the equation whose roots are the reciprocals of the roots of $5x^2 + 10x + 1 = 0$.

11. Find the equation whose roots are the squares of the reciprocals of the roots of $x^2 + 6x - 2 = 0$.

12. Find the equation whose roots are the cubes of the roots of $2x^2 + 4x + 1 = 0$.

Part C

Thinking/Inquiry/ Problem Solving

13. A cubic equation may be expressed as $ax^3 + bx^2 + cx + d = 0$ or as $(x - x_1)(x - x_2)(x - x_3) = 0$ where x_1, x_2, and x_3 are the roots of the equation. Use this fact to find the values of $(x_1 + x_2 + x_3)$, $(x_1x_2 + x_1x_3 + x_2x_3)$, and $(x_1x_2x_3)$ in terms of a, b, c, and d.

14. Using the result of Question 13, find a cubic equation (with integral coefficients) whose roots are $\frac{1}{2}$, 2, and 4.

Thinking/Inquiry/ Problem Solving

15. Find the equation whose roots are each two more than the roots of $x^3 - 4x^2 + 3x - 2 = 0$.

16. Using the method employed in Question 13, find the relationship between the coefficients in a quartic equation and the roots of that equation.

Section 2.5 — Solving Polynomial Inequalities

When the equal sign in an equation is replaced by any of $>$, $<$, $\geq$, or $\leq$, the equation becomes an inequality. You already know that linear inequalities can be easily solved algebraically. Quadratic and especially cubic or quartic inequalities are more easily solved with the help of a sketch or graph.

EXAMPLE 1

Solve $x^2 - x - 6 < 0$.

Solution

technology

Consider the graph of $y = x^2 - x - 6$
$= (x - 3)(x + 2)$.

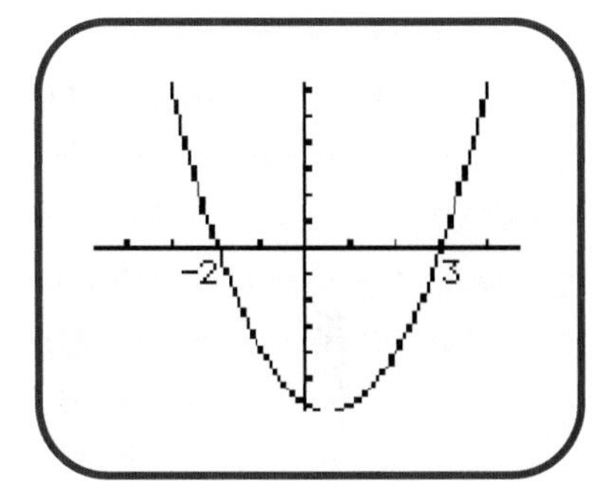

The values of x that satisfy the inequality $x^2 - x - 6 < 0$ are the same values for which the graph of $y = x^2 - x - 6$ is below the x-axis. From the graph, $x^2 - x - 6 < 0$ for $-2 < x < 3$.

EXAMPLE 2

Solve $x^3 - 5x^2 + 2x + 8 \geq 0$.

Solution

technology

We first graph $y = f(x) = x^3 - 5x^2 + 2x + 8$.

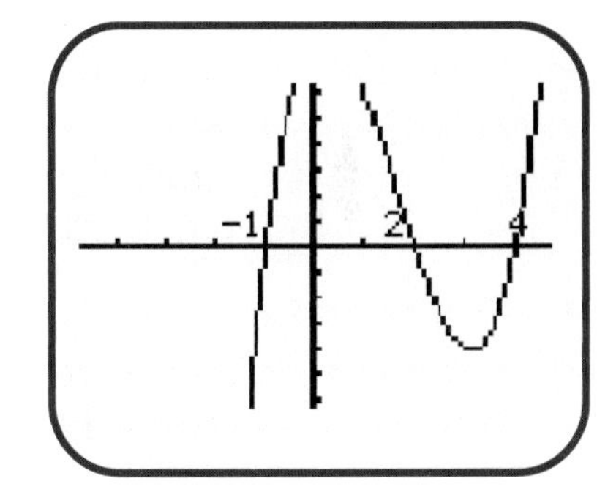

From the graph it appears that $x^3 - 5x^2 + 2x + 8 = 0$ if $x = -1$, 2, or 4. Since $f(-1) = f(2) = f(4) = 0$, the x-intercepts are -1, 2, and 4. The solution to the inequality $x^3 - 5x^2 + 2x + 8 \geq 0$ is the set of values of x for which the graph of $y = f(x)$ is on or above the x-axis.
The solution is $-1 \leq x \leq 2$ or $x \geq 4$.

EXAMPLE 3

Solve $2x^3 - 3x^2 - 9x + 5 < 0$.

Solution

technology

The solution to the inequality is the set of values for which the graph of $f(x) = 2x^3 - 3x^2 - 9x + 5$ is below the x-axis.

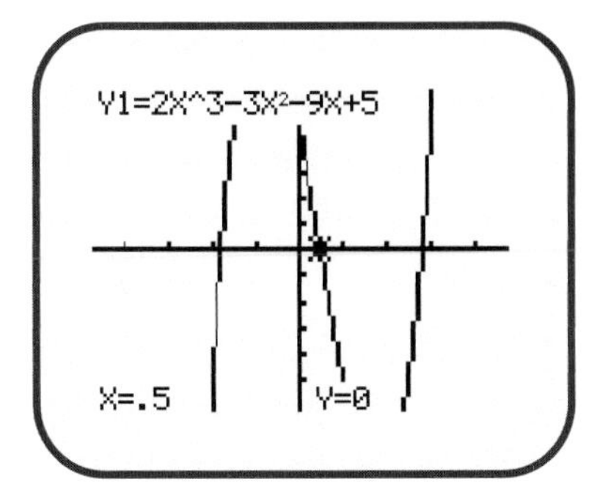

Using the graph and the TRACE function, it appears that the x-intercepts are approximately -1.8, 0.5, and 2.8.

If q is a divisor of 2 and p is a divisor of 5, possible values of x are $\frac{1}{2}$ and $\frac{5}{2}$.

Use **1:value** in the CALCULATE menu or substitution to obtain $f\left(\frac{5}{2}\right) = -5$ and $f\left(\frac{1}{2}\right) = 0$.

Since $f\left(\frac{1}{2}\right) = 0$, $2x - 1$ is a factor.

$$\begin{array}{r}
x^2 - x - 5 \\
2x - 1\overline{)2x^3 - 3x^2 - 9x + 5} \\
\underline{2x^3 - x^2} \\
-2x^2 - 9x \\
\underline{-2x^2 + x} \\
-10x + 5 \\
\underline{-10x + 5} \\
0
\end{array}$$

Then $2x^3 - 3x^2 - 9x + 5 = 0$

$(2x - 1)(x^2 - x - 5) = 0$

$x = \frac{1}{2}$ or $x = \frac{1 \pm \sqrt{21}}{2}$.

Now, from the graph, $2x^3 - 3x^2 - 9x + 5 < 0$

for $x < \frac{1 - \sqrt{21}}{2}$ or $\frac{1}{2} < x < \frac{1 + \sqrt{21}}{2}$.

If approximate answers are sufficient, then we can make conclusions without having to solve the equation completely. In the above example, using only the TRACE function, we might, depending on the given conditions, be satisfied with the solution $x < -1.8$, or $0.5 < x < 2.8$. In some situations an approximation is the best we can hope to achieve.

EXAMPLE 4

Solve $x^4 - 3x^3 - 7x^2 + 16x + 12 > 0$.

Solution

technology

The graph of $f(x) = x^4 - 3x^3 - 7x^2 + 16x + 12$ is shown. From the graph, there are no integer roots for the equation $f(x) = 0$. This means that there are no simple factors of the expression and, in fact, it does not factor at all. The best we can do is to approximate the intercepts using the TRACE function. Then, to one decimal place accuracy,

$x^4 - 3x^3 - 7x^2 + 16x + 12 > 0$

for $x < -2.2$, or $-0.6 < x < 2.5$, or $x > 3.3$.

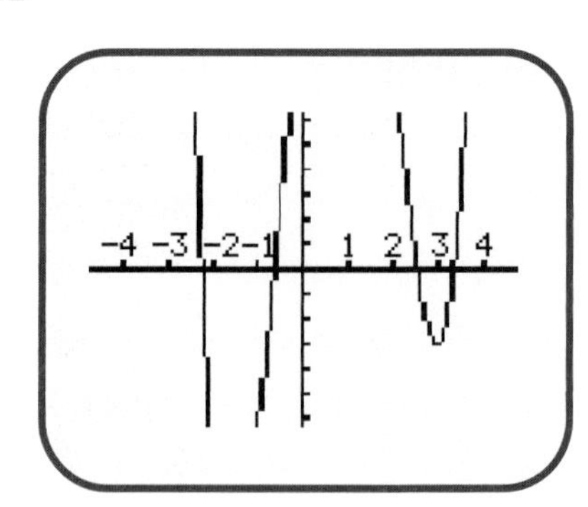

Exercise 2.5

Part A

Knowledge/Understanding

1. Use the graphs of the following functions to state when

(i) $f(x) > 0$ (ii) $f(x) < 0$

a.

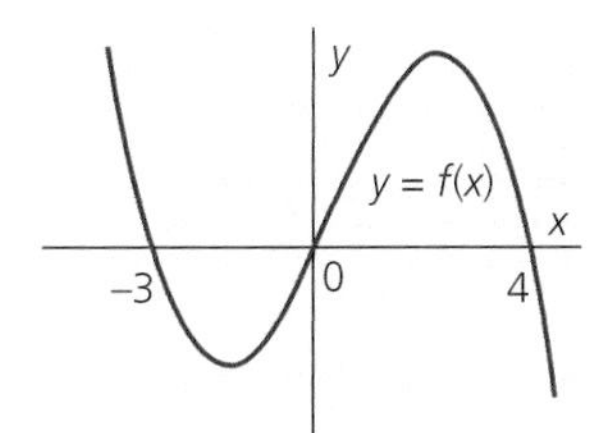

b.

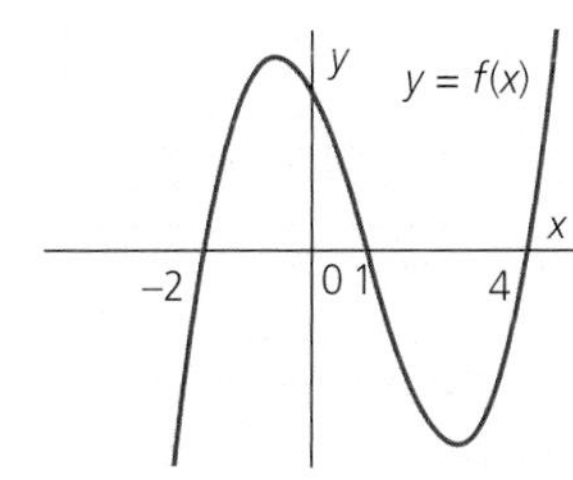

c.

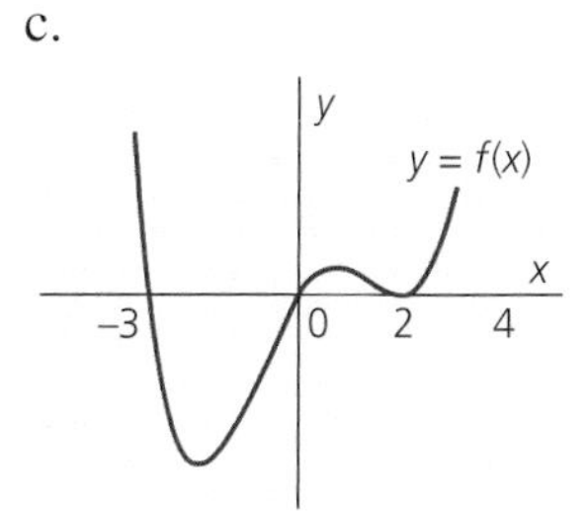

Part B

2. Solve each of the following, $x \in R$.

a. $x(x - 2) < 0$

b. $(x + 3)(x - 1) \leq 0$

c. $x^2 - 7x + 10 \leq 0$

d. $2x^2 + 5x - 3 > 0$

e. $-x^2 + 4x - 4 \geq 0$

f. $-x^3 + 9x \geq 0$

g. $x^3 - 5x^2 < x - 5$

h. $2x^3 + x^2 - 5x + 2 \leq 0$

i. $x^3 - 10x - 2 \geq 0$

j. $x^2 + 1 > 0$

technology

3. The viscosity, v, of oil used in cars is related to its temperature, t, by the formula $v = -t^3 + 9t^2 - 27t + 21$, where each unit of t is equivalent to 50°C.

a. Graph the function of $v = -t^3 + 9t^2 - 27t + 21$ on your graphing calculator.

b. Determine the value of t for $v > 0$, correct to two decimal places.

c. Determine the value of t for $v < -20$, correct to two decimal places.

Application

4. A projectile is shot upwards with an initial velocity of 30 m/s. Its height at time t is given by $h = 30t - 4.9t^2$. During what period of time is the projectile more than 40 m above the ground? Write your answer correct to two decimal places.

Thinking/Inquiry/Problem Solving

5. A rectangular solid is to be constructed with a special kind of wire along all the edges. The length of the base is to be twice the width of the base. The height of the rectangular solid is such that the total amount of wire used (for the whole figure) is 40 cm. Find the range of possible values for the width of the base so that the volume of the figure will lie between 2 cm^3 and 4 cm^3. Write your answer correct to two decimal places.

Section 2.6 — Absolute Value Functions

In manufacturing, quality control is very important. If the piston in an engine is too large, it will bind, and if it is too small, it will not work efficiently. The manufacturer might decide that a piston of radius 4 cm must not deviate more than 0.001 cm at this radius.

The margin of error, e, can be written as the inequality $-0.001 \leq e \leq 0.001$. This inequality can be written by the absolute value statement $|e| \leq 0.001$ and read as "the absolute value of e is less than or equal to 0.001."

A real number can be represented by a position on the number line. The absolute value of such a number is the positive distance between the origin and the number. For example, $|4| = 4$, $|-3| = 3$, $|0| = 0$, and so on.

When numbers are represented as points on a number line, $|x|$ is the distance (undirected) from x to 0 (the origin). So $|x| = 4$ means that x is a number four units distant from zero. If $|x| = 4$, x is either 4 or -4.

$$|x| = 4$$

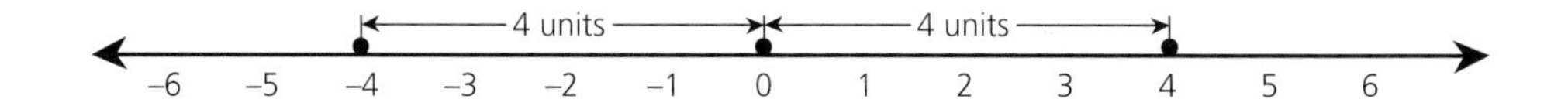

EXAMPLE 1 Evaluate $|5| - |-9| + 3|5 - 12|$.

Solution

$$\begin{aligned} |5| - |-9| + 3|5 - 12| &= 5 - 9 + 3|-7| \\ &= 5 - 9 + 3 \times 7 \\ &= 17 \end{aligned}$$

EXAMPLE 2 Solve for x if $|x - 7| = 3$.

Solution

Since $x - 7$ is three units from the origin, $x - 7 = 3$ or $x - 7 = -3$. Therefore, $x = 10$ or $x = 4$.

EXAMPLE 3 Solve $|x| < 3$.

Solution

Using the geometric definition of absolute value, this statement says that x is less than three units away from the origin. If we look at the real number line, this means that x must lie in the interval between -3 and $+3$.

Therefore, the values of x satisfying $|x| < 3$ are $-3 < x < 3, x \in R$.

EXAMPLE 4

Solve $|x - 3| > 5$.

Solution

Using the geometric definition of absolute value, this statement says that $x - 3$ is more than five units away from the origin. Looking at the real number line, this means that $x - 3$ must lie in the interval to the right of 5 *or* in the interval to the left of -5.

Therefore, $x - 3 > 5$ or $x - 3 < -5$.
Solving these inequalities for x gives us $x > 8$ or $x < -2$.
We now summarize the preceding discussion by giving the definition of the absolute value of any real number.

The Absolute Value of x, $x \in R$, is

$$|x| = \begin{cases} x, \text{ if } x \geq 0. \\ -x, \text{ if } x < 0. \end{cases}$$

EXAMPLE 5

Graph the absolute value function $f(x) = |x|, x \in R$.

Solution

The graph of $f(x) = |x|$ is shown at the right as it would appear on a graphing calculator or a computer.

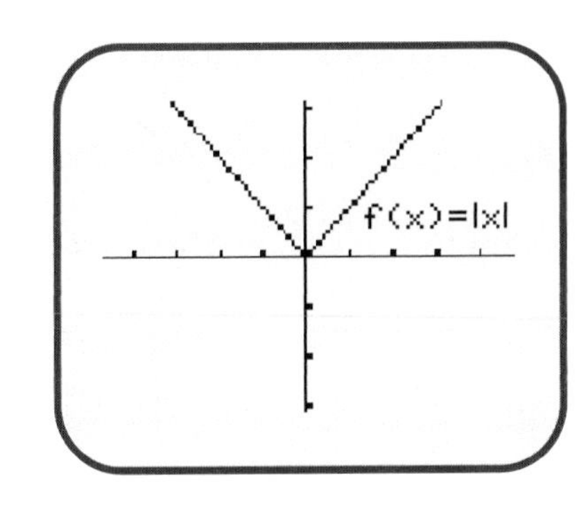

technology

To graph $f(x) = |x|$ on your calculator, first select [Y =] and then [MATH].
In the MATH menu, move the cursor to NUM and select **1:abs(**, the absolute value function.
Select [ENTER] to return to the y_1 screen.

Enter $y_1 = \text{abs}(x)$ and press GRAPH.

You might also use the following method to graph $f(x) = |x|$.
If $x \geq 0$, $|x| = x$ and the graph is the line $y = x$.
If $x < 0$, $|x| = -x$ and the graph is the line $y = -x$.

Another way of graphing $f(x) = |x|$ is to graph $f(x) = x$, then reflect the portion of the graph below the x-axis in the x-axis, as illustrated, to obtain the required graph.

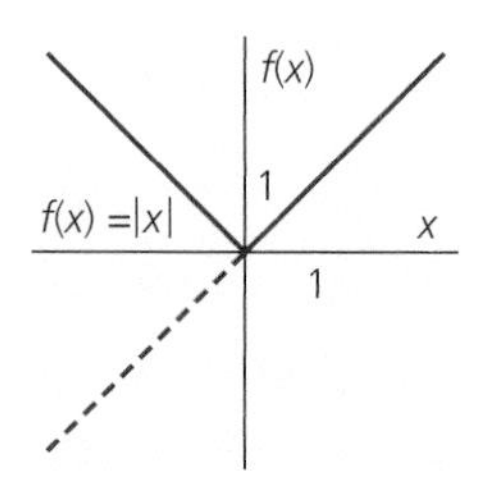

The definition of absolute value extends to functions, and the algebraic definition can be used in obtaining the graphs of such functions.

For a given function $f(x)$,

$$|f(x)| = \begin{cases} f(x), \text{ if } f(x) \geq 0. \\ -f(x), \text{ if } f(x) < 0. \end{cases}$$

This means that in order to obtain the graph of $y = |f(x)|$, we can sketch the graph $y = f(x)$ and reflect the portion(s) of the graph that are below the x-axis.

EXAMPLE 6 Graph $y = |2x + 1|$, $x \in R$.

Solution

To graph $y = |2x + 1|$, first graph $y = 2x + 1$. The portion of the graph below the x-axis is reflected in the x-axis as illustrated, to obtain the required graph. The graph $y = |2x + 1|$ is shown.
Note that if $x = 1$, $y = 3$, and if $x = -2$, $y = 3$.
The graph of $y = |2x + 1|$ contains the line $y = 2x + 1$ for $x \geq -\frac{1}{2}$, $x \in R$, and the line $y = -2x - 1$ for $x < -\frac{1}{2}$.

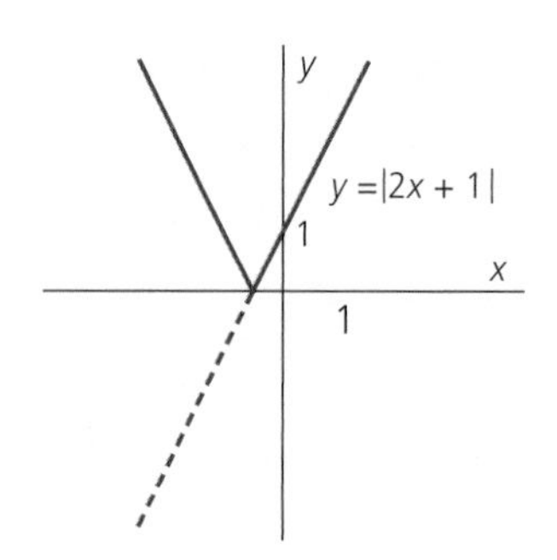

EXAMPLE 7

Graph $y = |x^2 - 4|, x \in R$.

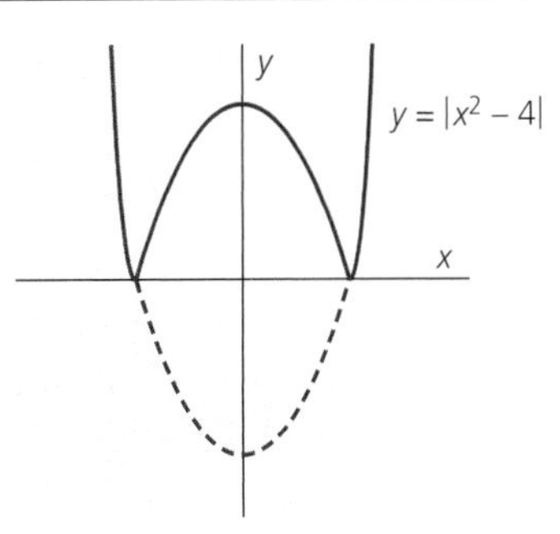

Solution

First graph the parabola $y = x^2 - 4$. Then reflect the portion of the graph that is below the x-axis in the x-axis, as illustrated, to obtain the required graph.

Exercise 2.6

Part A

Knowledge/Understanding

1. Evaluate each of the following:
   a. $|-3 - 7|$
   b. $|4| + |-15|$
   c. $|3| - |-5| + |3 - 9|$
   d. $|9 - 3| + 5|-3| - 3|7 - 12|$

2. Graph each of the following on the number line, for $x \in R$. Rewrite each statement without the absolute value bars.
   a. $|x| \leq 2$
   b. $|x| > 3$
   c. $|x| < 4$
   d. $|x| \geq 2$

Application

3. Graph each of the following absolute value functions, $x \in R$.
   a. $f(x) = |x - 3|$
   b. $g(x) = |x + 5|$
   c. $h(x) = |2x + 5|$
   d. $m(x) = |3x - 6|$
   e. $f(x) = |4 - 3x|$
   f. $g(x) = |1 - 2x|$

4. Graph each of the following absolute value functions, $x \in R$.
   a. $y = |x^2 - 4|$
   b. $y = |x^2 - 1|$
   c. $y = |x^2 - 2x|$
   d. $y = |x^2 + 4x|$
   e. $y = |x^3 - 1|$
   f. $y = |x^3|$

Part B

Communication

5. In your notebook, describe how you would sketch the graph of the absolute value of a function.

6. Graph each of the following functions:
   a. $y = |x^2 - x - 6|$
   b. $y = |-2x^2 + 4x - 3|$
   c. $y = |x^3 - x|$

7. Solve for x, $x \in R$.

a. $|2x - 1| = 7$ b. $|3x + 2| = 6$ c. $|x - 3| \leq 9$

d. $|x + 4| \geq 5$ e. $|2x - 3| < 4$ f. $|x| = -5$

Part C

technology

8. Use your graphing calculator to solve for x, $x \in R$.

a. $|x| = 3x + 4$ b. $|x - 5| = 4x + 1$

c. $|4x - 8| = 2x$ d. $|x - 1| < x$

e. $|2x + 4| \geq 12x$ f. $|3x - 1| \leq 5|3x - 1| - 16$

g. $|x - 2| + |x| = 6$ h. $|x + 4| - |x - 1| = 3$

Thinking/Inquiry/
Problem Solving

9. For which non-zero real numbers, x, is $\dfrac{|x - |x||}{x}$ a positive integer?

10. Graph $f(x) = \dfrac{|x - |x||}{x}$ for $x \in R$.

Key Concepts Review

Now that you have completed this chapter, you should be familiar with the following key concepts:

The Factor Theorem

- $(x - p)$ is a factor of $f(x)$ if and only if $f(p) = 0$.

Factor Theorem Extended

- A function $f(x) = a_n x^n + a_{n-1}x^{n-1} + \dots + a_0$ has a factor $(qx - p)$ if $f\left(\frac{p}{q}\right) = 0$, where q divides a_n and p divides a_0.

Solving Equations

- using grouping, using the Factor Theorem, using the graphing calculator and the Factor Theorem
- finding approximate roots using the graphing calculator
- finding the family of polynomial functions given the x-intercepts of the graph

Properties of the Roots of a Quadratic Equation

- sum of the roots $= -\frac{b}{a}$
- product of the roots $= \frac{c}{a}$

Solving Polynomial Inequalities

- consider when the graph of the polynomial function is above and below the x-axis

Absolute Value

- $|x| = \begin{cases} x, \text{ if } x \geq 0 \\ -x, \text{ if } x < 0 \end{cases}$
- graphs of $y = |f(x)|$ lie entirely above (or on) the x-axis

Career Link wrap-up investigate and apply

CHAPTER 2: RESEARCHING DOSE–RESPONSE RELATIONSHIPS

In this task, you will utilize the mathematical model used in the Career Link for predicting the side-effect response to medication.

The model states

$$R(t) = 5\left(t^4 - 4t^3 + \frac{19}{4}t^2 - \frac{3}{2}t\right)$$

where $[R(t)]$ is the temperature in degrees Celsius above or below the normal body temperature of 36.9°C caused by an experimental drug t hours after it was administered. Remember that due to the stress of temperature change on the body, a second drug is administered at the moment the patient's temperature starts to *exceed* 36.9°C. Complete the following questions:

a) Apply the Factor Theorem and the quadratic formula to determine the times when the patient's temperature is at the normal body temperature.

b) Predict when the second drug will be administered by applying your knowledge of solving polynomial inequalities.

c) The company has stated the maximum deviation, above or below normal body temperature, is 2.5°C. Express this statement in algebraic form using absolute-value notation and explaining your work. Describe how you would solve this on the graphing calculator. ●

Review Exercise

1. a. If $f(-3) = 0$, state a factor of $f(x)$.
   b. If $f\left(\frac{2}{3}\right) = 0$, find a factor of $f(x)$, with integral coefficients.

2. a. Find the family of cubic functions whose x-intercepts are 4, 1, and -2.
   b. Find the particular member of the above family whose graph passes through the point (3, 10).

3. a. Determine if $x + 2$ is a factor of $x^5 - 4x^3 + x^2 - 3$.
   b. Determine if $x - 3$ is a factor of $x^3 + x^2 - 11x - 3$.

4. Use the Factor Theorem to factor $x^3 - 6x^2 + 6x - 5$.

5. a. If $x - 1$ is a factor of $x^3 - 3x^2 + 4kx - 1$, what is the value of k?
   b. If $x + 3$ is a factor of $kx^3 + 4x^2 + 2kx - 1$, what is the value of k?

6. Factor each of the following:
   a. $x^3 - 2x^2 + 2x - 1$
   b. $x^3 - 6x^2 + 11x - 6$
   c. $8x^3 - 27y^3$
   d. $3(x + 2w)^3 - 3p^3r^3$

7. Use the Factor Theorem to prove that $x^2 - 4x + 3$ is a factor of $x^5 - 5x^4 + 7x^3 - 2x^2 - 4x + 3$.

8. Use your graphing calculator to factor each of the following:
   a. $2x^3 + 5x^2 + 5x + 3$
   b. $9x^3 + 3x^2 - 17x + 5$

9. If $f(x) = 5x^4 - 2x^3 + 7x^2 - 4x + 8$,
   a. is it possible that $f\left(\frac{5}{4}\right) = 0$?
   b. is it possible that $f\left(\frac{4}{5}\right) = 0$?

10. Factor fully:
    a. $3x^3 - 4x^2 + 4x - 1$
    b. $2x^3 + x^2 - 13x - 5$
    c. $30x^3 - 31x^2 + 10x - 1$

11. Solve for x, $x \in C$.
    a. $x^2 - 3x - 10 = 0$
    b. $x^3 - 25x = 0$
    c. $x^3 + 8 = 0$
    d. $x^3 - x^2 - 9x + 9 = 0$
    e. $x^4 - 12x^2 - 64 = 0$
    f. $x^3 - 4x^2 + 3 = 0$

g. $x^3 - 3x^2 + 3x - 2 = 0$ h. $x^6 - 26x^3 - 27 = 0$

i. $(x^2 + 2x)^2 - (x^2 + 2x) - 12 = 0$

technology

12. Use your graphing calculator to find the approximate roots of the following equations (correct to three decimal places):

a. $x^2 = 2$ b. $x^2 + 10x - 2 = 0$

c. $x^3 - x^2 - 4x - 1 = 0$ d. $2x^3 + x^2 + 2 = 0$

e. $x^4 - 10x^2 + 15 = 0$ f. $x^6 - 11x^5 + x^2 - 1 = 0$

13. If -2 is one root of $x^2 + kx - 6 = 0$, find the other root and the value of k.

14. Find the quadratic equation whose roots are the reciprocals of the roots of $2x^2 + 5x + 1 = 0$.

15. a. State the sum and product of the roots of $2x^2 - x + 4 = 0$.

b. Find a quadratic equation (with integral coefficients) whose roots have a sum of $\frac{1}{15}$ and a product of $-\frac{2}{15}$.

c. Find a quadratic equation (with integral coefficients) whose roots are $3 + 2i$ and $3 - 2i$.

d. If 2 is one root of the equation $3x^2 + 4kx - 4 = 0$, find the other root and the value of k.

e. Find an equation whose roots are each three less than the roots of $x^2 - 5x + 2 = 0$.

f. Find an equation whose roots are the reciprocals of the roots of $2x^2 + x - 4 = 0$.

16. Solve for x, $x \in R$.

a. $(x - 2)(x + 4) < 0$ b. $x^2 + x - 2 \geq 0$ c. $x^3 + 3x \leq 0$

d. $x^3 - 2x^2 - x + 2 > 0$ e. $x^4 \leq 0$ f. $x^4 + 5x^2 + 2 \geq 0$

g. $x^6 - 8x^4 + 2 < 0$ h. $x^9 - 2x^7 + 1 > 0$

17. Solve for x, $x \in R$.

a. $|3x - 1| = 11$ b. $|x + 1| < 3$ c. $|2x - 3| \geq 5$

18. Identical squares are cut from each corner of a rectangular sheet of tin 8 cm × 6 cm. The sides are bent upward to form an open box. If the volume of the box is 16 cm^3, what is the length of each side of the squares cut from the original sheet?

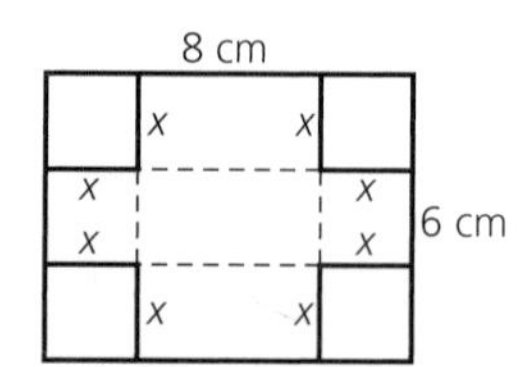

Chapter 2 Test

Achievement Category	Questions
Knowledge/Understanding	1, 2, 3, 4, 7
Thinking/Inquiry/Problem Solving	8
Communication	6
Application	5, 9

1. Without using long division, determine if $(x + 3)$ is a factor of $x^3 - 5x^2 + 9x - 3$.

2. Factor each of the following:

   a. $x^3 + 3x^2 - 2x - 2$

   b. $2x^3 - 7x^2 + 9$

   c. $x^4 - 2x^3 + 2x - 1$

3. Use your graphing calculator to factor $3x^3 + 4x^2 + 2x - 4$.

4. Solve for x, $x \in C$.

   a. $2x^3 - 54 = 0$

   b. $x^3 - 4x^2 + 6x - 3 = 0$

   c. $2x^3 - 7x^2 + 3x = 0$

   d. $x^4 - 5x^2 + 4 = 0$

5. Find the quadratic equation whose roots are each three greater than the roots of $x^2 - 2x + 5 = 0$.

6. The Math Wizard states that the x-intercepts of the graph of $f(x) = x^3 + 9x^2 + 26x + 24$ cannot be positive. Is the Math Wizard correct? Explain.

7. Solve for x, $x \in R$.

   a. $(x - 3)(x + 2)^2 < 0$

   b. $x^3 - 4x \geq 0$

   c. $|2x + 5| > 9$

8. What can you deduce about the zeros, the leading coefficient, and the least degree of the polynomial functions represented by the following graphs?

a.

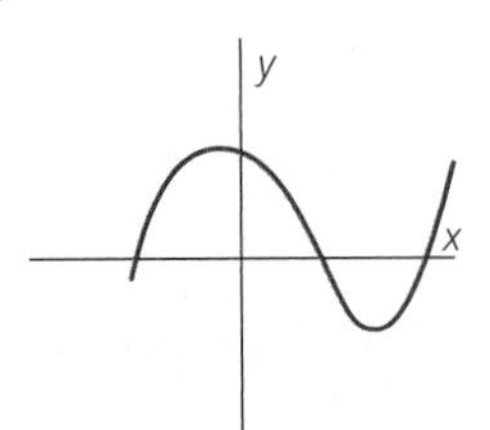

b.

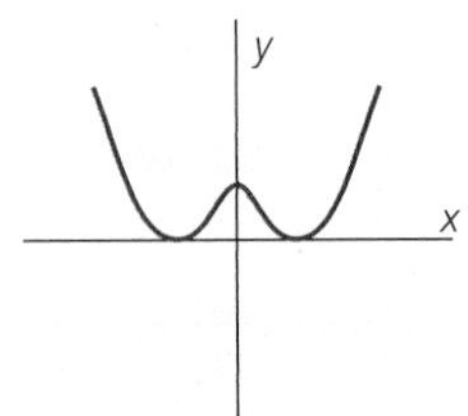

c.

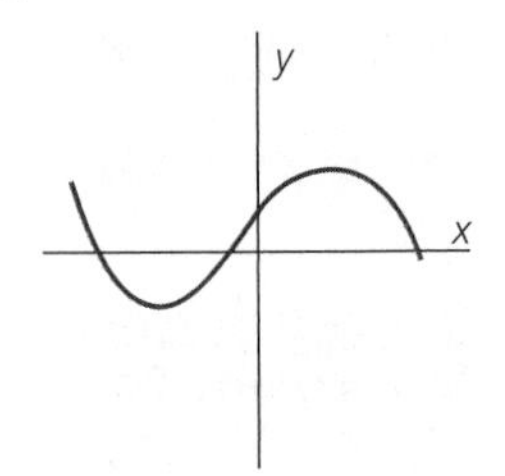

9. The free end of a diving board dips C centimetres when a diver of x kilograms stands on it. The relation is $C = 0.0002x^3 - 0.005x^2 + 0.5x$.

   a. Calculate the amount of dip when a 95 kg diver stands on the board. Give your answer to the nearest tenth of a centimetre.

   b. Calculate the mass of a diver, correct to one decimal place, if the diving board dips 40 cm.

Chapter 3

INTRODUCTION TO CALCULUS

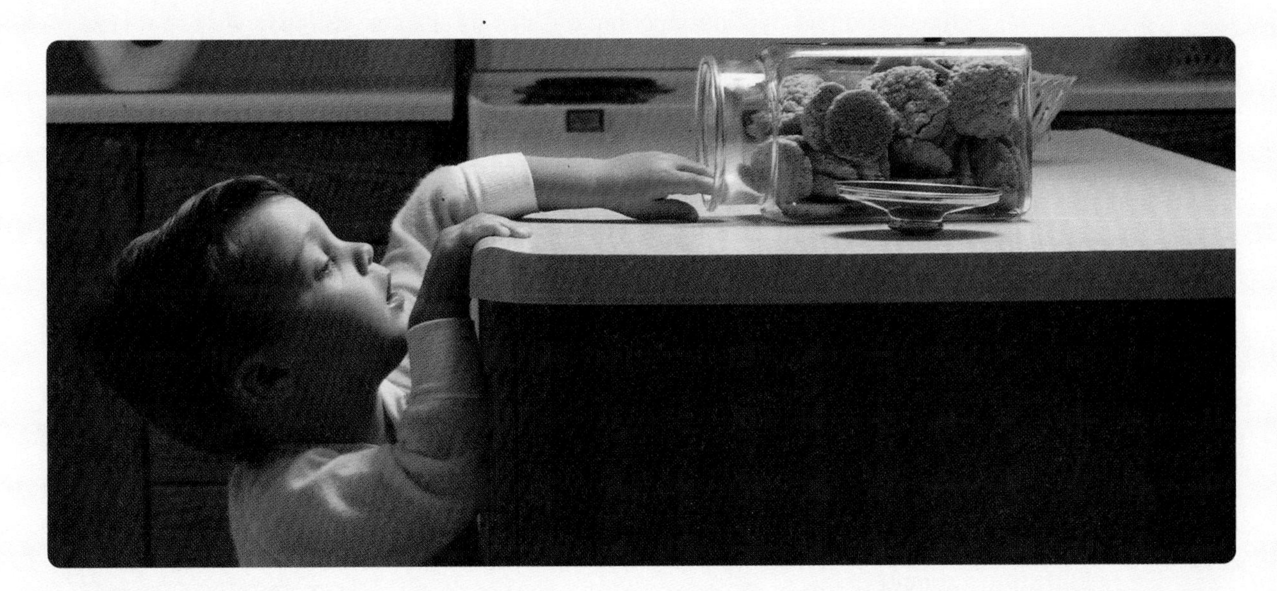

As a child, you learned how to communicate through words. You saw the cookie in the jar, pointed, and said, "Cookie!" Gradually, you learned to compose these words into sentences to more clearly communicate your meaning. As you got older, you studied the rules of grammar, and you learned that there was a correct way to form these sentences, with rules to follow.

Calculus developed in a very similar way: Sir Isaac Newton and Gottfried Wilhelm von Leibniz independently organized an assortment of ideas and methods that were circulating among the mathematicians of their time. As a tool in the service of science, calculus served its purpose very well, but it took over two centuries for mathematicians to identify and agree on its underlying principles—its grammar. In this chapter, you will see some of the ideas that were brought together to form the underlying principles of calculus.

CHAPTER EXPECTATIONS In this chapter, you will

- determine the equation of the tangent to a graph, **Section 3.1**
- understand the slope of the tangent to a curve, **Section 3.1**
- pose problems and formulate hypotheses regarding rates of change, **Section 3.2, Career Link**
- calculate and interpret average rates of change, **Section 3.2**
- estimate and interpret instantaneous rates of change, **Section 3.2**
- explain the difference between average and instantaneous rates of change, **Section 3.2**
- understand the slope of a secant on a curve and the slope of the tangent to a curve, **Section 3.1, 3.2, 3.4**
- make inferences from models of applications and compare the inferences with the original hypotheses regarding the rates of change, **Section 3.2**
- understand the instantaneous rate of change of a function, **Section 3.3, 3.4**
- determine properties of the graphs of polynomial functions, **Section 3.5**
- identify discontinuous functions, **Section 3.5**

Review of Prerequisite Skills

Before beginning this Introduction to Calculus chapter, you may wish to review the following concepts from previous courses and chapters:

- Determining the slope of a line
- Determining the equation of a line
- Using function notation for substituting into and evaluating functions
- Simplifying a radical expression with a monomial or a binomial radical in the denominator
- Factoring expressions
- Finding the domain of functions

Exercise

1. Determine the slope of the line passing through each of the following pairs of points:

   a. $(2, 5)$ and $(6, -7)$
   b. $(3, -4)$ and $(-1, 4)$
   c. $(-6, -1)$ and $(-5, 11)$
   d. $(0, 10)$ and $(10, 0)$
   e. $(-3, 6)$ and $(3, 2)$
   f. $(-3, 6)$ and $(6, 0)$
   g. though the origin and $(1, 4)$
   h. though the origin and $(-1, 4)$
   i. $(0, 1)$ and $(-6, 6)$
   j. $(-2, 4)$ and $(-6, 8)$
   k. $(-2.1, 4.41)$ and $(-2, 4)$
   l. $\left(\frac{3}{4}, \frac{1}{4}\right)$ and $\left(\frac{7}{4}, -\frac{3}{4}\right)$

2. Find the equation of a line determined by the given information.

   a. slope 4, y-intercept -2
   b. slope -2, y-intercept 5
   c. slope 0, y-intercept -5
   d. slope $\frac{2}{3}$, y-intercept 4
   e. through $(-1, 6)$ and $(4, 12)$
   f. through $(-2, 4)$ and $(-6, 8)$
   g. through $(0, 2)$ and $(-1, -4)$
   h. through the origin and $(-1, -4)$
   i. slope 7, through $(4, 1)$
   j. slope -3, through $(1, 3)$
   k. vertical, through $(-3, 5)$
   l. horizontal, through $(-3, 5)$

3. The domain of a function f is the set of all numbers x, and its values are given by $f(x) = \frac{x}{x^2 + 4}$. Find each of the following values:

   a. $f(-10)$
   b. $f(-3)$
   c. $f(0)$
   d. $f(10)$

4. A function f is defined for all x, and its values are given by

$$f(x) = \begin{cases} \sqrt{3 - x}, \text{ if } x < 0. \\ \sqrt{3 + x}, \text{ if } x \geq 0. \end{cases}$$

Compute each of the following:

a. $f(-33)$ b. $f(0)$ c. $f(78)$

5. A function s is defined for $t > -3$ by $s(t) = \begin{cases} \frac{1}{t}, \text{ if } -3 < t < 0. \\ 5, \text{ if } t = 0. \\ t^3, \text{ if } t > 0. \end{cases}$

Find each of the following:

a. $s(-2)$ b. $s(-1)$ c. $s(0)$ d. $s(1)$ e. $s(100)$

6. Rationalize each denominator.

a. $\frac{5}{\sqrt{2}}$ b. $\frac{6 + \sqrt{2}}{\sqrt{3}}$ c. $\frac{2\sqrt{3} + 4}{\sqrt{3}}$

d. $\frac{1}{3 + \sqrt{3}}$ e. $\frac{5}{\sqrt{7} - 4}$ f. $\frac{2\sqrt{3}}{\sqrt{3} - 2}$

g. $\frac{5\sqrt{3}}{2\sqrt{3} + 4}$ h. $\frac{3\sqrt{2}}{2\sqrt{3} - 5}$ i. $\frac{2\sqrt{5}}{2\sqrt{5} - 1}$

7. Rationalize each numerator.

a. $\frac{\sqrt{2}}{5}$ b. $\frac{\sqrt{3}}{6 + \sqrt{2}}$ c. $\frac{\sqrt{7} - 4}{5}$

d. $\frac{2\sqrt{3} - 5}{3\sqrt{2}}$ e. $\frac{\sqrt{3} - \sqrt{7}}{4}$ f. $\frac{2\sqrt{3} + \sqrt{7}}{5}$

8. Factor each of the following:

a. $x^2 - 4$ b. $x^3 - x$ c. $x^2 + x - 6$

d. $2x^2 - 7x + 6$ e. $x^3 + 2x^2 + x$ f. $x^3 + 8$

g. $27x^3 - 64$ h. $x^3 - 2x^2 + 3x - 6$ i. $2x^3 - x^2 - 7x + 6$

9. What is the domain of each of the following?

a. $3x + 2y - 7 = 0$ b. $y = x^2$ c. $y = \sqrt{x + 5}$

d. $y = x^3$ e. $y = \frac{3}{x - 1}$ f. $y = 4x + 5$

g. $y = -\sqrt{x - 9} + 7$ h. $y = \frac{x^2 + 4}{x}$ i. $y = \frac{4}{5 - x}$

j. $y = \frac{7}{x^2 - 3x - 4}$ k. $y = \frac{6x}{2x^2 - 5x - 3}$

l. $y = \frac{(x - 3)(x + 4)}{(x + 2)(x - 1)(x + 5)}$

Career Link investigate

CHAPTER 3: ASSESSING ATHLETIC PERFORMANCE

Differential calculus is fundamentally about the idea of *instantaneous rate of change*. A rate of change familiar to us is "heart rate." Elite athletes are keenly interested in the analysis of heart rates. Obviously, sporting performance is enhanced when an athlete is able to increase his or her heart rate at a slower pace (i.e., get tired less quickly). Heart rate is the *rate of change* of the number of heartbeats with respect to time. A heart rate is given for an *instant* in time. In calculus terminology, heart rate at an instant in time is known as the instantaneous rate of change of the number of heartbeats with respect to time. When a nurse or doctor counts our heartbeats then divides by the time elapsed, they are *not* determining the instantaneous rate of change but instead are calculating the average heart rate over a period of time (usually ten seconds). In this chapter, the idea of the **derivative** will be developed, progressing from the average rate of change being calculated over a smaller and smaller interval until a limiting value is reached at the instantaneous rate of change.

Time (in seconds)	Number of Heartbeats
10, 0.17	9
20, 0.33	19
30, 0.50	31
40, 0.67	44
50, 0.83	59
60, 1.00	75

Case Study—Assessing Elite Athlete Performance

The table below shows the number of heartbeats of an athlete who is undergoing a cardio-vascular fitness test. Complete the discussion questions to determine if this athlete is under his or her maximum desired heart rate of 65 beats per minute at precisely 30 seconds.

DISCUSSION QUESTIONS

1. Graph the number of heartbeats versus time (in minutes) on graph paper, joining the points to make a smooth curve. Draw a second relationship on the same set of axes showing the resting heart rate of 50 beats per minute. Use the slopes of the two relationships graphed to explain why the test results indicate that the person must be exercising.
2. Discuss how the average heart rate between two points in time could be calculated on this graph. Explain your reasoning.
3. Calculate the athlete's average heart rate at $t = 30$ s over the intervals of [0 s, 60 s], [10 s, 50 s] and [20 s, 40 s]. Show the progression of these average speed calculations on the graph as a series of secants.
4. Use the progression of your average heart rate secants to make a graphical prediction of the instantaneous heart rate at $t = 30$ s. Is the athlete's heart rate less than 65 beats per minute at precisely $t = 30$ s? Use this method to determine the heart rate after exactly 60 s. ●

What Is Calculus?

Two simple geometric problems originally led to the development of what is now called calculus. Both problems can be stated in terms of the graph of a function $y = f(x)$.

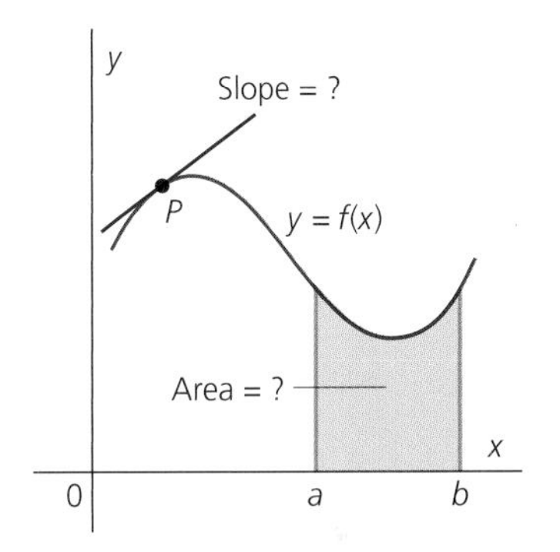

- **The problem of tangents:** What is the value of the slope of the tangent to the graph of a function at a given point P?
- **The problem of areas:** What is the area under a graph of a function $y = f(x)$ between $x = a$ and $x = b$?

Interest in the problem of tangents and the problem of areas dates back to scientists such as Archimedes of Syracuse (287–212 B.C.), who used his vast ingenuity to solve special cases of these problems. Further progress was made in the seventeenth century, most notably by Pierre de Fermat (1601–1665) and by Isaac Barrow (1630–1677), Isaac Newton's professor at the University of Cambridge, England. Professor Barrow recognized that there was a close connection between the problem of tangents and the problem of areas. However, it took the genius of both Sir Isaac Newton (1642–1727) and Gottfried Wilhelm von Leibniz (1646–1716) to show the way to handle both problems. Using the analytic geometry of René Descartes (1596–1650), Newton and Leibniz showed independently how these two problems could be solved by means of new operations on functions, called **differentiation** and **integration.** Their discovery is considered to be one of the major advances in the history of mathematics. Further research by mathematicians from many countries using these operations has created a problem-solving tool of immense power and versatility, which is known as calculus. It is a powerful branch of mathematics, used in applied mathematics, science, engineering, and economics.

We begin our study of calculus by discussing the meaning of a tangent and the related idea of rate of change. This leads us to the study of limits and, at the end of the chapter, to the concept of the derivative of a function.

Section 3.1 — The Slope of a Tangent

You are familiar with the concept of a tangent to a curve. What geometric interpretation can be given to a tangent to the graph of a function at a point P? A tangent is the straight line that most resembles the graph near that point. Its slope tells how steep the graph is at the point of tangency. In the figure, four tangents have been drawn.

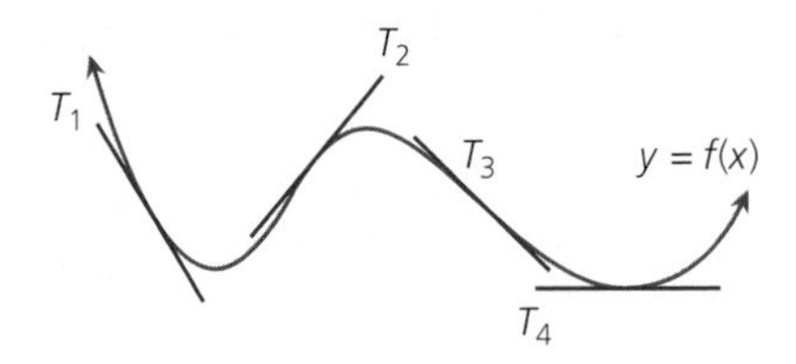

The goal of this section is to develop a method for determining the slope of a tangent at a given point on a curve. We begin with a brief review of slopes and lines.

Slopes and Lines

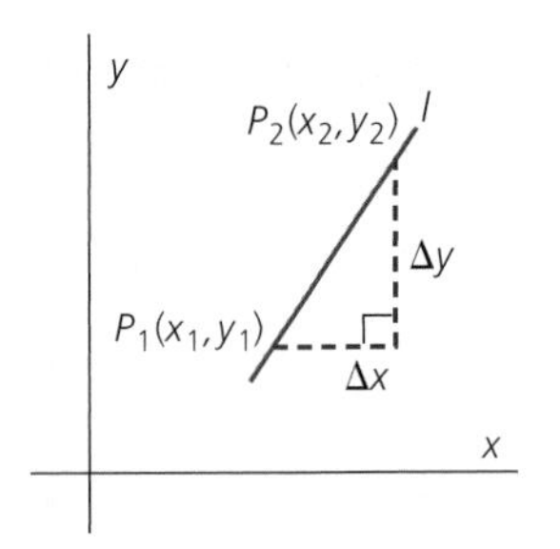

The slope m of the line joining points $P_1(x_1, y_1)$ and $P_2(x_2, y_2)$ is defined as

$$m = \frac{\Delta y}{\Delta x} = \frac{y_2 - y_1}{x_2 - x_1}.$$

The equation of the line l in slope-point form is

$$\frac{y - y_1}{x - x_1} = m \quad \text{or} \quad y - y_1 = m(x - x_1),$$

and in slope y-intercept form is $y = mx + b$, where b is the y-intercept of the line.

To find the equation of a tangent to a curve at a given point, we first need to know the slope of the tangent. What can we do when we only have one point? We proceed as follows:

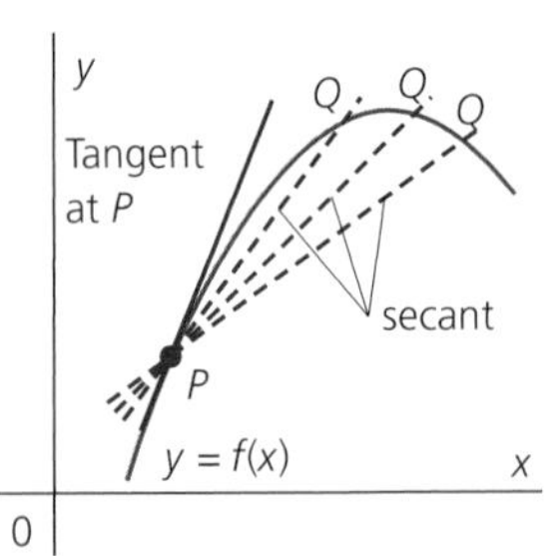

Consider a curve $y = f(x)$ and a point P that lies on the curve. Now consider another point Q on the curve. The line joining P and Q is called a **secant**. Think of Q as a moving point that slides along the curve towards P, so that the slope of the secant PQ becomes a progressively better estimate of the slope of the tangent at P.

This suggests the following definition of the slope of the tangent:

The slope of the tangent to a curve at a point P is the limiting slope of the secant PQ as the point Q slides along the curve towards P. In other words, the slope of the tangent is said to be the limit of the slope of the secant as Q approaches P along the curve.

We will illustrate this idea by finding the slope of the tangent to the parabola $y = x^2$ at $P(3, 9)$.

INVESTIGATION 1

1. Find the y-coordinates of the following points that lie on the graph of the parabola $y = x^2$.

   a. $Q_1(3.5, \quad)$ b. $Q_2(3.1, \quad)$ c. $Q_3(3.01, \quad)$ d. $Q_4(3.001, \quad)$

2. Find the slopes of the secants through $P(3, 9)$ and each of the points Q_1, Q_2, Q_3, and Q_4.

3. Find the y-coordinates of each point on the parabola and then repeat step 2 using the points.

   a. $Q_5(2.5, \quad)$ b. $Q_6(2.9, \quad)$ c. $Q_7(2.99, \quad)$ d. $Q_8(2.999, \quad)$

4. Use your results from steps 2 and 3 to estimate the slope of the tangent at point $P(3, 9)$.

5. Graph $y = x^2$ and the tangent to the graph at point $P(3, 9)$.

In this investigation, you found the slope of the tangent by finding the limiting value of the slopes of a sequence of secants. Since we are interested in points Q that are close to $P(3, 9)$ on the parabola $y = x^2$, it is convenient to write Q as $(3 + h, (3 + h)^2)$, where h is a very small non-zero number. The variable h determines the position of Q on the parabola. As Q slides along the parabola towards P, h will take on values successively smaller and closer to zero. We say that "h approaches zero" and use the notation "$h \to 0$."

INVESTIGATION 2

1. Using technology or graph paper, draw the parabola $f(x) = x^2$.

2. Let P be the point $(1, 1)$.

technology
APPENDIX P. 440

3. Find the slope of the secant through Q_1 and $P(1, 1)$, Q_2 and $P(1, 1)$, and so on, for points $Q_1(1.5, f(1.5))$, $Q_2(1.1, f(1.1))$, $Q_3(1.01, f(1.01))$, $Q_4(1.001, f(1.001))$, and $Q_5(1.0001, f(1.0001))$.

4. Graph these secants on the same utility you used in step 1.

5. Use your results to estimate the slope of the tangent to the graph of f at point P.

6. Draw the tangent at point $P(1, 1)$.

INVESTIGATION 3

1. Find the slope of the secant PQ through points $P(3, 9)$ and $Q(3 + h, (3 + h)^2)$, $h \neq 0$.

2. Explain how you could predict the slope of the tangent at point $P(3, 9)$ to the parabola $f(x) = x^2$.

The **slope of the tangent** to the parabola at point P is the limiting slope of the secant line PQ as point Q slides along the parabola; that is, as $h \to 0$. We write "$\lim_{h \to 0}$" as the abbreviation for "limiting value as h approaches 0."
Therefore, from the investigation, the slope of the tangent at a point P is $\lim_{h \to 0}$ (slope of the secant PQ).

EXAMPLE 1

Find the slope of the tangent to the graph of the parabola $f(x) = x^2$ at $P(3, 9)$.

Solution

Using points $P(3, 9)$ and $Q(3 + h, (3 + h)^2)$, $h \neq 0$, the slope of the secant PQ is

$$\begin{aligned} \frac{\Delta y}{\Delta x} &= \frac{y_2 - y_1}{x_2 - x_1} \\ &= \frac{(3 + h)^2 - 9}{3 + h - 3} \\ &= \frac{9 + 6h + h^2 - 9}{h} \\ &= \frac{h(6 + h)}{h} \\ &= (6 + h) \end{aligned}$$

As $h \to 0$, the value of $(6 + h)$ approaches 6 and thus $\lim_{h \to 0}(6 + h) = 6$.
We conclude the slope of the tangent at $P(3, 9)$ to the parabola $y = x^2$ is 6.

EXAMPLE 2

technology

a. Use your calculator to graph the parabola $y = -\frac{1}{8}(x + 1)(x - 7)$ and plot the points on the parabola from $x = -1$ to $x = 6$, where x is an integer.

b. Determine the slope of the secants using each point from part **a** and point $P(5, 1.5)$.

c. Use the result of part **b** to estimate the slope of the tangent at $P(5, 1.5)$.

Solution

a. Using the x-intercepts of -1 and 7, the equation of the axis of symmetry is $x = \frac{-1 + 7}{2} = 3$, so the x-coordinate of the vertex is 3. Substitute $x = 3$ into $y = -\frac{1}{8}(x + 1)(x - 7)$ and we get $y = -\frac{1}{8}(3 + 1)(3 - 7) = 2$.

Therefore, the vertex is (3, 2).

The y-intercept of the parabola is $\frac{7}{8}$.

The points on the parabola are $(-1, 0)$, (0, 0.875), (1, 1.5), (2, 1.875), (3, 2), (4, 1.875), (5, 1.5), and (6, 0.875).

Using graphing software, the parabola and the secants through each point and point $P(5, 1.5)$ are shown.

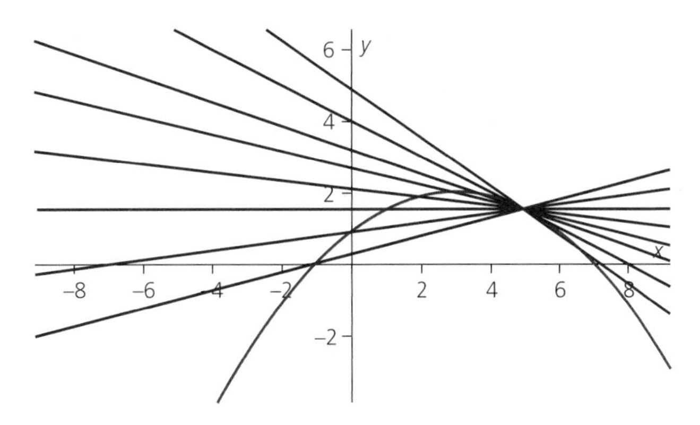

b. Using points $(-1, 0)$ and $P(5, 1.5)$, the slope is $m = \frac{1.5 - 0}{5 - (-1)} = 0.25$.

Similarly, using the other points and $P(5, 1.5)$, the slopes are 0.125, 0, -0.125, -0.25, -0.375, 0, and -0.625, respectively.

c. The slope of the tangent at $P(5, 1.5)$ is between -0.375 and -0.625. It can be determined to be -0.5 using additional points closer and closer to $P(5, 1.5)$ for values of x between 4 and 6.

The Slope of a Tangent at an Arbitrary Point

We can now generalize the method used above to derive a formula for the slope of the tangent to the graph of any function $y = f(x)$.

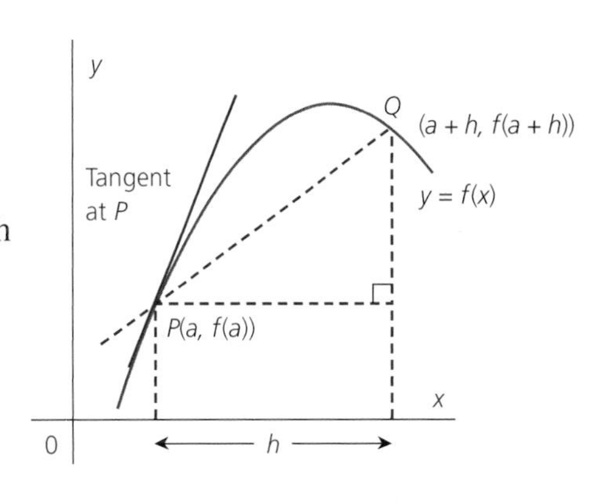

Let $P(a, f(a))$ be a fixed point on the graph of $y = f(x)$ and let $Q(x, y) = Q(x, f(x))$ represent any other point on the graph. If Q is a horizontal distance of h units from P, then $x = a + h$ and $y = f(a + h)$. Point Q then has coordinates $Q(a + h, f(a + h))$. The slope of the secant PQ is

$$\frac{\Delta y}{\Delta x} = \frac{f(a+h) - f(a)}{a + h - a} = \frac{f(a+h) - f(a)}{h}.$$

This quotient is fundamental to calculus and is referred to as the **difference quotient.** Therefore, the slope m of the tangent at $P(a, f(a))$ is $\lim_{h \to 0}$ (slope of the secant PQ), which may be written as $m = \lim_{h \to 0} \frac{f(a+h) - f(a)}{h}$.

The slope of the tangent to the graph $y = f(x)$ at point $P(a, f(a))$ is

$$m = \lim_{\Delta x \to 0} \frac{\Delta y}{\Delta x} = \lim_{h \to 0} \frac{f(a+h) - f(a)}{h}.$$

EXAMPLE 3

a. Using the definition of a derivative, determine the slope of the tangent to the curve $y = -x^2 + 4x + 1$ at the point determined by $x = 3$.
b. Determine the equation of the tangent.
c. Sketch the graph of $y = -x^2 + 4x + 1$ and the tangent at $x = 3$.

Solution

a. The slope of the tangent can be determined using the expression above. In this example, $f(x) = -x^2 + 4x + 1$ and $a = 3$.

Then $\quad f(3) = -(3)^2 + 4(3) + 1 = 4$

and $\quad f(3+h) = -(3+h)^2 + 4(3+h) + 1$

$\qquad\qquad = -h^2 - 2h + 4$

The slope of the tangent at (3, 4) is

$$\begin{aligned} m &= \lim_{h \to 0} \frac{f(3+h) - f(3)}{h} \\ &= \lim_{h \to 0} \frac{-h^2 - 2h + 4 - 4}{h} \\ &= \lim_{h \to 0} \frac{h(-h-2)}{h} \\ &= \lim_{h \to 0} (-h - 2) \\ &= -2. \end{aligned}$$

The slope of the tangent at $x = 3$ is -2.

b. The equation of the tangent at (3, 4) is $\frac{y-4}{x-3} = -2$, or $y = -2x + 10$.

c. Using graphing software, we obtain

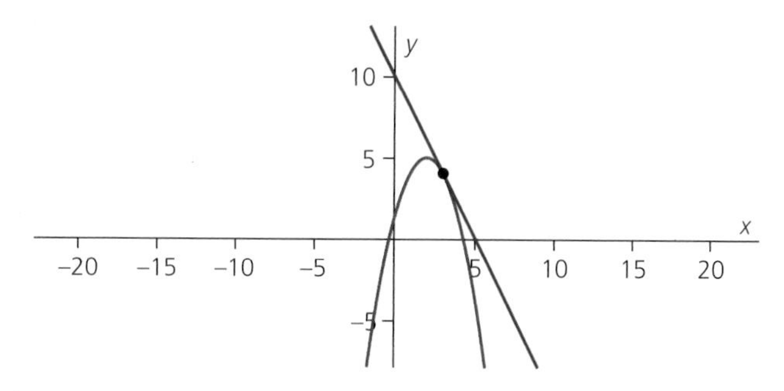

EXAMPLE 4

Determine the slope of the tangent to the rational function $f(x) = \frac{3x + 6}{x}$ at point (2, 6).

Solution

Using the definition, the slope of the tangent at (2, 6) is

$$\begin{aligned} m &= \lim_{h \to 0} \frac{f(2 + h) - f(2)}{h} \\ &= \lim_{h \to 0} \frac{\frac{6 + 3h + 6}{2 + h} - 6}{h} \\ &= \lim_{h \to 0} \frac{\frac{12 + 3h - 12 - 6h}{2 + h}}{h} \\ &= \lim_{h \to 0} \frac{-3h}{2 + h} \times \frac{1}{h} \\ &= \lim_{h \to 0} \frac{-3h}{h(2 + h)} \\ &= \lim_{h \to 0} \frac{-3}{(2 + h)} \\ &= -1.5. \end{aligned}$$

Therefore, the slope of the tangent to $f(x) = \frac{3x + 6}{x}$ at (2, 6) is -1.5.

EXAMPLE 5

Find the slope of the tangent to $y = f(x)$, where $f(x) = \sqrt{x}$, at $x = 9$.

Solution

At $x = 9, f(9) = \sqrt{9} = 3$.
At $x = 9 + h, f(9 + h) = \sqrt{9 + h}$.

Using the limit of the difference quotient, the slope of the tangent at $x = 9$ is

$$\begin{aligned} m &= \lim_{h \to 0} \frac{f(9+h) - f(9)}{h} \\ &= \lim_{h \to 0} \frac{\sqrt{9+h} - 3}{h} \\ &= \lim_{h \to 0} \frac{\sqrt{9+h} - 3}{h} \times \frac{\sqrt{9+h} + 3}{\sqrt{9+h} + 3} \\ &= \lim_{h \to 0} \frac{(9+h) - 9}{h(\sqrt{9+h} + 3)} \\ &= \lim_{h \to 0} \frac{h}{h(\sqrt{9+h} + 3)} \\ &= \lim_{h \to 0} \frac{1}{\sqrt{9+h} + 3} \\ &= \frac{1}{6}. \end{aligned}$$

Rationalizing the numerator of a quotient often helps to simplify the calculation of some limits. When the numerator has two terms, such as $\sqrt{9+h} - 3$, we multiply both the numerator and denominator by the conjugate radical; that is, by $\sqrt{9+h} + 3$.

Therefore, the slope of the tangent to the function $f(x) = \sqrt{x}$ at $x = 9$ is $\frac{1}{6}$.

INVESTIGATION 4 A graphing calculator can help us "guess" the approximate value of the slope of a tangent at a point, which can then be found using the definition of the slope of the tangent, from first principles, developed in this section. For example, suppose we wish to find the slope of the tangent to $y = f(x) = x^3$ at $x = 1$.

1. Graph $Y_1 = \frac{((x + 0.01)^3 - x^3)}{0.01}$.

technology

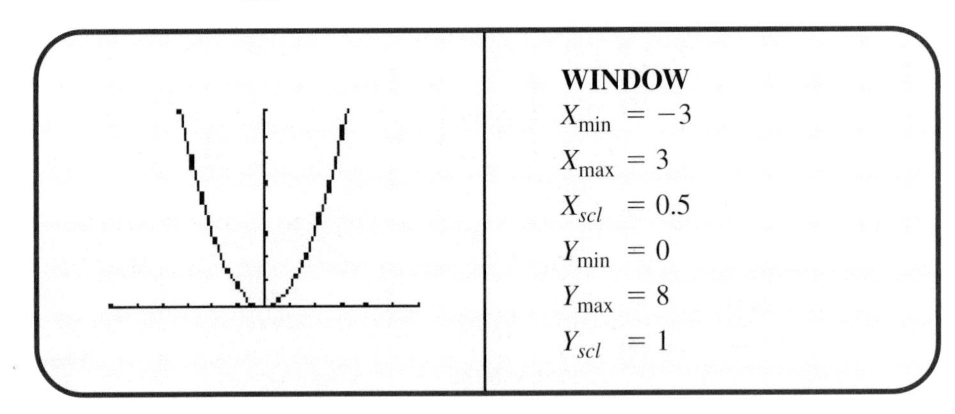

2. Explain why the values for the WINDOW were chosen.
   Looking at the graph, recognize Y_1 as the difference quotient $\frac{f(a+h) - f(a)}{h}$ for $f(x) = x^3$ and $h = 0.01$. Remember that this approximates the slope of the tangent and not the graph of $f(x) = x^3$.

3. Use the TRACE function to find $X = 1.0212766$, $Y = 3.159756$. This means the slope of the secant passing through the points where $x = 1$ and $x = 1 + 0.01 = 1.01$ is about 3.2; this could be used as an approximation for the slope of the tangent at $x = 1$.

4. Can you improve this approximation? Explain how you could improve your estimate. Also, if you use different WINDOW values you can see a different-sized or differently centred graph.

5. Try once again by setting $X_{min} = -9$, $X_{max} = 10$, and note the different appearance of the graph. Use the TRACE function to find $X = 0.904\ 255\ 32$, $Y = 2.480\ 260\ 7$, then $X = 1.106\ 383$, $Y = 3.705\ 541\ 4$. What is your guess for the slope of the tangent at $x = 1$ now? Explain why only estimation is possible.

6. Another way of using a graphing calculator to approximate the slope of the tangent is to consider h as the variable in the difference quotient. For this example, $f(x) = x^3$ at $x = 1$, look at

$$\frac{f(a + h) - f(a)}{h} = \frac{(1 + h)^3 - 1^3}{h}.$$

7. Trace values of h as $h \to 0$. You can use the table or graph functions of your calculator. Graphically, we say we are looking at $\frac{(1 + h)^3 - 1}{h}$ in the *neighbourhood* of $h = 0$. To do this, graph $y = \frac{(1 + x)^3 - 1}{x}$ and examine the value of the function as $x \to 0$.

Exercise 3.1

Part A

1. Find the slope of the line through each pair of points.

   a. $(2, 7), (-3, -8)$ b. $\left(\frac{1}{2}, \frac{3}{2}\right), \left(\frac{7}{2}, -\frac{7}{2}\right)$ c. $(6.3, -2.6), (1.5, -1)$

2. What is the slope of a line perpendicular to the following?

   a. $y = 3x - 5$ b. $13x - 7y - 11 = 0$

3. State the equation and sketch the graph of the following straight lines:

   a. passing through $(-4, -4)$ and $\left(-\frac{5}{3}, -\frac{5}{3}\right)$

   b. having slope 8 and y-intercept 6

   c. having x-intercept 5 and y-intercept -3

   d. passing through $(5, 6)$ and $(5, -9)$

4. Simplify each of the following:

   a. $\frac{(2 + h)^2 - 4}{h}$ b. $\frac{(5 + h)^3 - 125}{h}$ c. $\frac{(3 + h)^4 - 81}{h}$ d. $\frac{\frac{1}{1 + h} - 1}{h}$

   e. $\frac{3(1 + h)^2 - 3}{h}$ f. $\frac{(2 + h)^3 - 8}{h}$ g. $\frac{\frac{3}{4 + h} - \frac{3}{4}}{h}$ h. $\frac{\frac{-1}{2 + h} + \frac{1}{2}}{h}$

5. Rationalize each of the following numerators to obtain an equivalent expression.

a. $\frac{\sqrt{16 + h} - 4}{h}$ b. $\frac{\sqrt{h^2 + 5h + 4} - 2}{h}$ c. $\frac{\sqrt{5 + h} - \sqrt{5}}{h}$

Part **B**

6. Find the slope m, in simplified form, of each pair of points.

a. $P(1, 3)$, $Q(1 + h, f(1 + h))$ where $f(x) = 3x^2$

b. $R(1, 3)$, $S(1 + h, (1 + h)^3 + 2)$

c. $T(9, 3)$, $U(9 + h, \sqrt{9 + h})$

Knowledge/Understanding

7. Consider the function $f(x) = x^3$.

a. Copy and complete the following table of values; P and Q are points on the graph of $f(x)$.

P	*Q*	Slope of Line *PQ*
(2,)	(3,)	
(2,)	(2.5,)	
(2,)	(2.1,)	
(2,)	(2.01,)	

P	*Q*	Slope of Line *PQ*
(2,)	(1,)	
(2,)	(1.5,)	
(2,)	(1.9,)	
(2,)	(1.99,)	

b. Use the results of part **a** to approximate the slope of the tangent to the graph of $f(x)$ at point P.

c. Calculate the slope of the secant PR, where the x-coordinate of R is $2 + h$.

d. Use the result of part **c** to calculate the slope of the tangent to the graph of $f(x)$ at point P.

e. Compare your answers for parts **b** and **d.**

f. Sketch the graph of $f(x)$ and the tangent to the graph at point P.

8. Find the slope of the tangent to each curve at the point whose x-value is given.

a. $y = 3x^2$; $(-2, 12)$ b. $y = x^2 - x$ at $x = 3$ c. $y = x^3$ at $x = -2$

9. Find the slope of the tangent to each curve at the point whose x-value is given.

a. $y = \sqrt{x - 2}$; $(3, 1)$ b. $y = \sqrt{x - 5}$ at $x = 9$ c. $y = \sqrt{5x - 1}$ at $x = 2$

10. Find the slope of the tangent to each curve at the point whose x-value is given.

a. $y = \frac{8}{x}$; $(2, 4)$ b. $y = \frac{8}{3 + x}$ at $x = 1$ c. $y = \frac{1}{x + 2}$ at $x = 3$

Knowledge/ Understanding

11. Find the slope of the tangent to each curve at the given point.

a. $y = x^2 - 3x$; $(2, -2)$

b. $f(x) = \frac{4}{x}$; $(-2, -2)$

c. $y = 3x^3$ at $x = 1$

d. $y = \sqrt{x - 7}$ at $x = 16$

e. $f(x) = \sqrt{16 - x}$, where $y = 5$

f. $y = \sqrt{25 - x^2}$; $(3, 4)$

g. $y = \frac{4 + x}{x - 2}$ at $x = 8$

h. $y = \frac{8}{\sqrt{x + 11}}$ at $x = 5$

12. Sketch the graph of Question 11, part **f.** Show that the slope of the tangent can be found using the properties of circles.

Communication

13. Explain how you would approximate the slope of the tangent at a point without using first principles.

Communication

14. Sketch the graph of $y = \frac{3}{4}\sqrt{16 - x^2}$. Explain how the slope of the tangent at $P(0, 3)$ can be found without using first principles.

15. Copy the following figures. Draw an approximate tangent for each curve at point P.

a.

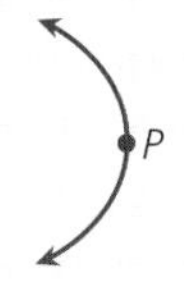

b.

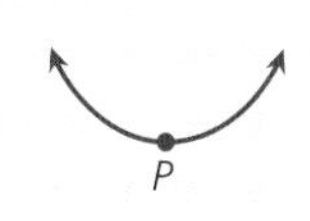

c.

d.

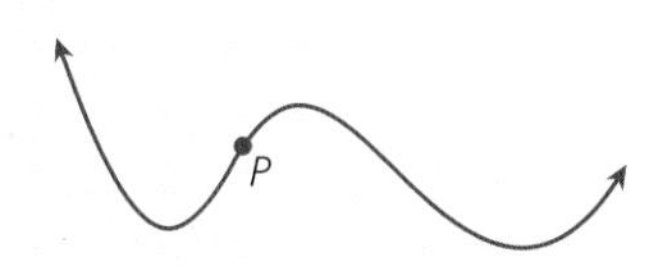

e.

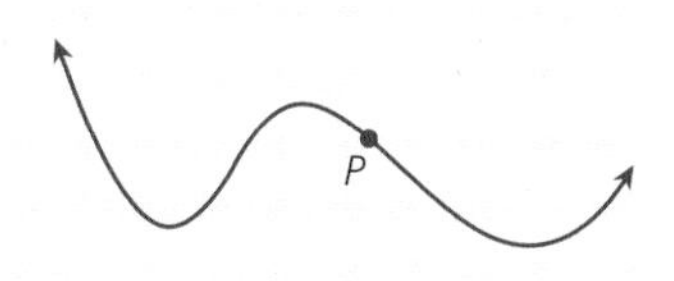

f.

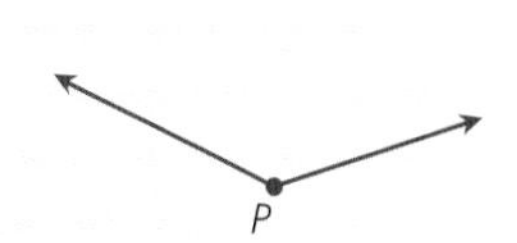

Application 16. Find the slope of the demand curve $D(p) = \frac{20}{\sqrt{p-1}}$, $p > 1$, at point $(5, 10)$.

Application 17. It is projected that t years from now, the circulation of a local newspaper will be $C(t) = 100t^2 + 400t + 5000$. Find how fast the circulation is increasing after 6 months. *Hint:* Find the slope of the tangent when t is equal to 6 months.

Thinking/Inquiry/ Problem Solving 18. Find the coordinates of the point on the curve $f(x) = 3x^2 - 4x$, where the tangent is parallel to the line $y = 8x$.

Thinking/Inquiry/ Problem Solving 19. Find the points on the graph of $y = \frac{1}{3}x^3 - 5x - \frac{4}{x}$ at which the slope of the tangent is horizontal.

Part C

20. Show that at the points of intersection of the quadratic functions $y = x^2$ and $y = \frac{1}{2} - x^2$, the tangents to each parabola are perpendicular.

Section 3.2 — Rates of Change

Many practical relationships involve interdependent quantities. For example, the volume of a balloon varies with its height above the ground, air temperature varies with elevation, and the surface area of a sphere varies with the length of the radius.

These and other relationships can be described by means of a function, often of the form $y = f(x)$. The **dependent variable,** y, can represent price, air temperature, area, and so forth. The **independent variable,** x, can represent time, elevation, length, and so on.

We are often interested in how rapidly the dependent variable changes when there is a change in the independent variable. This concept is called **rate of change.** In this section, we show that a rate of change can be calculated by finding the limit of a difference quotient, in the same way we find the slope of a tangent.

An object moving in a straight line is an example of a rate of change model. It is customary to use either a horizontal or a vertical line with a specified origin to represent the line of motion. On such lines, movement to the right (or upward) is considered to be in the positive direction, and movement to the left (or down) is considered to be in the negative direction. An example of an object moving along a line would be a vehicle entering a highway and travelling north 340 km in 4 h. The average velocity would be $\frac{340}{4} = 85$ km/h, since

$$\text{average velocity} = \frac{\text{change in distance}}{\text{change in time}}.$$

If $s(t)$ gives the position of the vehicle on a straight section of the highway at time t, then the average rate of change of the position of the vehicle over a time interval is

$$\text{average velocity} = \frac{\Delta s}{\Delta t}.$$

INVESTIGATION

You are driving with a broken speedometer on a highway. At any instant you do not know how fast the car is going. Your odometer readings are the following:

t (in hours)	0	1	2	2.5	3
$s(t)$ (in kilometres)	62	133	210	250	293

1. Determine the average velocity of the car over each interval.
2. The speed limit is 80 km/h. Do any of the results suggest that you were speeding at any time? If so, when?

3. Explain why there may be other times when you were travelling above the posted speed limit.

4. Compute your average velocity over the interval $4 \leq t \leq 7$ if $s(4) = 375$ km and $s(7) = 609$ km.

5. After 3 h of driving, you decide to continue driving from Goderich to Huntsville, a distance of 330 km. Using the average velocity from Question 4, how long would it take you to make this trip?

EXAMPLE 1

A pebble is dropped from a cliff with a height of 80 m. After t seconds, it is s metres above the ground, where $s(t) = 80 - 5t^2$, $0 \leq t \leq 4$.

a. Find the average velocity of the pebble between the times $t = 1$ s and $t = 3$ s.

b. Find the average velocity of the pebble between the times $t = 1$ s and $t = 1.5$ s.

c. Explain why the answers to parts **a** and **b** are different.

Solution

a. average velocity $= \frac{\Delta s}{\Delta t}$

$$s(1) = 75$$

$$s(3) = 35$$

$$\begin{aligned} \text{average velocity} &= \frac{s(3) - s(1)}{3 - 1} \\ &= \frac{35 - 75}{2} \\ &= \frac{-40}{2} \\ &= -20 \text{ m/s} \end{aligned}$$

The average velocity in this 2 s interval is -20 m/s.

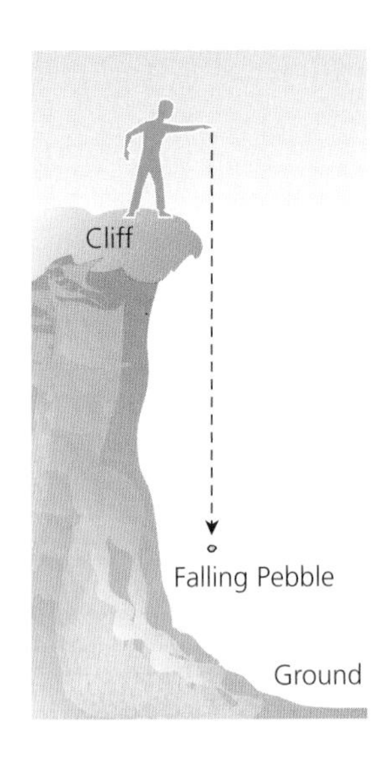

b. $s(1.5) = 80 - 5(1.5)^2$

$$= 68.75$$

$$\begin{aligned} \text{average velocity} &= \frac{s(1.5) - s(1)}{1.5 - 1} \\ &= \frac{68.75 - 75}{0.5} \\ &= -12.5 \text{ m/s} \end{aligned}$$

The average velocity in this 0.5 s interval is -12.5 m/s.

c. Since gravity causes the velocity to increase with time, the smaller interval of 0.5 s gives a lower average velocity, as well as giving a value closer to the actual velocity at time $t = 1$.

The following table shows the results of similar calculations of the average velocity over successively smaller time intervals.

Time Interval	Average Velocity (in metres per second)
$1 \leq t \leq 1.1$	-10.5
$1 \leq t \leq 1.01$	-10.05
$1 \leq t \leq 1.001$	-10.005

It appears that, as we shorten the time interval, the average velocity is approaching the value 10 m/s. The average velocity over the time interval $1 \leq t \leq 1 + h$ is

$$\begin{aligned}\text{average velocity} &= \frac{s(1+h) - s(1)}{h}\\ &= \frac{[80 - 5(+h)^2] - [80 - 5]}{h}\\ &= \frac{-(5 + 10h + 5h^2) + 5}{h}\\ &= -(10 + 5h),\ h \neq 0.\end{aligned}$$

If the time interval is very short, then h is small, so $5h$ is close to 0 and the average velocity is close to -10 m/s. The **instantaneous velocity** when $t = 1$ is defined to be the limiting value of these average values as h approaches 0. Therefore, the velocity (the word "instantaneous" is usually omitted) at time $t = 1$ s is

$$v = \lim_{h \to 0}(10 + 5h) = -10 \text{ m/s}.$$

In general, suppose that the position of an object at time t is given by the function $s(t)$. In the time interval from $t = a$ to $t = a + h$, the change in position is

$$\Delta s = s(a + h) - s(a).$$

The average velocity over this time interval is

$$\frac{\Delta s}{\Delta t} = \frac{s(a+h) - s(a)}{h}$$

which is the same as the slope of the secant PQ. The **velocity** at a particular time $t = a$ is calculated by finding the limiting value of the average velocity as $h \to 0$.

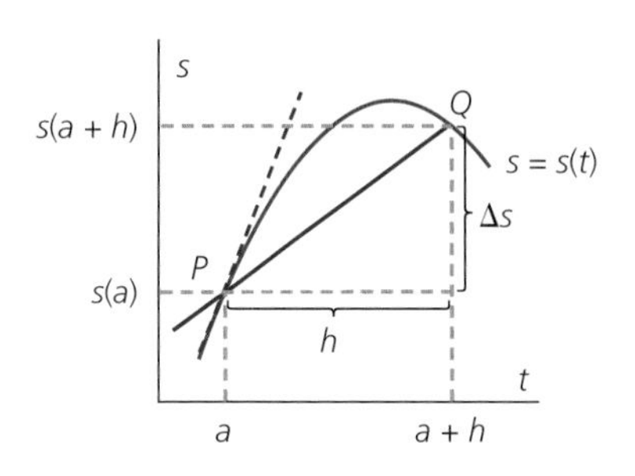

The velocity of an object, with position function $s(t)$, at time $t = a$, is

$$v(a) = \lim_{\Delta t \to 0} \frac{\Delta s}{\Delta t} = \lim_{h \to 0} \frac{s(a+h) - s(a)}{h}.$$

Note that the velocity $v(a)$ is the slope of the tangent to the graph of $s(t)$ at $P(a, s(a))$.

The **speed** of an object is the absolute value of its velocity. It indicates how fast an object is moving, whereas velocity indicates both speed and direction (relative to a given coordinate system).

EXAMPLE 2

A ball is tossed straight up so that its position s, in metres, at time t, in seconds, is given by $s(t) = -5t^2 + 30t + 2$. What is the velocity of the ball at $t = 4$?

Solution

Since $s(t) = -5t^2 + 30t + 2$,

$$\begin{aligned} s(4 + h) &= -5(4 + h)^2 + 30(4 + h) + 2 \\ &= -5h^2 - 10h + 42 \\ s(4) &= -5(4)^2 + 30(4) + 2 \\ &= 42. \end{aligned}$$

The velocity at $t = 4$ is

$$\begin{aligned} v(4) &= \lim_{h\to 0}\frac{s(4 + h) - s(4)}{h} \\ &= \lim_{h\to 0}\frac{[-10h - 5h^2]}{h} \\ &= \lim_{h\to 0}\frac{h(-10 - 5h)}{h} \\ &= \lim_{h\to 0}(-10 - 5h) \\ &= -10. \end{aligned}$$

Therefore, the velocity of the ball is 10 m/s downwards at $t = 4$.

Velocity is only one example of the concept of **rate of change.** In general, suppose that a quantity y depends on x according to the equation $y = f(x)$. As the independent variable changes from a to $a + h$, the corresponding change in the dependent variable y is $\Delta y = f(a + h) - f(a)$.

The difference quotient $\frac{\Delta y}{\Delta x} = \frac{f(a + h) - f(a)}{h}$ is called the average rate of change of y with respect to x over the interval from $x = a$ to $x = a + h$.

From the diagram, it follows that the average rate of change equals the slope of the secant PQ of the graph of $f(x)$. The rate of change of y with respect to x when $x = a$ is defined to be the limiting value of the average rate of change as $h \to 0$.

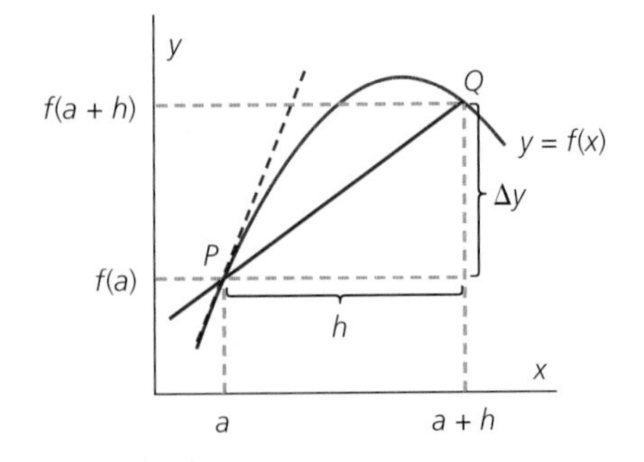

Therefore, we conclude that the rate of change of $y = f(x)$ with respect to x when $x = a$ is

$\lim_{\Delta x\to 0}\frac{\Delta y}{\Delta x} = \lim_{h\to 0}\frac{f(a + h) - f(x)}{h}$, provided the limit exists.

It should be noted that as with velocity, the rate of change of y with respect to x at $x = a$ equals the slope of the tangent to the graph of $y = f(x)$ at $x = a$.

EXAMPLE 3

The total cost of manufacturing x units of a product is given by $C(x) = 10\sqrt{x} + \$1000$.

a. What is the total cost of manufacturing 100 items of the product?
b. What is the rate of change of the total cost with respect to the number of units, x, being produced when $x = 100$?

Solution

a. $C(100) = 10\sqrt{100} + 1000$
$= 1100$

Therefore, the total cost of manufacturing 100 items is \$1100.

b. The rate of change of the cost at $x = 100$ is given by

$$\lim_{h \to 0} \frac{C(100 + h) - C(100)}{h}$$

$$= \lim_{h \to 0} \frac{10\sqrt{100 + h} + 1000 - 1100}{h}$$

$$= \lim_{h \to 0} \frac{10\sqrt{100 + h} - 100}{h} \times \frac{10\sqrt{100 + h} + 100}{10\sqrt{100 + h} + 100}$$

(Rationalizing the numerator)

$$= \lim_{h \to 0} \frac{100(100 + h) - 10\,000}{h(10\sqrt{100 + h} + 100)}$$

$$= \lim_{h \to 0} \frac{100h}{h(10\sqrt{100 + h} + 100)}$$

$$= \lim_{h \to 0} \frac{100}{(10\sqrt{100 + h} + 100)}$$

$$= \frac{100}{(10\sqrt{100 + 0} + 100)}$$

$$= 0.5.$$

Therefore, the rate of change of the total cost with respect to the number of items being produced when that number is 100 is \$0.50 per item.

An Alternative Form for Finding Rates of Change

In Example 1, we determined the velocity of the pebble at $t = 1$ by taking the limit of the average velocity over the interval $1 \le t \le 1 + h$ as h approaches 0. We can also determine the velocity at $t = 1$ by considering the average velocity over the interval from 1 to a general time t and letting t approach the value 1. Then,

$s(1) = 75$

$s(t) = 80 - 5t^2$

$$v(1) = \lim_{t \to 1} \frac{s(t) - s(1)}{t - 1}$$

$$= \lim_{t \to 1} \frac{5 - 5t^2}{t - 1}$$
$$= \lim_{t \to 1} \frac{5(1 - t)(1 + t)}{t - 1}$$
$$= \lim_{t \to 1} -5(1 + t)$$
$$= -10.$$

In general, the velocity of an object at time $t = a$ is $v(a) = \lim_{t \to a} \frac{s(t) - s(a)}{t - a}$. Similarly, the rate of change of $y = f(x)$ with respect to x when $x = a$ is $\lim_{x \to a} \frac{f(x) - f(a)}{x - a}$.

Exercise 3.2

Part A

Knowledge/Understanding

1. The velocity of an object is given by $v(t) = t(t - 4)^2$. At what times, in seconds, is the object at rest?

Communication

2. Give a geometrical interpretation of the following, where s is a position function.

   a. $\frac{s(9) - s(2)}{7}$ b. $\lim_{h \to 0} \frac{s(6 + h) - s(6)}{h}$

3. Give a geometrical interpretation of $\lim_{h \to 0} \frac{\sqrt{4 + h} - 2}{h}$.

4. Use the graph to answer each question.

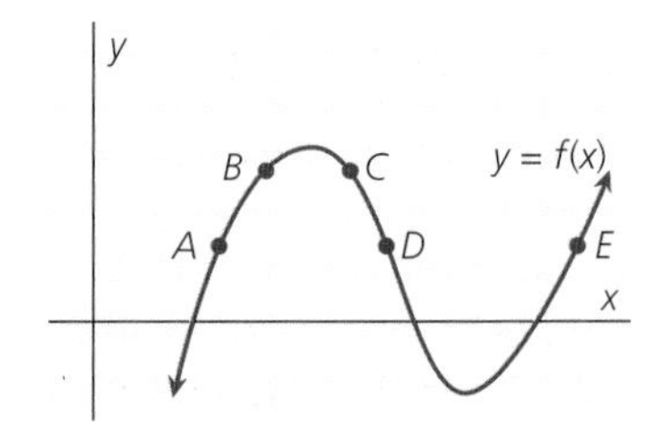

   a. Between which two consecutive points is the average rate of change of the function greatest?

   b. Is the average rate of change of the function between A and B greater than or less than the instantaneous rate of change at B?

   c. Sketch a tangent to the graph between points D and E such that the slope of the tangent is the same as the average rate of change of the function between B and C.

5. What is wrong with the statement "the speed of the cheetah was 65 km/h north"?

6. Is there anything wrong with the statement "a school bus had a velocity of 60 km/h for the morning run and that is why it was late on arrival"?

Part B

7. A construction worker drops a bolt while working on a high-rise building 320 m above the ground. After t seconds, the bolt has fallen a distance of s metres, where $s(t) = 320 - 5t^2$, $0 \leq t \leq 8$.

   a. Find the average velocity during the first, third, and eighth seconds.

   b. Find the average velocity for the interval $3 \leq t \leq 8$.

   c. Find the velocity at $t = 2$.

8. The function $s(t) = 8t(t + 2)$ describes the distance s, in kilometres, that a car has travelled after a time t, in hours, for $0 \leq t \leq 5$.

   a. Find the average velocity of the car during the following intervals:

      i) from $t = 3$ to $t = 4$

      ii) from $t = 3$ to $t = 3.1$

      iii) $3 \leq t \leq 3.01$

   b. Use the results of part **a** to approximate the instantaneous velocity of the car when $t = 3$.

   c. Find the velocity at $t = 3$.

Application

9. Suppose that a foreign-language student has learned $N(t) = 20t - t^2$ vocabulary terms after t hours of uninterrupted study.

   a. How many terms are learned between time $t = 2$ h and $t = 3$ h?

   b. What is the rate in terms per hour at which the student is learning at time $t = 2$ h?

Application

10. A medicine is administered to a patient. The amount, M, of the medicine, in milligrams, in 1 mL of the patient's blood t hours after the injection is given by $M(t) = -\frac{1}{3}t^2 + t$, where $0 \leq t \leq 3$.

    a. Find the rate of change of the amount, M, 2 h after the injection.

    b. What is the significance of the fact that your answer is negative?

11. The time, t, in seconds, taken for an object dropped from a height of s metres to reach the ground is given by the formula $t = \sqrt{\frac{s}{5}}$. Determine the rate of change of the time with respect to the height when the height of an object is 125 m above the ground.

12. Suppose that the temperature, T, in degrees Celsius, varies with the height h, in kilometres, above the earth's surface according to the equation $T(h) = \frac{60}{h + 2}$. Find the rate of change of temperature with respect to height at a height of 3 km.

13. A spaceship approaching touchdown on a distant planet has height h, in metres, at time t, in seconds, given by $h = 25t^2 - 100t + 100$. When and with what speed does it land on the surface?

Application

14. A manufacturer of soccer balls finds that the profit from the sale of x balls per week is given by $P(x) = 160x - x^2$ dollars.

   a. Find the profit on the sale of 40 soccer balls.

   b. Find the rate of change of the profit at the production level of 40 balls per week.

technology

   c. Using a graphing calculator, graph the profit function and from the graph determine for what sales levels of x the rate of change of profit is positive.

15. Use the alternate definition $\lim\limits_{x \to a} \frac{f(x) - f(a)}{x - a}$ to find the rate of change of $f(x)$ at each of the given points.

   a. $f(x) = -x^2 + 2x + 3$; $(-2, -5)$

   b. $f(x) = \frac{x}{x - 1}$, where $x = 2$

   c. $f(x) = \sqrt{x + 1}$, where $x = 24$

Part C

Thinking/Inquiry/Problem Solving

16. Let (a, b) be any point on the graph of $y = \frac{1}{x}$, $x > 0$. Prove that the area of the triangle formed by the tangent through (a, b) and the coordinate axes is 2.

17. A manufacturer's total weekly cost in producing x items can be written as $C(x) = F + V(x)$, where F, a constant, represents fixed costs such as rent and utilities, and $V(x)$ represents variable costs, which depend on production level x. Show that the rate of change of the cost is independent of fixed costs.

18. A circular oil slick on the ocean spreads outward. Find the approximate rate of change of the area of the oil slick with respect to its radius when the radius is 100 m.

19. Show that the rate of change of the volume of a cube with respect to its edge length is equal to half the surface area of the cube.

Section 3.3 — The Limit of a Function

The notation $\lim_{x \to a} f(x) = L$ is read "the limit of $f(x)$ as x approaches a equals L" and means that the value of $f(x)$ can be made arbitrarily close to L by choosing x sufficiently close to a (but not equal to a). The limit $\lim_{x \to a} f(x)$ exists if and only if the limiting value from the left equals the limiting value from the right. We shall use this definition to evaluate some limits.

Note: This is an intuitive explanation of the limit of a function. A more precise definition using inequalities is important for advanced work but is not necessary for our purposes.

INVESTIGATION 1 Find the limit of $y = x^2 - 1$, as x approaches 2.

1. Copy and complete the table of values.

x	1	1.5	1.9	1.99	1.999	2	2.001	2.01	2.1	2.5	3
$y = x^2 - 1$											

2. As x approaches 2 from the left, starting at $x = 1$, what is the approximate value of y?
3. As x approaches 2 from the right, starting at $x = 3$, what is the approximate value of y?
4. Graph $y = x^2 - 1$ using graphing software or graph paper.
5. Using arrows, illustrate that as we choose a value of x that is closer and closer to $x = 2$, the value of y gets closer and closer to a value of 3.
6. Explain why the limit of $y = x^2 - 1$ exists as x approaches 2, and give its approximate value.

INVESTIGATION 2 Find $\lim_{x \to 1} \frac{x^2 - 1}{x - 1}$ by graphing.

Solution

On a graphing calculator, display the graph of $f(x) = \frac{x^2 - 1}{x - 1}, x \neq 1$.

The graph shown on your calculator is a straight line ($f(x) = x + 1$) whereas it should be a line with the point (1, 2) deleted ($f(x) = x + 1, x \neq 1$). The WINDOW is $X_{min} = -10$, $X_{max} = 10$, $X_{scl} = -10$, and similarly for Y. Use the TRACE function to find $X = 0.851\,063\,83$, $Y = 1.851\,063\,8$; $X = 1.063\,829\,8$, and $Y = 2.063\,829\,8$.

Click ZOOM; select **4:ZDecimal,** ENTER.
Now, the graph of $f(x) = \frac{x^2 - 1}{x - 1}$ is displayed as a straight line with the point (1, 2) deleted. The WINDOW has new values, too.
Use the TRACE function to find $X = 0.9$, $Y = 1.9$; $X = 1$, Y has no value given; and $X = 1.1$, $Y = 2.1$.

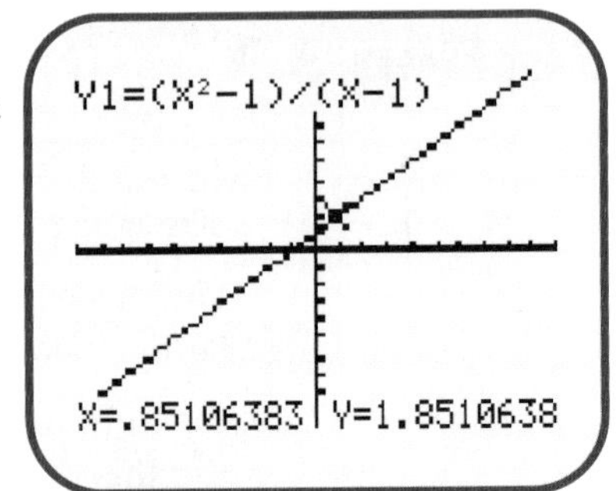

We can estimate $\lim_{x \to 1} f(x)$. As x approaches 1 from the left, written as $x \to 1^-$, we observe that $f(x)$ approaches the value 2 from below, and as x approaches 1 from the right, written as $x \to 1^+$, $f(x)$ approaches the value 2 from above.

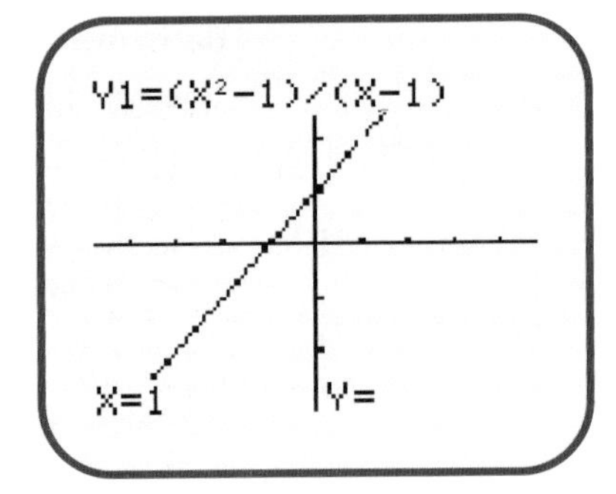

We say that the limit at $x = 1$ exists only if the value approached from the left is the same as the value approached from the right. From this investigation, we conclude that $\lim_{x \to 1}\left(\frac{x^2 - 1}{x - 1}\right) = 2$.

EXAMPLE 1

Find $\lim_{x \to 1}\frac{x^2 - 1}{x - 1}$ by using a table.

Solution

We select sequences of numbers for $x \to 1^-$ and $x \to 1^+$.

	x approaches 1 from the left →						← x approaches 1 from the right				
x	0	0.5	0.9	0.99	0.999	1	1.001	1.01	1.1	1.5	2
$\frac{x^2 - 1}{x - 1}$	1	1.5	1.9	1.99	1.999	undefined	2.001	2.01	2.1	2.5	3
$f(x) = \frac{x^2 - 1}{x - 1}$ approaches 2 from below →							← $f(x) = \frac{x^2 - 1}{x - 1}$ approaches 2 from above				

This pattern of numbers suggests $\lim_{x \to 1}\frac{x^2 - 1}{x - 1} = 2$, as we found when graphing in Investigation 2.

EXAMPLE 2

technology
APPENDIX P. 438

Sketch the graph of the function of

$$f(x) = \begin{cases} x - 1, \text{ if } x < 1. \\ 1, \text{ if } x = 1. \\ 2 + \sqrt{x - 1}, \text{ if } x > 1. \end{cases}$$

Determine $\lim_{x \to 1} f(x)$.

Solution

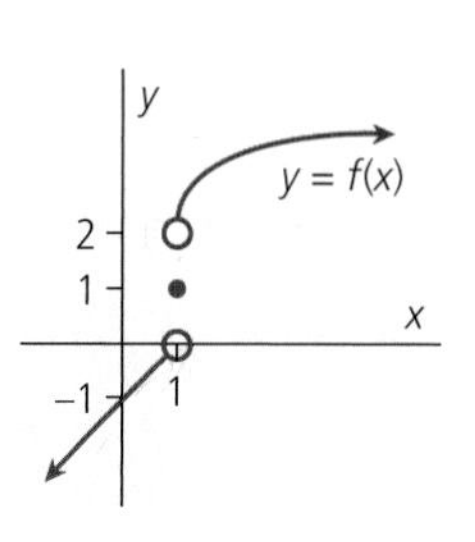

The graph of the function f consists of the line $y = x - 1$ for $x < 1$, the point $(1, 1)$ and the square root function $y = 2 + \sqrt{x - 1}$ for $x > 1$. From the graph of $f(x)$, observe that the limit of $f(x)$ as $x \to 1$ depends on whether $x < 1$ or $x > 1$. As $x \to 1^-$, $f(x)$ approaches the value of 0, from below. We write this as $\lim_{x \to 1^-} f(x) = \lim_{x \to 1^-} (x - 1) = 0$. Similarly, as $x \to 1^+$, $f(x)$ approaches the value 2, from above. We write this as $\lim_{x \to 1^+} f(x) = \lim_{x \to 1^+} (2 + \sqrt{x - 1}) = 2$. (This is the same value when $x = 1$ is substituted.) These two limits are referred to as one-sided limits, because in each case only values of x on one side of $x = 1$ are considered. However, the one-sided limits are unequal—$\lim_{x \to 1^-} f(x) = 0 \neq 2 = \lim_{x \to 1^+} f(x)$—or more briefly, $\lim_{x \to 1^-} f(x) \neq \lim_{x \to 1^+} f(x)$. This implies that $f(x)$ does not approach a **single value** as $x \to 1$. We say "the limit of $f(x)$ as $x \to 1$ does not exist" and write "$\lim_{x \to 1} f(x)$ does not exist." This may be surprising, since the function $f(x)$ was defined at $x = 1$; that is, $f(1) = 1$. We can now summarize the ideas introduced in these examples.

We say that the number L is the limit of a function $y = f(x)$ as x approaches the value a, written as $\lim_{x \to a} f(x) = L$, if $\lim_{x \to a^-} f(x) = L = \lim_{x \to a^+} f(x)$. Otherwise, $\lim_{x \to a} f(x)$ does not exist.

Exercise 3.3

Part A

1. What do you think is the appropriate limit of these sequences?
   a. 0.7, 0.72, 0.727, 0.7272, …
   b. 3, 3.1, 3.14, 3.141, 3.1415, 3.141 59, 3.141 592, …

Communication

2. Explain a process for finding a limit.

Communication

3. Write a concise description of the meaning of $\lim_{x \to 3} f(x) = 10$.

Knowledge/Understanding

4. Calculate each limit.

a. $\lim_{x \to -5} x$

b. $\lim_{x \to 3} (x + 7)$

c. $\lim_{x \to 10} x^2$

d. $\lim_{x \to -2} (4 - 3x^2)$

e. $\lim_{x \to 1} 4$

f. $\lim_{x \to 3} 2^x$

5. Find $\lim_{x \to 4} f(x)$, where $f(x) = \begin{cases} 1, & x \neq 4. \\ -1, & x = 4. \end{cases}$

Part B

6. For the function $y = f(x)$ in the graph below, find the following:

a. $\lim_{x \to -2^+} f(x)$

b. $\lim_{x \to 2^-} f(x)$

c. $\lim_{x \to 2^+} f(x)$

d. $f(2)$

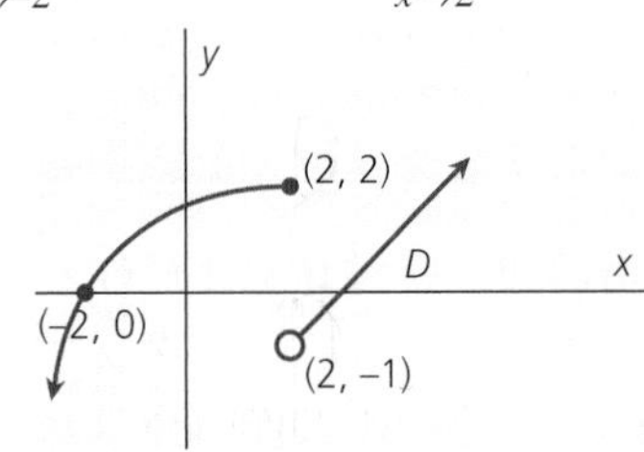

Knowledge/Understanding

7. Use the graph to find the limit, if it exists.

a. $\lim_{x \to 2} f(x)$

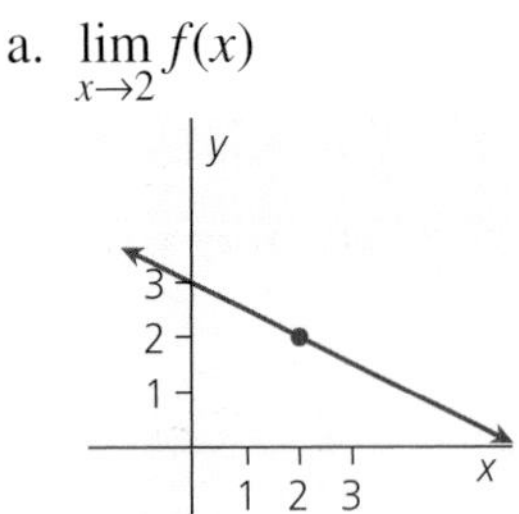

b. $\lim_{x \to 2} f(x)$

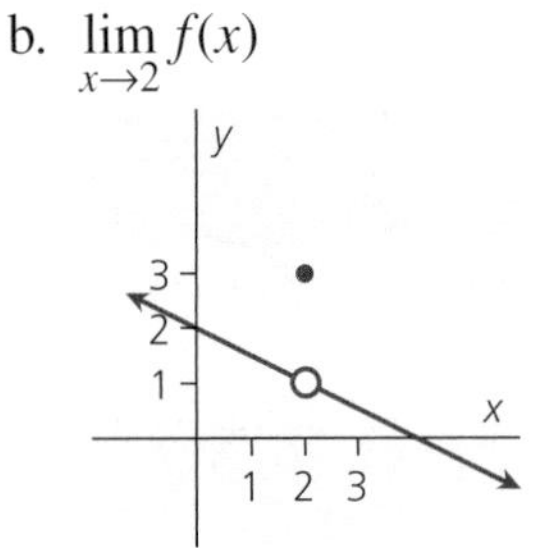

c. $\lim_{x \to 3} f(x)$

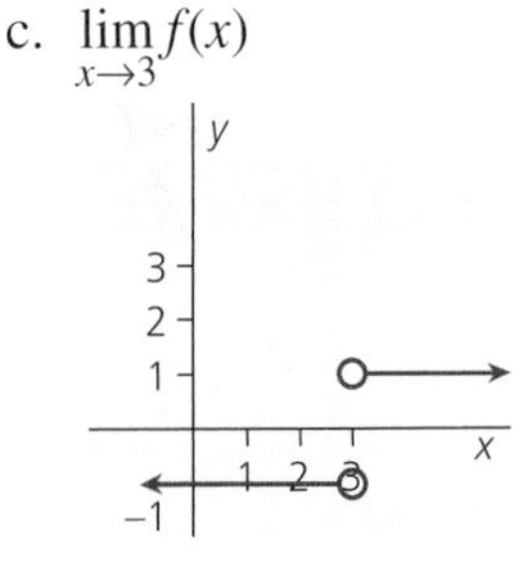

8. Evaluate each limit.

a. $\lim_{x \to -1} (9 - x^2)$

b. $\lim_{x \to 0} \sqrt{\frac{x + 20}{2x + 5}}$

c. $\lim_{x \to 5} \sqrt{x - 1}$

9. Find $\lim_{x \to 2} (x^2 + 1)$ and illustrate your result with a graph indicating the limiting value.

Communication

10. i) Evaluate the limits.

ii) If the limit does not exist, explain why.

a. $\lim_{x \to 0^+} x^4$

b. $\lim_{x \to 2^-} (x^2 - 4)$

c. $\lim_{x \to 3^-} (x^2 - 4)$

d. $\lim_{x \to 1^+} \frac{1}{x - 3}$

e. $\lim_{x \to 3^+} \frac{1}{x + 2}$

f. $\lim_{x \to 3} \frac{1}{x - 3}$

Knowledge/Understanding

11. In each of the following, find the indicated limit if it exists. Sketch the graph of the function.

a. $f(x) = \begin{cases} x + 2, x < -1 \\ -x + 2, x \geq -1 \end{cases}$; $\lim_{x \to -1} f(x)$

b. $f(x) = \begin{cases} -x + 4, x \leq 2 \\ -2x + 6, x > 2 \end{cases}$; $\lim_{x \to 2} f(x)$

c. $f(x) = \begin{cases} 4x, x \geq \frac{1}{2} \\ \frac{1}{x}, x < \frac{1}{2} \end{cases}$; $\lim_{x \to -\frac{1}{2}} f(x)$

d. $f(x) = \begin{cases} 1, x < -0.5 \\ x^2 - 0.25, x \geq -0.5 \end{cases}$; $\lim_{x \to -0.5} f(x)$

Application

12. Sketch the graph of any function that satisfies the given conditions in each case.

a. $f(1) = 1, \lim_{x \to 1^+} f(x) = 3, \lim_{x \to 1^-} f(x) = 2$

b. $f(2) = 1, \lim_{x \to 2} f(x) = 0$

c. $f(x) = 1$, if $x < 1$ and $\lim_{x \to 1^+} f(x) = 2$

d. $f(3) = 0, \lim_{x \to 3^+} f(x) = 0$

Thinking/Inquiry/Problem Solving

13. Let $f(x) = mx + b$, where m and b are constants.
If $\lim_{x \to 1} f(x) = -2$ and $\lim_{x \to -1} f(x) = 4$, find m and b.

Part C

Thinking/Inquiry/Problem Solving

14. Determine the real values of a, b, and c for the quadratic function $f(x) = ax^2 + bx + c$, $a \neq 0$, that satisfy the conditions $f(0) = 0$, $\lim_{x \to 1} f(x) = 5$, and $\lim_{x \to -2} f(x) = 8$.

15. The fish population (in thousands) in a lake at time t, in years, is modelled by the function

$$p(t) = \begin{cases} 3 + \frac{1}{12}t^2, 0 \leq t \leq 6 \\ 2 + \frac{1}{18}t^2, 6 < t \leq 12. \end{cases}$$

This function describes a sudden change in the population at time $t = 6$, due to a chemical spill.

a. Sketch the graph of $p(t)$.

b. Evaluate $\lim_{t \to 6^-} p(t)$ and $\lim_{x \to 6^+} p(t)$.

c. Determine how many fish were killed by the spill.

d. At what time did the population recover to the level before the spill?

Section 3.4 — Properties of Limits

The statement $\lim_{x \to a} f(x) = L$ says that the values of $f(x)$ become closer and closer to the number L as x gets closer and closer to the number a (from either side of a) such that $x \neq a$. This means that in finding the limit of $f(x)$ as x approaches a, there is no need to consider $x = a$. In fact, $f(a)$ need not even be defined. The only thing that matters is the behaviour of $f(x)$ near $x = a$.

EXAMPLE 1

Find $\lim_{x \to 2}(3x^2 + 4x - 1)$.

Solution

It seems clear that when x is close to 2, $3x^2$ is close to 12, and $4x$ is close to 8. Therefore, it appears that $\lim_{x \to 2}(3x^2 + 4x - 1) = 12 + 8 - 1 = 19$.

In Example 1, the limit was arrived at intuitively. It is possible to evaluate limits using the following properties of limits, which can be proved using the formal definition of limits. This is left for more advanced courses.

Properties of Limits

For any real number a, suppose f and g both have limits at $x = a$.

1. $\lim_{x \to a} k = k$ for any constant k
2. $\lim_{x \to a} x = a$
3. $\lim_{x \to a}[f(x) \pm g(x)] = \lim_{x \to a} f(x) \pm \lim_{x \to a} g(x)$
4. $\lim_{x \to a}[cf(x)] = c\left(\lim_{x \to a} f(x)\right)$ for any constant c
5. $\lim_{x \to a}[f(x)g(x)] = \left[\lim_{x \to a} f(x)\right]\left[\lim_{x \to a} g(x)\right]$
6. $\lim_{x \to a}\frac{f(x)}{g(x)} = \frac{\lim_{x \to a} f(x)}{\lim_{x \to a} g(x)}$ provided $\lim_{x \to a} g(x) \neq 0$
7. $\lim_{x \to a}[f(x)]^n = \left[\lim_{x \to a} f(x)\right]^n$, for n a rational number

---

EXAMPLE 2

Find $\lim_{x \to 2}(3x^2 + 4x - 1)$.

Solution

$\lim_{x \to 2}(3x^2 + 4x - 1) = \lim_{x \to 2}(3x^2) + \lim_{x \to 2}(4x) - \lim_{x \to 2}(1)$

$$= 3\lim_{x\to2}(x^2) + 4\lim_{x\to2}(x) - 1$$
$$= 3\left[\lim_{x\to2}x\right]^2 + 4(2) - 1$$
$$= 3(2)^2 + 8 - 1$$
$$= 19$$

Note: If f is a polynomial function, then $\lim_{x\to a} f(x) = f(a)$.

EXAMPLE 3

Evaluate $\lim_{x\to-1} \frac{x^2 - 5x + 2}{2x^3 + 3x + 1}$.

Solution

$$\lim_{x\to-1} \frac{x^2 - 5x + 2}{2x^3 + 3x + 1} = \frac{\lim_{x\to-1}(x^2 - 5x + 2)}{\lim_{x\to-1}(2x^3 + 3x + 1)}$$
$$= \frac{(-1)^2 - 5(-1) + 2}{2(-1)^3 + 3(-1) + 1}$$
$$= \frac{8}{-4}$$
$$= -2$$

EXAMPLE 4

Evaluate $\lim_{x\to5} \sqrt{\frac{x^2}{x - 1}}$.

Solution

$$\lim_{x\to5} \sqrt{\frac{x^2}{x - 1}} = \sqrt{\lim_{x\to5} \frac{x^2}{x - 1}}$$
$$= \sqrt{\frac{\lim_{x\to5} x^2}{\lim_{x\to5}(x - 1)}}$$
$$= \sqrt{\frac{25}{4}}$$
$$= \frac{5}{2}$$

Sometimes the limit of $f(x)$ as x approaches a cannot be found by direct substitution. This is of special interest when direct substitution results in an **indeterminate form** $\left(\frac{0}{0}\right)$. In such cases, we look for an equivalent function that agrees with f for all values except the troublesome value $x = a$. Here are some examples.

EXAMPLE 5

Find $\lim_{x\to 3} \frac{x^2 - 2x - 3}{x - 3}$.

Solution

If we try substitution, we obtain $\frac{0}{0}$, an indeterminate form. The next step is to simplify the function by factoring and reducing to see if the limit of the reduced form can be evaluated.

$$\lim_{x\to 3} \frac{x^2 - 2x - 3}{x - 3} = \lim_{x\to 3} \frac{(x + 1)(x - 3)}{x - 3} = \lim_{x\to 3} (x + 1)$$

This reduction is valid only if $x \neq 3$. This is not a problem, since $\lim_{x\to 3}$ is concerned with values as x approaches 3, not the value $x = 3$. Therefore,

$$\lim_{x\to 3} \frac{x^2 - 2x - 3}{x - 3} = \lim_{x\to 3} (x + 1) = 4.$$

EXAMPLE 6

A useful technique for finding limits is to rationalize either the numerator or the denominator to obtain an algebraic form that is not indeterminate.

Evaluate $\lim_{x\to 0} \frac{\sqrt{x + 1} - 1}{x}$.

Solution

$$\lim_{x\to 0} \frac{\sqrt{x + 1} - 1}{x} = \lim_{x\to 0} \frac{\sqrt{x + 1} - 1}{x} \times \frac{\sqrt{x + 1} + 1}{\sqrt{x + 1} + 1}$$

(Multiplying by $\frac{\sqrt{x + 1} + 1}{\sqrt{x + 1} + 1}$)

$$= \lim_{x\to 0} \frac{x + 1 - 1}{x(\sqrt{x + 1} + 1)}$$

$$= \lim_{x\to 0} \frac{x}{x(\sqrt{x + 1} + 1)}$$

$$= \lim_{x\to 0} \frac{1}{\sqrt{x + 1} + 1}$$

$$= \frac{1}{2}$$

INVESTIGATION

Here is an alternate technique for finding the value of a limit.

1. Find $\lim_{x\to 1} \frac{(x - 1)}{\sqrt{x} - 1}$ by rationalizing.

2. Let $u = \sqrt{x}$, and rewrite $\lim_{x\to 1} \frac{(x - 1)}{\sqrt{x} - 1}$ in terms of u. Since $x = u^2$, and $\sqrt{x} \geq 0$, and $u \geq 0$, it follows as x approaches the value of 1, u approaches the value of 1. Use this substitution to find $\lim_{u\to 1} \frac{(u^2 - 1)}{u - 1}$ by reducing the rational expression.

EXAMPLE 7 Evaluate $\lim\limits_{x\to 0}\dfrac{(x+8)^{\frac{1}{3}}-2}{x}$.

Solution

This quotient is indeterminate $\left(\frac{0}{0}\right)$ when $x = 0$. Rationalizing the term $(x + 8)^{\frac{1}{3}}$ is not so easy. However, the expression can be simplified by substitution.

Let $u = (x + 8)^{\frac{1}{3}}$. Then $u^3 = x + 8$ and $x = u^3 - 8$. As x approaches the value 0, u approaches the value 2. The given limit becomes

$$\begin{aligned}\lim_{x\to 0}\frac{(x+8)^{\frac{1}{3}}-2}{x} &= \lim_{u\to 2}\frac{u-2}{u^3-8}\\ &= \lim_{u\to 2}\frac{u-2}{(u-2)(u^2+2u+4)}\\ &= \lim_{u\to 2}\frac{1}{u^2+2u+4}\\ &= \frac{1}{12}.\end{aligned}$$

EXAMPLE 8 Evaluate $\lim\limits_{x\to 2}\dfrac{|x-2|}{x-2}$. Illustrate with a graph.

Solution

Consider

$$f(x) = \frac{|x-2|}{x-2} = \begin{cases}\dfrac{x-2}{x-2}, & \text{if } x > 2\\[2ex] \dfrac{-(x-2)}{x-2}, & \text{if } x < 2\end{cases}$$

$$= \begin{cases}1, & \text{if } x > 2.\\ -1, & \text{if } x < 2.\end{cases}$$

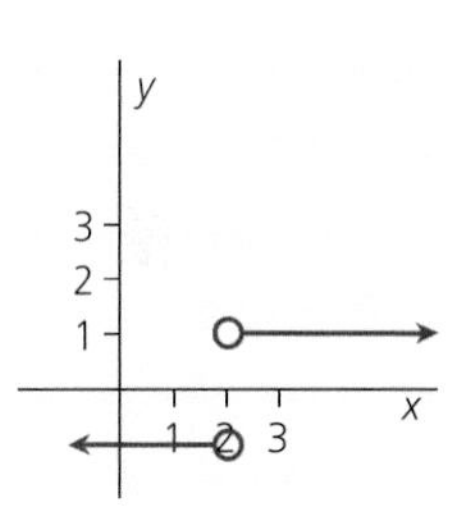

Notice that $f(2)$ is not defined and that we must consider left- and right-hand limits.

$$\lim_{x\to 2^{-1}} f(x) = \lim_{x\to 2^{-1}}(-1) = -1$$

$$\lim_{x\to 2^{+1}} f(x) = \lim_{x\to 2^{+1}}(1) = 1$$

Since the left- and right-hand limits are not the same, we conclude that

$\lim\limits_{x\to 2}\dfrac{|x-2|}{x-2}$ does not exist.

EXAMPLE 9

a. Evaluate $\lim_{x \to 3^-} \sqrt{9 - x^2}$.

b. Explain why the limit as x approaches 3^+ cannot be determined.

c. What can you conclude about the $\lim_{x \to 3} \sqrt{9 - x^2}$?

Solution

a. The graph of $f(x) = \sqrt{9 - x^2}$ is the semicircle $y = \sqrt{9 - x^2}$ as illustrated below.

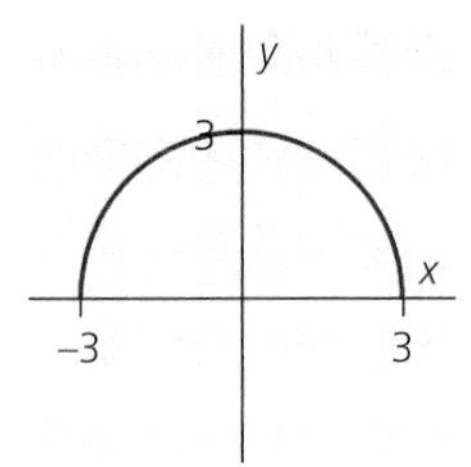

From the graph, the left-hand limit at $x = 3$ is 0. Therefore, $\lim_{x \to 3^-} \sqrt{9 - x^2} = 0$.

b. The function is not defined for $x > 3$.

c. $\lim_{x \to 3} \sqrt{9 - x^2}$ does not exist because the function is not defined on both sides of 3.

In this section, we have learned the properties of limits and developed algebraic methods for evaluating limits. The examples in this section have complemented the table of values and graphing techniques introduced in previous sections. Five techniques for evaluating simple limits that have indeterminate quotients were illustrated:

- direct substitution
- factoring
- rationalizing
- change of variable
- one-sided limits

In each case, a graph can be utilized to check your result.

Exercise 3.4

Part A

1. Is there a different value for the answers among $\lim_{x\to2}(3 + x)$, $\lim_{x\to2}3 + x$, and $\lim_{x\to2}(x + 3)$?

Communication

2. How do you find the limit of a rational function?

Communication

3. Once you know the $\lim_{x\to a^-} f(x)$ and $\lim_{x\to a^+} f(x)$ at an interior point of the domain of f, do you then know $\lim_{x\to a} f(x)$? Give reasons for your answer.

4. Evaluate each limit.

a. $\lim_{x\to2}\frac{3x}{x^2+2}$ b. $\lim_{x\to-1}(x^4 + x^3 + x^2)$ c. $\lim_{x\to9}\left(\sqrt{x} + \frac{1}{\sqrt{x}}\right)^2$

d. $\lim_{x\to2\pi}(x^3 + \pi^2 x - 5\pi^3)$ e. $\lim_{x\to0}\left(\sqrt{3 + \sqrt{1+x}}\right)$ f. $\lim_{x\to-3}\sqrt{\frac{x-3}{2x+4}}$

Part B

Knowledge/Understanding

5. Use a graphing calculator to graph the function and to estimate the limit. Then find the limit by substitution.

technology

a. $\lim_{x\to-2}\frac{x^3}{x-2}$ b. $\lim_{x\to1}\frac{2x}{\sqrt{x^2+1}}$

6. Show that $\lim_{t\to1}\frac{t^3 - t^2 - 5t}{6 - t^2} = -1$.

Knowledge/Understanding

7. Evaluate the limit of each indeterminate quotient.

a. $\lim_{x\to2}\frac{4 - x^2}{2 - x}$ b. $\lim_{x\to-2}\frac{4 - x^2}{2 + x}$ c. $\lim_{x\to0}\frac{7x - x^2}{x}$

d. $\lim_{x\to-1}\frac{2x^2 + 5x + 3}{x + 1}$ e. $\lim_{x\to-\frac{4}{3}}\frac{3x^2 + x - 4}{3x + 4}$ f. $\lim_{x\to3}\frac{x^3 - 27}{x - 3}$

g. $\lim_{x\to-2}\frac{x^3 + 2x^2 - 4x - 8}{x + 2}$ h. $\lim_{x\to2}\frac{2x^3 - 5x^2 + 3x - 2}{2x - 4}$ i. $\lim_{x\to0}\frac{\sqrt{x+1} - 1}{x}$

j. $\lim_{x\to0}\frac{2 - \sqrt{4+x}}{x}$ k. $\lim_{x\to4}\frac{\sqrt{x} - 2}{x - 4}$ l. $\lim_{x\to0}\frac{\sqrt{7-x} - \sqrt{7+x}}{x}$

m. $\lim_{x\to1}\frac{\sqrt{5-x} - \sqrt{3+x}}{x - 1}$ n. $\lim_{x\to4}\frac{2 - \sqrt{x}}{3 - \sqrt{2x+1}}$ o. $\lim_{x\to0}\frac{2^{2x} - 2^x}{2^x - 1}$

8. Evaluate the limit by change of variable.

a. $\lim_{x\to8}\frac{\sqrt[3]{x} - 2}{x - 8}$ b. $\lim_{x\to27}\frac{27 - x}{x^{\frac{1}{3}} - 3}$ c. $\lim_{x\to1}\frac{x^{\frac{1}{6}} - 1}{x - 1}$

d. $\lim_{x\to1}\frac{x^{\frac{1}{6}} - 1}{x^{\frac{1}{3}} - 1}$ e. $\lim_{x\to4}\frac{\sqrt{x} - 2}{\sqrt{x^3} - 8}$ f. $\lim_{x\to0}\frac{(x+8)^{\frac{1}{3}} - 2}{x}$

9. Evaluate each limit, if it exists, using any appropriate technique.

a. $\lim_{x \to 4} \frac{16 - x^2}{x^3 + 64}$

b. $\lim_{x \to 4} \frac{x^2 - 16}{x^2 - 5x + 6}$

c. $\lim_{x \to 1} \frac{x^3 + x^2 - 5x + 3}{x^2 - 2x + 1}$

d. $\lim_{x \to -1} \frac{x^2 + x}{x + 1}$

e. $\lim_{x \to 6^+} \frac{\sqrt{x^2 - 5x - 6}}{x - 3}$

f. $\lim_{x \to 0} \frac{(2x + 1)^{\frac{1}{3}} - 1}{x}$

g. $\lim_{x \to 2} \frac{x^2 - 4}{\left(\frac{1}{x}\right) - \frac{1}{2}}$

h. $\lim_{x \to 3} \frac{\sqrt{x + 1} - 2}{x - 3}$

i. $\lim_{x \to 0} \frac{x^2 - 9x}{5x^3 + 6x}$

j. $\lim_{x \to 0} \frac{\sqrt{x + 1} - 1}{x}$

k. $\lim_{h \to 0} \frac{(x + h)^2 - x^2}{h}$

l. $\lim_{x \to 1} \left(\frac{1}{x - 1}\right)\left(\frac{1}{x + 3} - \frac{2}{3x + 5}\right)$

10. By using one-sided limits, determine whether the limit exists. Illustrate the results geometrically by sketching the graph of each function.

a. $\lim_{x \to 5} \frac{|x - 5|}{x - 5}$

b. $\lim \frac{|2x - 5|(x + 1)}{2x - 5}$

c. $\lim_{x \to 2} \frac{x^2 - x - 2}{|x - 2|}$

d. $\lim_{x \to -2} \frac{(x + 2)^3}{|x + 2|}$

Application

11. **Charles' Law and Absolute Zero** Jacques Charles (1746–1823) discovered that the volume of gas at a constant pressure increases linearly with the temperature of the gas. In the table, one mole of hydrogen is held at a constant pressure of one atmosphere. The volume V is measured in litres and the temperature T is measured in degrees Celsius.

T	−40	−20	0	20	40	60	80
V	19.1482	20.7908	22.4334	24.0760	25.7186	27.3612	29.0038

a. By finding a difference row, show that T and V are related by a linear relation.

b. Find the linear equation V in terms of T.

c. Solve for T in terms of V for the equation in part **b.**

d. Show that $\lim_{V \to 0^+} T$ is approximately -273.15. *Note:* This represents the approximate number of degrees on the Celsius scale of absolute zero on the Kelvin scale (0 K).

e. Using the information found in parts **b** and **d,** draw a graph of V versus T.

Thinking/Inquiry/ Problem Solving

12. Show, using the properties of limits, that if $\lim_{x \to 5} f(x) = 3$, then $\lim_{x \to 5} \frac{x^2 - 4}{f(x)} = 7$.

13. If $\lim_{x \to 4} f(x) = 3$, use the properties of limits to evaluate each limit.

 a. $\lim_{x \to 4} [f(x)]^3$
 b. $\lim_{x \to 4} \frac{[f(x)]^2 - x^2}{f(x) + x}$
 c. $\lim_{x \to 4} \sqrt{3f(x) - 2x}$

Part C

14. If $\lim_{x \to 0} \frac{f(x)}{x} = 1$ and $g(0) \neq 0$, then evaluate each limit.

 a. $\lim_{x \to 0} f(x)$
 b. $\lim_{x \to 0} \frac{f(x)}{g(x)}$

15. If $\lim_{x \to 0} \frac{f(x)}{x} = 1$ and $\lim_{x \to 0} \frac{g(x)}{x} = 2$, then evaluate each limit.

 a. $\lim_{x \to 0} f(x)$
 b. $\lim_{x \to 0} g(x)$
 c. $\lim_{x \to 0} \frac{f(x)}{g(x)}$

16. Evaluate $\lim_{x \to 0} \frac{\sqrt{x + 1} - \sqrt{2x + 1}}{\sqrt{3x + 4} - \sqrt{2x + 4}}$ of the indeterminate quotient.

17. Does $\lim_{x \to 1} \frac{x^2 + |x - 1| - 1}{|x - 1|}$ exist? Illustrate your result by sketching a graph of the function.

18. For what value of b does $\lim_{x \to 1} \frac{x^2 + bx - 3}{x - 1}$ exist?

19. For what values of m and b is the statement $\lim_{x \to 0} \frac{\sqrt{mx + b} - 3}{x} = 1$?

Section 3.5 — Continuity

The idea of **continuity** may be thought of informally as the idea of being connected to one's neighbours. The concept arose from the notion of a graph "without breaks or jumps or gaps."

When we talk about a function being *continuous at a point*, we mean that the graph passes through the point without a break. A graph that is *not continuous at a point* (sometimes referred to as being *discontinuous at a point*) has a break of some type at the point. The following graphs illustrate these ideas.

a. Continuous for all values of the domain

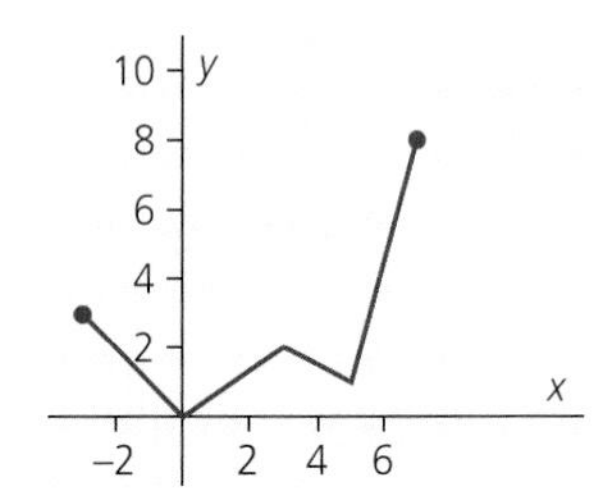

b. Discontinuous at $x = 1$

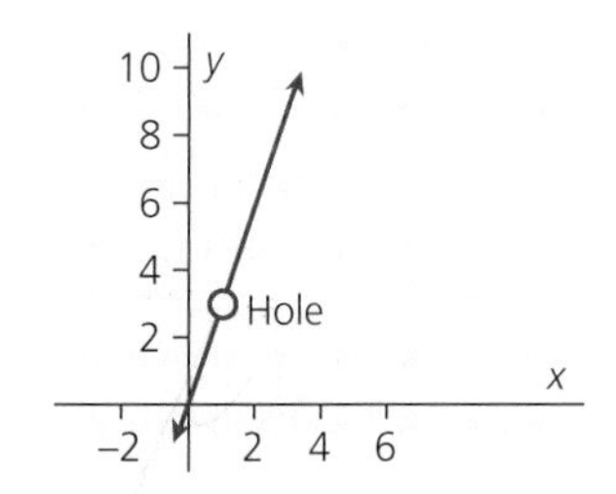

c. Discontinuous at $x = 1$

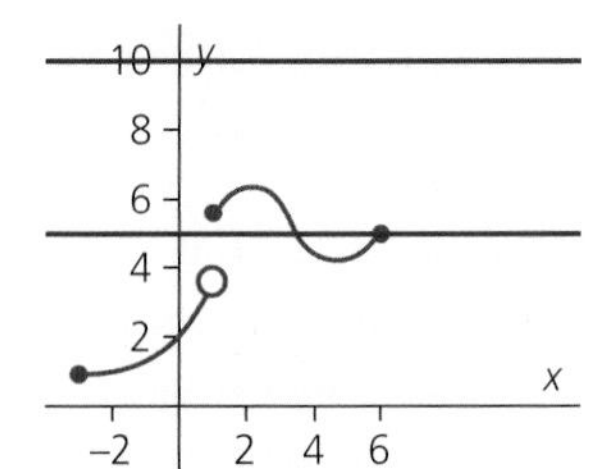

d. Discontinuous at $x = 1$

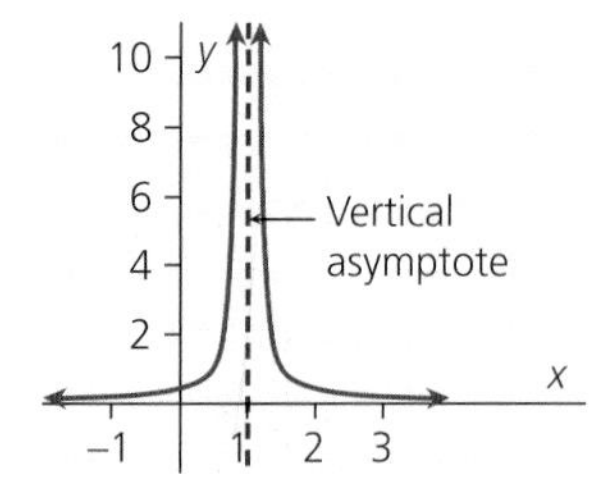

What conditions must be satisfied for a function f to be continuous at a? First, $f(a)$ must be defined. The curves in figure **b** and figure **d** are not continuous at $x = 1$ because they are not defined at $x = 1$.

A second condition for continuity at a point $x = a$ is that the function makes no jumps there. This means that if "x is close to a," then $f(x)$ must be close to $f(a)$. This condition is satisfied if $\lim_{x \to a} f(x) = f(a)$. Looking at the graph in figure **c**, we see that $\lim_{x \to 1} f(x)$ does not exist and the function is therefore not continuous at $x = 1$.

We can now define the **continuity of a function at a point.**

The function $f(x)$ is continuous at $x = a$ if $f(a)$ is defined and if

$$\lim_{x \to a} f(x) = f(a).$$

Otherwise, $f(x)$ is discontinuous at $x = a$.

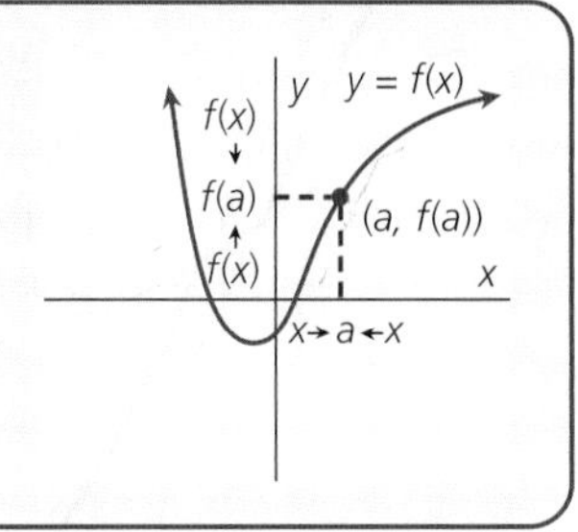

The geometrical meaning of f being continuous at $x = a$ is that as $x \to a$, the points $(x, f(x))$ on the graph of f converge at the point $(a, f(a))$ ensuring the graph of f is unbroken at $(a, f(a))$.

EXAMPLE 1

a. Graph the function $f(x) = \begin{cases} x^2 - 3, x \leq -1 \\ x - 1, x > -1. \end{cases}$

b. Find $\lim_{x \to -1} f(x)$.

c. Find $f(-1)$.

Solution

a.

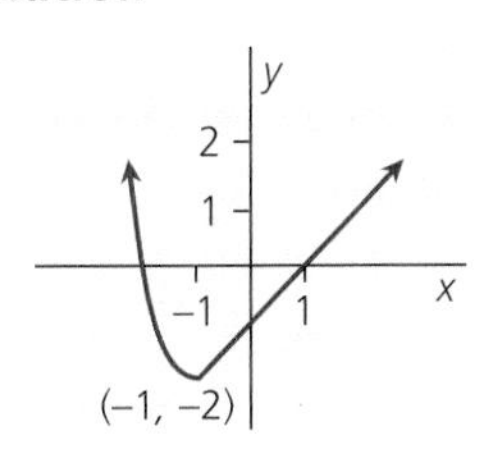

b. From the graph $\lim_{x \to -1} f(x) = -2$. *Note:* Both the left-hand and right-hand limits are equal.

c. $f(-1) = -2$

Therefore, $f(x)$ is continuous at $x = -1$.

EXAMPLE 2

Test the continuity of each of the following functions at $x = 2$. If a function is not continuous at $x = 2$, give a reason why it is not continuous.

a. $f(x) = x^3 - x$

b. $g(x) = \dfrac{x^2 - x - 2}{x - 2}$

c. $h(x) = \dfrac{x^2 - x - 2}{x - 2}$, if $x \neq 2$ and $h(2) = 3$

d. $F(x) = \dfrac{1}{(x - 2)^2}$

e. $G(x) = \begin{cases} 4 - x^2, \text{ if } x < 2 \\ 3, \text{ if } x \geq 2 \end{cases}$

Solution

a. The function f is continuous at $x = 2$ since $f(2) = 6 = \lim_{x \to 2} f(x)$. (Polynomial functions are continuous at all real values of x.)

b. The function g is not continuous at $x = 2$ because g is not defined at this point.

c. Since $\lim_{x \to 2} \frac{x^2 - x - 2}{x - 2} = \lim_{x \to 2} \frac{(x - 2)(x + 1)}{(x - 2)}$

$$= \lim_{x \to 2} (x + 1)$$

$$= 3$$

$$= h(2),$$

therefore, $h(x)$ is continous at $x = 2$.

d. The function F is not continuous at $x = 2$ because $F(2)$ is not defined.

e. Since $\lim_{x \to 2^-} G(x) = \lim_{x \to 2^-} (4 - x^2)$

$$= 0$$

and $\lim_{x \to 2^+} G(x) = \lim_{x \to 2^+} (3)$

$$= 3,$$

therefore, $\lim_{x \to 2} G(x)$ does not exist, since the function is not continuous at $x = 2$.

INVESTIGATION

technology

To test the definition of continuity by graphing, investigate the following:

1. Draw the graph for each function in Example 2.
2. Which of the graphs are continuous, contain a hole or a jump, or have a vertical asymptote?
3. Given only the defining sentence of a function $y = f(x)$ such as $f(x) = \frac{8x^3 - 9x + 5}{x^2 + 300x}$, explain why the graphing technique to test for continuity on an interval may be less suitable.
4. Find where $f(x) = \frac{8x^3 - 9x + 5}{x^2 + 300x}$ is not defined and the intervals where it is continuous.

Exercise 3.5

Part A

Communication

1. How can looking at a graph of a function help you tell where the function is continuous?

Communication

2. What does it mean for a function to be continuous over a given domain?

Knowledge/Understanding

3. What are the basic types of discontinuity? Give an example of each.

4. Find the value(s) of x at which the functions are discontinuous.

a. $f(x) = \frac{9 - x^2}{x - 3}$

b. $g(x) = \frac{7x - 4}{x}$

c. $h(x) = \frac{x^2 + 1}{x^3}$

d. $f(x) = \frac{x - 4}{x^2 - 9}$

e. $g(x) = \frac{13x}{x^2 + x - 6}$

f. $h(x) = \begin{cases} -x, x \leq 3 \\ 1 - x, x > 3 \end{cases}$

Part B

Knowledge/Understanding

5. Find all values of x for which the given functions are continuous.

a. $f(x) = 3x^5 + 2x^3 - x$

b. $g(x) = \pi x^2 - 4.2x + 7$

c. $h(x) = \frac{x^2 + 16}{x^2 - 5x}$

d. $f(x) = \sqrt{x + 2}$

e. $g(x) = 10^x$

f. $h(x) = \frac{16}{x^2 + 25}$

6. Examine the continuity of $g(x) = x + 3$ at the point $x = 2$.

7. Sketch a graph of $h(x) = \begin{cases} x - 1, x < 3 \\ 5 - x, x \geq 3 \end{cases}$

and determine if the function is continuous everywhere.

Knowledge/Understanding

8. Sketch a graph of $f(x) = \begin{cases} x^2, x < 0. \\ 3, x \geq 0. \end{cases}$ Is the function continuous?

Application

9. Recent postal rates for letter mail within Canada for non-standard and over-sized items are given in the following table. Maximum dimensions for over-sized letter mail are 380 mm × 270 mm × 20 mm.

100 g or Less	Between 100 g and 200 g	Between 200 g and 500 g
\$0.92	\$1.50	\$2.00

Draw a graph of the cost in dollars of mailing a non-standard envelope as a function of its mass in grams. Where are the discontinuities of this function?

Knowledge/Understanding

10. Determine whether $f(x) = \frac{x^2 - x - 6}{x - 3}$ is continuous at $x = 3$.

11. Examine the continuity of the function $f(x) = \begin{cases} x, \text{ if } x \leq 1. \\ 1, \text{ if } 1 < x \leq 2. \\ 3, \text{ if } x > 2. \end{cases}$

12. $g(x) = \begin{cases} x + 3, x \neq 3. \\ 2 + \sqrt{k}, x = 3. \end{cases}$ Find k, if $g(x)$ is continuous.

Part C

Thinking/Inquiry/ Problem Solving

13. Find constants a and b such that the function

$$f(x) = \begin{cases} -x, & \text{if } -3 \le x \le -2 \\ ax^2 + b, & \text{if } -2 < x < 0 \\ 6, & \text{if } x = 0 \end{cases}$$

is continuous for $-3 \le x \le 0$.

14. Consider the function $g(x) = \begin{cases} \dfrac{x|x-1|}{x-1}, & \text{if } x \neq 1. \\ 0, & \text{if } x = 1. \end{cases}$

a. Evaluate $\lim_{x \to 1^+} g(x)$ and $\lim_{x \to 1^-} g(x)$, then determine whether $\lim_{x \to 1} g(x)$ exists.

b. Sketch the graph of $g(x)$ and identify any points of discontinuity.

Key Concepts Review

We began our introduction to calculus by considering the slope of a tangent and the related idea of rate of change. This led us to the study of limits and laid the groundwork for Chapter 4 and the concept of the derivative of a function.

Consider the following brief summary to confirm your understanding of key concepts covered in Chapter 3.

- Slope of the tangent is the limit of the slope of the secant, as Q approaches P along the curve
- Slope of a tangent at an arbitrary point
- Rates of change, average velocity, and velocity
- The Limit of a Function exists when the limiting value from the left equals the limiting value from the right
- Properties of Limits and indeterminate forms $\frac{0}{0}$
- Continuity is described as a graph "without breaks or jumps or gaps"

Formulas

- The slope of the tangent to the graph $y = f(x)$ at point $P(a, f(a))$ is

  $$m = \lim_{\Delta x \to 0} \frac{\Delta y}{\Delta x} = \lim_{h \to 0} \frac{f(a + h) - f(a)}{h}.$$

- average velocity $= \dfrac{\text{change in distance}}{\text{change in time}}$

- The velocity (instantaneous) of an object, with position function $s(t)$, at time $t = a$ is

  $$v(a) = \lim_{\Delta t \to 0} \frac{\Delta s}{\Delta t} = \lim_{h \to 0} \frac{s(a + h) - s(a)}{h}.$$

- If f is a polynomial function, then $\lim_{x \to a} f(x) = f(a)$.

- The function $f(x)$ is continuous at $x = a$ if $f(a)$ is defined and if $\lim_{x \to a} f(x) = f(a)$.

Career Link wrap-up investigate and apply

CHAPTER 3: ASSESSING ATHLETIC PERFORMANCE

An Olympic coach has developed a six-minute fitness test for her team members that sets target values for heart rates. The monitor they have available counts the total number of heartbeats starting from a rest position at "time zero." Results for one of the team members are as follows:

Time (in minutes)	Number of Beats
0.0	0
1.0	55
2.0	120
3.0	195
4.0	280
5.0	375
6.0	480

a. The coach has established that each athlete's heart rate must not exceed 100 beats per minute at exactly 3 min. Using a graphical technique, determine if this athlete meets the coach's criteria.

b. The coach also needs to know the instant in time when an athlete's heart rate actually exceeds 100 beats per minute. Explain how you would solve this problem graphically. Would this be an efficient method? Explain. How is this question different from part **a**?

c. Build a mathematical model with the total number of heartbeats as a function of time ($n = f(t)$) by first determining the degree of the polynomial then using the graphing calculator to obtain an algebraic model.

d. Solve **b** algebraically by obtaining an expression for the instantaneous rate of change of number of heartbeats, heart rate, as a function of time ($r = f(t)$) using the methods presented in this chapter. Compare the accuracy and efficiency of solving this question graphically and algebraically. ●

Review Exercise

1. Consider the graph of the function $f(x) = 5x^2 - 8x$.

   a. Find the slope of the secant that joins the points on the graph given by $x = -2$ and $x = 3$.

   b. Determine the average rate of change as x changes from -1 to 4.

   c. Find an equation for the line tangent to the graph of the function at $x = 1$.

2. Find the slope of the tangent to the given function at the given point.

   a. $f(x) = \frac{3}{x+1}$, $P(2, 1)$

   b. $g(x) = \sqrt{x+2}$, $x = -1$

   c. $h(x) = \frac{2}{\sqrt{x+5}}$, $x = 4$

   d. $f(x) = \frac{5}{x-2}$, $x = 4$

3. Find the slope of the graph of $f(x) = \begin{cases} 4 - x^2, x \le 1 \\ 2x + 1, x > 1 \end{cases}$ at each of the following points:

   a. $P(-1, 3)$

   b. $P(2, 5)$

4. The height (in metres) that an object has fallen from a height of 180 m is given by the position function $s(t) = -5t^2 + 180$, where $t \ge 0$ and t is in seconds.

   a. Find the average velocity during each of the first two seconds.

   b. Find the velocity of the object when $t = 4$.

   c. At what velocity will the object hit the ground?

5. After t minutes of growth, a certain bacterial culture has a mass in grams of $M(t) = t^2$.

   a. How much does it grow during the time $3 \le t \le 3.01$?

   b. What is its average rate of growth during the time interval $3 \le t \le 3.01$?

   c. What is its rate of growth when $t = 3$?

6. It is estimated that t years from now, the amount of waste accumulated, Q, in tonnes, will be $Q(t) = 10^4(t^2 + 15t + 70)$ tonnes, $0 \le t \le 10$.

   a. How much waste has been accumulated up to now?

   b. What will be the average rate of change of this quantity over the next three years?

c. What is the present rate of change of this quantity?

d. When will the rate of change reach 3.0×10^5 tonnes per year?

7. The electrical power $p(t)$, in kilowatts, being used by a household as a function of time t, in hours, is modelled by the graph, where $t = 0$ corresponds to 06:00.

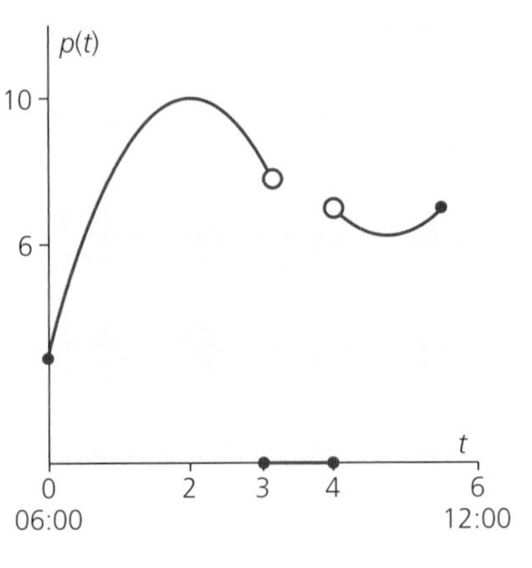

The graph indicates peak use at 08:00 and a power failure between 09:00 and 10:00.

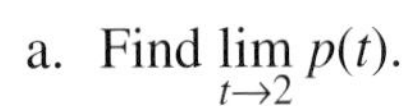

a. Find $\lim_{t \to 2} p(t)$.

b. Determine $\lim_{t \to 4^+} p(t)$ and $\lim_{t \to 4^-} p(t)$.

c. For what values of t is $p(t)$ discontinuous?

8. Sketch a graph of any function that satisfies the given conditions in each case.

a. $\lim_{x \to -1} f(x) = 0.5$ and f is discontinuous at $x = -1$.

b. $f(x) = -4$ if $x < 3$, f is an increasing function when $x > 3$, $\lim_{x \to 3^+} f(x) = 1$.

9. Sketch the graph of the function $f(x) = \begin{cases} x + 1, x < -1. \\ -x + 1, -1 \le x < 1. \\ x - 2, x > 1. \end{cases}$

a. Find all values at which the function is discontinuous.

b. Find the limits at those values, if they exist.

10. Determine whether $f(x) = \dfrac{x^2 - x - 6}{x - 3}$ is continuous at $x = 3$.

11. Consider the function $f(x) = \dfrac{2x - 2}{x^2 + x - 2}$.

a. For what values of x is f discontinuous?

b. At each point where f is discontinuous, determine the limit of $f(x)$, if it exists.

technology

12. Use a graphing calculator to graph the function and estimate the limits, if they exist.

a. $f(x) = \dfrac{1}{x^2}$, $\lim_{x \to 0} f(x)$

b. $g(x) = x(x - 5)$, $\lim_{x \to 0} g(x)$

c. $h(x) = \dfrac{x^3 - 27}{x^2 - 9}$, $\lim_{x \to 4} h(x)$ and $\lim_{x \to -3} h(x)$

technology

13. Complete each table and use the result to estimate the limit. Use a graphing calculator to graph the function to confirm your result.

a. $\lim_{x \to 2} \frac{x - 2}{x^2 - x - 2}$

x	1.9	1.99	1.999	2.001	2.01	2.1
$f(x)$						

b. $\lim_{x \to 1} \frac{x - 1}{x^2 - 1}$

x	0.9	0.99	0.999	1.001	1.01	1.1
$f(x)$						

14. Complete the table and use the results to estimate the limit. Then determine the limit using an algebraic technique and compare the answer with the estimate.

$\lim_{x \to 0} \frac{\sqrt{x + 3} - \sqrt{3}}{x}$

x	−0.1	−0.01	−0.001	0.001	0.01	0.1
$f(x)$						

15 a. Complete the table to approximate the limit of $f(x) = \frac{\sqrt{x + 2} - 2}{x - 2}$ as $x \to 2$.

x	2.1	2.01	2.001	2.0001
$f(x) = \frac{\sqrt{x+2} - 2}{x - 2}$				

technology

b. Use a graphing calculator to graph f and use the graph to approximate the limit.

c. Use the technique of rationalizing the numerator to find the $\lim_{x \to 2} \frac{\sqrt{x + 2} - 2}{x - 2}$.

16. Evaluate the limit of each difference quotient. In each case, interpret the limit as the slope of the tangent to a curve at a specific point.

a. $\lim_{h \to 0} \frac{(5 + h)^2 - 25}{h}$

b. $\lim_{h \to 0} \frac{\sqrt{4 + h} - 2}{h}$

c. $\lim_{h \to 0} \frac{\frac{1}{(4 + h)} - \frac{1}{4}}{h}$

d. $\lim_{h \to 0} \frac{(343 + h)^{\frac{1}{3}} - 7}{h}$

17. Evaluate each limit using one of the algebraic methods discussed in the text, if the limit exists.

a. $\lim_{x \to -2} \frac{x^2 - 7}{x^2 + x}$

b. $\lim_{x \to a} (5x^2 - 3x + 7)$

c. $\lim_{x \to -6} \frac{1}{6 + x}$

d. $\lim_{x\to 0} 10x$

e. $\lim_{x\to -6} \frac{x^2 - 36}{x + 6}$

f. $\lim_{x\to -4} \frac{x^2 + 12x + 32}{x + 4}$

g. $\lim_{x\to 2} \frac{x^2 - 4}{x^3 - 8}$

h. $\lim_{x\to a} \frac{(x + 4a)^2 - 25a^2}{x - a}$

i. $\lim_{x\to 0} \frac{x^2 + 3x}{3x^2 - 7x}$

j. $\lim_{x\to 2} \frac{x^2 - 1}{x^2 + 1}$

k. $\lim_{n\to 0} \frac{2^n}{4^n}$

l. $\lim_{x\to 0} \frac{5x^2 - 2x + 3}{7x^2 + 4x - 3}$

m. $\lim_{x\to 3} \frac{1}{\frac{1}{3} + \frac{1}{x}}$

n. $\lim_{x\to 0} \frac{4 - \sqrt{12 + x}}{x - 4}$

o. $\lim_{x\to 0} \frac{\sqrt{x + 5} - \sqrt{5 - x}}{x}$

p. $\lim_{x\to -3} \frac{x^2 + 3x}{x + 3}$

q. $\lim_{x\to -2} \frac{x^3 + x^2 - 8x - 12}{x + 2}$

r. $\lim_{x\to 2} \frac{x^3 + x^2 - 12}{x - 2}$

s. $\lim_{x\to -4} \frac{64 + x^3}{4 + x}$

t. $\lim_{x\to 0} \frac{1}{x}\left(\frac{1}{2 + x} - \frac{1}{2}\right)$

u. $\lim_{x\to -1} \frac{108(x^2 + 2x)(x + 1)^3}{(x^3 + 1)^3(x - 1)}$

18. Explain why the given limit does not exist.

a. $\lim_{x\to 3} \sqrt{x - 3}$

b. $\lim_{x\to 2} \frac{1}{\sqrt{x - 2}}$

c. $\lim_{x\to 2} \frac{x^2 - 4}{x^2 - 4x + 4}$

d. $\lim_{x\to 0} \frac{|x|}{x}$

e. $f(x) = \begin{cases} -5, & x < 1 \\ 2, & x \geq 1 \end{cases}$; $\lim_{x\to 1} f(x)$

f. $f(x) = \begin{cases} 5x^2, & x < -1 \\ 2x + 1, & x \geq -1 \end{cases}$; $\lim_{x\to -1} f(x)$

19. Write an essay about Sir Isaac Newton and his discovery of calculus.

20. Write an essay about Gottfried Leibniz and his discovery of calculus.

21. Write an essay about the controversy surrounding the discovery of calculus by Newton and Leibniz.

Chapter 3 Test

Achievement Category	Questions
Knowledge/Understanding	5–9, 11–14
Thinking/Inquiry/Problem Solving	4, 17
Communication	1, 2, 3
Application	10, 15, 16

1. Explain how you find the limit of a polynomial function.

2. Explain how you find the limit of a rational function.

3. Explain why the $\lim\limits_{x \to 1} \frac{1}{x-1}$ does not exist.

4. Give an example for which neither $\lim\limits_{x \to a} f(x)$ nor $\lim\limits_{x \to a} g(x)$ exists, but $\lim\limits_{x \to a} [f(x) + g(x)]$ does exist.

5. Consider the graph of the function $f(x) = 5x^2 - 8x$. Find the slope of the secant that joins the points on the graph given by $x = -2$ and $x = 1$.

6. State the slope of the line perpendicular to $y = \frac{3}{4}x + 5$.

7. State the y-intercept of the function $f(x) = \frac{\sqrt{x^2 + 100}}{5}$.

8. State the equation of the line through $(0, -2)$ with a slope of -1.

9. For the function in the diagram, find the following:

   a. $\lim\limits_{x \to 1} f(x)$ b. $\lim\limits_{x \to 2} f(x)$ c. $\lim\limits_{x \to 4^-} f(x)$

   d. values of x for which f is discontinuous.

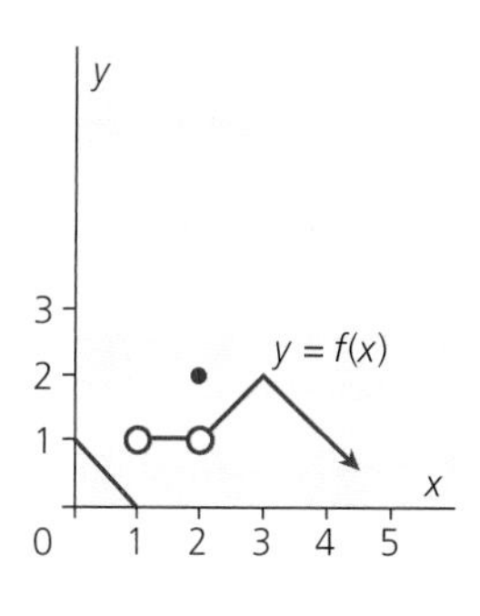

10. The population of a city grows from 100 000 people to an amount P given by the formula $P = 100\,000 + 4000t$, where t is measured in years.

    a. Find the number of people in the city in 20 years.

    b. Determine the growth rate, in people per year, at $t = 10$ years.

11. A weather balloon is rising vertically. After t hours, its distance, measured in kilometres above the ground, is given by the formula $s(t) = 8t - t^2$.

    a. Determine its average velocity from $t = 2$ h to $t = 5$ h.

    b. Find its velocity at $t = 3$ h.

12. Find the average rate of change of $f(x) = \sqrt{x + 11}$ with respect to x from $x = 5$ to $x = 5 + h$.

13. Find the slope of the tangent at $x = 4$ for the function $f(x) = \frac{x}{x^2 - 15}$.

14. Find the following limits:

    a. $\lim_{x \to 3} \frac{4x^2 - 36}{2x - 6}$

    b. $\lim_{x \to 2} \frac{2x^2 - x - 6}{3x^2 - 7x + 2}$

    c. $\lim_{x \to 5} \frac{x - 5}{\sqrt{x - 1} - 2}$

    d. $\lim_{x \to -1} \frac{x^3 + 1}{x^4 - 1}$

    e. $\lim_{x \to 3} \left(\frac{1}{x - 3} - \frac{6}{x^2 - 9} \right)$

    f. $\lim_{x \to 0} \frac{(x + 8)^{\frac{1}{3}} - 2}{x}$

15. Find constants a and b such that the function $f(x) = \begin{cases} ax + 3, \text{ if } x > 5 \\ 8, \text{ if } x = 5 \\ x^2 + bx + a, \text{ if } x < 5 \end{cases}$

    is continuous for all x.

16. Sketch a graph of a function with the following properties:

    a. $f(0) = 3$ b. $\lim_{x \to 1^+} f(x) = 3$ c. $\lim_{x \to 1^-} f(x) = 4$ d. $f(2) = -1$

17. For what value of k is the following a continuous function?

$$f(x) = \begin{cases} \frac{x - 2}{\sqrt{7x + 2} - \sqrt{6x + 4}}, \text{ if } x \geq -\frac{2}{7} \text{ and } x \neq 2 \\ k, \text{ if } x = 2 \end{cases}$$

Chapter 4

DERIVATIVES

Imagine a person speeding down the highway reaching speeds of 140 km/h. He hears the police siren in the distance, and his rear-view mirror is suddenly full of flashing red lights. As he pulls over and the police officer tells him he was going 140 km/h, he points out that because he has travelled the 200 km from home in two hours, his average speed is within the 100 km/h limit. Nice try, but we all know that police charge speeders based on their instantaneous speed, not their average speed. Furthermore, in business, responding rapidly to instantaneous changes is the key to success; opportunities can pass you by if you wait to observe long-term or average trends. In calculus, the derivative is a tool for finding instantaneous rates of change. This chapter shows how the derivative can be determined and applied in a great variety of circumstances.

CHAPTER EXPECTATIONS In this chapter, you will

- determine the limit of a function, and understand limits can give information about graphs of functions, **Section 4.1**
- understand and determine derivatives of polynomial and simple rational functions from first principles, **Section 4.1**
- identify examples of functions that are not differentiable, **Section 4.1**
- identify rate of change **Section 4.2**
- identify composition as two functions applied in succession, **Section 4.5**
- understand that the composition of functions exists only when the ranges overlap, **Section 4.5**
- determine the composition of two functions expressed in notation, and decompose a given composite function into its parts, **Section 4.5**
- justify and use the rules for determining derivatives, **Section 4.2, 4.3, 4.4, 4.6**
- describe the effect of the composition of inverse functions, $(f(f^{-1}(x)) = x)$, **Section 4.5**
- determine derivatives, using implicit differentiation, **Section 4.6**
- make inferences from models of applications and compare the inferences with the original hypotheses, **Section 4.1, 4.6**

Review of Prerequisite Skills

Before beginning your study of derivatives, it may be helpful to review the following concepts from previous courses and chapters:

- Finding the properties of exponents
- Simplifying radical expressions
- Finding the slopes of parallel and perpendicular lines
- Simplifying rational expressions
- Expanding and factoring algebraic expressions

Exercise

1. Use the exponent laws to simplify each of the following expressions. Express your answers with positive exponents.

   a. $5^4 \times 5^7$
   b. $a^5 \times a^3$
   c. $(4^9)^2$
   d. $(-2a^2)^3$
   e. $2m^6 \times 3m^7$
   f. $\frac{4p^7 \times 6p^9}{12p^{15}}$
   g. $(a^4b^{-5})(a^{-6}b^{-2})$
   h. $(3e^6)(2e^3)^4$
   i. $\frac{(3a^{-4})[2a^3(-b)^3]}{12a^5b^2}$

2. Simplify and write each expression in exponential form.

   a. $\left(x^{\frac{1}{2}}\right)\left(x^{\frac{2}{3}}\right)$
   b. $\left(8x^6\right)^{\frac{2}{3}}$
   c. $\frac{\sqrt{a}\sqrt[3]{a}}{\sqrt[6]{a}}$

3. Determine the slope of a line perpendicular to a tangent that has the following slopes:

   a. $\frac{2}{3}$
   b. $-\frac{1}{2}$
   c. $\frac{5}{3}$
   d. -1

4. Determine the equation of each of the following lines:

   a. passing through points $A(-3, 4)$ and $B(9, -2)$.

   b. passing through point $A(-2, 5)$ and parallel to the line with equation $3x - 2y = 5$.

   c. perpendicular to the line having the equation $y = \frac{3}{4}x - 6$, and passing through point $(4, -3)$.

5. Expand and collect like terms.

a. $(x - 3y)(2x + y)$
b. $(x - 2)(x^2 - 3x + 4)$
c. $(6x - 3)(2x + 7)$
d. $2(x + y) - 5(3x - 8y)$
e. $(2x - 3y)^2 + (5x + y)^2$
f. $3x(2x - y)^2 - x(5x - y)(5x + y)$

6. Simplify each expression.

a. $\dfrac{3x(x + 2)}{x^2} \times \dfrac{5x^3}{2x(x + 2)}$
b. $\dfrac{y}{(y + 2)(y - 5)} \times \dfrac{(y - 5)^2}{4y^3}$
c. $\dfrac{4}{(h + k)} \div \dfrac{9}{2(h + k)}$
d. $\dfrac{(x + y)(x - y)}{5(x - y)} \div \dfrac{(x + y)^3}{10}$
e. $\dfrac{x - 7}{2x} + \dfrac{5x}{x - 1}$
f. $\dfrac{x + 1}{x - 2} - \dfrac{x + 2}{x + 3}$

7. Factor completely.

a. $10a^2 - 6a$
b. $4k^2 - 9$
c. $x^2 + 4x - 32$
d. $y^2 - 11y - 42$
e. $3a^2 - 4a - 7$
f. $6y^2 + 17y + 10$
g. $x^4 - 1$
h. $x^3 - y^3$
i. $r^4 - 5r^2 + 4$

8. Use the Factor Theorem to factor the following:

a. $a^3 - b^3$
b. $a^5 - b^5$
c. $a^7 - b^7$
d. $a^n - b^n$

9. Rationalize the denominator in each of the following:

a. $\dfrac{3}{\sqrt{2}}$
b. $\dfrac{4 - \sqrt{2}}{\sqrt{3}}$
c. $\dfrac{2 + 3\sqrt{2}}{3 - 4\sqrt{2}}$
d. $\dfrac{3\sqrt{2} - 4\sqrt{3}}{3\sqrt{2} + 4\sqrt{3}}$

Career Link investigate

CHAPTER 4: THE ELASTICITY OF DEMAND

Have you ever wondered how businesses set prices for their goods and services? One of the most important ideas in marketing is the *elasticity of demand*, or the response of consumers to a change in price. Consumers respond very differently to a change in price of a staple item, such as bread, as compared to a luxury item such as jewellery. A family would probably still buy the same quantity of bread if the price increased by 20%. This is called *inelastic* demand. If the price of a gold chain, however, were increased by 20%, it is likely sales would decrease 40% or more. This is called *elastic* demand. Mathematically, elasticity is defined as the relative (percentage) change in the number demanded $\left(\frac{\Delta n}{n}\right)$ divided by the relative (percentage) change in the price $\left(\frac{\Delta p}{p}\right)$:

$$E = -\frac{\frac{\Delta n}{n}}{\frac{\Delta p}{p}}.$$

For example, if a store increased the price of a CD from \$17.99 to \$19.99 and the number sold per week went from 120 to 80, the elasticity would be

$$E = -\frac{\frac{(80 - 120)}{120}}{\frac{(19.99 - 17.99)}{17.99}} = 3.00.$$

The elasticity of 3.00 means that the change in demand is three times as large, in percentage terms, as the change in price. The CDs have an elastic demand because a small change in price can cause a large change in demand. In general, goods or services with elasticities greater than one ($E > 1$) are considered elastic (e.g., new cars), and those with elasticities less than one ($E < 1$) are inelastic (e.g., milk). In our example, we calculated the average elasticity between two price levels, but in reality, businesses want to know the elasticity at a specific or *instantaneous* price level. In this chapter, you will develop the rules of differentiation that will enable you to calculate the instantaneous rate of change for several classes of functions.

Case Study — Marketer: Product Pricing

In addition to developing advertising strategies, marketing departments also conduct research into and make decisions on pricing. The demand–price relationship for weekly movie rentals at a convenience store is $n(p) = \frac{500}{p}$, where $n(p)$ is demand and p is price.

DISCUSSION QUESTIONS

1. Generate two lists, each with at least five goods and services that you have purchased recently, classifying each of the goods and services as having elastic or inelastic demand.
2. Discuss how elasticity might be used in a business to make decisions about setting price levels. Give specific examples for elastic and inelastic goods.
3. Calculate and discuss the elasticity if the movie rental fee increases from \$1.99 to \$2.99.

Section 4.1 — The Derivative Function

In this chapter, we will extend the concepts of the slope of a tangent and the rate of change to introduce the **derivative**. We will be examining the methods of differentiation, which we can use to determine the derivatives of polynomial and rational functions. These methods include the use of the Power, Sum and Difference, Product and Quotient Rules, as well as the Chain Rule for the composition of functions.

In the previous chapter, we encountered limits of the form $\lim_{h\to 0} \frac{f(a+h)-f(a)}{h}$. This limit has two interpretations: the slope of the tangent to the graph $y = f(x)$ at the point $(a, f(a))$, and the rate of change of $y = f(x)$ with respect to x at $x = a$. Since this limit plays a central role in calculus, it is given a name and a concise notation. The limit is called the **derivative of $f(x)$ at $x = a$**. It is denoted by $f'(a)$ and is read as "f prime of a."

The derivative of f at the number a is given by

$$f'(a) = \lim_{h\to 0} \frac{f(a+h)-f(a)}{h}$$

provided this limit exists.

EXAMPLE 1

Find the derivative of $f(x) = x^2$ at $x = -3$.

Solution

Using the definition, the derivative at $x = -3$ is given by

$$\begin{aligned} f'(-3) &= \lim_{h\to 0} \frac{f(-3+h)-f(-3)}{h} \\ &= \lim_{h\to 0} \frac{(-3+h)^2-(-3)^2}{h} \\ &= \lim_{h\to 0} \frac{9-6h+h^2-9}{h} \\ &= \lim_{h\to 0} \frac{h(-6+h)}{h} \\ &= \lim_{h\to 0} (-6+h) \\ &= -6. \end{aligned}$$

Therefore, the derivative of $f(x) = x^2$ at $x = -3$ is -6.
An alternative way of writing the derivative of f at the number a is

$$f'(a) = \lim_{x \to a} \frac{f(x) - f(a)}{x - a}$$

In applications where we are required to find the value of the derivative for a number of particular values of x, using the definition repeatedly for each value is tedious.

The next example illustrates the efficiency of calculating the derivative of $f(x)$ at an arbitrary value of x and using the result to determine the derivatives at a number of particular x-values.

EXAMPLE 2

a. Find the derivative of $f(x) = x^2$ at an arbitrary value of x.

b. Determine the slopes of the tangents to the parabola $y = x^2$ at $x = -2$, 0, and 1.

Solution

a. Using the definition,

$$\begin{aligned} f'(x) &= \lim_{h \to 0} \frac{f(x + h) - f(x)}{h} \\ &= \lim_{h \to 0} \frac{(x + h)^2 - x^2}{h} \\ &= \lim_{h \to 0} \frac{x^2 + 2hx + h^2 - x^2}{h} \\ &= \lim_{h \to 0} \frac{h(2x + h)}{h} \\ &= \lim_{h \to 0} (2x + h) \\ &= 2x. \end{aligned}$$

The derivative of $f(x) = x^2$ at an arbitrary value of x is $f'(x) = 2x$.

b. The required slopes of the tangents to $y = x^2$ are obtained by evaluating the derivative $f'(x) = 2x$ at the given x-values. We obtain the slopes by substituting for x:

$$\begin{aligned} f'(-2) &= -4 \\ f'(0) &= 0 \\ f'(1) &= 2. \end{aligned}$$

The slopes are -4, 0, and 2, respectively.

The tangents to the parabola $y = x^2$ at $x = -2$, 0, and 1 are shown.

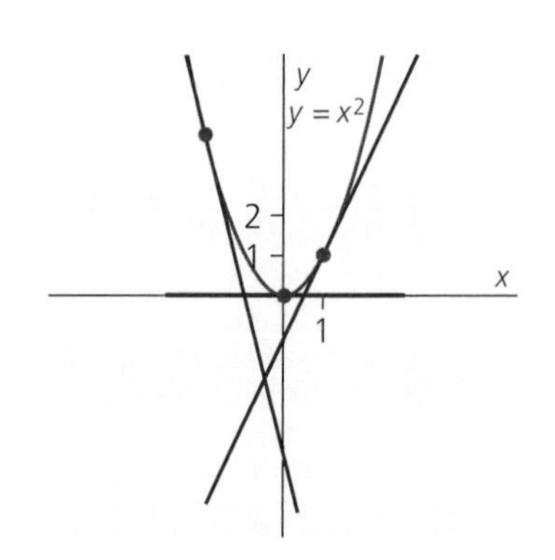

INVESTIGATION

1. Find the derivative with respect to x of each of the following functions:
   i) $f(x) = x^3$ ii) $f(x) = x^4$ iii) $f(x) = x$
2. In Example 2, we showed that the derivative of $f(x) = x^2$ is $f'(x) = 2x$. Referring to step 1, what pattern do you see developing?
3. Use the pattern of step 2 to predict the derivative of $f(x) = x^{39}$.
4. What do you think $f'(x)$ would be for $f(x) = x^n$, where n is a positive integer?

The Derivative Function

The derivative of f at $x = a$ is a number $f'(a)$. If we let a be arbitrary and assume a general value in the domain of f, the derivative f' is a function. For example, if $f(x) = x^2$, $f'(x) = 2x$, which is itself a function.

The derivative of $f(x)$ with respect to x is the function $f'(x)$ where

$$f'(x) = \lim_{h \to 0} \frac{f(x+h) - f(x)}{h},$$

provided this limit exists.

The limit $f'(x)$ is read "f prime of x." This notation was developed by Joseph Louis Lagrange (1736–1813), a French mathematician.

In Chapter 3, we discussed velocity at a point. We can now define (instantaneous) velocity as the derivative of position with respect to time. If a body's position at time t is $s(t)$, then the body's velocity at time t is

$$v(t) = s'(t) = \lim_{h \to 0} \frac{s(t+h) - s(t)}{h}.$$

Likewise, the (instantaneous) rate of change of $f(x)$ with respect to x is the function $f'(x)$, whose value is $f'(x) = \lim_{h \to 0} \frac{f(x+h) - f(x)}{h}$.

EXAMPLE 3

Find the derivative $f'(t)$ of the function $f(t) = \sqrt{t}$, $t \geq 0$.

Solution

Using the definition,

$$\begin{aligned} f'(t) &= \lim_{h \to 0} \frac{f(t+h) - f(t)}{h} \\ &= \lim_{h \to 0} \frac{\sqrt{t+h} - \sqrt{t}}{h} \\ &= \lim_{h \to 0} \frac{\sqrt{t+h} - \sqrt{t}}{h}\left(\frac{\sqrt{t+h} + \sqrt{t}}{\sqrt{t+h} + \sqrt{t}}\right) \quad \text{(Rationalizing the numerator)} \\ &= \lim_{h \to 0} \frac{(t+h) - t}{h(\sqrt{t+h} + \sqrt{t})} \end{aligned}$$

$$= \lim_{h \to 0} \frac{h}{h(\sqrt{t+h} + \sqrt{t})}$$
$$= \lim_{h \to 0} \frac{1}{\sqrt{t+h} + \sqrt{t}}$$
$$= \frac{1}{2\sqrt{t}}, \text{ for } t > 0.$$

Note that $f(t) = \sqrt{t}$ is defined for all $t \geq 0$, whereas its derivative $f'(t) = \frac{1}{2\sqrt{t}}$ is defined for only $t > 0$. From this, we can see that a function need not have a derivative throughout its entire domain.

EXAMPLE 4

Find an equation of the tangent to the graph of $f(x) = \frac{1}{x}$ at the point where $x = 2$.

Solution

When $x = 2$, $y = \frac{1}{2}$. The graph of $y = \frac{1}{x}$, the point $\left(2, \frac{1}{2}\right)$, and the tangent at the point are shown. First find $f'(x)$.

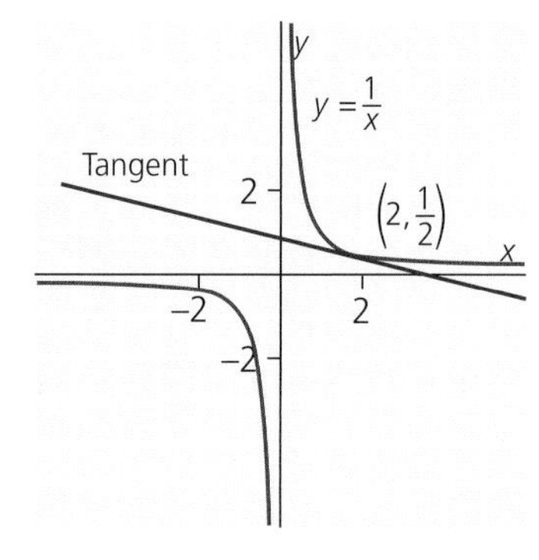

$$f'(x) = \lim_{h \to 0} \frac{f(x+h) - f(x)}{h}$$
$$= \lim_{h \to 0} \frac{\frac{1}{x+h} - \frac{1}{x}}{h} \qquad \left(f(x) = \frac{1}{x};\ f(x+h) = \frac{1}{x+h}\right)$$
$$= \lim_{h \to 0} \frac{x - (x+h)}{h(x+h)x} \qquad \text{(Simplify the fraction)}$$
$$= \lim_{h \to 0} \frac{-1}{(x+h)x}$$
$$= -\frac{1}{x^2}$$

The slope of the tangent at $x = 2$ is $m = f'(2) = -\frac{1}{4}$. The equation of the tangent is $y - \frac{1}{2} = -\frac{1}{4}(x - 2)$, or in standard form, $x + 4y - 4 = 0$.

EXAMPLE 5

Find an equation of the line that is perpendicular to the tangent to the graph of $f(x) = \frac{1}{x}$ at $x = 2$ and that intersects it at the point of tangency.

Solution

From Example 4, we found that the slope of the tangent is $f'(2) = -\frac{1}{4}$ and the point of tangency is $\left(2, \frac{1}{2}\right)$. The perpendicular line has slope 4, the negative reciprocal of $-\frac{1}{4}$. Therefore, the required equation is $y - \frac{1}{2} = 4(x - 2)$ or $8x - 2y - 15 = 0$.

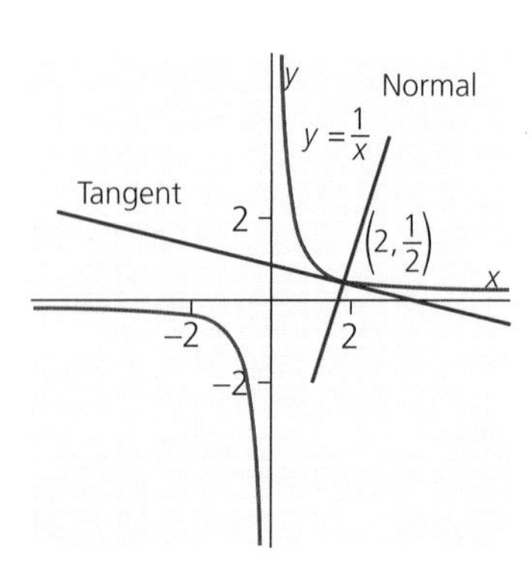

The line we found in Example 5 has a name.

The normal to the graph of f at point P is the line that is perpendicular to the tangent at P.

The Existence of Derivatives

A function f is said to be **differentiable** at a if $f'(a)$ exists. At points where f is not differentiable, we say that the *derivative does not exist*. Three common ways for a derivative to fail to exist are shown.

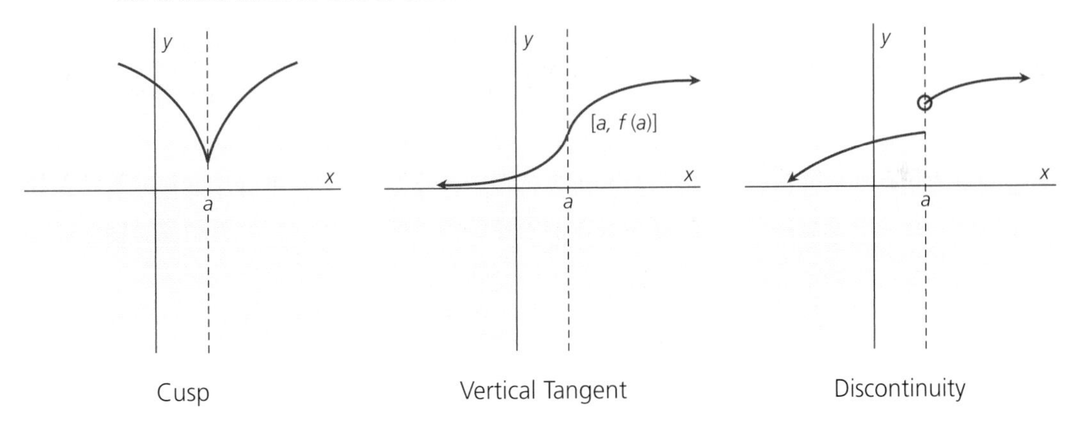

Cusp Vertical Tangent Discontinuity

EXAMPLE 6 Show that the absolute value function $f(x) = |x|$ is not differentiable at $x = 0$.

Solution

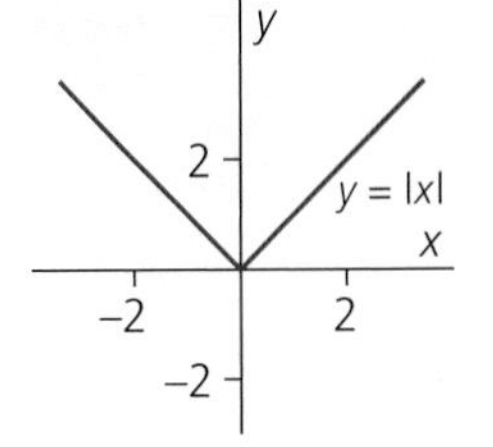

The graph of $f(x) = |x|$ is shown. Because the slope for $x < 0$ is -1 while the slope for $x > 0$ is $+1$, the graph has a "corner" at (0, 0), which prevents a unique tangent being drawn there. We can show this using the definition of a derivative.

$$\begin{aligned} f'(0) &= \lim_{h \to 0} \frac{f(0 + h) - f(0)}{h} \\ &= \lim_{h \to 0} \frac{f(h) - 0}{h} \\ &= \lim_{h \to 0} \frac{|h|}{h} \end{aligned}$$

Now, we will consider one-sided limits.
$|h| = h$ when $h > 0$ and $|h| = -h$ when $h < 0$.

$$\lim_{h \to 0^-} \frac{|h|}{h} = \lim_{h \to 0^-} \frac{-h}{h} = \lim_{h \to 0^-} (-1) = -1$$

$$\lim_{h \to 0^+} \frac{|h|}{h} = \lim_{h \to 0^+} \frac{h}{h} = \lim_{h \to 0^+} (1) = 1$$

Since the left-hand and right-hand limits are not the same, the derivative does not exist.

From Example 6, we conclude that it is possible for a function to be **continuous** at a point and yet to be *not differentiable* at that point.

Other Notation for Derivatives

Symbols other than $f'(x)$ are often used to denote the derivative. If $y = f(x)$, the symbols y' and $\frac{dy}{dx}$ are used instead of $f'(x)$. The notation $\frac{dy}{dx}$ was originally used by Leibniz and is read "dee y by dee x." For example, if $y = x^2$, the derivative is $y' = 2x$ or, in Leibniz notation, $\frac{dy}{dx} = 2x$. Similarly, in Example 4, we showed that if $y = \frac{1}{x}$, then $\frac{dy}{dx} = \frac{1}{x^2}$. The Leibniz notation reminds us of the process by which the derivative is obtained — namely, as the limit of a difference quotient:

$$\frac{dy}{dx} = \lim_{\Delta x \to 0} \frac{\Delta y}{\Delta x}.$$

By omitting y and f altogether, we can combine these statements and write $\frac{d}{dx}(x^2) = 2x$, which is read "the derivative of x^2 with respect to x is $2x$."
It is important to note that $\frac{dy}{dx}$ is *not a fraction.*

Exercise 4.1

Part A

1. State the domain on which f is differentiable.

a.

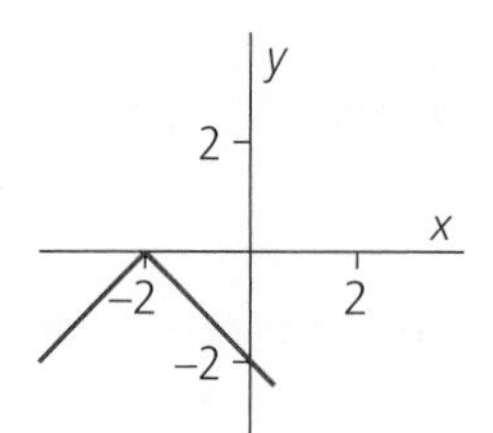

b.

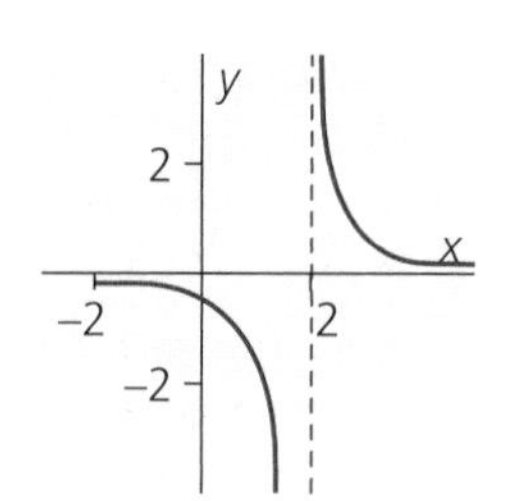

c.

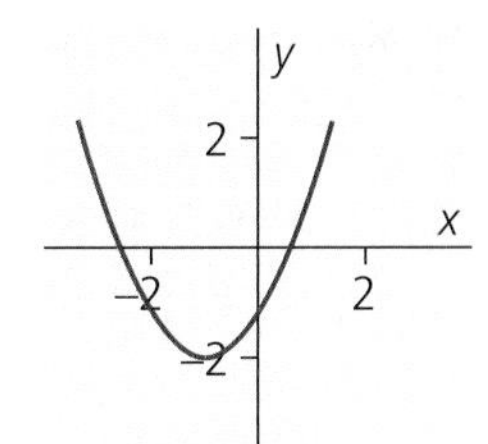

d.

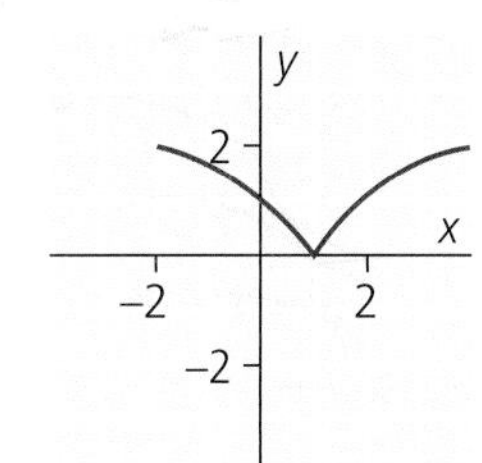

e.

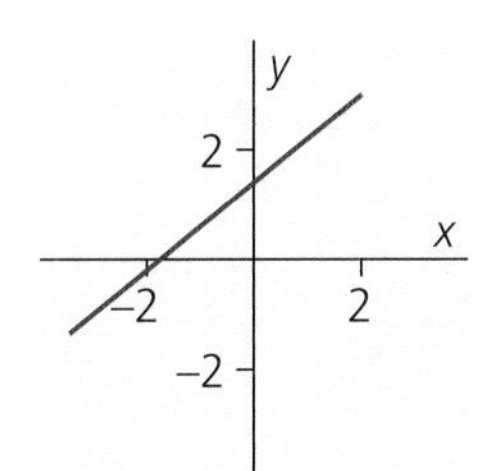

f.

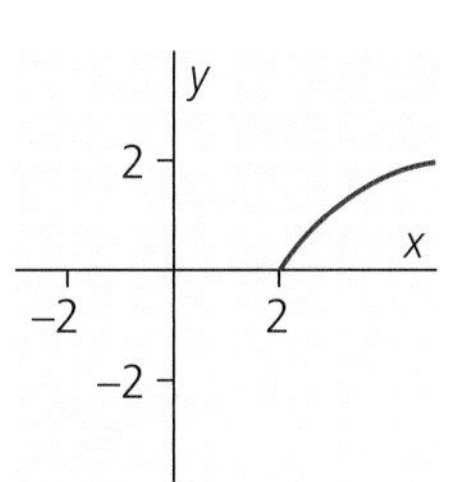

Communication

2. Explain what the derivative of a function represents.

Communication

3. Illustrate two situations in which a function does not have a derivative at $x = 1$.

Part B

Knowledge/Understanding

4. For each function, find the value of the derivative $f'(a)$ for the given value of a.

   a. $f(x) = x^2; a = 1$

   b. $f(x) = x^2 + 3x + 1; a = 3$

   c. $f(x) = \sqrt{x + 1}; a = 0$

5. Use the definition of the derivative to find $f'(x)$ for each function.

   a. $f(x) = x^2 + 3x$ b. $f(x) = \frac{3}{x + 2}$ c. $f(x) = \sqrt{3x + 2}$ d. $f(x) = \frac{1}{x^2}$

6. In each case, find the derivative $\frac{dy}{dx}$.

   a. $y = 6 - 7x$ b. $y = \frac{x + 1}{x - 1}$ c. $y = 3x^2$

7. Find the slope of the tangents to $y = 2x^2 - 4x$ when $x = 0$, $x = 1$, and $x = 2$. Sketch the graph, showing these tangents.

Application

8. An object moves in a straight line with its position at time t seconds given by $s(t) = -t^2 + 8t$ where s is measured in metres. Find the velocity when $t = 0$, $t = 4$, and $t = 6$.

Thinking/Inquiry/Problem Solving

9. Find an equation of the straight line that is tangent to the graph of $f(x) = \sqrt{x + 1}$ and parallel to $x - 6y + 4 = 0$.

10. For each function, use the definition of the derivative to determine $\frac{dy}{dx}$, where a, b, c, and m are constants.

a. $y = c$ b. $y = x$ c. $y = mx + b$ d. $y = ax^2 + bx + c$

Communication

11. Does the function $f(x) = x^3$ ever have a negative slope? If so, where? Give reasons for your answer.

Thinking/Inquiry/ Problem Solving

12. Match each function in graphs **a**, **b**, and **c** with its corresponding derivative, graphed in **d**, **e**, and **f.**

a.

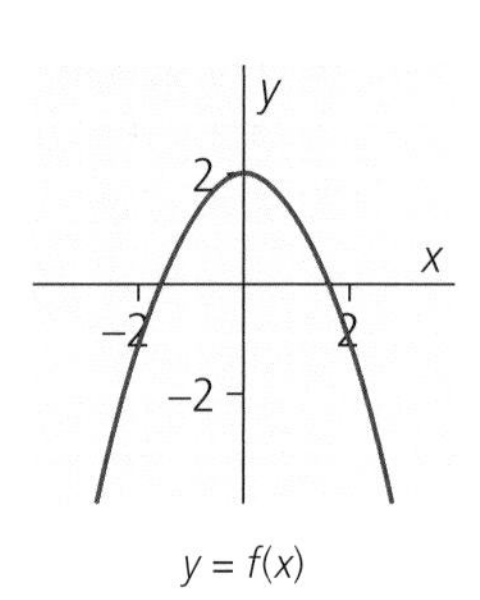

$y = f(x)$

b.

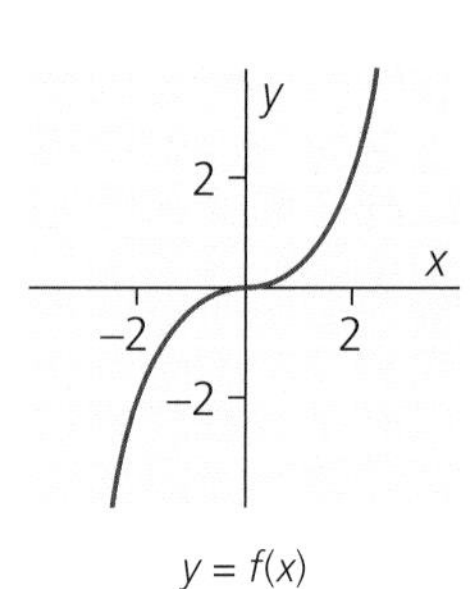

$y = f(x)$

c.

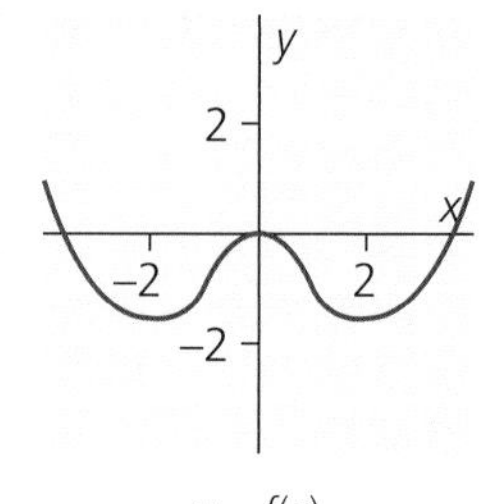

$y = f(x)$

d.

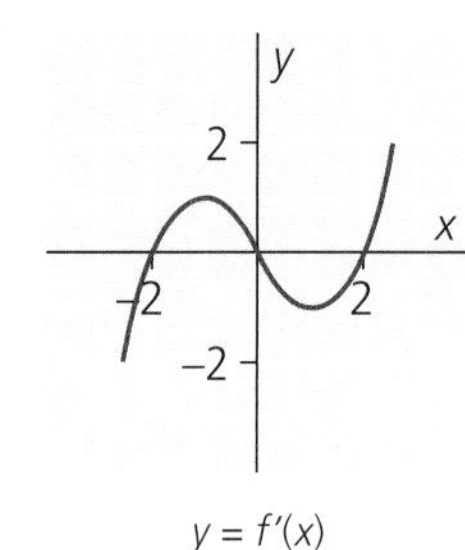

$y = f'(x)$

e.

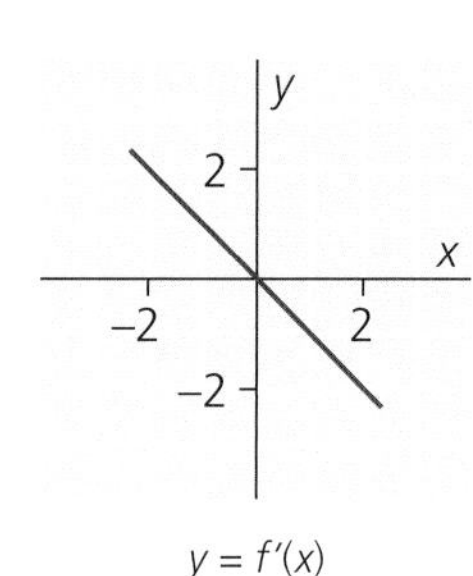

$y = f'(x)$

f.

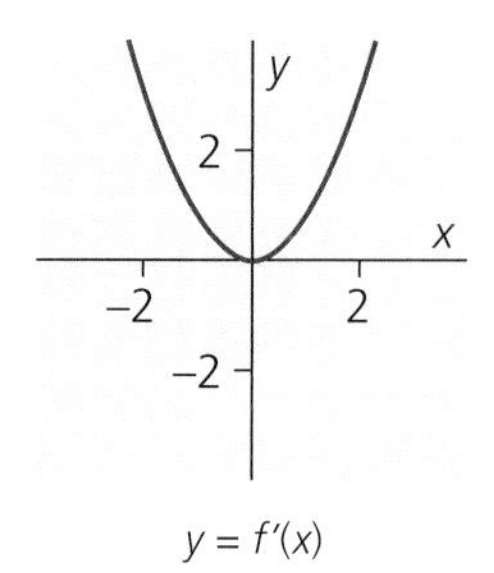

$y = f'(x)$

13. Find the slope of the tangent to the curve $\frac{1}{x} + \frac{1}{y} = 1$ at the point (2, 2).

Part C

14. For the function $f(x) = x|x|$, show that $f'(0)$ exists. What is the value?

Application

15. If $f(a) = 0$ and $f'(a) = 6$, find $\lim_{h \to 0} \frac{f(a + h)}{2h}$.

Thinking/Inquiry/ Problem Solving

16. Give an example of a function that is continuous on $-\infty < x < \infty$ but that is not differentiable at $x = 3$.

Section 4.2 — The Derivatives of Polynomial Functions

We have seen that derivatives of functions are of practical use because they represent instantaneous rates of change.

Computing derivatives from the definition, as we did in Section 4.1, is tedious and time-consuming. In this section, we will develop some rules that simplify the process of differentiation.

We will begin developing the rules of differentiation by looking at the constant function, $f(x) = k$. Since the graph of any constant function is a horizontal line with slope zero at each point, the derivative should be zero.

For example, if $f(x) = -4$ then $f'(3) = 0$.

Alternatively, we can write $\frac{d}{dx}(3) = 0$.

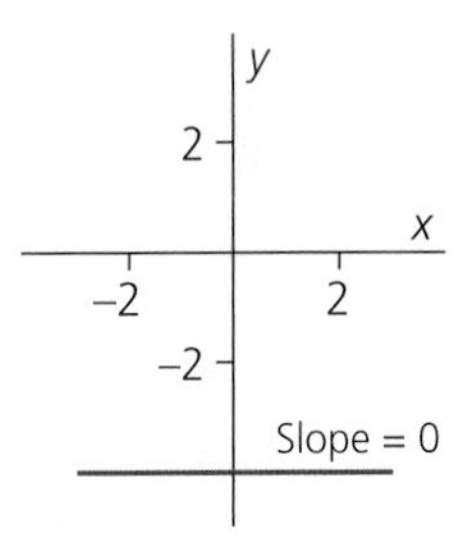

The Constant Function Rule
If $f(x) = k$, where k is a constant, then $f'(x) = 0$.

In Leibniz notation, $\frac{d}{dx}(k) = 0$.

Proof

$$\begin{aligned} f'(x) &= \lim_{h \to 0} \frac{f(x+h) - f(x)}{h} \\ &= \lim_{h \to 0} \frac{k - k}{h} \qquad \text{(Since } f(x) = k \text{ and } f(x+h) = k \text{ for all } h\text{)} \\ &= \lim_{h \to 0} 0 \\ &= 0 \end{aligned}$$

EXAMPLE 1

a. If $f(x) = 5, f'(x) = 0$.

b. If $y = \frac{\pi}{2}, \frac{dy}{dx} = 0$.

A **power function** is a function of the form $f(x) = x^n$, where n is a real number. In the previous section, we observed that for $f(x) = x^2$, $f'(x) = 2x$; for $g(x) = \sqrt{x} = x^{\frac{1}{2}}$, $g'(x) = \frac{1}{2}x^{-\frac{1}{2}} = \frac{1}{2\sqrt{x}}$; and for $h(x) = \frac{1}{x^2} = x^{-2}$, $h'(x) = -2x^{-3}$. We also hypothesized that $\frac{d}{dx}(x^n) = nx^{n-1}$. In fact, this is true, and is called the **Power Rule**.

The Power Rule
If $f(x) = x^n$, where n is a real number, then $f'(x) = nx^{n-1}$.

In Leibniz notation, $\frac{d}{dx}(x^n) = nx^{n-1}$.

EXAMPLE 2

a. If $f(x) = x^7$, then $f'(x) = 7x^6$.

b. If $g(x) = \frac{1}{x^3} = x^{-3}$, then $g'(x) = -3x^{-3-1} = -3x^{-4} = -\frac{3}{x^4}$.

c. If $s = t^{\frac{3}{2}}$, $\frac{ds}{dt} = \frac{3}{2}t^{\frac{1}{2}} = \frac{3}{2}\sqrt{t}$.

d. $\frac{d}{dx}(x) = 1x^{1-1} = x^0 = 1$

Proof of the Power Rule

(Where n is a positive integer.)
Using the definition of the derivative,

$$f'(x) = \lim_{h \to 0} \frac{f(x+h) - f(x)}{h}, \quad \text{where } f(x) = x^n$$

$$= \lim_{h \to 0} \frac{(x+h)^n - x^n}{h}$$

$$= \lim_{h \to 0} \frac{(x + h - x)\left[(x+h)^{n-1} + (x+h)^{n-2}x + \ldots + (x+h)x^{n-2} + x^{n-1}\right]}{h}$$ (Factoring a difference of nth powers)

$$= \lim_{h \to 0} \left[(x+h)^{n-1} + (x+h)^{n-2}x + \ldots + (x+h)x^{n-2} + x^{n-1}\right]$$ (Reduce the fraction)

$$= (x)^{n-1} + x^{n-2}x + \ldots + (x)x^{n-2} + x^{n-1}$$

$$= x^{n-1} + x^{n-1} + \ldots + x^{n-1} + x^{n-1}$$ (Since there are n terms)

$$= nx^{n-1}.$$

The proof for any real number n will be investigated in Chapter 8.

The Constant Multiple Rule
If $f(x) = kg(x)$, where k is a constant, then $f'(x) = kg'(x)$.

In Leibniz notation, $\frac{d}{dx}(ky) = k\frac{dy}{dx}$.

Proof of the Constant Multiple Rule

Let $f(x) = kg(x)$. By the definition of the derivative,

$$\begin{aligned} f'(x) &= \lim_{h \to 0} \frac{f(x + h) - f(x)}{h} \\ &= \lim_{h \to 0} \frac{kg(x + h) - kg(x)}{h} \\ &= \lim_{h \to 0} k\left[\frac{g(x + h) - g(x)}{h}\right] \\ &= k \lim_{h \to 0} \left[\frac{g(x + h) - g(x)}{h}\right] && \text{(Property of Limits)} \\ &= kg'(x). \end{aligned}$$

EXAMPLE 3

Differentiate the following:

a. $f(x) = 7x^3$

b. $y = 12x^{\frac{4}{3}}$

Solution

a. $f(x) = 7x^3$

$$f'(x) = 7\frac{d}{dx}(x^3) = 7(3x^2) = 21x^2$$

b. $y = 12x^{\frac{4}{3}}$

$$\frac{dy}{dx} = 12\frac{d}{dx}\left(x^{\frac{4}{3}}\right) = 12\left(\frac{4}{3}x^{\frac{4}{3} - 1}\right) = 16x^{\frac{1}{3}}$$

We conclude this section on Rules of Differentiation with the Sum and Difference Rules.

The Sum Rule
If functions $p(x)$ and $q(x)$ are differentiable and $f(x) = p(x) + q(x)$, then $f'(x) = p'(x) + q'(x)$.

In Leibniz notation, $\frac{d}{dx}(f(x)) = \frac{d}{dx}(p(x)) + \frac{d}{dx}(q(x))$.

Proof of the Sum Rule

Let $f(x) = p(x) + q(x)$. By the definition of the derivative,

$$\begin{aligned}
f'(x) &= \lim_{h\to 0} \frac{f(x+h) - f(x)}{h} \\
&= \lim_{h\to 0} \frac{[p(x+h) + q(x+h)] - [p(x) + q(x)]}{h} \\
&= \lim_{h\to 0} \left\{ \frac{[p(x+h) - p(x)]}{h} + \frac{[q(x+h) - q(x)]}{h} \right\} \\
&= \lim_{h\to 0} \left\{ \frac{[p(x+h) - p(x)]}{h} \right\} + \lim_{h\to 0} \left\{ \frac{[q(x+h) - q(x)]}{h} \right\} \quad \text{(Sum Property of Limits)} \\
&= p'(x) + q'(x)
\end{aligned}$$

The proof of the Difference Rule is similar to that of the Sum Rule.

The Difference Rule
If $f(x) = p(x) - q(x)$, then $f'(x) = p'(x) - q'(x)$.

EXAMPLE 4

Differentiate the following functions:

a. $f(x) = 3x^2 - 5\sqrt{x}$

b. $y = (3x + 2)^2$

Solution

We apply the Constant Multiple, Power, Sum, and Difference Rules.

a. $f(x) = 3x^2 - 5\sqrt{x}$

$$\begin{aligned}
f'(x) &= \frac{d}{dx}(3x^2) - \frac{d}{dx}\left(5x^{\frac{1}{2}}\right) \\
&= 3\frac{d}{dx}(x^2) - 5\frac{d}{dx}\left(x^{\frac{1}{2}}\right) \\
&= 3(2x) - 5\left(\frac{1}{2}x^{-\frac{1}{2}}\right) \\
&= 6x - \frac{5}{2}x^{-\frac{1}{2}}
\end{aligned}$$

b. We first expand $y = (3x + 2)^2$.

$$y = 9x^2 + 12x + 4$$

$$\frac{dy}{dx} = 18x + 12$$

EXAMPLE 5

Find the equation of the tangent to the graph of $f(x) = -x^3 + 3x^2 - 2$ at $x = 1$.

technology

Solution

The slope of the tangent to the graph of f at any point is given by the derivative $f'(x)$.

For $\quad f(x) = -x^3 + 3x^2 - 2$

$$f'(x) = -3x^2 + 6x$$

Now, $\quad f'(1) = -3(1)^2 + 6(1)$

$$= -3 + 6$$

$$= 3.$$

The slope of the tangent at $x = 1$ is 3. The point of tangency is $(1, f(1)) = (1, 0)$.

The equation of the tangent is $y - 0 = 3(x - 1)$ or $y = 3x - 3$.

Solution Using the Graphing Calculator

Draw the graph using a graphing calculator and draw the tangent at $x = 1$. The point is $(1, 0)$. Input $y_1 = -x^3 + 3x^2 - 2$.

Select ZOOM 4.

Select 2nd PRGM (DRAW) for the DRAW program.

Select **5:Tangent(.**

Select VARS and then Y-VARS and **1:Function.**

Press ENTER for the y_1 function.

Complete the instructions so the window looks like Tangent $(y_1, 1)$.

Press ENTER to see the graph.

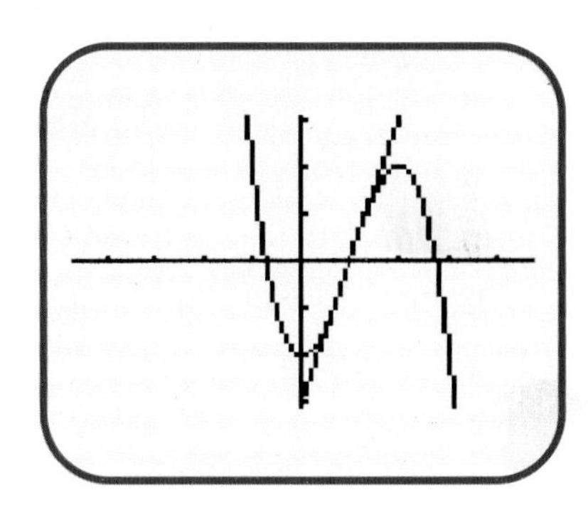

EXAMPLE 6

Find the points on the graph in Example 5 where the tangents are horizontal.

Solution

Horizontal lines have slope 0. We need to find the values of x that satisfy $f'(x) = 0$.

$$-3x^2 + 6x = 0$$

$$-3x(x - 2) = 0$$

$$x = 0 \text{ or } x = 2$$

The graph of $f(x) = -x^3 + 3x^2 - 2$ has horizontal tangents at $(0, -2)$ and $(2, 2)$.

Exercise 4.2

Part A

Communication

1. What rules do you know for calculating derivatives? Give examples of each.

2. Find $f'(x)$ for each of the following:

a. $f(x) = 4x - 7$ b. $f(x) = 7$ c. $f(x) = 2x^2 + x - 5$

d. $f(x) = \sqrt{x}$ e. $f(x) = 4x^3 + 2$ f. $f(x) = x^3 - x^2$

g. $f(x) = -x^2 + 5x + 8$ h. $f(x) = \sqrt[3]{x}$ i. $f(x) = \frac{1}{4}x^4$

j. $f(x) = (3x)^2$ k. $f(x) = \left(\frac{x}{2}\right)^4$ l. $f(x) = x^{-3}$

Knowledge/Understanding

3. Differentiate each function. Use either the Leibniz notation or prime notation, depending on which is appropriate.

a. $y = x^2 - 3x + 1$ b. $f(x) = 2x^3 + 5x^2 - 4x - 3.75$

c. $v(t) = 6t^3 - 4t^5$ d. $s(t) = \frac{1}{t^2}, t > 0$

e. $f(x) = (x^3)^2$ f. $h(x) = (2x + 3)(x + 4)$

g. $s = t^2(t^2 - 2t)$ h. $g(x) = \frac{4}{x^{-5}}$

i. $y = \frac{1}{5}x^5 + \frac{1}{3}x^3 - \frac{1}{2}x^2 + 1$ j. $g(x) = 5(x^2)^4$

k. $s(t) = \frac{t^5 - 3t^2}{2t}, t > 0$ l. $g(x) = 7f(x) + 5$

m. $h(x) = -\frac{3}{x^7}$ n. $y = mx + b$

4. Apply the differentiation rules of this section to find the derivatives of the following:

a. $f(x) = 10x^{\frac{1}{5}}$ b. $y = 3x^{\frac{5}{3}}$ c. $y = 6x^{-\frac{3}{2}}$

d. $y = x^8 - x^{-8}$ e. $y = 3x^{\frac{2}{3}} - 6x^{\frac{1}{3}} + x^{-\frac{1}{3}}$ f. $y = 4x^{-\frac{1}{2}} - \frac{6}{x}$

g. $y = \frac{6}{x^3} + \frac{2}{x^2} - 3$ h. $y = 9x^{-2} + 3\sqrt{x}$ i. $y = 20x^5 + 3\sqrt[3]{x} + 17$

j. $y = \sqrt{x} + 6\sqrt{x^3} + \sqrt{2}$ k. $y = x^{1.5} - 12x^{-0.25}$ l. $y = \frac{1 + \sqrt{x}}{x}$

Part B

5. Let s represent the position of a moving object at time t. Find the velocity $v = \frac{ds}{dt}$ at time t.

a. $s = -2t^2 + 7t$ b. $s = 18 + 5t - \frac{1}{3}t^3$ c. $s = (t - 3)^2$

6. Find $f'(a)$ for the given function $f(x)$ at the given value of a.

a. $f(x) = x^3 - \sqrt{x};\ a = 4$

b. $f(x) = 7 - 6\sqrt{x} + 5x^{\frac{2}{3}};\ a = 64$

Application

7. Find the slope of the tangent to each of the curves at the given point.

a. $y = 3x^4$ at $(1, 3)$

b. $y = \frac{1}{x^{-5}}$ at $(-1, -1)$

c. $y = \frac{2}{x}$ at $(-2, -1)$

d. $y = \sqrt{16x^3}$ at $(4, 32)$

8. Find the slope of the tangent to the graph of the function at the point whose x-coordinate is given.

a. $y = 2x^3 + 3x;\ x = 1$

b. $y = 2\sqrt{x} + 5;\ x = 4$

c. $y = \frac{16}{x^2};\ x = -2$

d. $y = x^{-3}(x^{-1} + 1);\ x = 1$

9. Write an equation of a tangent to each of the curves at the given point.

a. $y = 2x - \frac{1}{x}$ at $P(0.5, -1)$

b. $y = \frac{3}{x^2} - \frac{4}{x^3}$ at $P(-1, 7)$

c. $y = \sqrt{3x^3}$ at $P(3, 9)$

d. $y = \frac{1}{x}\left(x^2 + \frac{1}{x}\right)$ at $P(1, 2)$

e. $y = \left(\sqrt{x} - 2\right)\left(3\sqrt{x} + 8\right)$ at $P(4, 0)$

f. $y = \frac{\sqrt{x} - 2}{\sqrt[3]{x}}$ at $P(1, -1)$

Communication

10. What is a normal to the graph of a function? Find the equation of the normal to the graph of the function in Question 9, part **b** at the given point.

Thinking/Inquiry/ Problem Solving

11. Find the values of x so that the tangent to the function $y = \frac{3}{\sqrt[3]{x}}$ is parallel to the line $x + 16y + 3 = 0$.

Communication

12. Do the functions $y = \frac{1}{x}$ and $y = x^3$ ever have the same slope? If so, where?

13. Tangents are drawn to the parabola $y = x^2$ at $(2, 4)$ and $(-\frac{1}{8}, \frac{1}{64})$. Prove that these lines are perpendicular. Illustrate with a sketch.

14. Find the point on the parabola $y = -x^2 + 3x + 4$ where the slope of the tangent is 5. Illustrate your answer with a sketch.

15. Find the coordinates of the points on the graph of $y = x^3 + 2$ at which the slope of the tangent is 12.

16. Show that there are two tangents to the curve $y = \frac{1}{5}x^5 - 10x$ that have a slope of 6.

Application

17. Find the equations of the tangents to the curve $y = 2x^2 + 3$ that pass through the following:

    a. point $(2, 3)$
    b. point $(2, -7)$

18. Find the value of a, given that the line $ax - 4y + 21 = 0$ is tangent to the graph of $y = \frac{a}{x^2}$ at $x = -2$.

Application

19. It can be shown that from a height of h metres, a person can see a distance d kilometres to the horizon, where $d = 3.53\sqrt{h}$.

    a. When the elevator of the CN Tower passes the 200 m height, how far can the passengers in the elevator see across Lake Ontario?
    b. Find the rate of change of this distance with respect to height when the height of the elevator is 200 m.

20. A subway train travels from one station to the next in 2 min. Its distance, in kilometres, from the first station after t minutes is $s(t) = t^2 - \frac{1}{3}t^3$. At what times will the train have a velocity of 0.5 km/min?

21. A construction worker drops a bolt while working on a high-rise building 320 m above the ground. After t seconds, the bolt has fallen a distance of s metres, where $s(t) = 5t^2$, $0 \leq t \leq 8$. The function that gives the height of the bolt above ground at time t is $R(t) = 320 - 5t^2$. Use this function to determine the velocity of the bolt at $t = 2$.

22. Tangents are drawn from the point $(0, 3)$ to the parabola $y = -3x^2$. Find the coordinates of the points at which these tangents touch the curve. Illustrate your answer with a sketch.

23. The tangent to the cubic function defined by $y = x^3 - 6x^2 + 8x$ at point $A(3, -3)$ intersects the curve at another point, B. Find the coordinates of B. Illustrate with a sketch.

Part C

Thinking/Inquiry/ Problem Solving

24. Let $P(a, b)$ be a point on the curve $\sqrt{x} + \sqrt{y} = 1$. Show that the slope of the tangent at P is $-\sqrt{\frac{b}{a}}$.

Thinking/Inquiry/ Problem Solving

25. For the power function $f(x) = x^n$, find the x-intercept of the tangent to its graph at point $(1, 1)$. What happens to the x-intercept as n increases without bound $(n \rightarrow +\infty)$? Explain the result geometrically.

Application

26. For each function, sketch the graph of $y = f(x)$ and find an expression for $f'(x)$. Indicate any points at which $f'(x)$ does not exist.

    a. $f(x) = \begin{cases} x^2, x < 3 \\ x + 6, x \geq 3 \end{cases}$
    b. $f(x) = |3x^2 - 6|$
    c. $f(x) = ||x| - 1|$

Section 4.3 — The Product Rule

In this section, we will develop a rule for differentiating the product of two functions, such as $f(x) = (3x^2 - 1)(x^3 + 8)$ and $g(x) = (x - 3)^3(x + 2)^2$, without first expanding the expressions.

You might suspect that the derivative of a product of two functions is simply the product of the separate derivatives. An example shows that this is not so.

EXAMPLE 1

Let $h(x) = f(x)g(x)$, where $f(x) = (x^2 + 2)$ and $g(x) = (x + 5)$.
Show that $h'(x) \neq f'(x)g'(x)$.

Solution

The expression $h(x)$ can be simplified.

$$\begin{aligned} h(x) &= (x^2 + 2)(x + 5) \\ &= x^3 + 5x^2 + 2x + 10 \end{aligned}$$

The derivative of $h(x)$ is $h'(x) = 3x^2 + 10x + 2$.
The derivatives of the functions $f(x)$ and $g(x)$ are

$$f'(x) = 2x \text{ and } g'(x) = 1.$$

The product $f'(x)g'(x) = (2x)(1) = 2x$.

Since $2x$ is not the derivative of $h(x)$, we have shown that $h'(x) \neq f'(x)g'(x)$.

The correct method for differentiating a product of two functions uses the following rule.

The Product Rule
If $h(x) = f(x)g(x)$, then $h'(x) = f'(x)g(x) + f(x)g'(x)$.
If u and v are functions of x, $\frac{d}{dx}(uv) = \frac{du}{dx}v + u\frac{dv}{dx}$.

In words, the Product Rule says, "the derivative of the product of two functions is equal to the derivative of the first function times the second function plus the first function times the derivative of the second function."

Proof of the Product Rule

$h(x) = f(x)g(x)$; then using the definition of the derivative,

$$h'(x) = \lim_{h \to 0} \frac{f(x + h)g(x + h) - f(x)g(x)}{h}.$$

In Section 4.1, we saw that $f'(x) = \lim_{h \to 0} \left[\frac{f(x+h) - f(x)}{h}\right]$,

and $g'(x) = \lim_{h \to 0} \left[\frac{g(x+h) - g(x)}{h}\right]$. To evaluate $h'(x)$ we subtract and add terms in the numerator.

$$
\begin{aligned}
\text{Now } h'(x) &= \lim_{h \to 0} \frac{f(x+h)g(x+h) - f(x)g(x+h) + f(x)g(x+h) - f(x)g(x)}{h} \\
&= \lim_{h \to 0} \left\{\left[\frac{f(x+h) - f(x)}{h}\right] g(x+h) + f(x)\left[\frac{g(x+h) - g(x)}{h}\right]\right\} \\
&= \lim_{h \to 0} \left[\frac{f(x+h) - f(x)}{h}\right] \lim_{h \to 0} g(x+h) + \lim_{h \to 0} f(x) \lim_{h \to 0} \left[\frac{g(x+h) - g(x)}{h}\right] \\
&= f'(x)g(x) + f(x)g'(x).
\end{aligned}
$$

EXAMPLE 2 Differentiate $h(x) = (x^2 - 3x)(x^5 + 2)$, using the Product Rule.

Solution

$$h(x) = (x^2 - 3x)(x^5 + 2)$$

Using the Product Rule, we get

$$
\begin{aligned}
h'(x) &= (2x - 3)(x^5 + 2) + (x^2 - 3x)(5x^4) \\
&= 2x^6 - 3x^5 + 4x - 6 + 5x^6 - 15x^5 \\
&= 7x^6 - 18x^5 + 4x - 6.
\end{aligned}
$$

We can, of course, differentiate the function after we first expand. The Product Rule will be essential, however, when we work with products of polynomials such as $f(x) = (x^2 + 9)(x^3 + 5)^4$ or non-polynomial functions such as $f(x) = (x^2 + 9)\sqrt{x^3 + 5}$.

It is not necessary to simplify the expression when you are asked to calculate the derivative at a particular value of x. Because many expressions derived using differentiation rules are cumbersome, it is easier to substitute, as in the preceding example.

The next example can be determined by multiplying out the two polynomials and then calculating the derivative of the resulting polynomial at $x = -1$. Instead we shall apply the Product Rule.

EXAMPLE 3 Find the value $h'(-1)$ for the function $h(x) = (5x^3 + 7x^2 + 3)(2x^2 + x + 6)$.

Solution

$h(x) = (5x^3 + 7x^2 + 3)(2x^2 + x + 6)$

Using the Product Rule, we get

$$\begin{aligned} h'(x) &= (15x^2 + 14x)(2x^2 + x + 6) + (5x^3 + 7x^2 + 3)(4x + 1) \\ h'(-1) &= [15(-1)^2 + 14(-1)][2(-1)^2 + (-1) + 6] + [5(-1)^3 \\ &\quad + 7(-1)^2 + 3][4(-1) + 1] \\ &= (1)(7) + (5)(-3) \\ &= -8. \end{aligned}$$

The following example illustrates the extension of the Product Rule to more than two functions.

EXAMPLE 4 Find an expression for $p'(x)$ if $p(x) = f(x)g(x)h(x)$.

Solution

We temporarily regard $f(x)g(x)$ as a single function.

$$p(x) = [f(x)g(x)]h(x)$$

By the Product Rule,

$$p'(x) = [f(x)g(x)]'h(x) + [f(x)g(x)]h'(x).$$

A second application of the Product Rule yields

$$\begin{aligned} p'(x) &= [f'(x)g(x) + f(x)g'(x)]h(x) + f(x)g(x)h'(x) \\ &= f'(x)g(x)h(x) + f(x)g'(x)h(x) + f(x)g(x)h'(x). \end{aligned}$$

This expression gives us the **Extended Product Rule** for the derivative of the product of three functions. Its symmetric form makes it easy to extend the process to the product of four or more functions.

The Power of a Function Rule for Positive Integers

Suppose that we now wish to differentiate functions such as

$y = (x^2 - 3)^4$ or $y = (x^2 + 3x + 5)^6$.

These functions are of the form $y = u^n$, where n is a positive integer and $u = g(x)$ is a function whose derivative we can find. Using the Product Rule, we can develop an efficient method for differentiating such functions.

For the case $n = 2$, $$h(x) = [g(x)]^2$$ $$h(x) = g(x)g(x)$$

and using the Product Rule,

$$h'(x) = g'(x)g(x) + g(x)g'(x) = 2g'(x)g(x).$$

Similarly, for $n = 3$, we can use the Extended Product Rule.

Thus
$$\begin{aligned} h(x) &= [g(x)]^3 \\ &= g(x)g(x)g(x) \\ h'(x) &= g'(x)g(x)g(x) + g(x)g'(x)g(x) + g(x)g(x)g'(x) \\ &= 3[g(x)]^2g'(x). \end{aligned}$$

These results suggest a generalization of the Power Rule.

The Power of a Function Rule for Positive Integers

If u is a function of x, and n is a positive integer, then $\frac{d}{dx}(u^n) = nu^{n-1}\frac{du}{dx}$.

In function notation, if $f(x) = [g(x)]^n$, then $f'(x) = n[g(x)]^{n-1}g'(x)$.

The Power of a Function Rule is a *special case* of the Chain Rule, which we will discuss later in this chapter. We are now able to differentiate any polynomial, such as $h(x) = (x^2 + 3x + 5)^6$ or $h(x) = (1 - x^2)^4(2x + 6)^3$, without multiplying out the brackets.

EXAMPLE 5

For $h(x) = (x^2 + 3x + 5)^6$, find $h'(x)$.

Solution

Here $h(x)$ has the form $h(x) = [g(x)]^6$, where the "inside" function is $g(x) = x^2 + 3x + 5$.

By the Power of a Function Rule, we get $h'(x) = 6(x^2 + 3x + 5)^5(2x + 3)$.

EXAMPLE 6

The position s, in centimetres, of an object moving in a straight line is given by $s = t(6 - 3t)^4$, $t \geq 0$, where the time t is in seconds. Determine its velocity at time $t = 2$.

Solution

The velocity of the object at any time $t \geq 0$ is $v = \frac{ds}{dt}$.

$$v = \frac{d}{dt}\left[t(6 - 3t^4)\right]$$
$$= (1)(6 - 3t)^4 + (t)\frac{d}{dt}\left[(6 - 3t)^4\right] \quad \text{(Product Rule)}$$
$$= (6 - 3t)^4 + (t)\left[4(6 - 3t)^3(-3)\right] \quad \text{(Power of a Function Rule)}$$

At $t = 2$,
$$v = 0 + (2)[4(0)(-3)]$$
$$= 0.$$

We conclude that the object is at rest at time $t = 2$.

Notice that if the derivative is required at a particular value of the independent variable, it is not necessary to simplify before substituting.

Exercise 4.3

Part A

1. Use the Product Rule to differentiate each function. Simplify your answers.
   a. $h(x) = x(x - 4)$
   b. $h(x) = x^2(2x - 1)$
   c. $h(x) = (3x + 2)(2x - 7)$
   d. $h(x) = (8 - x)(4x + 6)$
   e. $h(x) = (5x^7 + 1)(x^2 - 2x)$
   f. $s(t) = (t^2 + 1)(3 - 2t^2)$

Knowledge/ Understanding

2. Use the Product Rule and the Power of a Function Rule to differentiate the following. Do not simplify.
   a. $y = (5x + 1)^3(x - 4)$
   b. $y = (3x^2 + 4)(3 + x^3)^5$
   c. $y = (1 - x^2)^4(2x + 6)^3$

Communication

3. When is it not appropriate to use the Product Rule? Give examples.

Part B

4. Find the value of $\frac{dy}{dx}$ for the given value of x.
   a. $y = (2 + 7x)(x - 3)$, $x = 2$
   b. $y = (1 - 2x)(1 + 2x)$, $x = \frac{1}{2}$
   c. $y = (3 - 2x - x^2)(x^2 + x - 2)$, $x = -2$
   d. $y = (4x^2 + 2x)(3 - 2x - 5x^2)$, $x = 0$
   e. $y = x^3(3x + 7)^2$, $x = -2$

f. $y = (2x + 1)^5(3x + 2)^4$, $x = -1$

g. $y = x(5x - 2)(5x + 2)$, $x = 3$

h. $y = 3x(x - 4)(x + 3)$, $x = 2$

5. Find the equation of the tangent to the curve $y = (x^3 - 5x + 2)(3x^2 - 2x)$ at the point $(1, -2)$.

6. Find the point(s) where the tangent to the curve is horizontal.

a. $y = 2(x - 29)(x + 1)$

b. $y = (x^2 + 2x + 1)(x^2 + 2x + 1)$

7. Use the Extended Product Rule to differentiate the following. Do not simplify.

a. $y = (x + 1)^3(x + 4)(x - 3)^2$

b. $y = x^2(3x^2 + 4)^2(3 - x^3)^4$

Communication

8. Find the slope of the tangent to $h(x) = 2x(x + 1)^3(x^2 + 2x + 1)^2$ at $x = -2$. Explain how to find the equation of the normal at $x = -2$.

Part C

Thinking/Inquiry/ Problem Solving

9. a. Find an expression for $f'(x)$ if $f(x) = g_1(x)g_2(x)g_3(x) \ldots g_{n-1}(x)g_n(x)$.

b. If $f(x) = (1 + x)(1 + 2x)(1 + 3x) \ldots (1 + nx)$, find $f'(0)$.

10. Determine a quadratic function $f(x) = ax^2 + bx + c$ whose graph passes through the point $(2, 19)$ and that has a horizontal tangent at $(-1, -8)$.

11. Sketch the graph of $f(x) = |x^2 - 1|$.

a. For what values of x is f not differentiable?

b. Find a formula for f' and sketch the graph of f'.

c. Find f' at $x = -2$, 0, and 3.

12. Show that the line $4x - y + 11 = 0$ is tangent to the curve $y = \frac{16}{x^2} - 1$.

Section 4.4 — The Quotient Rule

In the previous section, we found that the derivative of the product of two functions is not the product of their derivatives. The Quotient Rule gives the derivatives of a function that is the quotient of two functions. It is derived from the Product Rule.

The Quotient Rule

If $h(x) = \frac{f(x)}{g(x)}$, then $h'(x) = \frac{f'(x)g(x) - f(x)g'(x)}{[g(x)]^2}$, $g(x) \neq 0$.

In Leibniz notation, $\frac{d}{dx}\left(\frac{u}{v}\right) = \frac{\frac{du}{dx}v - u\frac{dv}{dx}}{v^2}$.

Memory Aid for the Product and Quotient Rules

It is worth noting that the Quotient Rule is similar to the Product Rule in that both have $f'(x)g(x)$ and $f(x)g'(x)$. For the Product Rule, we put an addition sign $(+)$ between both terms. For the Quotient Rule, we put a subtraction sign $(-)$ between the terms and then divide the result by the square of the original denominator.

Proof of the Quotient Rule

We wish to find $h'(x)$, given that

$$h(x) = \frac{f(x)}{g(x)},\ g(x) \neq 0.$$

We rewrite this as a product:

$$h(x)g(x) = f(x).$$

Using the Product Rule,

$$h'(x)g(x) + h(x)g'(x) = f'(x).$$

Solving for $h'(x)$, we get

$$h'(x) = \frac{f'(x) - h(x)g'(x)}{g(x)}$$

$$= \frac{f'(x) - \frac{f(x)}{g(x)}g'(x)}{g(x)}$$

$$= \frac{f'(x)g(x) - f(x)g'(x)}{[g(x)]^2}.$$

The Quotient Rule enables us to differentiate rational functions.

EXAMPLE 1

Find the derivative of $h(x) = \frac{3x - 4}{x^2 + 5}$.

Solution

Since $h(x) = \frac{f(x)}{g(x)}$, where $f(x) = 3x - 4$ and $g(x) = x^2 + 5$, we use the Quotient Rule to find $h'(x)$.

Using the Quotient Rule, we get
$$\begin{aligned} h'(x) &= \frac{(3)(x^2 + 5) - (3x - 4)(2x)}{(x^2 + 5)^2} \\ &= \frac{3x^2 + 15 - 6x^2 + 8x}{(x^2 + 5)^2} \\ &= \frac{-3x^2 + 8x + 15}{(x^2 + 5)^2}. \end{aligned}$$

EXAMPLE 2

Using a graphing calculator, graph $y = \frac{2x}{x^2 + 1}$ and the tangent to it at $x = 0$. Find the equation of the tangent.

technology

Solution

The slope of the tangent to the graph of y at any point is given by the derivative $\frac{dy}{dx}$.

By the Quotient Rule,

$$\frac{dy}{dx} = \frac{(2)(x^2 + 1) - (2x)(2x)}{(x^2 + 1)^2}.$$

At $x = 0$,

$$\frac{dy}{dx} = \frac{(2)(0 + 1) - (0)(0)}{(0 + 1)^2} = 2.$$

Since the slope of the tangent at $x = 0$ is 2 and the point of tangency is $(0, 0)$, the equation of the tangent is $y = 2x$.

Solution Using the Calculator

Use the DRAW function to draw a tangent at the point $(0, 0)$.

In this case, input $y_1 = \frac{2x}{x^2 + 1}$.

Select ZOOM **4:ZDecimal** for your domain and range.

Select GRAPH.

Select 2nd PRGM (DRAW) and choose **5:Tangent(** to obtain the graph window.

Select $x = 0$ and then press ENTER to graph the tangent.

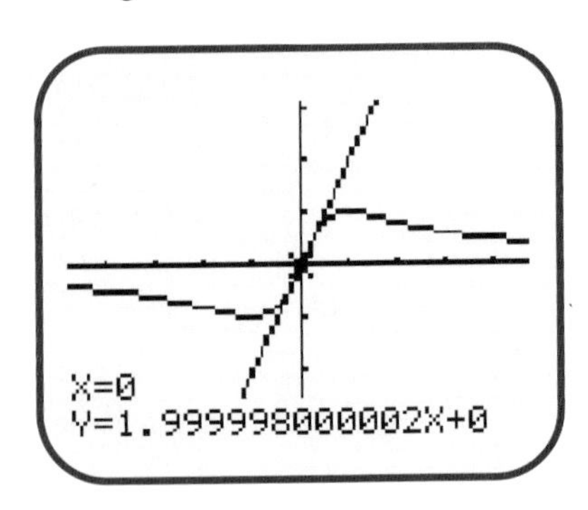

EXAMPLE 3 Find the coordinates of each point on the graph of $f(x) = \frac{2x + 8}{\sqrt{x}}$ where the tangent is horizontal.

Solution

The slope of the tangent at any point on the graph is given by $f'(x)$.
Using the Quotient Rule,

$$f'(x) = \frac{(2)(\sqrt{x}) - (2x + 8)\left(\frac{1}{2}x^{-\frac{1}{2}}\right)}{(\sqrt{x})^2}$$

$$= \frac{2\sqrt{x} - \frac{2x + 8}{2\sqrt{x}}}{x}$$

$$= \frac{\frac{2x}{\sqrt{x}} - \frac{x + 4}{\sqrt{x}}}{x}$$

$$= \frac{x - 4}{x^{\frac{3}{2}}}.$$

The tangent will be horizontal when $f'(x) = 0$, that is, when $x = 4$. The point on the graph where the tangent is horizontal is (4, 8).

Exercise 4.4

Part A

Communication

1. What are the Exponential Rules? Give examples of each rule.

2. Copy and complete the table *without* using the Quotient Rule.

Function	Rewrite	Differentiate and simplify, if necessary
$f(x) = \frac{x^2 + 3x}{x}, x \neq 0$		
$g(x) = \frac{3x^{\frac{5}{3}}}{x}, x \neq 0$		
$h(x) = \frac{1}{10x^5}, x \neq 0$		
$y = \frac{8x^3 + 6x}{2x}, x \neq 0$		
$s = \frac{t^2 - 9}{t - 3}, t \neq 3$		

Communication

3. What rule do we use to find the derivative of a rational function?

Part B

Knowledge/Understanding

4. Use the Quotient Rule to differentiate each function. Simplify your answers.

a. $h(x) = \frac{x}{x+1}$ b. $h(x) = \frac{x^2}{x+1}$ c. $h(t) = \frac{2t-3}{t+5}$

d. $h(x) = \frac{2x-1}{x+3}$ e. $h(x) = \frac{x^3}{2x^2-1}$ f. $h(x) = \frac{1}{x^2+3}$

g. $y = \frac{x(3x+5)}{1-x^2}$ h. $y = \frac{x^2-x+1}{x^2+3}$ i. $y = \frac{x^2-1}{x(3x+1)}$

5. Find $\frac{dy}{dx}$ at the given value of x.

a. $y = \frac{3x+2}{x+5}, x = -3$ b. $y = \frac{x^3}{x^2+9}, x = 1$

c. $y = \frac{x^2-25}{x^2+25}, x = 2$ d. $y = \frac{(x+1)(x+2)}{(x-1)(x-2)}, x = 4$

6. Find the slope of the tangent to the curve $y = \frac{x^3}{x^2-6}$ at point (3, 9).

7. Find the points on the graph of $y = \frac{3x}{x-4}$, where the slope of the tangent is $-\frac{12}{25}$.

Thinking/Inquiry/Problem Solving

8. Show that there are no tangents to the graph of $f(x) = \frac{5x+2}{x+2}$ that have a negative slope.

9. Find the point(s) at which the tangent to the curve is horizontal.

a. $y = \frac{2x^2}{x-4}$ b. $y = \frac{x^2-1}{x^2+x-2}$

Application

10. An initial population, p, of 1000 bacteria grows in number according to the equation $p(t) = 1000\left(1 + \frac{4t}{t^2+50}\right)$, where t is in hours. Find the rate at which the population is growing after 1 h and after 2 h.

Application

11. Determine the equation of the tangent to the curve $y = \frac{x^2-1}{3x}$ at $x = 2$.

12. A motorboat coasts toward a dock with its engine off. Its distance s, in metres, from the dock t seconds after the engine is turned off is

$s(t) = \frac{10(6-t)}{t+3}$ for $0 \leq t \leq 6$.

a. How far is the boat from the dock initially?

b. Find the boat's velocity when it bumps into the dock.

Part C

Thinking/Inquiry/Problem Solving

13. Consider the function $f(x) = \frac{ax+b}{cx+d}, x \neq -\frac{d}{c}$, where a, b, c, and d are non-zero constants. What condition on a, b, c, and d ensures that each tangent to the graph of f has positive slope?

Section 4.5 — Composite Functions

Many functions can be thought of as the combination of simpler functions. If $f(x) = x^3$ and $g(x) = 2x$, then $h(x) = x^3 + 2x$ can be expressed as $h(x) = f(x) + g(x)$. It is often helpful to regard complicated functions as being built from simpler ones.

For example, if
$$y = h(x) = (2x - 1)^5,$$
we can consider this as the fifth power of $2x - 1$. That is,
$$y = u^5, \text{ where } u = 2x - 1.$$

If we let $f(u) = u^5$ and $g(x) = 2x - 1$,
then $y = h(x) = f(g(x))$
$= (2x - 1).$

As another example, consider
$$h(x) = \sqrt{25 - x^2},$$
which can be considered to be made up of
$$g(x) = 25 - x^2 \text{ and } f(x) = \sqrt{x},$$
and once again,
$$h(x) = f(g(x)) = \sqrt{25 - x^2}.$$

This process of combining functions is called **composition**. We start with a number x in the domain of g, find its image $g(x)$, and then take the value of f at $g(x)$, providing $g(x)$ is in the domain of f. The result is the new function $h(x) = f(g(x))$ which is called the **composite function** of f and g and is denoted $f \circ g$.

Given two functions f and g, the composite function $f \circ g$ is defined by $(f \circ g)(x) = f(g(x))$.

The domain of $f \circ g$ is the set of all x in the domain of g such that $g(x)$ is in the domain of f. We say that g is the **inner** function and that f is the **outer** function. A good way to picture the composition $f \circ g$ is by imagining a machine.

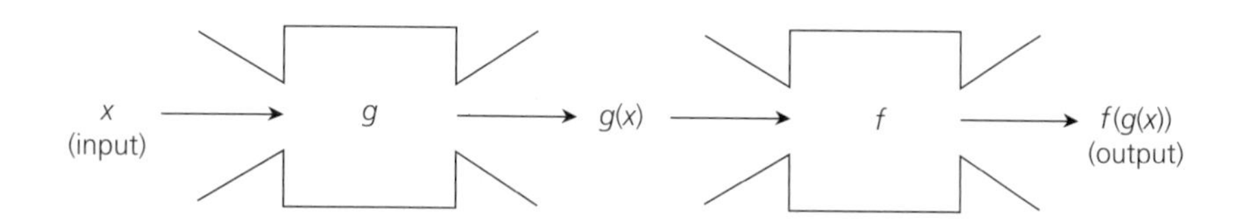

EXAMPLE 1

If $f(x) = \sqrt{x}$ and $g(x) = x + 5$, find each of the following:

a. $f(g(4))$ b. $g(f(4))$ c. $f(g(x))$ d. $g(f(x))$

Solution

a. Since $g(4) = 9$, we have $f(g(4)) = f(9) = 3$.

b. Since $f(4) = 2$, we have $g(f(4)) = g(2) = 7$. *Note:* $f(g(4)) \neq g(f(4))$.

c. $f(g(x)) = f(x + 5) = \sqrt{x + 5}$

d. $g(f(x)) = g\left(\sqrt{x}\right) = \sqrt{x} + 5$ *Note:* $f(g(x)) \neq g(f(x))$.

EXAMPLE 2

We are given that $h(x) = f(g(x)) = \frac{1}{1 + x^2}$.

a. If $f(x) = \frac{1}{x}$, what is $g(x)$?

b. If $g(x) = x^2$, what is $f(x)$?

Solution

a. Since $f(x) = \frac{1}{x}$, then $f(g(x)) = \frac{1}{g(x)} = \frac{1}{1 + x^2}$. We conclude that $g(x) = 1 + x^2$.

b. Since $g(x) = x^2$, then $f(g(x)) = f(x^2) = \frac{1}{1 + x^2}$. Since x^2 has been substituted for x in f, we conclude that $f(x) = \frac{1}{1 + x}$.

Exercise 4.5

Part A

1. Given $f(x) = \sqrt{x}$ and $g(x) = x^2 - 1$, find the following:

   a. $f(g(1))$ b. $g(f(1))$ c. $g(f(0))$

   d. $f(g(-4))$ e. $f(g(x))$ f. $g(f(x))$

2. For each of the following pairs of functions, find the composite functions $f \circ g$ and $g \circ f$. What is the domain of each composite function? Are the composite functions equal?

   a. $f(x) = x^2$, $g(x) = \sqrt{x}$

   b. $f(x) = \frac{1}{x}$, $g(x) = x^2 + 1$

   c. $f(x) = \frac{1}{x}$, $g(x) = \sqrt{x + 2}$

Part B

3. Use the functions $f(x) = 3x + 1$, $g(x) = x^3$, $h(x) = \frac{1}{x + 1}$, and $u(x) = \sqrt{x}$ to find expressions for the indicated composite function.

a. $f \circ u$ b. $u \circ h$ c. $g \circ f$

d. $u \circ g$ e. $h \circ u$ f. $f \circ g$

g. $h \circ (f \circ u)$ h. $(f \circ g) \circ u$ i. $g \circ (h \circ u)$

4. Express h as the composition of two functions f and g, such that $h(x) = f(g(x))$.

   a. $h(x) = (2x^2 - 1)^4$
   b. $h(x) = \sqrt{5x - 1}$
   c. $h(x) = \frac{1}{x - 4}$
   d. $h(x) = (2 - 3x)^{\frac{5}{2}}$
   e. $h(x) = x^4 + 5x^2 + 6$
   f. $h(x) = (x + 1)^2 - 9(x + 1)$

5. If $f(x) = \sqrt{2 - x}$ and $f(g(x)) = \sqrt{2 - x^3}$, then what is $g(x)$?

6. If $g(x) = \sqrt{x}$ and $f(g(x)) = (\sqrt{x} + 7)^2$, then what is $f(x)$?

7. Let $g(x) = x - 3$. Find a function f so that $f(g(x)) = x^2$.

8. Let $f(x) = x^2$. Find a function g so that $f(g(x)) = x^2 + 8x + 16$.

9. Let $f(x) = x + 4$ and $g(x) = (x - 2)^2$. Find a function u so that $f(g(u(x))) = 4x^2 - 8x + 8$.

10. If $f(x) = \frac{1}{1 - x}$ and $g(x) = 1 - x$, determine

    a. $g(f(x))$
    b. $f(g(x))$

11. If $f(x) = 3x + 5$ and $g(x) = x^2 + 2x - 3$, determine x such that $f(g(x)) = g(f(x))$.

12. If $f(x) = 2x - 7$ and $g(x) = 5 - 2x$,

    a. determine $f \circ f^{-1}$ and $f^{-1} \circ f$.
    b. show that $(f \circ g)^{-1} = g^{-1} \circ f^{-1}$.

Section 4.6 — The Derivative of a Composite Function

The Chain Rule tells us how to compute the derivative of the composite function $h(x) = f(g(x))$ in terms of the derivatives f and g.

The Chain Rule
If f and g are functions having derivatives, then the composite function $h(x) = f(g(x))$ has a derivative given by
$h'(x) = f'(g(x))g'(x)$.

In words, the Chain Rule says, "the derivative of a composite function is the product of the derivative of the outer function evaluated at the inner function and the derivative of the inner function."

EXAMPLE 1

Differentiate $h(x) = \left(x^2 + x\right)^{\frac{3}{2}}$.

Solution

The inner function is $g(x) = x^2 + x$ and the outer function is $f(x) = x^{\frac{3}{2}}$.
The derivative of the inner function is $g'(x) = 2x + 1$.
The derivative of the outer function is $f'(x) = \frac{3}{2}x^{\frac{1}{2}}$.
The derivative of the outer function evaluated at the inner function $g(x)$ is
$f'(x^2 + x) = \frac{3}{2}\left(x^2 + x\right)^{\frac{1}{2}}$.
By the Chain Rule,
$h'(x) = \frac{3}{2}\left(x^2 + x\right)^{\frac{1}{2}}(2x + 1)$.

Proof of the Chain Rule

By the definition of the derivative, $[f(g(x))]' = \lim_{h\to 0} \frac{f(g(x + h)) - f(g(x))}{h}$.

Assuming $g(x + h) - g(x) \neq 0$, then we can write

$$[f(g(x))]' = \lim_{h\to 0}\left[\left(\frac{f(g(x + h)) - f(g(x))}{g(x + h) - g(x)}\right)\left(\frac{g(x + h) - g(x)}{h}\right)\right]$$

$$= \lim_{h\to 0}\left[\frac{f(g(x + h)) - f(g(x))}{g(x + h) - g(x)}\right]\left[\lim_{h\to 0}\frac{g(x + h) - g(x)}{h}\right].$$

(Property of Limits)

Since $\lim_{h\to 0}[g(x + h) - g(x)] = 0$, let $g(x + h) - g(x) = k$ and $k \to 0$ as $h \to 0$, we obtain

$$[f(g(x))]' = \lim_{h\to 0}\left[\frac{f(g(x)+k)) - f(g(x))}{k}\right]\left[\lim_{h\to 0}\frac{g(x+h)-g(x)}{h}\right].$$

Therefore, $\quad [f(g(x))]' = f'(g(x))g'(x).$

This proof is not valid for all circumstances, since dividing by $g(x+h) - g(x)$, we assume $g(x+h) - g(x) \neq 0$. A more advanced proof can be found in advanced calculus texts.

The Chain Rule in Leibniz Notation

If $y = f(u)$, where $u = g(x)$, then y is a composite function and

$$\frac{dy}{dx} = \frac{dy}{du}\frac{du}{dx}.$$

If we interpret derivatives as rates of change, the Chain Rule states that if y is a function of x through the intermediate variable u, then the rate of change of y with respect to x is equal to the product of the rate of change of y with respect to u and the rate of change of u with respect to x.

EXAMPLE 2

If $y = u^3 - 2u + 1$, where $u = 2\sqrt{x}$, find $\frac{dy}{dx}$ at $x = 4$.

Solution

Using the Chain Rule,

$$\frac{dy}{dx} = \frac{dy}{du}\frac{du}{dx} = \left(3u^2 - 2\right)\left[2\left(\frac{1}{2}x^{-\frac{1}{2}}\right)\right]$$
$$= \left(3u^2 - 2\right)\left(\frac{1}{\sqrt{x}}\right).$$

It is not necessary to write the derivative entirely in terms of x.
When $x = 4$, $u = 2\sqrt{4} = 4$ and

$$\frac{dy}{dx} = \left[3(4^2) - 2\right]\left(\frac{1}{\sqrt{4}}\right) = (46)\left(\frac{1}{2}\right) = 23.$$

EXAMPLE 3

An environmental study of a certain suburban community suggests that the average daily level of carbon monoxide in the air may be modelled by the formula $C(p) = \sqrt{0.5p^2 + 17}$ parts per million when the population is p thousand. It is estimated that t years from now, the population of the community will be $p(t) = 3.1 + 0.1t^2$ thousand. At what rate will the carbon monoxide level be changing with respect to time three years from now?

Solution

We are asked to find the value of $\frac{dC}{dt}$, when $t = 3$.

We can find the value of change by using the Chain Rule.

Therefore, $$\frac{dC}{dt} = \frac{dC}{dP}\frac{dP}{dt}$$

$$= \left[\frac{1}{2}\left(0.5p^2 + 17\right)^{-\frac{1}{2}}(0.5)(2p)\right](0.2t).$$

When $t = 3$,

$$p(3) = 3.1 + 0.1(3)^2 = 4,$$

so $$\frac{dC}{dt} = \left[\frac{1}{2}\left(0.5(4)^2 + 17\right)^{-\frac{1}{2}}(0.5)(2(4))\right](0.2(3))$$

$$= 0.24.$$

The carbon monoxide level will be changing at the rate of 0.24 parts per million. This level will be increasing because the sign of $\frac{dC}{dt}$ is positive.

EXAMPLE 4

If $y = (x^2 - 5)^7$, find $\frac{dy}{dx}$.

Solution

The inner function is $g(x) = x^2 - 5$ and the outer function is $f(x) = x^7$.
By the Chain Rule,

$$\frac{dy}{dx} = 7(x^2 - 5)^6(2x)$$

$$= 14x(x^2 - 5)^6.$$

Example 4 is a special case of the Chain Rule in which the outer function is a power function of the form $y = [g(x)]^n$. This leads to a generalization of the Power Rule.

Power of a Function Rule
If n is a real number and $u = g(x)$,

then $$\frac{d}{dx}(u^n) = nu^{n-1}\frac{du}{dx}$$

or $$\frac{d}{dx}\left[g(x)\right]^n = n\left[g(x)\right]^{n-1}g'(x).$$

EXAMPLE 5

technology

Using graphing technology, sketch the graph of the function $f(x) = \frac{8}{x^2 + 4}$.
Find the equation of the tangent at the point (2, 1) on the graph.

Solution

From graphing technology, the graph is

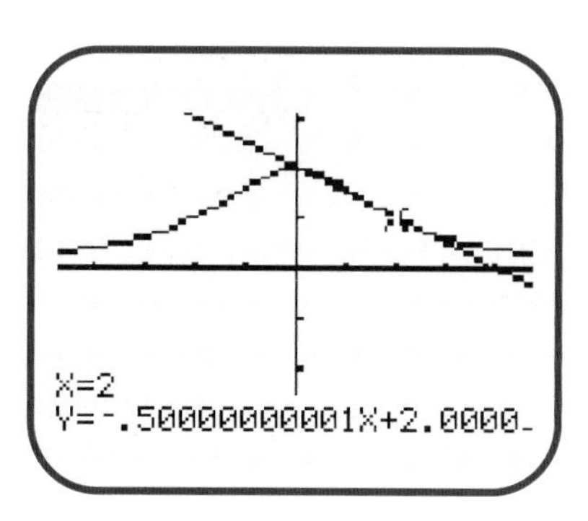

The slope of the tangent at point (2, 1) is given by $f'(2)$.

We first write the function as $f(x) = 8(x^2 + 4)^{-1}$.

By the Power of a Function Rule, $\quad f'(x) = -8(x^2 + 4)^{-2}(2x)$.

The slope at (2, 1) is
$$\begin{aligned} f'(2) &= -8(4 + 4)^{-2}(4) \\ &= -\frac{32}{(8)^2} \\ &= -0.5. \end{aligned}$$

The equation of the tangent is $y - 1 = -\frac{1}{2}(x - 2)$ or $x + 2y - 4 = 0$.

EXAMPLE 6

If $y = f(3x^4)$, and $f'(3) = -4$, find $\frac{dy}{dx}$ at $x = 1$.

Solution

Here the inner function is $g(x) = 3x^4$.

By the Chain Rule, $\quad \frac{dy}{dx} = f'(3x^4)\left[12x^3\right]$.

When $x = 1$,
$$\begin{aligned} \frac{dy}{dx} &= f'(3)\left[12(1)^3\right] \\ &= (-4)(12) \\ &= -48. \end{aligned}$$

EXAMPLE 7

Differentiate $h(x) = \sqrt[3]{\frac{x}{1 - 2x}}$. Express your answer in a simplified factored form.

Solution

We write $h(x) = \left(\frac{x}{1 - 2x}\right)^{\frac{1}{3}}$, where $u = \frac{x}{1 - 2x}$ is the inner function and $u^{\frac{1}{3}}$ is the outer function.

$$\begin{aligned} \text{Then } h'(x) &= \frac{1}{3}\left(\frac{x}{1 - 2x}\right)^{\frac{1}{3} - 1}\frac{d}{dx}\left(\frac{x}{1 - 2x}\right) && \text{(Chain Rule)} \\ &= \frac{1}{3}\left(\frac{x}{1 - 2x}\right)^{-\frac{2}{3}}\left[\frac{(1)(1 - 2x) - (x)(-2)}{(1 - 2x)^2}\right] && \text{(Quotient Rule)} \\ &= \frac{1}{3}\left(\frac{x}{1 - 2x}\right)^{-\frac{2}{3}}\left[\frac{1}{(1 - 2x)^2}\right] \\ &= \frac{1}{3x^{\frac{2}{3}}\left(1 - 2x\right)^{\frac{4}{3}}}. \end{aligned}$$

Exercise 4.6

Part A

Communication

1. What is the rule for calculating the derivative of the composition of two differentiable functions? Give examples and show how the derivative is determined.

2. Differentiate each function. Do not expand any expression before differentiating.

a. $f(x) = (2x + 3)^4$
b. $y = (5 - x)^6$
c. $g(x) = (x^2 - 4)^3$
d. $y = (7 - x^3)^5$
e. $h(x) = (2x^2 + 3x - 5)^4$
f. $y = (5x - x^2)^5$
g. $f(x) = (\pi^2 - x^2)^3$
h. $y = (1 - x + x^2 - x^3)^4$
i. $f(x) = [(2 - x)^4 + 16]^3$
j. $g(x) = (4x + 1)^{\frac{1}{2}}$
k. $h(x) = \sqrt{5x + 7}$
l. $y = \sqrt{x^2 - 3}$
m. $f(x) = \dfrac{1}{(x^2 - 16)^5}$
n. $y = \dfrac{1}{\sqrt{x^2 + 4}}$
o. $h(x) = \dfrac{1}{\sqrt{x} + 1}$
p. $f(u) = \left(1 + u^{\frac{1}{3}}\right)^6$
q. $y = \sqrt{(2x - 5)^3}$
r. $y = \left(\dfrac{x + 2}{\sqrt[3]{x}}\right)^3$

Part B

Knowledge/Understanding

3. Rewrite each of the following in the form $y = u^n$ or $y = ku^n$, and then differentiate.

a. $y = \dfrac{3}{x^2}$
b. $y = -\dfrac{2}{x^3}$
c. $y = \dfrac{1}{x + 1}$
d. $y = \dfrac{1}{x^2 - 4}$
e. $y = \left(\dfrac{2}{x}\right)^2$
f. $y = \dfrac{3}{9 - x^2}$
g. $y = \dfrac{1}{5x^2 + x}$
h. $y = \dfrac{1}{(x^2 + x + 1)^4}$
i. $y = \left(\dfrac{1 + \sqrt{x}}{\sqrt[3]{x^2}}\right)^3$

4. Differentiate each function. Express your answer in a simplified factored form.

a. $f(x) = (x + 4)^3(x - 3)^6$
b. $y = \dfrac{3x + 5}{1 - x^2}$
c. $g(x) = (2x - 1)^4(2 - 3x)^4$
d. $y = \dfrac{3x^2 + 2x}{x^2 + 1}$
e. $h(x) = x^3(3x - 5)^2$
f. $y = \dfrac{(2x - 1)^2}{(x - 2)^3}$
g. $y = x^4(1 - 4x^2)^3$
h. $y = \left(\dfrac{x^2 - 3}{x^2 + 3}\right)^4$

i. $y = (x^2 + 3)^3(x^3 + 3)^2$

j. $h(x) = \frac{x}{\sqrt{1 + x^2}}$

k. $s = (4 - 3t^3)^4(1 - 2t)^6$

l. $h(x) = \frac{\sqrt{1 - x^2}}{1 - x}$

5. Find the rate of change of each function at the given value of t. Leave your answers as rational numbers, or in terms of roots and the number π.

   a. $s(t) = t^{\frac{1}{3}}(4t - 5)^{\frac{2}{3}}$, $t = 8$

   b. $s(t) = \left(\frac{t - \pi}{t + 6\pi}\right)^{\frac{1}{3}}$, $t = 2\pi$

6. For what values of x do the curves $y = (1 + x^3)^2$ and $y = 2x^6$ have the same slope?

7. Find the slope of the tangent to the curve $y = (3x + x^2)^{-2}$ at $\left(-2, \frac{1}{4}\right)$.

8. Find the equation of the tangent to the curve $y = (x^3 - 7)^5$ at $x = 2$.

9. Use the Chain Rule, in Leibniz notation, to find $\frac{dy}{dx}$ at the indicated value of x.

   a. $y = 3u^2 - 5u + 2$, $u = x^2 - 1$, $x = 2$

   b. $y = u^3 - 5(u^3 - 7u)^2$, $u = \sqrt{x}$, $x = 4$

   c. $y = 2u^3 + 3u^2$, $u = x + x^{\frac{1}{2}}$, $x = 1$

   d. $y = u(u^2 + 3)^3$, $u = (x + 3)^2$, $x = -2$

   e. $y = \frac{u^3}{u + 1}$, $u = (x^2 + 1)^3$, $x = 1$

   f. $y = \frac{1}{(1 + u^2)^2}$, $u = \sqrt{x} - 1$, $x = 4$

   g. $y = u^5 + u^3$, $u = \frac{3}{v} - 4v$, $v = 3 - x^2$, $x = 2$

10. Let $y = f(x^2 + 3x - 5)$. Find $\frac{dy}{dx}$ when $x = 1$, given that $f'(-1) = 2$.

Application

11. Let $y = g(h(x))$ where $h(x) = \frac{x^2}{x + 2}$. If $g'\left(\frac{9}{5}\right) = -2$, find $\frac{dy}{dx}$ when $x = 3$.

Application

12. Find $h'(2)$ given that $h(x) = f(g(x))$, $f(u) = u^2 - 1$, $g(2) = 3$, and $g'(2) = -1$.

Part C

Application

13. a. Write an expression for $h'(x)$ if $h(x) = p(x)q(x)r(x)$.

    b. If $h(x) = x(2x + 7)^4(x - 1)^2$, find $h'(-3)$.

14. Show that the tangent to the curve $y = (x^2 + x - 2)^3 + 3$ at the point $(1, 3)$ is also the tangent to the curve at another point.

Thinking/Inquiry/Problem Solving

15. Differentiate $y = \frac{x^2(1 - x)^3}{(1 + x)^3}$.

Application **16.** Use mathematical induction to prove that if u is a function of x and n is a positive integer, then $\frac{d}{dx}(u^n) = nu^{n-1}\frac{du}{dx}$.

17. If $f(x) = ax + b$ and $g(x) = cx + d$, find the condition (involving a, b, c, and d) such that $f(g(x)) = g(f(x))$.

Technology Extension

Numerical derivatives can be approximated on a TI-83 Plus using **nDeriv(**. To approximate $f'(0)$ for $f(x) = \frac{2x}{x^2 + 1}$:

technology

Press MATH and scroll down to **8:nDeriv(** under the MATH menu.

Press ENTER and the display on the screen will be **nDeriv(**.

To find the derivative, key in the *expression*, the *variable*, the *value* at which we want the derivative, and a value for $\in$.

For this example, the display will be **nDeriv(** 2x/(x^2 + 1), x, 0, .01).

Press ENTER and the value **1.9998002** will be returned.

Therefore, $f'(0)$ is approximately 1.999 800 02.

A better approximation can be found by using a smaller value for $\in$, for example, $\in = 0.0001$. The default value for $\in$ is 0.001.

a. Use the **nDeriv(** function on a graphing calculator to find the value of the derivative of each of the following functions at the given point.

b. Determine the actual value of the derivative at the given point using the Rules of Differentiation.

i) $f(x) = x^2$ at $x = 3$

ii) $f(x) = x^3$ at $x = -1$

iii) $f(x) = x^4$ at $x = 2$

iv) $f(x) = x^3 - 6x$ at $x = -2$

v) $f(x) = \sqrt{25 - x^2}$ at $x = 3$

vi) $f(x) = (x^2 + 1)(2x - 1)^4$ at $x = 0$

vii) $f(x) = x^2 + \frac{16}{x} - 4\sqrt{x}$ at $x = 4$

viii) $f(x) = \frac{x^2 - 1}{x^2 + x - 2}$ at $x = -1$

The TI-89 and TI-92 can find exact symbolic and numerical deriviatives. If you have access to either model, try some of the above questions and compare your answers to those found using a TI-83 Plus. Press DIFFERENTIATE under the CALCULATE menu, key d(2x/(x^2 + 1), x) $|$x = 0 and press ENTER.

Key Concepts Review

Now that you have completed your study of derivatives in Chapter 4, you should be familiar with such concepts as derivatives of polynomial functions, the Product Rule, the Quotient Rule, the Power Rule for Rational Exponents, and the Chain Rule. Consider the following summary to confirm your understanding of key concepts.

- The derivative of f at a is given by $f'(a) = \lim_{h \to 0} \frac{f(a + h) - f(a)}{h}$ or, alternatively, by $f'(a) = \lim_{x \to a} \frac{f(x) - f(a)}{x - a}$.
- The derivative function of $f(x)$ with respect to x is $f'(x) = \lim_{h \to 0} \frac{f(x + h) - f(x)}{h}$.
- The normal at point P is the line that is perpendicular to the tangent at point P.
- For two functions f and g, the composite function $f \circ g$ is defined by $(f \circ g)(x) = f(g(x))$.

Summary of Differentiation Techniques

Rule	Function Notation	Leibniz Notation
Constant	$f(x) = k$, $f'(x) = 0$	$\frac{d}{dx}(k) = 0$
Linear	$f(x) = x$, $f'(x) = 1$	$\frac{d}{dx}(x) = 1$
Constant Multiple	$f(x) = kg(x)$, $f'(x) = kg'(x)$	$\frac{d}{dx}(ky) = k\frac{dy}{dx}$
Sum or Difference	$f(x) = p(x) \pm q(x)$, $f'(x) = p'(x) \pm q'(x)$	$\frac{d}{dx}[f(x) \pm g(x)] = \frac{d}{dx}f(x) \pm \frac{d}{dx}g(x)$
Product	$h(x) = f(x)g(x)$ $h'(x) = f'(x)g(x) + f(x)g'(x)$	$\frac{d}{dx}[f(x)g(x)] = \left[\frac{d}{dx}f(x)\right]g(x) + f(x)\left[\frac{d}{dx}g(x)\right]$
Quotient	$h(x) = \frac{f(x)}{g(x)}$ $h'(x) = \frac{f'(x)g(x) - f(x)g'(x)}{[g(x)]^2}$	$\frac{d}{dx}\left[\frac{f(x)}{(x)}\right] = \frac{\left[\frac{d}{dx}f(x)\right]g(x) - f(x)\left[\frac{d}{dx}g(x)\right]}{[g(x)]^2}$
Chain	$y = f(g(x)), \frac{dy}{dx} = f'(g(x))g'(x)$	$\frac{dy}{dx} = \frac{dy}{du}\frac{du}{dx}$, where u is a function of x.
General Power	$y = [f(x)]^n$, $\frac{dy}{dx} = n[f(x)]^{n-1}f'(x)$	$y = u^n$, $\frac{dy}{dx} = nu^{n-1}\frac{du}{dx}$, where u is a function of x.

Career Link wrap-up investigate and apply

CHAPTER 4: THE ELASTICITY OF DEMAND

An electronics retailing chain has established the monthly price (p) – demand (n_d) relationship for a Nintendo™ game as

$$n_d(p) = 1000 - 10\frac{(p-1)^{\frac{4}{3}}}{\sqrt[3]{p}}.$$

They are trying to set a price level that will provide maximum revenue (R). They know that when demand is *elastic* ($E > 1$), a drop in price will result in higher overall revenues ($R = n_dp$) and that when demand is *inelastic* ($E < 1$), an increase in price will result in higher overall revenues. To complete the questions in this task, you will have to use the elasticity definition of

$$E = -\frac{\frac{\Delta n_d}{n_d}}{\frac{\Delta p}{p}}$$

converted into differential $\left(\frac{\Delta n}{\Delta p} = \frac{dn}{dp}\right)$ notation.

a. Determine the elasticity of demand at \$20 and \$80, classifying these price points as having elastic or inelastic demand. What does this say about where the optimum price is in terms of generating the maximum revenue? Explain. Also calculate the revenue at the \$20 and \$80 price points.

b. Approximate the demand curve as a linear function (tangent) at a price point of \$50. Plot the demand function and its linear approximation on the graphing calculator. What do you notice? Explain this by looking at the demand function.

c. Use your linear approximation to determine the price point that will generate the maximum revenue. (*Hint:* Think about the specific value of E where you won't want to increase or decrease the price to generate higher revenues.) What revenue is generated at this price level?

d. A second game has a price–demand relationship of

$$n_d(p) = \frac{12\ 500}{p - 25}.$$

The price is currently set at \$50. Should the company increase or decrease the price? Explain. ●

Review Exercise

1. Describe the process of finding a derivative using the definition for $f'(x)$.

2. Use the definition of the derivative to find $f'(x)$ of each of the following functions:

   i) $y = 2x^2 - 5x$ ii) $y = \sqrt{x - 6}$ iii) $y = \dfrac{x}{4 - x}$

3. Differentiate each of the following:

   a. $y = x^2 - 5x + 4$ b. $y = 8 - x^3$ c. $f(x) = x^{\frac{3}{4}}$

   d. $y = -5x^{-4}$ e. $y = \dfrac{7}{3x^4}$ f. $y = \dfrac{1}{x - 3}$

   g. $y = \dfrac{1}{x^2 + 5}$ h. $y = \dfrac{3}{(3 - x^2)^2}$ i. $y = \sqrt{2 - x}$

   j. $y = \sqrt{7x^2 + 4x + 1}$ k. $y = (5x^4 + \pi)^3$ l. $y = x^{-4} + \left(x^3 - 4\right)^{-\frac{2}{5}}$

4. Find the derivative of the given function. In some cases, it will save time if you rearrange the function before differentiating.

   a. $f(x) = \dfrac{2x^3 - 1}{x^2}$ b. $g(x) = \sqrt{x}(x^3 - x)$

   c. $h(x) = \dfrac{8}{3x\sqrt{x}}$ d. $y = \dfrac{3 - \frac{1}{x}}{x}$

   e. $y = \dfrac{x}{3x - 5}$ f. $y = \sqrt{x - 1}(x + 1)$

   g. $f(x) = (\sqrt{x} + 2)^{-\frac{2}{3}}$ h. $y = \sqrt{(x + 3)(x - 3)}$

   i. $y = \dfrac{x^2 + 5x + 4}{x + 4}$ j. $y = \dfrac{x^3 - 27}{x - 3}$

5. Find the derivative, and give your answer in a simplified form.

   a. $y = x^4(2x - 5)^6$ b. $y = x\sqrt{x^2 + 1}$

   c. $y = \dfrac{(2x - 5)^4}{(x + 1)^3}$ d. $y = \dfrac{x}{\sqrt[3]{x^2 + 5}}$

   e. $y = \left(\dfrac{10x - 1}{3x + 5}\right)^6$ f. $y = \dfrac{(x^2 - 1)^3}{(x^2 + 1)^3}$

   g. $y = \dfrac{x}{\sqrt{x^2 - 1}}$ h. $y = (x - 2)^3(x^2 + 9)^4$

   i. $y = (1 - x^2)^3(6 + 2x)^{-3}$ j. $y = (3x^2 - 2)^2\sqrt{x^2 - 5}$

6. If f is a differentiable function, find an expression for the derivative of each of the following functions:

a. $g(x) = f(x^2)$ b. $h(x) = 2xf(x)$

7. a. If $y = 5u^2 + 3u - 1$ and $u = \frac{18}{x^2 + 5}$, find $\frac{dy}{dx}$ when $x = 2$.

b. If $y = \frac{u + 4}{u - 4}$ and $u = \frac{\sqrt{x} + x}{10}$, find $\frac{dy}{dx}$ when $x = 4$.

c. If $y = f(\sqrt{x^2 + 9})$ and $f'(5) = -2$, find $\frac{dy}{dx}$ when $x = 4$.

8. Find the slope of the line tangent to the graph of $f(x) = (9 - x^2)^{\frac{2}{3}}$ at point $(1, 4)$.

technology

9. For what values of x does the curve $y = -x^3 + 6x^2$ have a slope of -12? Of -15? Use a graphing calculator to graph the function and confirm your results.

technology

10. a. Find the values of x where the given graph has a horizontal tangent.

i) $y = (x^2 - 4)^5$ ii) $y = (x^3 - x)^2$

b. Use a graphing calculator to graph the function and its tangent at the point to confirm your result.

11. Find the equation of the tangent to each function at the point given.

a. $y = (x^2 + 5x + 2)^4$ at $(0, 16)$ b. $y = (3x^{-2} - 2x^3)^5$ at $(1, 1)$

12. A tangent to the parabola $y = 3x^2 - 7x + 5$ is perpendicular to $x + 5y - 10 = 0$. Determine the equation of the tangent.

13. The line $y = 8x + b$ is tangent to the curve $y = 2x^2$. Find the point of tangency and the value of b.

technology

14. a. Using a graphing calculator, graph the function $f(x) = \frac{x^3}{x^2 - 6}$.

b. Using the DRAW function or an equivalent function on your calculator or graphing software, find the equations of the tangents where the slope is zero.

c. Setting $f'(x) = 0$, find the coordinates of the points where the slope is zero.

d. Find the slope of the tangent to the graph at $(2, -4)$. Use the graph to verify that your answer is reasonable.

15. Consider the function $f(x) = 2x^{\frac{5}{3}} - 5x^{\frac{2}{3}}$.

 a. Find the slope of the tangent at the point where the graph crosses the x-axis.

 b. Find the value of a.

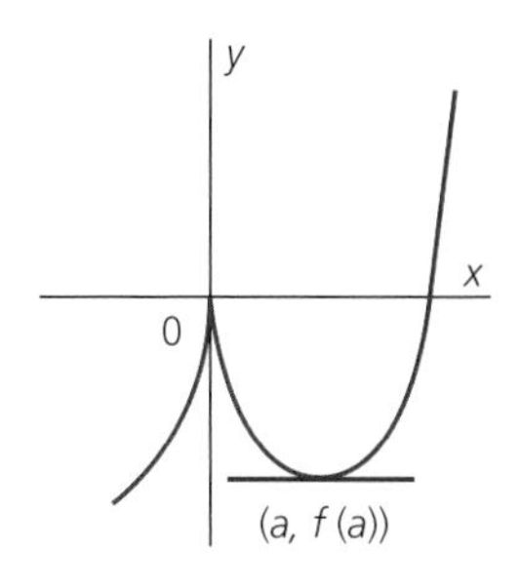

16. A rested student is able to memorize M words after t minutes, where $M = 0.1t^2 - 0.001t^3$.

 a. How many words are memorized in the first 10 min? The first 15 min?

 b. What is the memory rate at $t = 10$? At $t = 15$?

17. A grocery store determines that after t hours on the job, a new cashier can ring up $N(t) = 20 - \frac{30}{\sqrt{9 + t^2}}$ items per minute.

 a. Find $N'(t)$, the rate at which the cashier's productivity is changing.

 b. According to this model, does the cashier ever stop improving? Why?

18. An athletic-equipment supplier experiences weekly costs of $C(x) = \frac{1}{3}x^3 + 40x + 700$ in producing x baseball gloves per week.

 a. Find the marginal cost, $C'(x)$.

 b. Find the production level x, at which the marginal cost is \$76 per glove.

19. A manufacturer of kitchen appliances experiences revenues from the sale of x refrigerators per month of $R(x) = 750x - \frac{x^2}{6} - \frac{2}{3}x^3$ dollars.

 a. Find the marginal revenue, $R'(x)$.

 b. Find the marginal revenue when 10 refrigerators per month are sold.

20. An economist has found that the demand function for a particular new product is given by $D(p) = \frac{20}{\sqrt{p - 1}}$, $p > 1$. Find the slope of the demand curve at the point (5, 10).

Chapter 4 Test

Achievement Category	Questions
Knowledge/Understanding	3–7
Thinking/Inquiry/Problem Solving	11
Communication	1, 2
Application	8–10

1. Explain when you need to use the Chain Rule.

2. The following graph shows the graphs of a function and its derivative function. Label the graphs f and f' and write a short paragraph stating the criteria you used in making your selection.

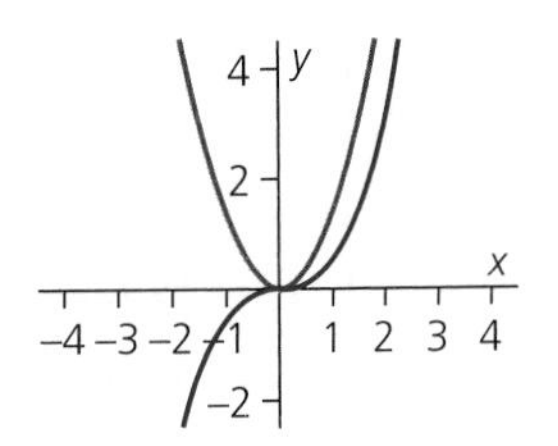

3. Use the definition of the derivative to find $\frac{d}{dx}(x - x^2)$.

4. Find $\frac{dy}{dx}$ for each of the following:

   a. $y = \frac{1}{3}x^3 - 3x^{-5} + 4\pi$

   b. $y = 6(2x - 9)^5$

   c. $y = \frac{2}{\sqrt{x}} + \frac{x}{\sqrt{3}} + 6\sqrt[3]{x}$

   d. $y = \left(\frac{x^2 + 6}{3x + 4}\right)^5$ Leave your answer in a simplified factored form.

   e. $y = x^2\sqrt[3]{6x^2 - 7}$ Simplify your answer.

   f. $y = \frac{4x^5 - 5x^4 + 6x - 2}{x^4}$ Simplify your answer.

5. Find the slope of the tangent to the graph of $y = (x^2 + 3x - 2)(7 - 3x)$ at $(1, 8)$.

6. Find $\frac{dy}{dx}$ at $x = -2$ for $y = 3u^2 + 2u$ and $u = \sqrt{x^2 + 5}$.

7. Find the equation of the tangent to $y = (3x^{-2} - 2x^3)^5$ at point $(1, 1)$.

8. The amount of pollution in a certain lake is $P(t) = \left(t^{\frac{1}{4}} + 3\right)^3$, where t is measured in years, and P is measured in parts per million (p.p.m.). At what rate is the amount of pollution changing after 16 years?

9. At what point on the curve $y = x^4$ does the normal have a slope of 16?

10. Find the points on the curve $y = x^3 - x^2 - x + 1$ where the slope of the tangent is horizontal.

11. For what values of a and b will the parabola $y = x^2 + ax + b$ be tangent to the curve $y = x^3$ at point $(1, 1)$?

Cumulative Review

CHAPTERS 1–4

1. Sketch the graph of $y = (x - 4)(x - 1)(x + 3)$.

2. Sketch the graph of $y = -(x + 1)^2(x - 2)$.

3. Find the polynomial function whose graph passes through the following points: $(1, -25)$, $(2, -20)$, $(3, 3)$, $(4, 56)$, $(5, 151)$.

4. a. Divide $x^3 - 3x^2 + 4$ by $x - 2$.

   b. Divide $3x^3 - 4x^2 + 11x - 2$ by $x + 3$.

   c. Divide $x^4 - 5x^2 + x - 1$ by $x^2 - x + 1$.

5. Find the remainder when $2x^3 - x^2 + 7x + 1$ is divided by $x - 2$.

6. When $3x^5 - 6x^3 + kx + 2$ is divided by $x - 1$, the remainder is 5. Find the value of k.

7. If $x - 3$ is a factor of $x^3 + kx^2 - 4x + 12$, where $k \in R$, find the value of k.

8. Determine whether or not $x - 2$ is a factor of $x^4 - 2x^3 + 5x^2 - 6x - 8$.

9. One factor of $x^3 - 2x^2 - 5x + 6$ is $x + 2$. Determine the other factors.

10. Factor fully.

    a. $x^3 + 3x^2 - 18x - 40$

    b. $x^3 + 5x^2 - 4x - 20$

    c. $2x^3 + x^2 - 8x - 4$

    d. $5x^3 + 8x^2 + 21x - 10$

11. Solve for x ($x \in C$).

    a. $x^3 + 3x^2 - 4 = 0$

    b. $x^4 + 5x^2 - 36 = 0$

    c. $x^3 + 4x^2 + x - 6 = 0$

    d. $2x^3 - x^2 - 2x + 1 = 0$

    e. $x^3 + x^2 - 5x + 3 = 0$

    f. $3x^3 - 4x^2 + 4x - 1 = 0$

12. Find the sum and product of the roots of $2x^2 + 8x + 5 = 0$.

13. Find the quadratic equation whose roots are the squares of the roots of $x^2 - 9x + 2 = 0$.

14. Solve each of the following, $x \in R$:

a. $x^2 - x - 6 < 0$

b. $(x + 2)(x - 1)(x - 3) \geq 0$

15. Solve for x.

a. $|x - 2| < 5$

b. $|2x - 3| \leq 5$

c. $|3x + 1| > 16$

16. The displacement (in metres) of an object is given by $s(t) = 2t^2 + 3t + 1$, where t is the time in seconds.

a. Find the average velocity from $t = 1$ to $t = 4$.

b. Find the instantaneous velocity at $t = 3$.

17. A cylinder has a volume of 200π cm^3. Its height is 3 cm greater than its radius. Determine the radius of the cylinder. (The volume of a cylinder is $V = \pi r^2 h$.)

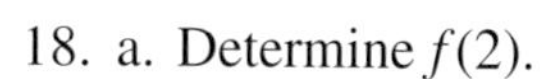

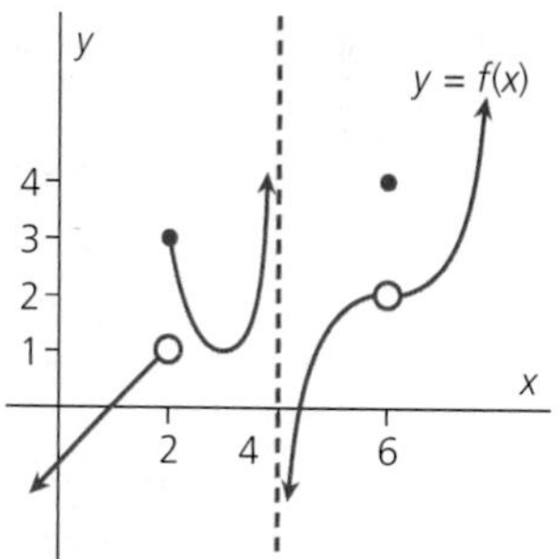

18. a. Determine $f(2)$.

b. Determine $\lim_{x \to 2^-} f(x)$.

c. Determine $\lim_{x \to 2^+} f(x)$.

d. Determine $\lim_{x \to 6} f(x)$.

e. Does $\lim_{x \to 4} f(x)$ exist? Justify your answer.

19. Sketch a function $f(x)$ that satisfies the following conditions:

- $f(x)$ is increasing;
- $\lim_{x \to 2^-} f(x) = 5$;
- $\lim_{x \to 2^+} f(x) = 8$.

20.
$$f(x) = \begin{cases} x^2 + 1, x < 2 \\ 2x + 1, x = 2 \\ -x + 5, x > 2 \end{cases}$$

Determine where $f(x)$ is discontinuous and justify your answer.

21. Use your graphing calculator to estimate $\lim_{x \to 1} \frac{x^4 + 2x^3 - 2x^2 + 2x - 3}{x^2 + 2x - 3}$.

22. If $\lim_{h \to 0} \frac{(4 + h)^3 - 64}{h}$ is the slope of the tangent to $y = f(x)$ at $x = 4$, what is $f(x)$?

23. Use algebraic methods to evaluate each of the following (if they exist):

a. $\lim_{x \to 0} \frac{2x^2 + 1}{x - 5}$ b. $\lim_{x \to 5} \frac{1}{x - 5}$ c. $\lim_{x \to -3} \frac{\frac{1}{x} + \frac{1}{3}}{x + 3}$

d. $\lim_{x \to 0} \frac{x^3 + 4x^2 + 2x}{3x^5 + 2x^3 + x}$ e. $\lim_{x \to 2} \frac{x - 2}{x^3 - 8}$ f. $\lim_{x \to 3} \frac{\sqrt{x + 1} - 2}{x - 3}$

24. Use the definition of derivative to find $f'(x)$ if

a. $f(x) = 3x^2 + x + 1.$ b. $f(x) = \frac{1}{x}.$

25. Use any of the rules you have learned to find the derivatives of the following functions:

a. $y = x^3 - 4x^2 + 5x + 2$ b. $y = \sqrt{2x^3 + 1}$

c. $y = \frac{2x}{x + 3}$ d. $y = (x^2 + 3)^2 (4x^5 + 5x + 1)$

e. $y = \frac{(4x^2 + 1)^5}{(3x - 2)^3}$ f. $y = [x^2 + (2x + 1)^3]^5$

26. Find the equation of the tangent to $y = \frac{18}{(x + 2)^2}$ at point (1, 2).

27. Find the equation of the tangent to $y = x^2 - 4x + 1$ that is perpendicular to the line with equation $3x + 6y - 2 = 0$.

28. If $y = 6u^3 + 2u^2 + 5u - 2$ and $u = \frac{1}{x^3 + 2}$, find $\frac{dy}{dx}$.

29. Find the slope of the tangent to $y = x^2 + 9x + 9$ at the point where the curve intersects the line at $y = 3x$.

30. In 1980, the population of Smalltown, Ontario, was 1100. After a time t, in years, the population is given by $p(t) = 2t^2 + 6t + 1100$.

a. Find $p'(t)$, the function that describes the rate of change of the population.

b. Find the rate of change of the population in 1990.

c. In what year is the rate of change of the population 94 people per year?

Chapter 5

APPLICATIONS OF DERIVATIVES

We live in a world that is always in flux. Sir Isaac Newton's name for calculus was "the method of fluxions." He recognized in the 17th century, as you probably recognize today, that understanding change is important. Newton was what we might call a "mathematical physicist." He developed his method of fluxions as a means to better understand the natural world, including motion and gravity. But change is not limited to the natural world, and since Newton's time, the use of calculus has spread to include applications in the social sciences. Psychology, business, and economics are just a few of the areas in which calculus has been an effective problem-solving tool. As we shall see in this chapter, anywhere that functions can be used as models, the derivative is certain to be meaningful and useful.

CHAPTER EXPECTATIONS In this chapter, you will

- justify the rules for determining derivatives, **Section 5.1**
- determine derivatives of polynomial and rational functions using rules for determining derivatives, **Section 5.1**
- solve problems of rates of change, **Section 5.1**
- determine second derivatives, **Section 5.2**
- solve related-rates problems, **Section 5.3**
- determine key features of the graph of a function, **Section 5.4**
- determine key features of a mathematical model, pose questions, and answer them by analyzing mathematical models, **Section 5.5**
- solve optimization problems, **Section 5.5, 5.6, Career Link**
- communicate findings clearly and concisely, **Section 5.6**

Review of Prerequisite Skills

Now that you have developed your understanding of derivatives and differentiation techniques in Chapter 4, we will consider a variety of applications of derivatives. The following skills will help you in your work in this chapter:

- Graphing polynomial and simple rational functions
- Drawing circles, ellipses, and hyperbolas in both standard position and when translated
- Solving polynomial equations
- Finding the equations of tangents and normals
- You should also be familiar with the following formulas:

Circle:	$C = 2\pi r$, $A = \pi r^2$
Right Circular Cylinder:	$S = 2\pi rh + 2\pi r^2$, $V = \pi r^2 h$
Sphere:	$S = 4\pi r^2$, $V = \frac{4}{3}\pi r^3$
Right Circular Cone:	$V = \frac{1}{3}\pi r^2 h$

Exercise

1. Sketch the graph of each function.
   a. $2x + 3y - 6 = 0$ b. $3x - 4y = 12$ c. $y = \sqrt{x}$
   d. $y = \sqrt{x - 2}$ e. $y = x^2 - 4$ f. $y = -x^2 + 9$

2. Draw each of the following circles:
   a. $x^2 + y^2 = 9$ b. $(x - 2)^2 + (y - 3)^2 = 9$
   c. $(x + 4)^2 + (y - 1)^2 = 49$

3. Draw each of the following ellipses:
   a. $4x^2 + 9y^2 = 36$ b. $x^2 + 4y^2 = 100$ c. $\frac{(x + 4)^2}{49} + \frac{(y - 1)^2}{4} = 1$

4. Draw each hyperbola defined by the following equations:
   a. $xy = 4$ b. $4x^2 - 9y^2 = 36$ c. $x^2 - 4y^2 = -100$

5. Solve $x, t \in R$.
   a. $3(x - 2) + 2(x - 1) - 6 = 0$ b. $\frac{1}{3}(x - 2) + \frac{2}{5}(x + 3) = \frac{x - 5}{2}$
   c. $t^2 - 4t + 3 = 0$ d. $2t^2 - 5t - 3 = 0$

e. $\frac{6}{t} + \frac{t}{2} = 4$

f. $x^3 + 2x^2 - 3x = 0$

g. $x^3 - 8x^2 + 16x = 0$

h. $4t^3 + 12t^2 - t - 3 = 0$

i. $4t^4 - 13t^2 + 9 = 0$

6. Solve each inequality, $x \in R$.

a. $3x - 2 > 7$ b. $x(x - 3) > 0$ c. $-x^2 + 4x > 0$

7. Find the area of the figure described. Leave your answers in terms of π.

a. Square: perimeter 20 cm

b. Rectangle: length 8 cm, width 6 cm

c. Circle: radius 7 cm

d. Circle: circumference 12π cm

8. Two measures of a right circular cylinder are given. Find the two remaining measures.

	Radius r	Height h	Surface Area $S = 2\pi rh + 2\pi r^2$	Volume $V = \pi r^2 h$
a.	4 cm	3 cm		
b.	4 cm			96π cm^3
c.		6 cm		216π cm^3
d.	5 cm		120π cm^2	

9. One measure of a sphere is given. Find the two remaining measures.

	Radius r	Volume $V = \frac{4}{3}\pi r^3$	Surface Area $S = 4\pi r^2$
a.	9 cm		
b.	3 cm		
c.		36π cm^3	
d.			1000π cm^2

10. Two measures of a right circular cone are given. Find the remaining measure.

	r	h	$V = \frac{1}{3}\pi r^2 h$
a.	4 cm	3 cm	
b.	3 cm		27π cm^3
c.		4 cm	27π cm^3

11. Find the total surface area and volume of a cube with each of the following dimensions:

a. 3 cm b. $\sqrt{5}$ cm c. $2\sqrt{3}$ cm d. $2k$ cm

Career Link investigate

CHAPTER 5: MAXIMIZING PROFITS

We live in a world that demands we determine the best, the worst, the maximum, and the minimum. Through mathematical modelling, calculus can be used to establish optimum operating conditions for processes that seem to have competing variables. For example, minimizing transportation costs for a delivery truck would seem to require the driver to travel as fast as possible to reduce hourly wages. Higher rates of speed, however, increase the cost of gas consumption. With calculus, an optimal speed can be established that minimizes the total cost of driving the delivery vehicle considering both gas consumption and hourly wages. In this chapter, calculus tools will be utilized in realistic contexts to solve optimization problems from business applications (e.g., minimizing cost) to psychology (e.g., maximizing learning).

Case Study — Entrepreneurship

In the last ten years, the Canadian economy has seen a dramatic increase in the number of small businesses. An ability to interpret the marginal profit on graphs, a calculus concept, will help an entrepreneur to make good business decisions. A person with an old family recipe for gourmet chocolates decides to open her own business. Her weekly total revenue (*TR*) and total cost (*TC*) curves are plotted on the set of axes below.

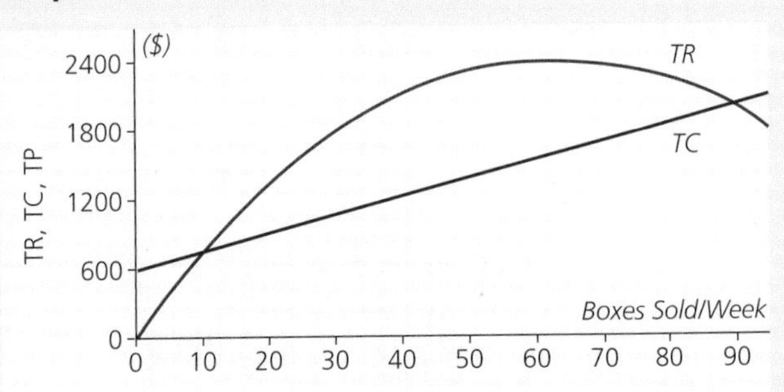

DISCUSSION QUESTIONS

Make a rough sketch of the graph in your notes and answer the following questions:

1. What range of sales would keep the company profitable? What do we call these values?
2. Superimpose the total profit (*TP*) curve over the *TR* and *TC* curves. What would the sales level have to be for maximum profits to occur? Estimate the slopes on the *TR* and *TC* curves at this level of sales. Should they be the same? Why or why not?
3. On a set of separate axes, draw a rough sketch of the marginal profit $\left(MP = \frac{dTP}{dx}\right)$, the extra profit earned by selling one more box of chocolates. What can you say about the marginal profit as the level of sales progress from just less than the maximum to the maximum to just above the maximum? Does this make sense? Explain.

Section 5.1 — Implicit Differentiation

In previous chapters, most functions were written in the form $y = f(x)$, in which y is defined **explicitly** as a function of x. Examples of functions that are defined explicitly include $y = x^3 - 4x$ and $y = \frac{7}{x^2 + 1}$. However, functions can also be defined **implicitly** by relations such as the circle $x^2 + y^2 = 25$.

Since there are x-values that correspond to two y-values, y is not a function of x on the entire circle. Solving for y gives $y = \pm\sqrt{25 - x^2}$, where $y = \sqrt{25 - x^2}$ represents the upper semicircle and $y = -\sqrt{25 - x^2}$ is the lower semicircle. The given relation defines two different functions of x.

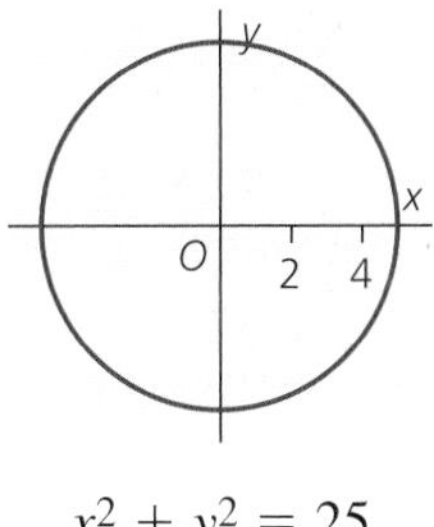

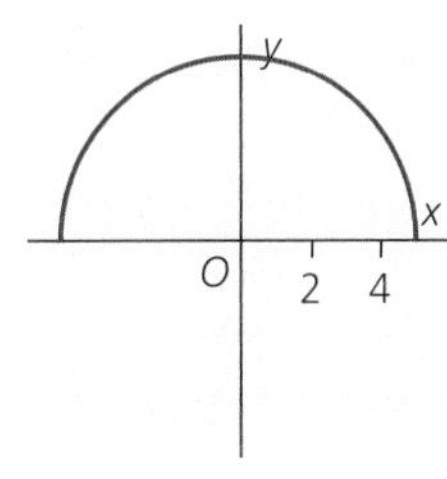

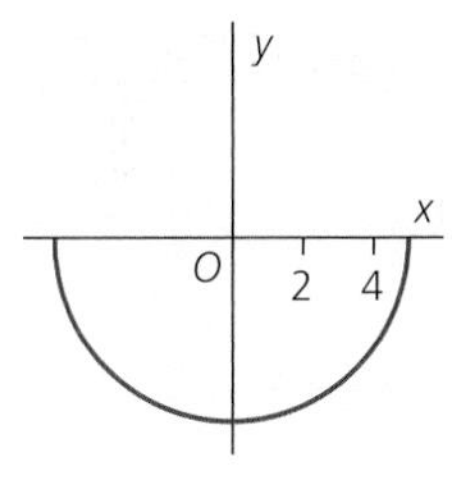

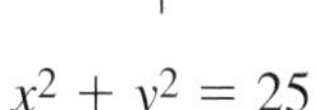

$x^2 + y^2 = 25$ $\qquad$ $y = \sqrt{25 - x^2}$ $\qquad$ $y = -\sqrt{25 - x^2}$

Consider the problem of finding the slope of the tangent line to the circle $x^2 + y^2 = 25$ at the point $(3, -4)$. Since this point lies on the lower semicircle, we could differentiate the function $y = -\sqrt{25 - x^2}$ and substitute $x = 3$. An alternative, which avoids having to solve for y explicitly in terms of x, is to use the method of **implicit differentiation**. Example 1 illustrates this method.

EXAMPLE 1

a. If $x^2 + y^2 = 25$, find $\frac{dy}{dx}$.

b. Find the slope of the tangent line to the circle $x^2 + y^2 = 25$ at the point $(3, -4)$.

Solution

a. Differentiate both sides of the equation with respect to x:

$$\frac{d}{dx}(x^2 + y^2) = \frac{d}{dx}(25)$$

$$\frac{d}{dx}(x^2) + \frac{d}{dx}(y^2) = \frac{d}{dx}(25)$$

To find $\frac{d}{dx}(y^2)$, use the Chain Rule.

$$\begin{aligned}\frac{d}{dx}(y^2) &= \frac{d}{dy}(y^2) \bullet \frac{dy}{dx} \\ &= 2y\frac{dy}{dx}\end{aligned}$$

Therefore, $\frac{d}{dx}(x^2) + \frac{d}{dx}(y^2) = \frac{d}{dx}(25)$

$$2x + 2y\frac{dy}{dx} = 0$$

and
$$\frac{dy}{dx} = -\frac{x}{y}.$$

The derivative in part **a** depends on both x and y. At the point $(3, -4)$, $x = 3$ and $y = -4$.
The slope of the tangent line to $x^2 + y^2 = 25$ at $(3, -4)$ is $\frac{dy}{dx} = -\frac{3}{-4} = \frac{3}{4}$.

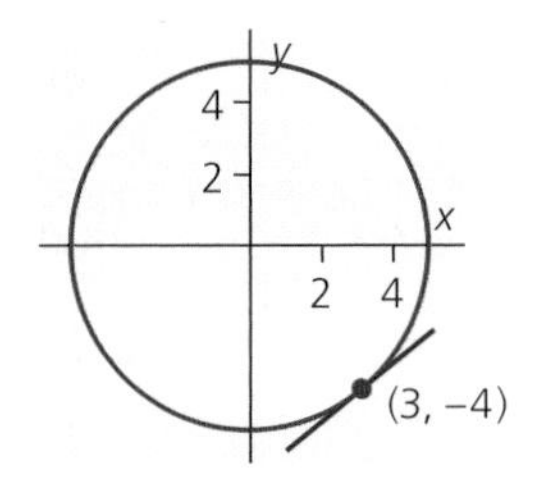

In Example 1, the derivative could be found either by implicit differentiation or by solving for y in terms of x and using the techniques introduced earlier in the text. There are many situations in which solving for y in terms of x is very difficult, and in some cases impossible. In such cases, implicit differentiation is the only method available to us.

EXAMPLE 2

Find $\frac{dy}{dx}$ for $2xy - y^3 = 4$.

Solution

We differentiate both sides of the equation with respect to x as follows:

$$\frac{d}{dx}(2xy) - \frac{d}{dx}(y^3) = \frac{d}{dx}(4).$$

Use the Product Rule to differentiate the first term and the Chain Rule for the second.

$$\left(\frac{d}{dx}(2x)\right)y + 2x\frac{dy}{dx} - \frac{d}{dy}(y^3) \bullet \frac{dy}{dx} = \frac{d}{dx}(4)$$

$$2y + 2x\frac{dy}{dx} - 3y^2\frac{dy}{dx} = 0$$

$$(2x - 3y^2)\frac{dy}{dx} = -2y$$

$$\frac{dy}{dx} = -\frac{2y}{2x - 3y^2}$$

Procedure for Implicit Differentiation
Suppose an equation defines y implicitly as a differentiable function of x.
To find $\frac{dy}{dx}$:

Step 1. **Differentiate both sides of the equation with respect to x. Remember to use the Chain Rule when differentiating terms containing y.**

Step 2. **Solve for $\frac{dy}{dx}$.**

Note that implicit differentiation leads to a derivative whenever the derivative does not have a zero in the denominator. The derivative expression usually includes terms in both x and y.

EXAMPLE 3

Find the slope of the tangent to the ellipse $x^2 + 4y^2 = 25$ at the point $(-3, 2)$. Illustrate the tangent on the graph of the ellipse.

Solution

Differentiating implicitly with respect to x, we obtain

$$2x + 4\left(2y\frac{dy}{dx}\right) = 0 \text{ or } 2x + 8y\frac{dy}{dx} = 0.$$

At point $(-3, 2)$,

$$2(-3) + 8(2)\frac{dy}{dx} = 0$$

$$\frac{dy}{dx} = \frac{6}{16}$$

$$= \frac{3}{8}.$$

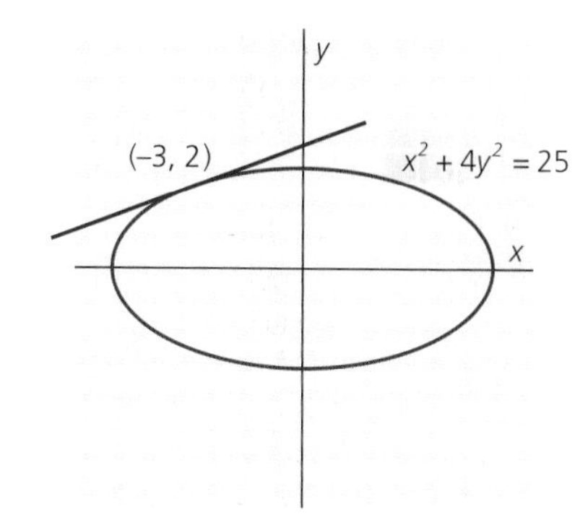

Therefore, the slope of the tangent to the ellipse at $(-3, 2)$ is $\frac{3}{8}$.

technology

Using your graphing calculator:

Step 1. To graph the ellipse, write $x^2 + 4y^2 = 25$ as

$$4y^2 = 25 - x^2$$

$$y^2 = \frac{25 - x^2}{4}$$

$$y = \pm\sqrt{\frac{25 - x^2}{4}}.$$

First, graph $y_1 = \sqrt{\frac{25 - x^2}{4}}$ as $\sqrt{((25 - x^2) \div 4)}$.

Step 2. To graph $y = -\sqrt{\frac{25 - x^2}{4}}$, select $y_2 = -$ and then select the VARS function.

Then select Y-VARS and press ENTER twice.

Then select GRAPH.

Use $x_{min} = -9.4$, $x_{max} = 9.4$, $y_{min} = -6.4$, and $y_{max} = 6.4$ as your window.

Step 3. To graph the tangent at $(-3, 2)$ from the GRAPH window, select

2nd PRGM (DRAW) to get the DRAW function. Select **5:Tangent(**. Move the cursor to $(-3, 2)$ and press ENTER to get the tangent.

Exercise 5.1

Part A

Communication

1. State the Chain Rule. Outline a procedure for implicit differentiation.

Knowledge/Understanding

2. Find $\frac{dy}{dx}$ for each of the following in terms of x and y using implicit differentiation.

a. $x^2 + y^2 = 36$
b. $y^2 = x^2 - 16$
c. $15y^2 = 2x^3$
d. $3xy^2 + y^3 = 8$
e. $5y^4 = x^3 + 13$
f. $9x^2 - 16y^2 = -144$
g. $\frac{x^2}{16} + \frac{3y^2}{13} = 1$
h. $3x^2 + 4xy^3 = 9$
i. $x^2 + y^2 + 5y = 10$
j. $x^3 + y^3 = 6xy$
k. $x^3y^3 = 144$
l. $x = y + y^5$
m. $xy^3 - x^3y = 2$
n. $\sqrt{x} + \sqrt{y} = 5$
o. $(x + y)^2 = x^2 + y^2$

3. For each curve, find the equation of the tangent at the given point.

a. $x^2 + y^2 = 13$ at $(2, -3)$
b. $x^2 + 4y^2 = 100$ at $(-8, 3)$
c. $\frac{x^2}{25} - \frac{y^2}{36} = -1$ at $(5\sqrt{3}, -12)$
d. $\frac{x^2}{81} - \frac{5y^2}{162} = 1$ at $(-11, -4)$

Part B

4. At what point is the tangent to the curve $x + y^2 = 1$ parallel to the line $x + 2y = 0$?

5. The equation $5x^2 - 6xy + 5y^2 = 16$ represents an ellipse.

   a. Find $\frac{dy}{dx}$ at $(1, -1)$.

   b. Find two points on the ellipse at which the tangent is horizontal.

Application

6. Find the slope of the tangent to the ellipse $5x^2 + y^2 = 21$ at point $A(-2, -1)$.

7. Find the equation of the normal at $(2, 3)$ to the curve $x^3 + y^3 - 3xy = 17$ at point $(2, 3)$.

8. Find the equation of the normal to $y^2 = \frac{x^3}{2 - x}$ at point $(1, -1)$.

9. The equation $4x^2y - 3y = x^3$ implicitly defines y as a function of x.

   a. Use implicit differentiation to find $\frac{dy}{dx}$.

   b. Write y as an explicit function of x and compute $\frac{dy}{dx}$ directly. Show that the results of parts **a** and **b** are equivalent.

technology

10. Graph each relation using a graphing calculator or a computer. For each graph, decide the number of tangents that exist at $x = 1$.

    a. $y = \sqrt{3 - x}$

    b. $y = -\sqrt{5 - x}$

    c. $y = x^7 - x$

    d. $x^3 + 4x^2 + (x - 4)y^2 = 0$ (This curve is known as the *strophoid*.)

11. Show that for the relation $\sqrt{\frac{x}{y}} + \sqrt{\frac{y}{x}} = 10, x \neq y \neq 0, \frac{dy}{dx} = \frac{y}{x}$.

Part C

12. Find the equations of the lines that are tangent to the ellipse $x^2 + 4y^2 = 16$ and that also pass through the point $(4, 6)$.

13. The angle between two intersecting curves is defined as the angle between their tangents at the point of intersection. If this angle is 90°, the two curves are said to be *orthogonal*. Prove that the curves defined by $x^2 - y^2 = k$ and $xy = p$ intersect orthogonally for all values of the constants k and p. Illustrate your proof with a sketch.

14. Let l be any tangent to the curve $\sqrt{x} + \sqrt{y} = \sqrt{k}$. Show that the sum of the intercepts of l is k.

15. Two circles of radius $3\sqrt{2}$ are tangent to the graph $y^2 = 4x$ at point $(1, 2)$. Find the equations of these two circles.

Section 5.2 — Higher-Order Derivatives, Velocity, and Acceleration

Derivatives arise in the study of motion. The velocity of a car represents the rate of change of distance with respect to time.

Up to this point, we have developed the rules of differentiation and learned how to interpret them at a point on a curve. We can now extend the applications of differentiation to higher-order derivatives. This will allow us to discuss the application of the first and second derivatives to rates of change as an object moves in a straight line, either vertically or horizontally, such as a space shuttle taking off into space or a car moving along a road.

Higher-Order Derivatives

The derivative of $10x^4$ with respect to x is $40x^3$. If we differentiate $40x^3$, we obtain $120x^2$. This new function is called the second derivative of $10x^4$.
For $y = 2x^3 - 5x^2$, the first derivative is $\frac{dy}{dx} = 6x^2 - 10x$ and the second derivative is $\frac{d^2y}{dx^2} = 12x - 10$.

Note the location of the superscripts in the second derivative. The reason for this choice of notation is that the second derivative is the derivative of the first derivative; that is, we write $\frac{d}{dx}\left(\frac{dy}{dx}\right) = \frac{d^2y}{dx^2}$.

Other notations used to represent first and second derivatives of $y = f(x)$ are

$$\frac{dy}{dx} = f'(x) = y' \text{ and } \frac{d^2y}{dx^2} = f''(x) = y''$$

EXAMPLE 1

Find the second derivative of $f(x) = \frac{x}{1+x}$ at $x = 1$.

Solution
Differentiate $f(x) = \frac{x}{1+x}$ using the Quotient Rule.

$$\begin{aligned} f'(x) &= \frac{(1)(1+x) - x(1)}{(1+x)^2} \\ &= \frac{1+x-x}{(1+x)^2} \\ &= \frac{1}{(1+x)^2} \\ &= (1+x)^{-2} \end{aligned}$$

Differentiating again to determine the second derivative,

$$f''(x) = -2(1 + x)^{-3}(1) \quad \text{(Power of a Function Rule)}$$
$$= \frac{-2}{(1 + x)^3}.$$

At $x = 1$, $f''(1) = \frac{-2}{(1 + 1)^3}$

$$= \frac{-2}{8}$$
$$= -\frac{1}{4}.$$

Velocity and Acceleration — Motion on a Straight Line

One reason for introducing the derivative is the need to calculate rates of change. Consider the motion of an object along a straight line. Examples are a car moving along a straight section of road, a ball being dropped from the top of a building, and a rocket in the early stages of flight.

When studying motion along a line, we assume the object is moving along a coordinate line, which gives us an origin of reference and positive and negative directions. The position of the object on the line relative to the origin is a function of time, t, and is denoted by $s(t)$. The rate of change of $s(t)$ with respect to time is the object's **velocity**, $v(t)$, and the rate of change of the velocity with respect to time is its **acceleration**, $a(t)$. The absolute value of the velocity is called **speed**.

Motion on a Straight Line

An object that moves along a straight line with its position determined by the function $s(t)$ has a velocity of $v(t) = s'(t)$ and *acceleration* of $a(t) = v'(t) = s''(t)$.

In Leibniz notation,

$$v = \frac{ds}{dt} \text{ and } a = \frac{dv}{dt} = \frac{d^2s}{dt^2}.$$

The *speed* of an object is $|v(t)|$.

The dimensions of velocity are length divided by time; typical units are m/s. The dimensions of acceleration are length divided by $(\text{time})^2$; typical units are m/s^2.

If $v(t) > 0$, the object is moving to the right, and if $v(t) < 0$, it is moving to the left. If $v(t) = 0$, the object is *stationary*, or at rest. The object is *accelerating* if the product of $a(t)$ and $v(t)$ is positive and *decelerating* if the product is negative.

EXAMPLE 2

An object is moving along a straight line.
Its distance, $s(t)$, to the right of a fixed point is given by the graph shown.

When is the object moving to the right, when is it moving to the left, and when is it at rest?

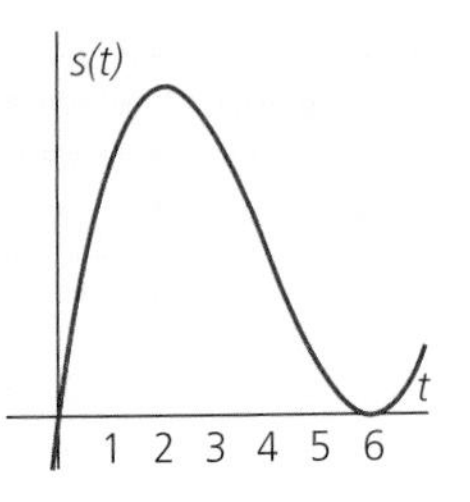

Solution

The object is moving to the right whenever $s(t)$ is increasing, or $v(t) > 0$.
From the graph, $s(t)$ is increasing for $0 < t < 2$ and for $t > 6$.
For $2 < t < 6$, the value of $s(t)$ is decreasing, so the object is moving to the left.
At $t = 6$, the direction of motion of the object changes from left to right, so the object is stationary at $t = 6$.

The motion of the object along the distance lines can be illustrated by the following diagram:

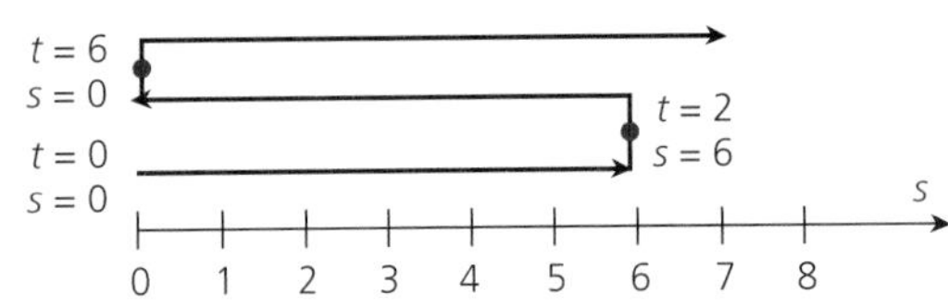

EXAMPLE 3

The position of an object moving on a line is given by $s(t) = 6t^2 - t^3$, $t \geq 0$, where s is in metres and t is in seconds.

a. Find the object's velocity and acceleration at $t = 2$.

b. At what time(s) is the object at rest?

c. In which direction is the object moving at $t = 5$?

d. When is the object moving in a positive direction?

e. When does the object return to its initial position?

Solution

a. The velocity at time t is

$$v(t) = s'(t) = 12t - 3t^2.$$

At $t = 2$, $v(2) = 12(2) - 3(2)^2 = 12.$

The acceleration at time t is

$$a(t) = v'(t) = s''(t) = 12 - 6t.$$

At $t = 2$, $a(2) = 12 - 6(2) = 0.$

At $t = 2$, the velocity is 12 m/s and the acceleration is 0.

We note that at $t = 2$, the object is neither speeding up nor slowing down.

b. The object is at rest when the velocity is 0, that is, $v(t) = 0$.

$$12t - 3t^2 = 0$$
$$3t(4 - t) = 0$$
$$t = 0 \text{ or } t = 4$$

The object is at rest at $t = 0$ s and at $t = 4$ s.

c. $v(5) = 12(5) - 3(5^2)$
$= -15$

The object is moving in a negative direction at $t = 5$.

d. The object moves in a positive direction when $v(t) > 0$;

that is, when $v(t) = 12t - 3t^2 > 0$

$t^2 - 4t < 0$, (Divide by −3)

therefore, $0 < t < 4$.

The graph of the velocity function is a parabola opening downward, as shown.

From the graph, we conclude that $v(t) > 0$ for $0 < t < 4$.

The object is moving to the right during the interval $0 < t < 4$.

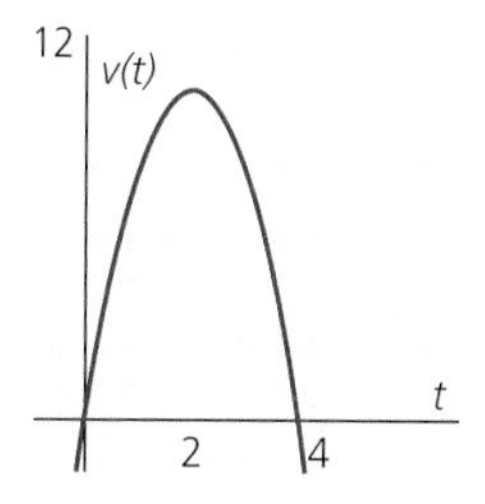

e. At $t = 0$, $s(0) = 0$. Therefore, the object's initial position is at 0.

To find other times when the object is at this point, we solve $s(t) = 0$.

$$6t^2 - t^3 = 0$$
$$t^2(6 - t) = 0$$
$$t = 0 \text{ or } t = 6$$

The object returns to its initial position after 6 s.

EXAMPLE 4

Discuss the motion of an object moving on a horizontal line if its position is given by $s(t) = t^2 - 10t$, $0 \leq t \leq 12$, where s is in metres and t is in seconds. Include the initial velocity, final velocity, and any acceleration in your discussion.

Solution

The initial position of the object occurs at time $t = 0$. Since $s(0) = 0$, the object starts at the origin.

The velocity at time t is

$$v(t) = s'(t) = 2t - 10$$
$$= 2(t - 5).$$

The object is at rest when $v(t) = 0$.

$$2(t - 5) = 0$$
$$t = 5$$

$v(t) > 0$ for $5 < t \leq 12$, therefore the object is moving to the right.

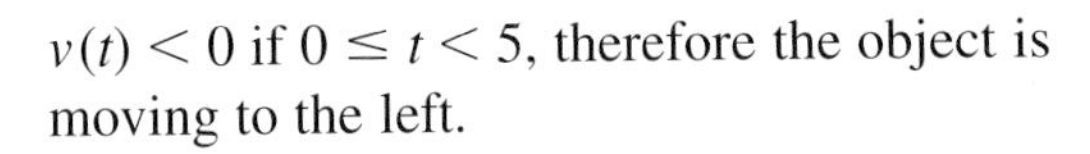

$v(t) < 0$ if $0 \leq t < 5$, therefore the object is moving to the left.

The initial velocity is $v(0) = -10$.

At $t = 12$, $v(12) = 14$.

The acceleration at time t is

$$a(t) = v'(t) = s''(t) = 2.$$

The object moves to the left for $0 \leq t < 5$ and to the right for $5 < t \leq 12$. The initial velocity is -10 m/s, the final velocity is 14 m/s, and the acceleration is 2 m/s^2.

The following diagram is a schematic of the motion. (The actual path of the object is back and forth on a line.)

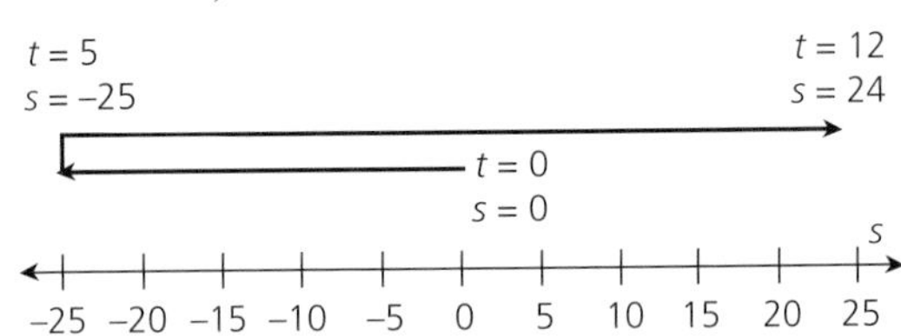

Motion Under Gravity Near the Surface of the Earth

EXAMPLE 5

A fly ball is hit vertically upward. The position function $s(t)$, in metres, of the ball is $s(t) = -5t^2 + 30t + 1$ where t is in seconds.

a. Find the maximum height reached by the ball.

b. Find the velocity of the ball when it is caught 1 m above the ground.

Solution

a. The maximum height occurs when the velocity of the ball is zero, that is, when the slope of the tangent to the graph is zero.

The velocity function is

$$v(t) = s'(t)$$
$$= -10t + 30.$$

On solving $v(t) = 0$, we obtain $t = 3$. Therefore, the maximum height reached by the ball is $s(3) = 46$ m.

b. When the ball is caught, $s(t) = 1$. To find the time at which this occurs, solve

$$1 = -5t^2 + 30t + 1$$
$$0 = -5t(t - 6)$$
$$t = 0 \text{ or } t = 6.$$

Since $t = 0$ is the time at which the ball left the bat, the time at which the ball was caught is $t = 6$.

The velocity of the ball when it was caught is $v(6) = -30$ m/s.

This negative value is reasonable, since the ball is falling (moving in a negative direction) when it is caught.

Note, however, that the graph of $s(t)$ does not represent the path of the ball. We think of the ball as moving in a straight line along a vertical s-axis, with the direction of motion reversing when $s = 46$.

To see this, note that the ball is at the same height at time $t = 1$, when $s(1) = 26$, and at time $t = 5$, when $s(5) = 26$.

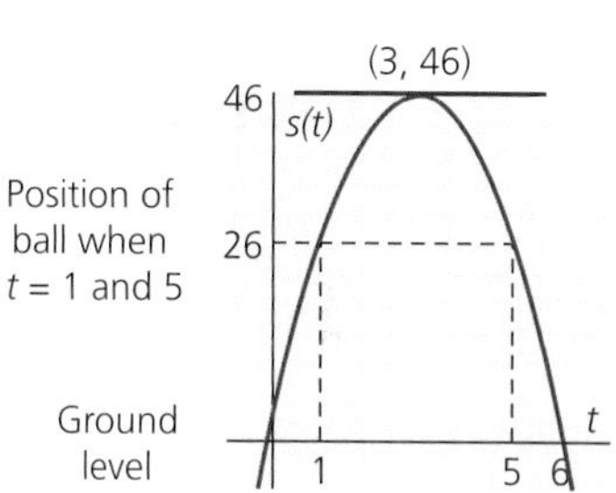

Exercise 5.2

Part A

Communication

1. Explain and discuss the difference in velocity at times $t = 1$ and $t = 5$ for $v(t) = 2t - t^2$.

2. Find the second derivative of each of the following:

   a. $y = x^{10} + 3x^6$ b. $f(x) = \sqrt{x}$ c. $y = (1 - x)^2$

Knowledge/ Understanding

3. For the following position functions, each of which describes the motion of an object along a straight line, find the velocity and acceleration as functions of t, $t \geq 0$.

a. $s(t) = 5t^2 - 3t + 15$ b. $s(t) = 2t^3 + 36t - 10$ c. $s(t) = t - 8 + \frac{6}{t}$

d. $s(t) = (t - 3)^2$ e. $s(t) = \sqrt{t + 1}$ f. $s(t) = \frac{9t}{t + 3}$

4. Consider the following positive time graphs.
   i) When is the velocity zero?
   ii) When is the object moving in a positive direction?
   iii) When is the object moving in a negative direction?

a.

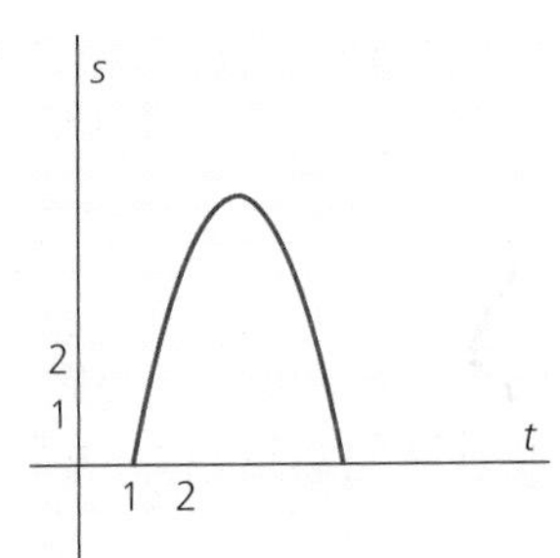

b.

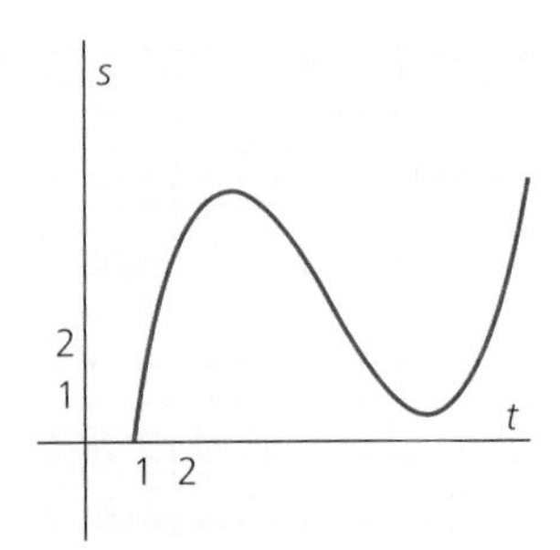

5. A particle moves along a straight line with the equation of motion $s = \frac{1}{3}t^3 - 2t^2 + 3t$, $t \geq 0$. Find the particle's velocity and acceleration at any time, t. When does the direction of the motion of the particle change? When does the particle return to its initial position?

Part **B**

6. Each function describes the position of an object that moves along a straight line. Determine whether the object is moving in a positive or in a negative direction at time $t = 1$ and at time $t = 4$.

   a. $s(t) = -\frac{1}{3}t^2 + t + 4$ b. $s(t) = t(t - 3)^2$ c. $s(t) = t^3 - 7t^2 + 10t$

7. Starting at $t = 0$, a particle moves along a line so that its position after t seconds is $s(t) = t^2 - 6t + 8$, where s is in metres.
   a. What is its velocity at time t?
   b. When is its velocity zero?

8. When an object is launched vertically from the ground level with an initial velocity of 40 m/s, its position after t seconds will be $s(t) = 40t - 5t^2$ metres above ground level.
   a. When does the object stop rising?
   b. What is its maximum height?

9. An object moves in a straight line, and its position, s, in metres after t seconds is $s(t) = 8 - 7t + t^2$.

   a. Find the velocity when $t = 5$.

   b. Find the acceleration when $t = 5$.

Application

10. The position function of a moving object is $s(t) = t^{\frac{5}{2}}(7 - t)$, $t \geq 0$, in metres, at time t in seconds.

   a. Find the object's velocity and acceleration at any time, t.

   b. After how many seconds does the object stop?

   c. When does the direction of motion of the object change?

   d. When is its acceleration positive?

   e. When does the object return to its original position?

11. A ball is thrown upwards so that its height, h, in metres above the ground after t seconds is given by $h(t) = -5t^2 + 25t$, $t \geq 0$.

   a. Find the ball's initial velocity.

   b. Find its maximum height.

   c. When does the ball strike the ground and what is its velocity at this time?

12. A dragster races down a 400 m strip in 8 s. Its distance, in metres, from the starting line after t seconds is $s(t) = 6t^2 + 2t$.

   a. Find the dragster's velocity and acceleration as it crosses the finish line.

   b. How fast was it moving 60 m down the strip?

13. For each of the following position functions, discuss the motion of an object moving on a horizontal line where s is in metres and t is in seconds. Make a graph similar to that in Example 4 showing the motion for $t \geq 0$. Find the velocity and acceleration, and determine the extreme positions (farthest left or right) for $t \geq 0$.

   a. $s = 10 + 6t - t^2$

   b. $s = t^3 - 12t - 9$

14. If the position function of an object is $s(t) = t^5 - 10t^2$, at what time, t, in seconds, will the acceleration be zero? Is the object moving towards or away from the origin at that instant?

Thinking/Inquiry/ Problem Solving

15. The distance–time relationship for a moving object is given by $s(t) = kt^2 + (6k^2 - 10k)t + 2k$, where k is a non-zero constant.

   a. Show that the acceleration is constant.

   b. Find the time at which the velocity is zero, and determine the position of the object when this occurs.

Thinking/Inquiry/
Problem Solving

16. Newton's laws of motion imply simple formulas for $s(t)$ and $v(t)$, and the functions of altitude (in metres) and vertical velocity (in m/s): altitude is $s(t) = s_0 + v_0 t - 5t^2$, and vertical velocity is $v(t) = v_0 - 10t$, where s_0 is the metres above ground, and v_0 is the upward velocity at $t = 0$. According to the 1998 *Guinness Book of Records*, the roof of the SkyDome in Toronto, Ontario, is the world's only retractable roof. It covers 3.2 ha (8 acres), spans 209 m at its widest point, and rises 86 m. It takes 20 min to retract the roof fully.

Could a major-league pitcher hit the 86 m ceiling of the SkyDome? *Hint:* Assume the pitcher can throw the ball horizontally at 50 m/s, at about 35 m/s straight up, and that he throws the ball from the pitcher's mound.

Part C

17. An elevator is designed to start from a resting position without a jerk. It can do this if the acceleration function is continuous.

   a. Show that for the position function $s(t) = \begin{cases} 0, & \text{if } t < 0 \\ \dfrac{t^3}{t^2 + 1}, & \text{if } t \geq 0 \end{cases}$, the acceleration is continuous at $t = 0$.

   b. What happens to the velocity and acceleration for very large values of t?

18. An object moves so that its velocity, v, is related to its position, s, according to $v = \sqrt{b^2 + 2gs}$, where b and g are constants. Show that the acceleration of the object is constant.

19. Newton's law of motion for a particle of mass m moving in a straight line says that $F = ma$, where F is the force acting on the particle and a is the acceleration of the particle. In relativistic mechanics, this law is replaced by

$$F = \frac{m_0 \frac{d}{dt} v}{\sqrt{1 - \left(\frac{v}{c}\right)^2}},$$ where m_0 is the mass of the particle measured at rest

and c is the velocity of light. Show that $F = \dfrac{m_0 a}{\left(1 - \left(\frac{v}{c}\right)^2\right)^{\frac{3}{2}}}$.

Section 5.3 — Related Rates

Oil spilled from a tanker spreads in a circle whose area increases at a constant rate of 6 km^2/h. How fast is the radius of the spill increasing when the area is 9π km^2? Knowing the rate of increase of the radius is important in planning the containment operation.

In this section, you will encounter some interesting problems that will help you to understand the applications of derivatives and how they can be used to describe and predict the phenomena of change. In many practical applications, several quantities vary in relation to one another. The rates at which they vary are also related to one another. With calculus, we can describe and calculate such rates.

EXAMPLE 1

When a raindrop falls into a still puddle, ripples spread out in concentric circles from the point where the raindrop hits. The radii of these circles grow at the rate of 3 cm/s.

a. Find the rate of increase of the circumference of one circle.

b. Find the rate of increase of the area of the circle that has an area of 81π cm^2.

Solution

The circumference of a circle is $C = 2\pi r$, and the area of a circle is $A = \pi r^2$.

We are given that $\frac{dr}{dt} = 3$.

a. To find $\frac{dC}{dt}$ at any time, it is necessary to differentiate the equation $C = 2\pi r$ with respect to t.

$$\frac{dC}{dt} = 2\pi\frac{dr}{dt}$$

At time t, since $\frac{dr}{dt} = 3$,

$$\frac{dC}{dt} = 2\pi(3)$$

$$= 6\pi.$$

Therefore, the circumference is increasing at a constant rate of 6π cm/s.

b. To find $\frac{dA}{dt}$, differentiate $A = \pi r^2$ with respect to t.

$$\frac{dA}{dt} = 2\pi r\frac{dr}{dt}$$

We know that $\frac{dr}{dt} = 3$, so we need to determine r.

Since $A = 81\pi$ and $A = \pi r^2$,

then $$\pi r^2 = 81\pi$$
$$r^2 = 81$$
$$r = 9,\ r > 0,$$

and $$\frac{dA}{dt} = 2\pi(9)(3)$$
$$= 54\pi.$$

The area of the circle is increasing at a rate of 54π cm^2/s at the given instant.

EXAMPLE 2

Many related-rate problems involve right triangles and the Pythagorean Theorem. In these problems, the lengths of the sides of the triangle vary with time. These quantities and related rates can be represented quite simply on the Cartesian plane.

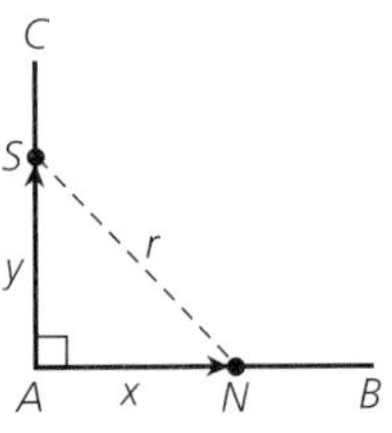

Natalie and Shannon start from point A and drive along perpendicular roads AB and AC respectively as shown. Natalie drives at a speed of 45 km/h and Shannon travels at a speed of 40 km/h. If Shannon begins one hour before Natalie, at what rate are their cars separating three hours after Shannon leaves?

Solution

Let x represent the distance Natalie's car has travelled along AB, and let y represent the distance Shannon has travelled along AC.

Therefore $\frac{dx}{dt} = 45$ and $\frac{dy}{dt} = 40$.

Let r represent the distance between the two cars at time t.
Therefore, $x^2 + y^2 = r^2$.
Differentiate both sides of the equation with respect to time.

$$\frac{d}{dt}(x^2) + \frac{d}{dt}(y^2) = \frac{d}{dt}(r^2)$$

$$2x\frac{dx}{dt} + 2y\frac{dy}{dt} = 2r\frac{dr}{dt}$$

or $$x\frac{dx}{dt} + y\frac{dy}{dt} = r\frac{dr}{dt} \qquad ①$$

Natalie has travelled for 2 h or $2 \times 45 = 90$ km.
Shannon has travelled for 3 h or $3 \times 40 = 120$ km.

The distance between the cars is

$$90^2 + 120^2 = r^2$$
$$r = 150.$$

Substituting into equation ①,

$x = 90, \frac{dx}{dt} = 45, y = 120, \frac{dy}{dt} = 40$, and $r = 150$

$90 \times 45 + 120 \times 40 = 150\frac{dr}{dt}.$

Therefore, the distance between Natalie's and Shannon's cars is increasing at a rate of 59 km/h after two hours.

EXAMPLE 3

Water is pouring into an inverted right circular cone at a rate of π m^3/min. The height and the diameter of the base of the cone are both 10 m. How fast is the water level rising when its depth is 8 m?

Solution

Let V denote the volume, r the radius, and h the height of water in the cone at time t. The volume of water in the cone at any time is $V = \frac{1}{3}\pi r^2 h$.
Since we want to find $\frac{dh}{dt}$ when $h = 8$, we solve for r in terms of h from the ratio determined from the similar triangles $\frac{r}{h} = \frac{5}{10}$ or $r = \frac{1}{2}h$.

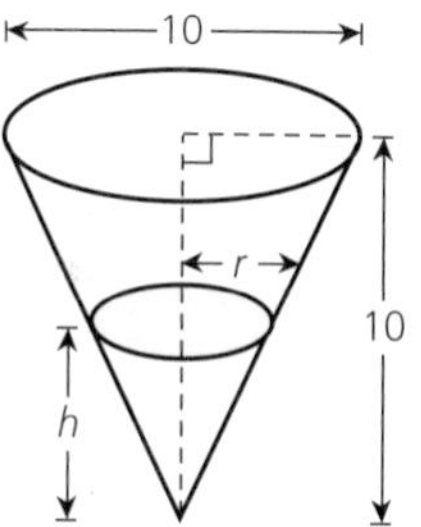

Substituting into $V = \frac{1}{3}\pi r^2 h$,

we get

$$V = \frac{1}{3}\pi\left(\frac{1}{2}h\right)^2 h$$
$$V = \frac{1}{3}\pi\left(\frac{1}{4}h^2\right)h$$
$$V = \frac{1}{12}\pi h^3.$$

Differentiating with respect to time, we find

$$\frac{dV}{dt} = \frac{1}{4}\pi h^2 \frac{dh}{dt}.$$

At a specific time, when $h = 8$ and $\frac{dV}{dt} = \pi$,

$$\pi = \frac{1}{4}\pi(8)^2 \frac{dh}{dt}$$
$$\frac{1}{16} = \frac{dh}{dt}.$$

Therefore, at the moment when the depth of the water is 8 m, the level is rising at 0.0625 m/min.

EXAMPLE 4

A student 1.6 m tall walks directly away from a lamppost at a rate of 1.2 m/s. A light is situated 8 m above the ground on the lamppost. Show that the student's shadow is lengthening at a rate of 0.3 m/s when she is 20 m from the base of the lamppost.

Solution

Let x be the length of her shadow and y be the distance she is from the lamppost, in metres, as shown. Let t denote the time, in seconds.

We are given that $\frac{dy}{dt} = 1.2$ m/s and we wish to determine $\frac{dx}{dt}$ when $y = 20$ m.

To find a relationship between x and y, use similar triangles.

$$\frac{x + y}{8} = \frac{x}{1.6}$$

$$1.6x + 1.6y = 8x$$

$$1.6y = 6.4x$$

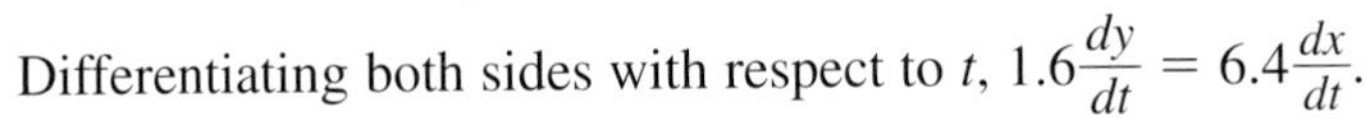

Differentiating both sides with respect to t, $1.6\frac{dy}{dt} = 6.4\frac{dx}{dt}$.

When $y = 20$ and $\frac{dy}{dt} = 1.2$,

$$1.6(1.2) = 6.4\frac{dx}{dt}$$

$$\frac{dx}{dt} = 0.3.$$

Therefore, her shadow is lengthening at 0.3 m/s. (Note that the shadow is lengthening at a constant rate, independent of her distance from the lamppost.)

Guidelines for Solving Related-Rate Problems

1. Make a sketch and label the quantities, if applicable.
2. Introduce variables to represent the quantities that change.
3. Identify the quantities to be determined.
4. Find an equation that relates the variables.
5. Implicitly differentiate both sides of the equation with respect to time t, regarding all variables as functions of t.
6. Substitute into the differentiated equation all known values for the variables and their rates of change.
7. Solve the equation for the required rate of change.
8. Write a conclusion that includes the units.

Exercise 5.3

Part A

Communication

1. Express the following statements in symbols:
   a. The area, A, of a circle is increasing at a rate of 4 m^2/s.
   b. The surface area, S, of a sphere is decreasing at a rate of 3 m^2/min.
   c. After travelling for 15 min, the speed of a car is 70 km/h.
   d. The x- and y-coordinates of a point are changing at equal rates.
   e. The head of a short-distance radar dish is revolving at three revolutions per minute.

Part B

2. The function $T(x) = \frac{200}{1 + x^2}$ represents the temperature in degrees Celsius perceived by a person standing x metres from a fire.
   a. If the person moves away from the fire at 2 m/s, how fast is the temperature changing when the person is 5 m away?
   b. Using a graphing calculator, determine the distance from the fire when the perceived temperature is changing the fastest.
   c. What other calculus techniques could be used to check the result?

Knowledge/Understanding

3. The side of a square is increasing at a rate of 5 cm/s. At what rate is the area changing when the side is 10 cm long? At what rate is the perimeter changing?

4. Each edge of a cube is expanding at a rate of 4 cm/s.
   a. How fast is the volume changing when each edge is 5 cm?
   b. At what rate is the surface area changing when each edge is 7 cm?

5. One side of a rectangle increases at 2 cm/s, while the other side decreases at 3 cm/s. How fast is the area of the rectangle changing when the first side equals 20 cm and the second side equals 50 cm?

6. The area of a circle is decreasing at the rate of 5 m^2/s when its radius is 3 m.
   a. At what rate is the radius decreasing at that moment?
   b. At what rate is the diameter decreasing at that moment?

Application

7. Oil spilled from a ruptured tanker spreads in a circle whose area increases at a constant rate of 6 km^2/h. How fast is the radius of the spill increasing when the area is 9π km^2?

8. The top of a 5 m wheeled ladder rests against a vertical wall. If the bottom of the ladder rolls away from the base of the wall at a rate of $\frac{1}{3}$ m/s, how fast is the top of the ladder sliding down the wall when it is 3 m above the base of the wall?

9. How fast must someone let out line if the kite that she is flying is 30 m high, 40 m away from her horizontally, and continuing to move away from her horizontally at the rate of 10 m/min?

10. If the rocket shown in the figure is rising vertically at 268 m/s when it is 1220 m up, how fast is the camera-to-rocket distance changing at that instant?

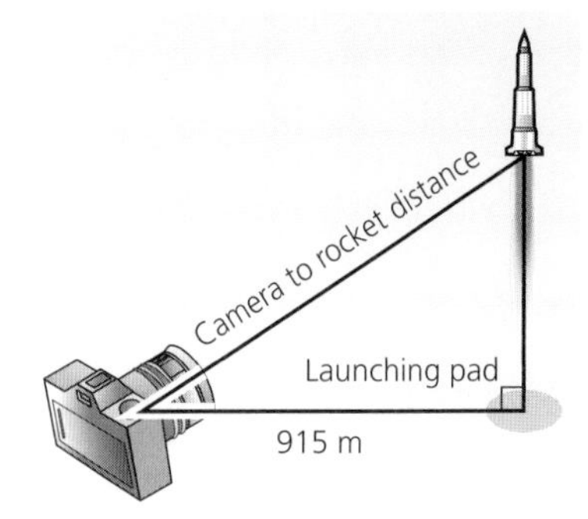

11. Two cyclists depart at the same time from a starting point along routes making an angle of $\frac{\pi}{3}$ radians with each other. The first is travelling at 15 km/h, while the second is moving at 20 km/h. How fast are the two cyclists moving apart after 2 h?

12. A spherical balloon is being filled with helium at a rate of 8 cm^3/s. At what rate is its radius increasing
    a. when the radius is 12 cm?
    b. when the volume is 1435 cm^3? (Your answer should be correct to the nearest hundredth.)
    c. when it has been filling for 33.5 s?

13. A cylindrical tank with height 15 m and diameter 2 m is being filled with gasoline at a rate of 500 L/min. At what rate is the fluid level in the tank rising? (1 L = 1000 cm^3). About how long will it take to fill the tank?

Communication

14. If $V = \pi r^2 h$, find $\frac{dV}{dt}$ if r and h are both variables. In your journal, write three problems that involve the rate of change of the volume of a cylinder such that
    i) r is a variable and h is a constant;
    ii) r is a constant and h is a variable;
    iii) r and h are both variables.

15. The trunk of a tree is approximately cylindrical in shape and has a diameter of 1 m when the height is 15 m. If the radius is increasing at 0.003 m per

annum and the height is increasing at 0.4 m per annum, find the rate of increase of the volume of the trunk.

16. A conical paper cup of radius 5 cm and height 15 cm is leaking water at the rate of 2 cm^3/min. At what rate is the level of water decreasing when the water is 3 cm deep?

17. Derive the formula for the volume of a trough whose cross-section is an equilateral triangle and whose length is 10 m.

18. The cross-section of a water trough is an equilateral triangle with a horizontal top edge. If the trough is 5 m long and 25 cm deep, and water is flowing in at a rate of 0.25 m^3/min, how fast is the water level rising when the water is 10 cm deep at the deepest point?

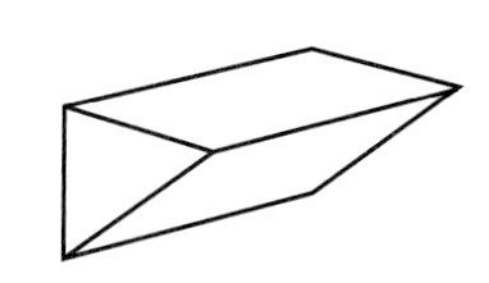

19. The shadow cast by a man standing 1 m from a lamppost is 1.2 m long. If the man is 1.8 m tall and walks away from the lamppost at a speed of 120 m/min, at what rate is the shadow lengthening after 5 s?

Part C

20. A railroad bridge is 20 m above, and at right angles to, a river. A person in a train travelling at 60 km/h passes over the centre of the bridge at the same instant that a person in a motorboat travelling at 20 km/h passes under the centre of the bridge. How fast are the two people separating 10 s later?

21. Liquid is being poured into the top of a funnel at a steady rate of 200 cm^3/s. The funnel is in the shape of an inverted right circular cone with a radius equal to its height. It has a small hole in the bottom where the liquid is flowing out at a rate of 20 cm^3/s. How fast is the height of the liquid changing when the liquid in the funnel is 15 cm deep?

    At the instant when the height of the liquid is 25 cm, the funnel becomes clogged at the bottom and no more liquid flows out. How fast does the height of the liquid change just after this occurs?

22. A ladder of length l standing on level ground is leaning against a vertical wall. The base of the ladder begins to slide away from the wall. Introduce a coordinate system so that the wall lies along the y-axis, the ground is on the x-axis, and the base of the wall is the origin.

    What is the equation of the path followed by the midpoint of the ladder? What is the equation of the path followed by any point on the ladder? (*Hint:* Let k be the distance from the top of the ladder to the point in question.)

23. A ball is dropped from a height of 20 m, 12 m away from the top of a 20 m lamppost. The ball's shadow, created by the light at the top of the lamppost, is moving along the level ground. How fast is the shadow moving one second after the ball is released?

Section 5.4 — Maximum and Minimum on an Interval

INVESTIGATION

The purpose of this investigation is to determine how the derivative can be used in determining the maximum (largest) value or the minimum (smallest) value of a function on a given interval.

1. For each of the following functions, determine, by completing the square, the value of x that produces a maximum or minimum function value on the given interval.
   a. $f(x) = -x^2 + 6x - 3$, interval $0 \le x \le 5$
   b. $f(x) = -x^2 - 2x + 11$, interval $-3 \le x \le 4$
   c. $f(x) = 4x^2 - 12x + 7$, interval $-1 \le x \le 4$
2. For each function, determine the value of c such that $f'(c) = 0$.
3. Compare the values obtained in Questions 1 and 2 for each function.

technology
APPENDIX P. 444

4. Using your calculator, graph each of the following functions and determine all values of x that produce a maximum or minimum function value on the given interval.
   a. $f(x) = x^3 - 3x^2 - 8x + 10$, interval $-2 \le x \le 4$
   b. $f(x) = x^3 - 12x + 5$, interval $-3 \le x \le 3$
   c. $f(x) = 3x^3 - 15x^2 + 9x + 23$, interval $0 \le x \le 4$
   d. $f(x) = -2x^3 + 12x + 7$, interval $-2 \le x \le 2$
   e. $f(x) = -x^3 - 2x^2 + 15x + 23$, interval $-4 \le x \le 3$
5. For each function in Question 4, determine all values of c such that $f'(c) = 0$.
6. Compare the values obtained in Questions 4 and 5 for each function.

technology

7. From your conclusions in Questions 3 and 6, state a method for using the derivative of a function to determine values of the variable that determine maximum or minimum values of the function.
8. Repeat Question 4 for the following functions, using the indicated intervals.
   a. $f(x) = -x^2 + 6x - 3$, interval $4 \le x \le 8$
   b. $f(x) = 4x^2 - 12x + 7$, interval $2 \le x \le 6$
   c. $f(x) = x^3 - 3x^2 - 9x + 10$, interval $-2 \le x \le 6$
   d. $f(x) = x^3 - 12x + 5$, interval $0 \le x \le 5$
   e. $f(x) = x^3 - 5x^2 + 3x + 7$, interval $-2 \le x \le 5$

9. In Questions 3 and 6, you saw that a maximum or minimum can occur at points $(c, f(c))$ where $f'(c) = 0$. From your observations in Question 8, state other values of the variable that can produce a maximum or minimum in a given interval.

Checkpoint: Check Your Understanding

The maximum value of a function that has a derivative at all points in an interval occurs at a "peak" ($f'(c) = 0$) or at an end point of the interval. The minimum value occurs at a "valley" ($f'(c) = 0$) or at an end point. This is true no matter how many peaks and valleys the graph has in the interval.

In the following three graphs, the derivative equals zero at two points.

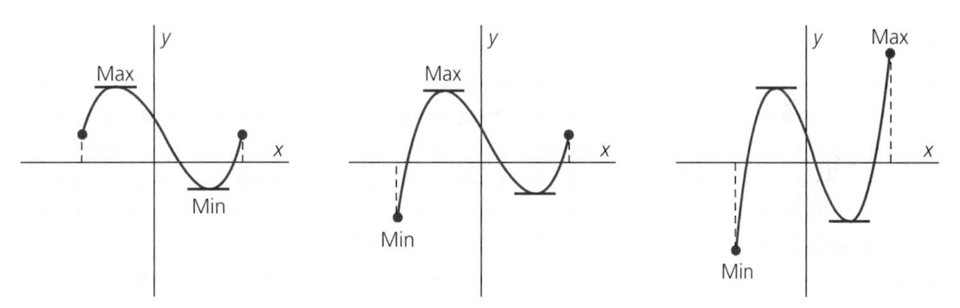

Algorithm for Maximum or Minimum (Extreme Values)
If a function $f(x)$ has a derivative at every point in the interval $a \leq x \leq b$, calculate $f(x)$ at

- **all points in the interval $a \leq x \leq b$ where $f'(x) = 0$;**
- **the end points $x = a$ and $x = b$.**

The maximum value of $f(x)$ on the interval $a \leq x \leq b$ is the largest of these values, and the minimum value of $f(x)$ on the interval is the smallest of these values.

EXAMPLE 1

Find the extreme values of the function $f(x) = -2x^3 + 9x^2 + 4$ on the interval $-1 \leq x \leq 5$.

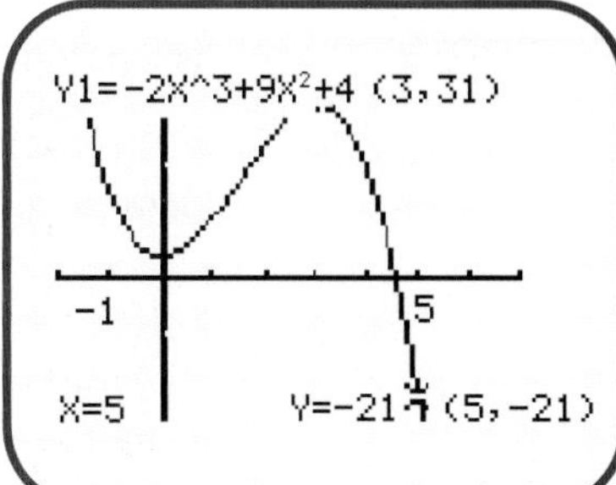

Solution

The derivative is $f'(x) = -6x^2 + 18x$.

If we set $f'(x) = 0$, we obtain

$$-6x(x - 3) = 0,$$

so $x = 0$ or $x = 3$.

Both values lie in the given domain.

We can then evaluate $f(x)$ for these values and at the end points $x = -1$ and $x = 5$, to obtain

$$\begin{aligned} f(-1) &= 15 \\ f(0) &= 4 \\ f(3) &= 31 \\ f(5) &= -21. \end{aligned}$$

Therefore, the maximum value of $f(x)$ on the interval $-1 \leq x \leq 5$ is $f(3) = 31$, and the minimum value is $f(5) = -21$.

EXAMPLE 2

The amount of current in an electrical system is given by the function $C(t) = -t^3 + t^2 + 21t$, where t is the time in seconds and $0 \leq t \leq 5$. Determine the times at which the current is maximal and minimal and the amount of current in the system at these times.

Solution

The derivative is $\frac{dC}{dt} = -3t^2 + 2t + 21$.

If we set $\frac{dC}{dt} = 0$, we obtain

$$\begin{aligned} 3t^2 - 2t - 21 &= 0 \\ (3t + 7)(t - 3) &= 0, \end{aligned}$$

therefore, $t = -\frac{7}{3}$ or 3.

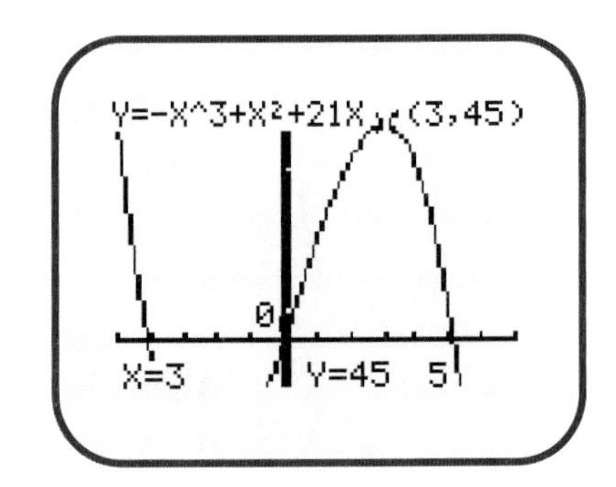

Only $t = 3$ is in the given interval, so we evaluate $C(t)$ at $t = 0$, $t = 3$, and $t = 5$ as follows:

$$\begin{aligned} C(0) &= 0 \\ C(3) &= -3^3 + 3^2 + 21(3) = 45 \\ C(5) &= -5^3 + 5^2 + 21(5) = 5. \end{aligned}$$

The maximum is 45 units at time $t = 3$ s, and the minimum is zero units at time $t = 0$ s.

EXAMPLE 3

The amount of light intensity on a point is given by the function $I(t) = \frac{t^2 + 2t + 16}{t + 2}$, where t is the time in seconds and $0 \leq t \leq 14$. Determine the time of minimal intensity.

Solution

Note that the function is not defined for $t = -2$. Since this value is not in the given interval, we need not worry about it.
The derivative is

$$I'(t) = \frac{(2t + 2)(t + 2) - (t^2 + 2t + 16)(1)}{(t + 2)^2}$$

$$= \frac{2t^2 + 6t + 4 - t^2 - 2t - 16}{(t + 2)^2}$$

$$= \frac{t^2 + 4t - 12}{(t + 2)^2}.$$

If we set $I'(t) = 0$, we obtain

$$t^2 + 4t - 12 = 0$$
$$(t + 6)(t - 2) = 0$$
$$t = -6 \text{ or } t = 2.$$

Only $t = 2$ is in the given interval, so we evaluate $I(t)$ for $t = 0, 2$, and 14:

$$I(0) = 8$$

$$I(2) = \frac{4 + 4 + 16}{4} = 6$$

$$I(14) = \frac{14^2 + 2(14) + 16}{16} = 15.$$

Note that the calculation can be greatly reduced by rewriting the function, as shown:

$$I(t) = \frac{t^2 + 2t}{t + 2} + \frac{16}{t + 2}$$

$$= t + 16(t + 2)^{-1}.$$

Then $$I'(t) = 1 - 16(t + 2)^{-2}$$

$$= 1 - \frac{16}{(t + 2)^2}.$$

Setting $I'(t) = 0$ gives

$$1 = \frac{16}{(t + 2)^2}$$

$$t^2 + 4t + 4 = 16$$
$$t^2 + 4t - 12 = 0.$$

As before, $t = -6$ or $t = 2$.

The evaluations are also simplified:

$$I(0) = 0 + 8 = 8$$

$$I(2) = 2 + \frac{16}{4} = 6$$

$$I(14) = 14 + \frac{16}{16} = 15.$$

Exercise 5.4

Part A

Communication

1. State, with reasons, why the maximum/minimum algorithm can or cannot be used to determine the maximum and minimum values for the following:

   a. $y = x^3 - 5x^2 + 10$ on $-5 \leq x \leq 5$

   b. $y = \dfrac{3x}{x - 2}$ on $-1 \leq x \leq 3$

   c. $y = \dfrac{x}{x^2 - 4}$ on $0 \leq x \leq 5$

   d. $y = \dfrac{x^2 - 1}{x + 3}$ on interval $-2 \leq x \leq 3$

2. State the value of the maximum and the minimum for each function. In each of the following graphs, the function is defined in the interval shown.

a.

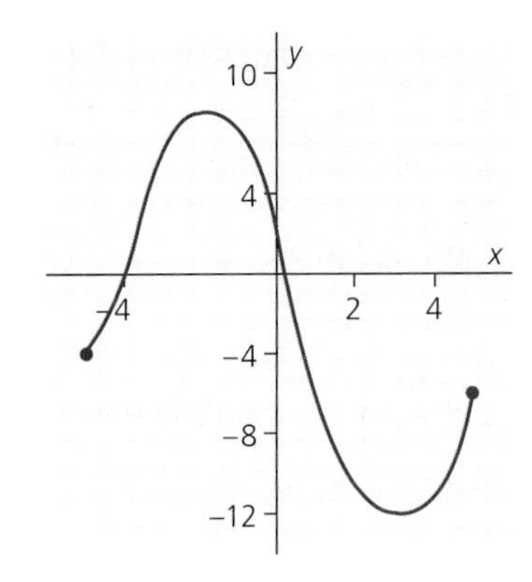

b.

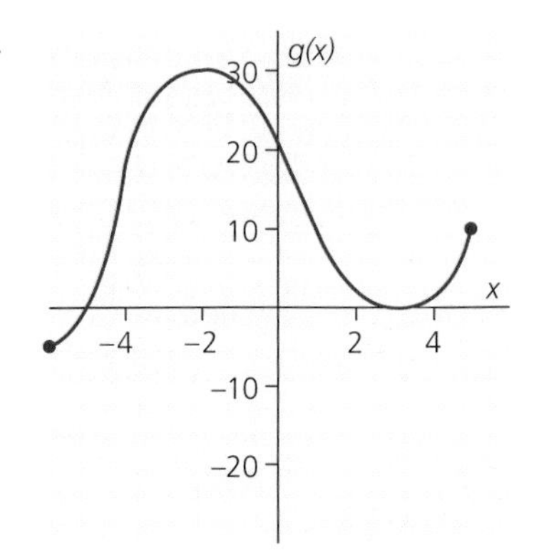

c.

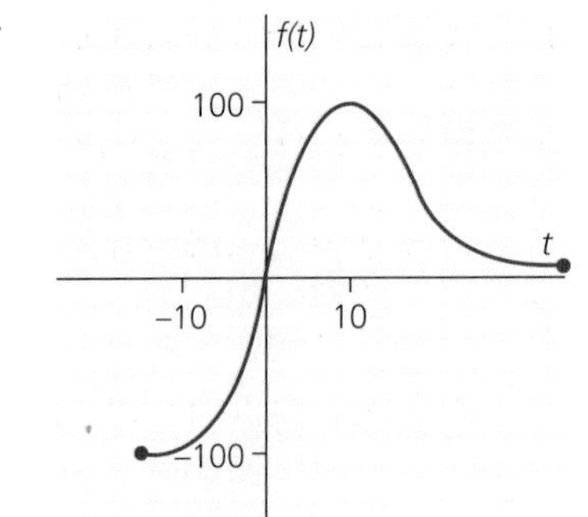

d.

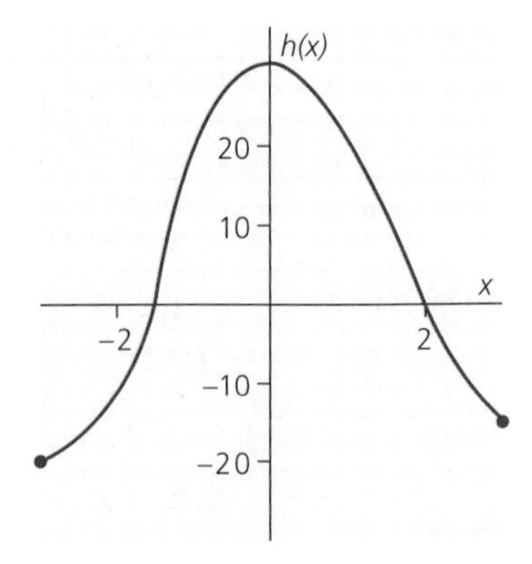

Knowledge/Understanding

technology

3. Find the maximum or minimum value of each function on the given interval, using the algorithm for maximum or minimum values. Illustrate your results by sketching the graph of each function.

a. $f(x) = x^2 - 4x + 3, 0 \leq x \leq 3$

b. $f(x) = (x - 2)^2, 0 \leq x \leq 2$

c. $f(x) = x^3 - 3x^2, -1 \leq x \leq 3$

d. $f(x) = x^3 - 3x^2, -2 \leq x \leq 1$

e. $f(x) = 2x^3 - 3x^2 - 12x + 1, -2 \leq x \leq 0$

f. $f(x) = \frac{1}{3}x^3 - \frac{5}{2}x^2 + 6x, 0 \leq x \leq 4$

Part B

4. Find the extreme values of each function on the given interval, using the algorithm for maximum or minimum values.

a. $f(x) = x + \frac{4}{x}, 1 \leq x \leq 10$

b. $f(x) = 4\sqrt{x} - x, 2 \leq x \leq 9$

c. $f(x) = \frac{1}{x^2 - 2x + 2}, 0 \leq x \leq 2$

d. $f(x) = 3x^4 - 4x^3 - 36x^2 + 20, -3 \leq x \leq 4$

e. $f(x) = \frac{4x}{x^2 + 1}, -2 \leq x \leq 4$

f. $f(x) = \frac{4x}{x^2 + 1}, 2 \leq x \leq 4$

5. a. An object moves in a straight line. Its velocity in m/s at time t is $v(t) = \frac{4t^2}{4 + t^3}, t \geq 0$. Find the maximum and minimum velocities over the time interval $1 \leq t \leq 4$.

b. Repeat part **a** if $v(t) = \frac{4t^2}{1 + t^2}, t \geq 0$.

Application

6. A swimming pool is treated periodically to control the growth of bacteria. Suppose that t days after a treatment, the concentration of bacteria per cubic centimetre is $C(t) = 30t^2 - 240t + 500$. Find the lowest concentration of bacteria during the first week after the treatment.

7. The fuel efficiency, E, (in litres per hundred kilometres) of a car driven at speed v (in km/h) is $E(v) = \frac{1600v}{v^2 + 6400}$.

a. If the speed limit is 100 km/h, find the legal speed that will maximize the fuel efficiency.

b. Repeat part **a** using a speed limit of 50 km/h.

8. The concentration $C(t)$ (in milligrams per cubic centimetre) of a certain medicine in a patient's bloodstream is given by $C(t) = \frac{0.1t}{(t + 3)^2}$, where t is the number of hours after the medicine is taken. Find the maximum and minimum concentrations between the first and sixth hours after the patient is given the medicine.

9. Technicians working for the Ministry of Natural Resources have found that the amount of a pollutant in a certain river can be represented by $P(t) = 2t + \frac{1}{(162t + 1)}$, $0 \leq t \leq 1$, where t is the time (in years) since a clean-up campaign started. At what time was the pollution at its lowest level?

10. A truck travelling at x km/h, where $30 \leq x \leq 120$, uses gasoline at the rate of $r(x)$ L/km, where $r(x) = \frac{1}{400}\left(\frac{4900}{x} + x\right)$. If fuel costs \$0.45/L, what speed will result in the lowest fuel cost for a trip of 200 km? What is the lowest total cost for the trip?

Part C

Thinking/Inquiry/ Problem Solving

11. In a certain manufacturing process, when the level of production is x units, the cost of production (in dollars) is $C(x) = 3000 + 9x + 0.05x^2$, $1 \leq x \leq 300$. What level of production x will minimize the unit cost $U(x) = \frac{C(x)}{x}$? Keep in mind that the production level must be an integer.

12. Repeat Question 11 using a cost of production of $C(x) = 6000 + 9x + 0.05x^2$, $1 \leq x \leq 300$.

Section 5.5 — Optimization Problems

We frequently encounter situations in which we are asked to do the best we can. Such a request is vague unless we are given some conditions. Asking us to minimize the cost of making tables and chairs is not clear. Asking us to make the maximum number of tables and chairs possible so that the costs of production are minimized and given that the amount of material available is restricted allows us to construct a function describing the situation. We can then determine the minimum (or maximum) of the function.

Such a procedure is called **optimization.** To optimize a situation is to realize the best possible outcome, subject to a set of restrictions. Because of these restrictions, the domain of the function is usually restricted. As you have seen earlier, in such situations, the absolute maximum or minimum can be identified through the use of calculus, but might also occur at the ends of the domain.

A farmer has 800 m of fencing and wishes to enclose a rectangular field. One side of the field is against a country road which is already fenced, so the farmer needs to fence only the remaining three sides of the rectangular field. The farmer wishes to enclose the maximum possible area and wishes to use all of the fencing. How does he determine the dimensions that achieve this?

The farmer can achieve his goal by determining a function that describes the area, subject to the condition that the amount of fencing used is to be exactly 800 m, and by finding the absolute maximum of the function. To do so, he would proceed as follows:

Let the width of the enclosed area be x m. Then the length of the area is $(800 - 2x)$ m. The area of the field can be represented by the function $A(x)$ where

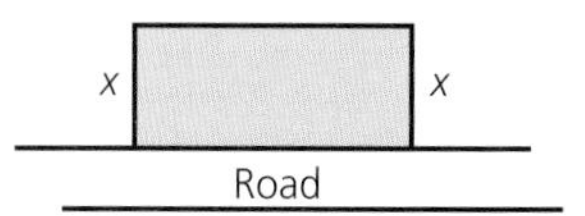

$$A(x) = x(800 - 2x)$$
$$= 800x - 2x^2.$$

The domain of the function is $0 \le x \le 400$ since the amount of fencing is 800 m. To find the minimum and maximum values, determine $A'(x)$:

$$A'(x) = 800 - 4x.$$

Setting $A'(x) = 0$, we obtain $800 - 4x = 0$

$$x = 200.$$

The minimum and maximum values can occur at $x = 200$ or at the ends of the domain, $x = 0$ and $x = 400$.

$$\begin{aligned} A(0) &= 0 \\ A(200) &= 200(800 - 400) \\ &= 80\,000 \\ A(400) &= 400(800 - 800) \\ &= 0 \end{aligned}$$

The maximum area he can enclose is 80 000 m^2, within a field 200 m by 400 m. The procedure used here can be summarized as follows:

An Algorithm for Solving Optimization Problems

1. Understand the problem and identify quantities that can vary. Determine a function that represents the quantity to be optimized. Be sure that this function only depends on one variable.
2. Whenever possible, draw a diagram, labelling the given and required quantities.
3. Determine the domain of the function to be optimized, using information given in the problem.
4. Use the algorithm for extreme values to find the absolute maximum or minimum function value on the domain.
5. Use the results of step 4 to answer the original problem.

EXAMPLE 1

A piece of sheet metal 60 cm by 30 cm is to be used to make a rectangular box with an open top. Find the dimensions that will give the box with the largest volume.

Solution

From the diagram, making the box requires that the four corner squares be cut out and discarded. Let each side of the squares be x cm.

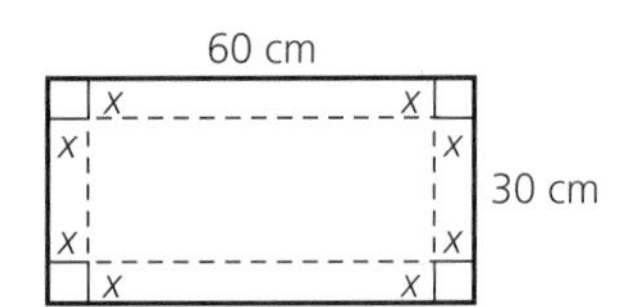

Therefore, height $= x$
length $= 60 - 2x$
width $= 30 - 2x$.

Since all dimensions are non-negative, $0 \le x \le 15$.

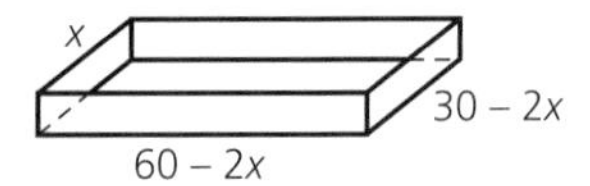

The volume of the box is given by the function $V(x)$, where

$$\begin{aligned} V(x) &= x(60 - 2x)(30 - 2x) \\ &= 4x^3 - 180x^2 + 1800x \end{aligned}$$

For extreme values, set $V'(x) = 0$.

$$\begin{aligned} V'(x) &= 12x^2 - 360x + 1800 \\ &= 12(x^2 - 30x + 150) \end{aligned}$$

Setting $V'(x) = 0$, we obtain $x^2 - 30x + 150 = 0$.

$$\begin{aligned} x &= \frac{30 \pm \sqrt{300}}{2} \\ &= 15 \pm 5\sqrt{3} \\ x &\doteq 23.7 \text{ or } x \doteq 6.3 \end{aligned}$$

Since $x \leq 15$, $x = 15 - 5\sqrt{3} \doteq 6.3$.

To find the largest volume, substitute $x = 0$, 6.3, and 15 in $V(x) = 4x^3 - 180x^2 + 1800x$.

$$\begin{aligned} V(0) &= 0 \\ V(6.3) &= 4(6.3)^3 - 180(6.3)^2 + 1800(6.3) \\ &\doteq 5196 \\ V(15) &= 0 \end{aligned}$$

The maximum volume is obtained by cutting out corner squares of side 6.3 cm. The length of the box is $60 - 2 \times 6.3 = 47.4$ cm, the width is $30 - 2 \times 6.3 = 17.4$ cm, and the height is 6.3 cm.

EXAMPLE 2

Ian and Ada are both training for a marathon. Ian's house is located 20 km north of Ada's house. At 9:00 one Saturday morning, Ian leaves his house and jogs south at 8 km/h. At the same time, Ada leaves her house and jogs east at 6 km/h. When are Ian and Ada closest together, given that they both run for 2.5 h?

Solution

If Ian starts at point I, he reaches point J after time t hours. Then $IJ = 8t$ km and $JA = (20 - 8t)$ km.

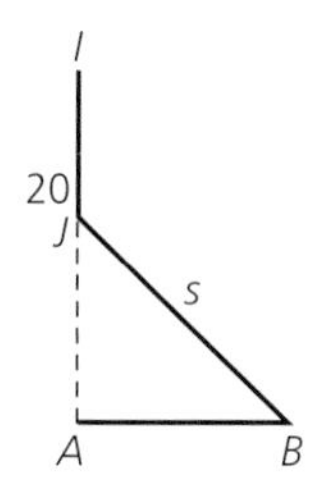

If Ada starts at point A, she reaches point B after t hours and $AB = 6t$ km.

Now the distance they are apart is $s = JB$, and s can be expressed as a function of t by

$$
\begin{aligned}
s(t) &= \sqrt{JA^2 + AB^2} \\
&= \sqrt{(20 - 8t)^2 + (6t)^2} \\
&= \sqrt{100t^2 - 320t + 400}.
\end{aligned}
$$

The domain for t is $0 \leq t \leq 2.5$.

$$
\begin{aligned}
s'(t) &= \frac{1}{2}(100t^2 - 320t + 400)^{-\frac{1}{2}}(200t - 320) \\
&= \frac{100t - 160}{\sqrt{100t^2 - 320t + 400}}
\end{aligned}
$$

To obtain a minimum or maximum value, let $s'(t) = 0$.

$$
\begin{aligned}
\frac{100t - 160}{\sqrt{100t^2 - 320t + 400}} &= 0 \\
100t - 160 &= 0 \\
t &= 1.6
\end{aligned}
$$

Using the algorithm for extreme values,

$$
\begin{aligned}
s(0) &= \sqrt{400} \\
&= 20 \\
s(1.6) &= \sqrt{100(1.6)^2 - 320(1.6) + 400} \\
&= \sqrt{144} \\
&= 12 \\
s(2.5) &= \sqrt{225} \\
&= 15.
\end{aligned}
$$

Therefore, the minimum value of $s(t)$ is 12 km and occurs at time 10:36.

Exercise 5.5

Part A

1. A piece of wire 100 cm long is to be bent to form a rectangle. Determine the rectangle of maximum area.

Communication

2. Discuss the result of maximizing the area of a rectangle given a fixed perimeter.

Knowledge/Understanding

3. A farmer has 600 m of fence and he wants to enclose a rectangular field beside the river on his property. Find the dimensions of the field so that a maximum area is enclosed. (Fencing is required only on three sides.)

Application

4. A rectangular piece of cardboard 100 cm by 40 cm is to be used to make a rectangular box with an open top. Find the dimensions (to one decimal place) for the box with the largest volume.

Part **B**

5. The volume of a square-based rectangular cardboard box is to be 1000 cm^3. Find the dimensions so that the quantity of material used to manufacture all 6 faces is a minimum. Assume that there will be no waste material. The machinery available cannot fabricate material smaller in length than 2 cm.

6. Find the area of the largest rectangle that can be inscribed inside a semicircle with radius of 10 units. Place the length of the rectangle along the diameter.

Application

7. A cylindrical-shaped tin can is to have a capacity of 1000 cm^3.
   a. Find the dimensions of the can that require the minimum amount of tin. (Assume no waste material.) The marketing department has specified that the smallest can the market will accept has a diameter of 6 cm and a height of 4 cm.
   b. Express the answer for part **a** as a ratio of height to diameter.

Thinking/Inquiry/ Problem Solving

8. a. Find the area of the largest rectangle that can be inscribed in a right triangle with legs adjacent to the right angle of lengths 5 cm and 12 cm. The two sides of the rectangle lie along the legs.
   b. Repeat part **a** with the right triangle that has sides 8 cm by 15 cm.
   c. Hypothesize a conclusion for any right triangle.

Thinking/Inquiry/ Problem Solving

9. a. An isosceles trapezoidal drainage gutter is to be made so that the angles at A and B, in the cross-section $ABCD$ are each 120°. If the 5-m-long sheet of metal that has to be bent to form the open topped gutter has a width of 60 cm, then find the dimensions so that the cross-sectional area will be a maximum.

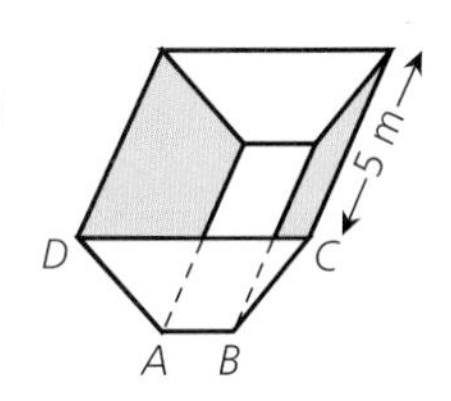

   b. Calculate the maximum volume of water that can be held by this gutter.

10. A piece of window framing material is 6 m long. A carpenter wants to build a frame for a rural gothic style window where ΔABC is equilateral. The window must fit inside a space 1 m wide and 3 m high.

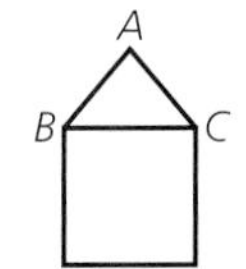

   a. Find the dimensions that should be used for the 6 pieces so that the
   maximum amount of light will be admitted. Assume no waste of material for corner cuts, etc.
   b. Would the carpenter get more light if he built a window in the shape of an equilateral triangle only? Explain.

11. A train leaves the station at 10:00 and travels due south at a speed of 60 km/h. Another train has been heading due west at 45 km/h and reaches the same station at 11:00. At what time were the two trains closest together?

Part C

Thinking/Inquiry/ Problem Solving

12. In Question 8, you looked at two specific right triangles and observed that the rectangle of maximum area that could be inscribed inside the triangle always had dimensions equal to half the lengths of the sides adjacent to the rectangle. Prove that this is true for any right triangle.

13. Prove that any cylindrical can of volume k cubic units that is to be made using a minimum amount of material must have the height equal to the diameter.

14. A piece of wire 100 cm long is cut into two pieces. One piece is bent to form a square, and the other is bent to form a circle. How should the wire be cut so that the total area enclosed is

    a. a maximum?

    b. a minimum?

15. Determine the minimal distance from point $(-3, 3)$ to the curve given by $y = (x - 3)^2$.

16. A chord joins any two points A and B on the parabola whose equation is $y^2 = 4x$. If C is the midpoint of AB, and CD is drawn parallel to the x-axis to meet the parabola at D, prove that the tangent at D is parallel to chord AB.

17. A rectangle lies in the first quadrant with one vertex at the origin and two of the sides along the coordinate axes. If the fourth vertex lies on the line defined by $x + 2y - 10 = 0$, then find the maximum area of the rectangle.

18. The base of a rectangle lies along the x-axis, and the upper two vertices are on the curve defined by $y = k^2 - x^2$. Find the maximum area of the rectangle.

Section 5.6 — Optimizing in Economics and Science

In the world of business, it is extremely important to manage costs effectively. Good control will allow for a minimization of costs and a maximization of profit. At the same time, there are human considerations. If your company is able to maximize profit but antagonizes its customers or employees in the process, there may be a very significant penalty to pay in the future. For this reason, it may be important that, in addition to any mathematical constraints, you consider other, more practical constraints on the domain when you are constructing a workable function.

The following examples will illustrate economic situations and the domain constraints that you may encounter.

EXAMPLE 1

A cylindrical chemical storage tank with a capacity of 1000 m^3 is to be constructed in a warehouse that is 12 m by 15 m and has a height of 11 m. The specifications call for the base to be made of sheet steel, which costs \$100/m^2, the top of sheet steel, which costs \$50/m^2, and the wall of sheet steel costing \$80/m^2.

a. Determine whether it is possible for a tank of this capacity to fit in the warehouse. If it *is* possible, find the restrictions on the radius.

b. Determine, if the tank is possible, the proportions of the tank that meet the conditions and that minimize the cost of construction.

All calculations should be accurate to two decimal places.

Solution

a. The radius of the tank cannot exceed 6 m, and the maximum height is 11 m. The volume, using $r = 6$ and $h = 11$, is

$$V = \pi r^2 h$$
$$\cong 1244.$$

It is possible to build a tank of 1000 m^3.
There are limits on the radius and the height.
Clearly, $r \leq 6$.
Also, if $h = 11$, then $\pi r^2(11) \geq 1000$
$$r \geq 5.38.$$

The tank can be constructed to fit in the warehouse. Its radius must be $5.38 \leq r \leq 6$.

b. If the height is h m and the radius is r m, then
- the cost of the base is $\$100(\pi r^2)$,
- the cost of the top is $\$50(\pi r^2)$, and
- the cost of the wall is $\$80(2\pi rh)$.

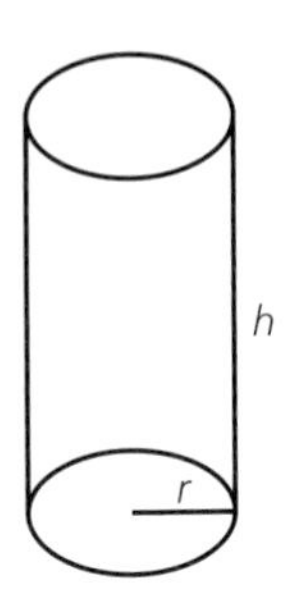

The cost of the tank is $C = 150\pi r^2 + 160\pi rh$.
Here we have two variable quantities, r and h.

However, since $V = \pi r^2 h = 1000$,

$$h = \frac{1000}{\pi r^2}.$$

Substituting for h, we have a cost function in terms of r:

$$C(r) = 150\pi r^2 + 160\pi r\left(\frac{1000}{\pi r^2}\right)$$

or $$C(r) = 150\pi r^2 + \frac{160\,000}{r}.$$

From part **a,** we know that the domain is $5.38 \leq r \leq 6$.
For critical points, set $C'(r) = 0$.

$$300\pi r - \frac{160\,000}{r^2} = 0$$
$$300\pi r = \frac{160\,000}{r^2}$$
$$r^3 = \frac{1600}{3\pi}$$
$$r \cong 5.54$$

This value is within the given domain, so we use the algorithm for maximum and minimum.

$$C(5.38) = 150\pi(5.38)^2 + \frac{160\,000}{5.38} \cong 43\,380$$
$$C(5.54) = 150\pi(5.54)^2 + \frac{160\,000}{5.54} \cong 43\,344$$
$$C(6) = 150\pi(6^2) + \frac{160\,000}{6} \cong 43\,631$$

The minimal cost is \$43 344 with a tank of radius 5.54 m and a height of $\frac{1000}{\pi(5.54)^2} = 10.37$ m.

EXAMPLE 2 A commuter train carries 2000 passengers daily from a suburb into a large city. The cost to ride the train is \$7.00 per person. Market research shows that 40 fewer people would ride the train for each \$0.10 increase in the fare, and 40 more people would ride the train for each \$0.10 decrease. If the capacity of the train is 2600 passengers, and contracts with the rail employees require that at least 1600 passengers be carried, what fare should the railway charge to get the largest possible revenue?

Solution

In order to maximize revenue, we require a revenue function. We know that

$$\text{revenue} = (\text{number of passengers}) \times (\text{fare per passenger}).$$

In forming a revenue function, the most straightforward choice for the independent variable comes from noticing that both the number of passengers and the fare per passenger change with each \$0.10 increase or decrease in the fare. If we let x represent the number of \$0.10 increases in the fare (e.g., $x = 3$ represents a \$0.30 increase in the fare, while $x = -1$ represents a \$0.10 decrease in the fare), then we can write expressions for both the number of passengers and the fare per passenger in terms of x, as follows:

the fare per passenger is $7 + 0.10x$
the number of passengers is $2000 - 40x$.

Since the number of passengers must be at least 1600, $2000 - 40x \geq 1600$, and $x \leq 10$, and since the number of passengers cannot exceed 2600,
$2000 - 40x \leq 2600$, and $x \geq -15$.
The domain is $-15 \leq x \leq 10$.

The revenue function is

$$\begin{aligned} R(x) &= (7 + 0.10x)(2000 - 40x) \\ &= -4x^2 - 80x + 140\,000. \end{aligned}$$

From a practical standpoint, we also require that x be an integer, in order that the fare only varies by increments of \$0.10. We do not wish to consider fares that are other than multiples of 10 cents.

Therefore the problem is now to find the absolute maximum value of the revenue function.

$$\begin{aligned} R(x) &= (7 + 0.10x)(2000 - 40x) \\ &= -4x^2 - 80x + 14\,000 \end{aligned}$$

on the interval $-15 \leq x \leq 10$, where x must be an integer.

$$\begin{aligned} R'(x) &= -8x - 80 \\ R'(x) &= 0, \text{ when } -8x - 80 = 0 \\ x &= -10 \end{aligned}$$

$R'(x)$ is never undefined. The only critical point for R occurs at $x = 10$, which is in the domain. To determine the absolute maximum revenue, we evaluate

$$\begin{aligned} R(-15) &= -4(-15)^2 - 80(-15) + 14\,000 \\ &= 11\,900 \\ R(-10) &= -4(-10)^2 - 80(-10) + 14\,000 \\ &= 14\,400 \\ R(10) &= -4(10)^2 - 80(10) + 14\,000 \\ &= 12\,800. \end{aligned}$$

Therefore, the maximum revenue occurs when there are -10 fare increases of \$0.10 each, or a fare decrease of $10(0.10) = \$1.00$. At a fare of \$6.00, the daily revenue is \$14 400 and the number of passengers is $2000 - 40(-10) = 2400$.

EXAMPLE 3

In this example, we consider soot deposits from a smokestack. Suppose that a smokestack deposits soot on the ground with a concentration that is inversely proportional to the square of the distance from the foot of the stack (we ignore the height of the stack). For an object located x km from a smokestack, the concentration of soot is modelled by the function $S(x) = \frac{k}{x^2}$, where $k > 0$ is the constant of proportionality that depends on the quantity of smoke emitted by the stack.

If two smokestacks are located 20 km apart, and one is emitting 7 times as much smoke as the other, where on the (straight line) road between the two stacks should a building be built so that the concentration of soot deposit is minimal?

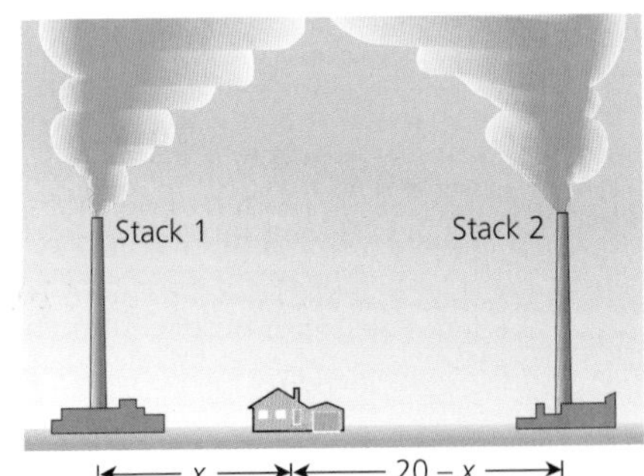

Solution

Let the distance from the building to the stack with lesser emissions be x km. Then the distance from the building to the second stack is $(20 - x)$ km.

Let the constant of proportionality of the first stack be $k > 0$.
Then the constant of proportionality of the second stack (with greater emissions) is 7 k.

The concentration of soot deposit from the first stack is $\frac{k}{x^2}$.

The concentration of soot deposit from the second stack is $\frac{7k}{(20 - x)^2}$.

The total concentration is given by

$$S(x) = \frac{k}{x^2} + \frac{7k}{(20 - x)^2},$$

and since the building is between the stacks, $0 < x < 20$.

To find the critical points of $S(x)$, set $S'(x) = 0$.

$$S'(x) = -\frac{2k}{x^3} + \frac{14k}{(20 - x)^3}$$

If $S'(x) = 0$, $-\frac{2k}{x^3} + \frac{14k}{(20 - x)^3} = 0$

or $$\frac{7k}{(20 - x)^3} = \frac{k}{x^3}$$ (and k has no impact)

$$7x^3 = (20 - x)^3$$
$$\sqrt[3]{7}x = 20 - x$$
$$(1 + \sqrt[3]{7})x = 20$$
$$x = \frac{20}{1 + \sqrt[3]{7}}$$
$$\cong 6.9.$$

There is one critical value at $x \cong 6.9$.
Since there are no fixed domain end points, we use the first derivative test to determine whether this gives a minimal value.

If $0 < x < 6.9$, $\quad S'(x) = -\frac{2k}{x^3} + \frac{14k}{(20 - x)^3}$

$$= -2k\left[\frac{1}{x^3} - \frac{7}{(20 - x)^3}\right]$$
$$< 0.$$

Then $S(x)$ is decreasing.

If $6.9 < x < 20$, $\quad S'(x) = -2k\left[\frac{1}{x^3} - \frac{7}{(20 - x)^3}\right]$

$$> 0.$$

Then $S(x)$ is increasing.
Then a relative minimum occurs at $x = 6.9$, and by the test it is an absolute minimum. The building should be 6.9 km from the smokestack with fewer emissions.

In summary, when solving real-life optimization problems, there are often many factors that can affect the required functions and their domains. Such factors may not be obvious from the statement of the problem. We must do research and ask many questions to address all of the factors. Solving an entire problem is a series of many steps, and optimization using calculus techniques is only one step that is used in determining a solution.

Exercise 5.6

Part A

Knowledge/ Understanding

1. The cost, in dollars, to produce x litres of maple syrup for the Elmira Maple Syrup Festival is $C(x) = 75(\sqrt{x} - 10)$, $x \geq 400$.
   a. What is the average cost of producing 625 L?
   b. The marginal cost is $C'(x)$, and similarly, the marginal revenue is $R'(x)$. What is the marginal cost at 1225 L?
   c. How much production is needed to achieve a marginal cost of \$0.50/L?

Application

2. A sociologist determines that a foreign-language student has learned $N(t) = 20t - t^2$ vocabulary terms after t hours of uninterrupted study.

   a. How many terms are learned between times $t = 2$ and $t = 3$ h?

   b. What is the rate in terms per hour at which the student is learning at time $t = 2$ h?

   c. What is the maximum rate in terms per hour at which the student is learning?

3. A researcher found that the level of antacid in a person's stomach t minutes after a certain brand of antacid tablet is taken is found to be $L(t) = \frac{6t}{t^2 + 2t + 1}$.

   a. Find the value of t for which $L'(t) = 0$.

   b. Find $L(t)$ for the value found in part **a**.

   c. Using your graphing calculator, graph $L(t)$.

   d. From the graph, what can you predict about the level of antacid in a person's stomach after 1 min?

   e. What is happening to the level of antacid in a person's stomach from $2 \leq t \leq 8$ min?

4. The running cost, C, in dollars per hour for an airplane cruising at a height of h metres and an air speed of 200 km/h is given by $C = 4000 + \frac{h}{15} + \frac{15\,000\,000}{h}$ for the domain $1000 \leq h \leq 20\,000$. Find the height at which the operating cost is at a minimum and find the operating cost per hour.

Application

5. A rectangular piece of land is to be fenced in using two kinds of fencing. Two opposite sides will be fenced using standard fencing that costs \$6/m, while the other two sides will require heavy-duty fencing that costs \$9/m. What are the dimensions of the rectangular lot of greatest area that can be fenced in for a cost of \$9000?

Thinking/Inquiry/ Problem Solving

6. A 20 000 m^3 rectangular cistern is to be made from reinforced concrete so that the interior length will be twice the height. If the cost is \$40/m^2 for the base, \$100/m^2 for the side walls, and \$200/m^2 for the roof, then find the interior dimensions (correct to one decimal place) that will keep the cost to a minimum. To protect the water table, the building code specifies that no excavation can be more than 22 m deep. It also specifies that all cisterns must be at least 1 m in depth.

7. The cost of producing an ordinary cylindrical tin can is determined by the materials used for the wall and the end pieces. If the end pieces are twice as expensive per square centimetre as the wall, find the dimensions (to the nearest millimetre) to make a 1000 cm^3 can at minimal cost.

8. A lighthouse, L, is located on a small island 4 km west of point A on a straight north-south coastline. A power cable is to be laid from L to the nearest source of power at point B on the shoreline, 12 km north of point A. The cost of laying cable under water is \$6000/km and the cost of laying cable along the shoreline is \$2000/km. To minimize the cost, the power line will be built from L underwater to a point C on the shoreline and then along the shoreline from C to B. Find the location of point C (to the nearest metre) on the shoreline where the power cable should enter the water.

9. A bus service carries 10 000 people daily between Cyberville and Steeptown, and the company has space to serve up to 15 000 people per day. The cost to ride the bus is \$20. Market research shows that if the fare is increased by \$0.50, 200 fewer people will ride the bus. What fare should be charged to get maximum revenue, given that the bus company must have at least \$130 000 in fares a day to cover operating costs.

10. The fuel cost per hour for running a ship is approximately one half the cube of the speed plus additional fixed costs of \$216 per hour. Find the most economical speed to run the ship for a 500-nautical-mile trip. *Note:* This assumes that there are no major disturbances such as heavy tides or stormy seas.

11. A truck crossing the prairies at a constant speed of 110 km/h gets 8 km/L of gas. Gas costs \$0.68/L. The truck loses 0.10 km/L in fuel efficiency for each km/h increase in speed. Drivers are paid \$35/h in wages and benefits. Fixed costs for running the truck are \$15.50/h. If a trip of 450 km is planned, what speed will minimize operating expenses?

Communication

12. Your neighbours operate a successful bake shop. One of their specialties is a very rich whipped-cream-covered cake. They buy the cakes from a supplier who charges \$6.00 per cake, and they sell 200 cakes weekly at a price of \$10.00 each. Research shows that profit from the cake sales can be increased by increasing the price. Unfortunately, for every increase of \$0.50 cents, sales will drop by seven.

    a. What is the optimal sales price for the cake to obtain a maximal weekly profit?

    b. The supplier, unhappy with reduced sales, informs the owners that if they purchase fewer than 165 cakes weekly, the cost per cake will increase to \$7.50. Now what is the optimal sales price per cake and what is the total weekly profit?

    c. Situations like this occur regularly in retail trade. Discuss the implications of reduced sales with increased total profit versus greater sales with smaller profits. For example, a drop in the number of customers means fewer sales of associated products.

Part C

13. If the cost of producing x items is given by the function $C(x)$, and the total revenue when x items are sold is $R(x)$, then the profit function is $P(x) = R(x) - C(x)$. Show that the profit function has a critical point when the marginal revenue equals the marginal cost.

14. A fuel tank is being designed to contain 200 m^3 of gasoline; however, the maximum length tank that can be safely transported to clients is 16 m long. The design of the tank calls for a cylindrical part in the middle with hemispheres at each end. If the hemispheres are twice as expensive per unit area as the cylindrical wall, then find the radius and height of the cylindrical part so that the cost of manufacturing the tank will be minimal. Give the answer correct to the nearest centimetre.

15. The illumination of an object by a light source is directly proportional to the strength of the source and inversely proportional to the square of the distance from the source. If two light sources, one three times as strong as the other, are placed 10 m apart, where should an object be placed on the line between the two lights so as to receive the least illumination?

16. During a cough, the diameter of the trachea decreases. The velocity, v, of air in the trachea during a cough may be modelled by the formula $v(r) = Ar^2(r_0 - r)$, where A is a constant, r is the radius of the trachea during the cough, and r_0 is the radius of the trachea in a relaxed state. Find the radius of the trachea when the velocity is the greatest, and find the associated maximum velocity of air. Note that the domain for the problem is $0 \leq r \leq r_0$.

Key Concepts Review

In Chapter 5, you have considered a variety of applications of derivatives.

You should now be familiar with the following concepts:

- $y = f(x)$ defines y explicitly as a function of x. For example, $y = x^3 - 4x + 2$.
- An equation involving both x and y, as in $x = y^2 + 1$, is said to define y implicitly as a function of x. For implicit differentiation, we differentiate both sides of the equation with respect to x. The Chain Rule is used when differentiating terms containing y.
- The position, velocity, and acceleration functions are $s(t)$, $v(t)$, and $a(t)$ respectively, where $v(t) = s'(t)$ and $a(t) = v'(t) = s''(t)$
- The algorithm for maximum and minimum values
- Derivatives in the social sciences that involve cost, revenue, and profit
- Related-rate problems
- Optimization problems. Remember that you must first create a function to analyze and that restrictions in the domain may be crucial.

CHAPTER 5: MAXIMIZING PROFITS

A construction company has been offered a build-operate contract for $7.8 million to construct and operate a trucking route for five years to transport ore from a mine site to a smelter. The smelter is located on a major highway and the mine is 3 km into the bush off the road.

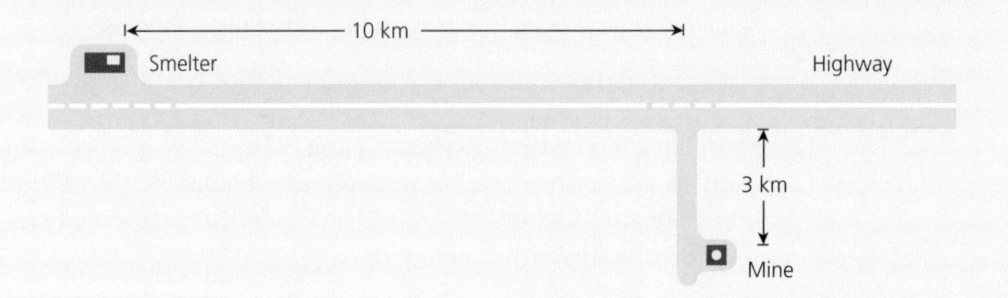

Construction (capital) costs are estimated as follows:

- Upgrade to the highway (i.e., repaving) will be $200 000/km.
- New gravel road from the mine to the highway will be $500 000/km.

Operating conditions are as follows:

- There will be 100 return trips each day for 300 days a year for each of the five years the mine will be open.
- Operating costs on the gravel road will be $65/h and average speed will be 40 km/h.
- Operating costs on the highway will be $50/h and average speed will be 70 km/h.

Use calculus to determine if the company will accept the contract and the distances of the paved and gravel road sections producing optimum conditions (maximum profit). What is the maximum profit? Do not consider the time value of money in your calculations.

Review Exercise

1. Find $\frac{dy}{dx}$ for each of the following:

   a. $x^3 + y^5 = 6$ b. $\frac{1}{x^2} + \frac{1}{y^2} = 5$ c. $y^3 = \frac{x-1}{x+1}$

   d. $x^2y^{-3} + 3 = y$ e. $y^7 - 2x^7y^5 = 10$ f. $x^{\frac{2}{5}} + y^{\frac{3}{5}} = x$

2. Find $\frac{dy}{dx}$ at the indicated point.

   a. $x^3 + y^3 = 18xy$ at $(8, 4)$ b. $(x^2 + y^2)^2 = 4x^2y$ at $(1,1)$

3. Find the slopes of the lines tangent to the graph of $x^{-2}y^6 + 2y^{-2} - 6 = 0$ at the point $(0.5, 1)$ and at the point $(0.5, -1)$.

4. Find f' and f'', if $f(x) = x^4 - \frac{1}{x^4}$.

5. For $y = x^9 - 7x^3 + 2$, find $\frac{d^2y}{dx^2}$.

6. For the relation $3x^2 - y^2 = 7$, show that $y'' = -\frac{21}{y^3}$.

7. Find the velocity and acceleration of an object that moves along a straight line in such a way that its coordinate $s(t)$ is $s(t) = t^2 + (2t - 3)^{\frac{1}{2}}$.

8. Find the velocity and acceleration as functions of time, t, for $s(t) = t - 7 + \frac{5}{t}$, $t \neq 0$.

9. A pellet is shot into the air. Its position above the ground at any time, t, is defined by $s(t) = 45t - 5t^2$ metres. For what values of t seconds, $t \geq 0$, is the upward velocity of the pellet positive? Zero? Negative? Draw a graph to represent the velocity of the pellet.

10. Determine the maximum and minimum of each function on the given interval.

    a. $f(x) = 2x^3 - 9x^2$, $-2 \leq x \leq 4$

    b. $f(x) = 12x - x^3$, $-3 \leq x \leq 5$

    c. $f(x) = 2x + \frac{18}{x}$, $1 \leq x \leq 5$

11. A motorist starts braking when she sees a stop sign. After t seconds, the distance (in metres) from the front of her car to the sign is $s(t) = 62 - 16t + t^2$.

a. How far was the front of the car from the sign when she started braking?

b. Does the car go beyond the stop sign before stopping?

c. Explain why it is unlikely that the car would hit another vehicle that is travelling perpendicular to the motorist's road when her car first comes to a stop at the intersection.

12. Find the equation of the tangent to the graph $y^3 - 3xy - 5 = 0$ at the point $(2, -1)$.

13. The position function of an object that moves in a straight line is $s(t) = 1 + 2t - \frac{8}{t^2 + 1}$, $0 \leq t \leq 2$. Find the maximum and minimum velocities of the object over the given time interval.

14. Suppose that the cost (in dollars) of manufacturing x items is approximated by $C(x) = 625 + 15x + 0.01x^2$, for $1 \leq x \leq 500$. The unit cost (the cost of manufacturing one item) would then be $U(x) = \frac{C(x)}{x}$. How many items should be manufactured in order to ensure that the unit cost is minimized?

15. For each of the following cost functions, find, in dollars,

a. the cost of producing 400 items.

b. the average cost of each of the first 400 items produced.

c. the marginal cost when $x = 400$, as well as the cost of producing the 401st item.

i) $C(x) = 3x + 1000$

ii) $C(x) = 0.004x^2 + 40x + 8000$

iii) $C(x) = \sqrt{x} + 5000$

iv) $C(x) = 100x^{-\frac{1}{2}} + 5x + 700$

16. Find the production level that minimizes the average cost per unit for the cost function $C(x) = 0.004x^2 + 40x + 16\,000$. Show that it is a minimum by using a graphing calculator to sketch the graph of the average cost function.

17. a. The position of an object moving along a straight line is described by the function $s(t) = 3t^2 - 10$ for $t \geq 0$. Is the object moving away from or towards its starting position when $t = 3$?

b. Repeat the problem using $s(t) = -t^3 + 4t^2 - 10$ for $t \geq 0$.

18. Sand is being poured onto a conical pile at the rate of 9 m^3/h. Friction forces in the sand are such that the slope of the sides of the conical pile is always $\frac{2}{3}$.

    a. How fast is the altitude increasing when the radius of the base of the pile is 6 m?

    b. How fast is the radius of the base increasing when the height of the pile is 10 m?

19. Digging in his backyard, Dennis accidentally breaks a pipe attached to his water-sprinkling system. Water bubbles up at a rate of 1 cm^3/s, forming a circular pond of depth 0.5 cm in his yard. How quickly is the surface area of the pond covering his lawn?

20. The surface area of a cube is changing at a rate of 8 cm^2/s. How fast is the volume changing when the surface area is 60 cm^2?

21. A coffee filter has the shape of an inverted cone. Water drains out of the filter at a rate of 10 cm^3/min. When the depth of water in the cone is 8 cm, the depth is decreasing at 2 cm/min. What is the ratio of the height of the cone to its radius?

22. A floodlight that is 15 m away and at ground level illuminates a building. A man 2 m tall walks away from the light directly towards the building at 2 m/s. Is the length of his shadow on the building increasing or decreasing? Find the rate of change of the length of his shadow when he is 4 m from the light.

23. A particle moving along a straight line will be s cm from a fixed point at time t seconds, where $t > 0$ and $s = 27t^3 + \frac{16}{t} + 10$.

    a. Find when the velocity will be zero.

    b. Is this a maximum or a minimum velocity?

    c. Is the particle accelerating? Explain.

24. A box with a square base and no top must have a volume of 10 000 cm^3. If the smallest dimension in any direction is 5 cm, then determine the dimensions of the box that minimize the amount of material used.

25. An animal breeder wishes to create five adjacent rectangular pens, each with an area of 2400 m^2. To ensure that the pens are large enough for grazing, the minimum for either dimension must be 10 m. Find the dimensions for the pens in order to keep the amount of fencing used to a minimum.

26. You are given a piece of sheet metal that is twice as long as it is wide and the area of the sheet is 800 square decametres. Find the dimensions of the rectangular box that would contain a maximum volume if it were constructed from this piece of metal. The box will not have a lid. Give your answer correct to one decimal place.

27. A cylindrical can is to hold 500 cm^3 of apple juice. The design must take into account that the height must be between 6 and 15 cm, inclusive. How should the can be constructed so that a minimum amount of material will be used in the construction? (Assume that there will be no waste.)

28. In oil pipeline construction, the cost of pipe to go under water is 60% more than the cost of pipe used in dry land situations. A pipeline comes to a 1-km-wide river at point A, and it must be extended to a refinery, R, on the other side that is 8 km down a straight river. Find the best way to cross the river so that the total cost of the pipe is kept to a minimum. (Answer to the nearest metre.)

29. A train leaves the station at 10:00 and travels due north at a speed of 100 km/h. Another train has been heading due west at 120 km/h and reaches the same station at 11:00. At what time were the two trains closest together?

30. A store sells portable CD players for $100 each, and at this price the store sells 120 CD players every month. The owner of the store wishes to increase his profit, and he estimates that for every $2 increase in the price of CD players, one less CD player will be sold each month. If each CD player costs the store $70, at what price should the store sell the CD players to maximize profit?

31. An offshore oil well, P, is located in the ocean 5 km from the nearest point on the shore, A. A pipeline is to be built to take oil from P to a refinery that is 20 km along the straight shoreline from A. If it costs $100 000 per kilometre to lay pipe underwater and only $75 000 per kilometre to lay pipe on land, what route from the well to the refinery will be the cheapest? (Give your answer correct to the nearest metre.)

Chapter 5 Test

Achievement Category	Questions
Knowledge/Understanding	All questions
Thinking/Inquiry/Problem Solving	9, 11
Communication	5b
Application	4, 5, 6, 10

1. Find $\frac{dy}{dx}$ if $x^2 + 4xy - y^2 = 8$.

2. Find the equation of the tangent to $3x^2 + 4y^2 = 7$ at $P(-1, 1)$.

3. An object starts at rest and moves along a horizontal trail. Its position, s, in metres, after t seconds is given by $s(t) = t^3 - 9t^2 + 24t + 5$, $t \geq 0$.
   a. Find the average velocity from $t = 1$ s to $t = 6$ s.
   b. At what time(s) is the object at rest?
   c. Determine its acceleration after 5 s.
   d. Is the object moving towards or away from the origin when $t = 3$ s? Justify your answer.

These formulas may be helpful for the following questions.

Sphere $V = \frac{4}{3}\pi r^3$, $S = 4\pi r^2$ **Cone** $V = \frac{1}{3}\pi r^2 h$

Cylinder $V = \pi r^2 h$, $S = 2\pi rh + 2\pi r^2$ **Circle** $C = 2\pi r$, $A = \pi r^2$

4. Assume that oil spilled from a ruptured tanker spreads in a circular pattern whose radius increases at a constant rate of 2 m/s. How fast is the area of the spill increasing when the radius of the spill is 60 m?

5. The radius of a sphere is increasing at a rate of 2 m/min.
   a. Find the rate of change of the volume when the radius is 8 m.
   b. Explain why the rate of change of the volume of the sphere is not constant even though $\frac{dr}{dt}$ is constant.

6. At a certain instant, each edge of a cube is 5 cm long and the volume is increasing at a rate of 2 cm^3/min. How fast is the surface area of the cube increasing?

7. An inverted conical water tank has a radius of 10 m at the top and is 24 m high. If water flows into the tank at a rate of 20 m^3/min, how fast is the depth of the water increasing when the water is 16 m deep?

8. Determine the extreme values of the function $f(x) = \frac{x^2 - 1}{x + 2}$ on the domain $-1 \leq x \leq 3$.

9. A figure skater is directly beneath a spotlight 10 m above the ice. If she skates away from the light at a rate of 6 m/s and the spot follows her, how fast is her shadow's head moving when she is 8 m from her starting point? The skater is (almost) 1.6 m tall with her skates on.

10. A man has purchased 2000 m of used wire fencing at an auction. He and his wife want to use the fencing to create three adjacent rectangular paddocks. Find the dimensions of the paddocks so the fence encloses the largest possible area.

11. An engineer working on a new generation of computer called The Beaver is using very compact VLSI circuits. The container design for the CPU is to be determined by marketing considerations and must be a rectangular solid in shape. It must contain exactly 10 000 cm^3 of interior space, and the length must be twice the height. If the cost of the base is \$0.02/cm^2, the cost of the side walls is \$0.05/cm^2, and the cost of the upper face is \$0.10/cm^2, find the dimensions to the nearest millimetre that will keep the cost of the container to a minimum.

Chapter 6

THE EXPONENTIAL FUNCTION

Are you thinking of buying a computer? Moore's Law suggests that the processing power of computers doubles every eighteen months, which means that in a year and a half from today, computers will be twice as powerful as they are now! This is an example of exponential growth. In this chapter, you will study the exponential functions that can be used to describe and make predictions about the growth of biological populations, including human populations and populations of cancerous cells, the growth of financial investments, the growth of the Internet, and the decaying of radioactive substances. Another application of exponential functions occurs in psychology, where it has been noted that, in certain circumstances, there is an exponential relationship between the size of a stimulus and a nerve's response to the stimulus. The common feature in all these situations and many others is that the amount of growth or decline at any point in time is directly proportional to the size of the thing that is growing or declining.

CHAPTER EXPECTATIONS In this chapter, you will

- identify key properties of exponential functions, **Section 6.1, 6.2**
- determine intercepts and positions of the asymptotes to a graph, **Section 6.2, 6.3**
- describe graphical implications of changes in parameters, **Section 6.3**
- describe the significance of exponential growth or decay, **Section 6.4, 6.5**
- pose and solve problems related to models of exponential functions, **Section 6.4, 6.5, Career Link**
- predict future behaviour by extrapolating from a mathematical model, **Section 6.5**

Review of Prerequisite Skills

In this chapter, you will be studying the exponential function. You will require a knowledge of rational exponents, such as the following:

- $x^0 = 1$
- $x^{-n} = \frac{1}{x^n}, x \neq 0$
- $a^{\frac{p}{q}} = (\sqrt[q]{a})^p$ or $\sqrt[q]{a^p}$

In this chapter you will also be working with transformations.

Exercise

1. Find the value of each of the following:

   a. 4^3 b. $(-3)^2$ c. -3^3 d. $\left(\frac{3}{4}\right)^2$

2. Write the following with positive exponents:

   a. x^{-7} b. $5m^{-2}$ c. $(3b)^{-3}$ d. $\frac{1}{w^{-5}}$ e. $\left(\frac{2}{3}\right)^{-2}$

3. Evaluate the following:

   a. 5^{-2} b. $\left(\frac{2}{3}\right)^{-1}$ c. $\left(\frac{3}{4}\right)^{-3}$ d. $\frac{2^{-1} + 2^{-2}}{3^{-1}}$

4. Evaluate the following:

   a. $4^{\frac{1}{2}}$ b. $27^{\frac{1}{3}}$ c. $\left(\frac{1}{8}\right)^{\frac{1}{3}}$

5. a. Sketch the following functions on the same grid:

   $y_1 = x^2$, $y_2 = x^2 + 4$, and $y_3 = x^2 - 3$.

   b. Describe

   i) the transformation of the graph of y_1 to y_2.

   ii) the transformation of the graph of y_1 to y_3.

   c. Without sketching, describe the transformation of the graph of $y = x^2 - 2$ to the graph of $y = x^2 + 2$.

   d. Describe what happens when a positive or negative constant is added to a function.

6. a. Sketch the following functions on the same grid:

   $y_1 = x^2$, $y_2 = \frac{1}{2}x^2$, and $y_3 = -2x^2$.

   b. Describe

      i) the transformation of the graph of y_1 to y_2.

      ii) the transformation of the graph of y_1 to y_3.

   c. Without sketching, describe the transformation of the graph of $y = x^2$ to the graph of $y = 3x^2 + 25$.

   d. Describe what happens when a function is multiplied by a constant c, where $c < 0$, $0 < c < 1$, and $c > 1$.

7. a. Sketch the following functions on the same grid:

   $y_1 = x^2$, $y_2 = (x - 5)^2$, and $y_3 = -(x + 3)^2$.

   b. Describe

      i) the transformation of the graph of y_1 to y_2.

      ii) the transformation of the graph of y_1 to y_3.

   c. Without sketching, describe the transformation of the graph of $y = x^2$ to the graph of $y = (x + 6)^2 - 7$.

   d. Describe what happens when a positive or negative constant is added to the variable in a function.

Career Link investigate

CHAPTER 6: DISCOVERING EXPONENTIAL GROWTH PATTERNS

If you have suffered from the bacterial infection streptococcal pharyngitis, better known as strep throat, you have had first-hand experience with exponential growth. Not all applications of exponential growth are so negative, however. Bacteria are used in a multitude of biotechnology applications, including the destruction of hazardous wastes such as PCBs, toxins that otherwise would be very difficult to remove from our natural environment. Other applications with exponential patterns include the mathematics of investment (growth) and the carbon dating of archeological relics (decay). In this chapter, you will investigate patterns in exponential graphs, solve problems following exponential growth and decay patterns, and build and manipulate mathematical models following exponential patterns.

Case Study — Agricultural Entomologist

Faced with changing weather patterns bringing more severe weather events, Canada's agricultural sector is attempting to create disease- and insect-resistant crops that are adaptable to both dry and wet climates. As part of this process, the population dynamics of insects are thoroughly investigated. An entomologist, an insect researcher, is examining the birth and death patterns of an insect that destroys soy crops. The researcher notices that if no deaths were to occur, the population would grow by 50% each day. She has also observed that 10% of the population, including the new births, dies every day. The starting population is 1000.

DISCUSSION QUESTIONS

1. Complete a table showing the population dynamics to day 5 with the following column headings, then draw a rough sketch of the Start-of-Day versus End-of-Day Population.

Day	Population Start of Day	Births	Deaths	Population End of Day
0	—	—	—	1000
	1000			
5				

2. Considering the relationships you have studied to date (linear, quadratic, higher-degree polynomial, periodic, rational, geometric series), what does this pattern most closely resemble? Explain your reasoning.
3. For "steady-state" conditions to exist (no population growth or decline), what percentage of the population would have to die each day? Explain.
4. Identify at least two other relationships in nature or technology that follow exponential growth or decay patterns (that were not mentioned on this page). Explain why these relationships follow exponential patterns.

At the end of this chapter, you will build, modify, and manipulate an algebraic and graphical mathematical population dynamics model for two insects in an ecosystem.

Section 6.1 — Laws of Exponents

Your study of calculus will require an ability to manipulate rational and negative exponents. The exponent laws enable us to simplify and evaluate expressions involving exponents. Here is a summary of the exponent laws.

Exponent Laws

$a^m \times a^n = a^{m+n}$	$x^{-n} = \frac{1}{x^n}, x \neq 0$
$\frac{a^m}{a^n} = a^{m-n}, a \neq 0$	$\frac{1}{x^{-n}} = x^n, x \neq 0$
$(a^m)^n = a^{mn}$	$\left(\frac{a}{b}\right)^{-n} = \left(\frac{b}{a}\right)^n, a, b \neq 0$
$(ab)^m = a^m b^m$	$a^{\frac{p}{q}} = (\sqrt[q]{a})^p$ or $\sqrt[q]{a^p}$
$\left(\frac{a}{b}\right)^m = \frac{a^m}{b^m}, b \neq 0$	
$x^0 = 1$	Alternatively, $a^{\frac{p}{q}} = \left(a^{\frac{1}{q}}\right)^p$ or $(a^p)^{\frac{1}{q}}$

EXAMPLE 1

Evaluate each of the following:

a. $\frac{5^{-2}}{3^{-3}}$ b. $\frac{2^{-1} + 4^{-1}}{3^{-2}}$ c. $\frac{4^{\frac{3}{2}} - 8^{\frac{1}{3}}}{16^{\frac{1}{4}} \times 25^{\frac{1}{2}}}$

Solution

a. $\frac{5^{-2}}{3^{-3}} = \frac{3^3}{5^2}$

$= \frac{27}{25}$

b. $\frac{2^{-1} + 4^{-1}}{3^{-2}} = \frac{\frac{1}{2} + \frac{1}{4}}{\frac{1}{3^2}}$

$= \frac{\frac{3}{4}}{\frac{1}{9}}$

$= \frac{3}{4} \times \frac{9}{1}$

$= \frac{27}{4}$

c. $\frac{4^{\frac{3}{2}} - 8^{\frac{1}{3}}}{16^{\frac{1}{4}} \times 25^{\frac{1}{2}}} = \frac{8 - 2}{2 \times 5}$

$= \frac{6}{10}$

$= \frac{3}{5}$

EXAMPLE 2

Simplify each of the following, using the laws of exponents.

a. $\sqrt[3]{b^4} \times (b^2)^3$ b. $\frac{a^{\frac{3}{4}} \times a^{\frac{1}{3}}}{a^{\frac{1}{2}}}$

Solution

a. $\sqrt[3]{b^4} \times (b^2)^3 = b^{\frac{4}{3}} \times b^6$

$= b^{\frac{22}{3}}$

b. $\frac{a^{\frac{3}{4}} \times a^{\frac{1}{3}}}{a^{\frac{1}{2}}} = a^{\frac{3}{4} + \frac{1}{3} - \frac{1}{2}}$

$= a^{\frac{9+4-6}{12}}$

$= a^{\frac{7}{12}}$

EXAMPLE 3 Simplify, using the laws of exponents.

a. $x^{\frac{2}{3}} \div x^{-\frac{4}{3}}$

b. $\dfrac{(x^2y - xy^2)^3}{(xy)^4}$

Solution

a. $x^{\frac{2}{3}} \div x^{-\frac{4}{3}} = x^{\frac{2}{3}-\left(-\frac{4}{3}\right)}$

$= x^2$

b. $\dfrac{(x^2y - xy^2)^3}{(xy)^4} = \dfrac{[xy(x - y)]^3}{(xy)^4}$

$= \dfrac{(xy)^3(x - y)^3}{(xy)^4}$

$= \dfrac{(x - y)^3}{xy}$

Exercise 6.1

Part A

1. Evaluate each of the following, using the laws of exponents.

a. $(7^3)^2 \div 7^4$
b. $(0.4)^5 \div (0.4)^3$
c. $(\sqrt{3})^5 \times (\sqrt{3})^3$
d. $25^{\frac{3}{2}}$
e. $(-8)^{\frac{2}{3}}$
f. $(-2)^3 \times (-2)^3$
g. $4^{-2} - 8^{-1}$
h. $(a^4 \div a^7) \times a^3$
i. $(0.3)^3 \div (0.3)^5$
j. $(p^2)^3 \div (p^3)^2$
k. $(3^2)^3 \div 3^{-2}$
l. $(3^{-1})^3 \times 3^2$
m. $(-2)^3 \times 2^{-4}$
n. $(2^3)^{-2} \times (2^{-2})^2$
o. $(6^3)^4 \div 12^6$

Knowledge/Understanding

2. Simplify each of the following, using the laws of exponents.

a. $\dfrac{x^5y^2}{x^3y^4}$
b. $(xy^2)(x^3y^2)$
c. $\dfrac{(3a^2b)^2}{(ab^2)^3}$
d. $\dfrac{2^3g^2h^4}{(gh^2)^3}$
e. $(xy^2)^3$
f. $\dfrac{(b^2)^3c^4}{(bc)^5}$
g. $\dfrac{5x^3y^{-4}}{2x^{-2}y^2}$
h. $\dfrac{\pi x^2y}{4xy^3}$
i. $(5x^2y)^{-2}$
j. $(a^2bc^{-1})^3$
k. $(a^2b^{-1})^{-3}$
l. $(ab)^4\left(\dfrac{a^{-2}}{b^{-2}}\right)^2$

Knowledge/Understanding

3. Simplify each of the following:

a. $(3x^{-2}y^3)^{-1}$
b. $(a^{\frac{1}{4}}b^{-\frac{1}{3}})^{-2}$
c. $\left(\dfrac{x^{-3}}{x^{-1}}\right)^{-2}$
d. $\dfrac{(4x^2y^{\frac{1}{3}})^{\frac{1}{2}}}{(8xy^{\frac{1}{4}})^{\frac{1}{3}}}$
e. $\dfrac{(4a^{-2})(2a^3b^2)}{12a^4b^3}$
f. $\dfrac{(5x^{-2}y^0)^3}{(25x^2y)^{\frac{1}{2}}}$

Part B

4. Simplify, using the laws of exponents.

a. $(64x^4)^{\frac{1}{2}}$ b. $\sqrt[4]{16^3}$ c. $(27)^{\frac{4}{3}}$

d. $\sqrt{2a^{\frac{1}{2}}} \times \sqrt{32a^{\frac{3}{4}}}$ e. $\sqrt[3]{27p^6}$ f. $\sqrt[5]{32a^{10}}$

g. $a^{3.4} \times a^{2.6}$ h. $\sqrt[3]{5^2} \div \sqrt[4]{5^5}$ i. $(\sqrt[3]{t})^2 \times \sqrt{t^5}$

Application

5. Simplify, using the laws of exponents.

a. $\dfrac{3^{-1} + 3^{-2}}{3^{-3}}$ b. $\dfrac{ab^2c + a^2bc}{abc}$ c. $\dfrac{(p^2q + pq^3)^3}{p^3q^4}$

d. $\dfrac{x^{-2} - x^{-3}}{2x}$ e. $\dfrac{3t - 2t^{-1}}{t^3}$ f. $\dfrac{3p^2 - p^{-3}}{p^4}$

Thinking/Inquiry/ Problem Solving

6. Simplify each of the following:

a. $\dfrac{x^{\frac{3}{2}} - x^{\frac{1}{2}} - x^{-1}}{x^{-\frac{1}{2}}}$ b. $\dfrac{4 - \sqrt{x}}{x^{\frac{3}{2}}}$ c. $\dfrac{x - 9}{x^{\frac{1}{2}} - 3}$ d. $\dfrac{x - 1}{\sqrt{x} - x}$

Communication

7. Using the laws of exponents, explain why $64^{\frac{1}{6}} = 8^{\frac{1}{3}}$.

Section 6.2 — Investigating $f(x) = b^x$

In this section, you will be investigating the exponential function $f(x) = b^x$. Since you will be drawing several curves on each grid, remember to label each curve with its equation.

INVESTIGATION

technology

1. a. Use your graphing calculator or graphing software to draw the graph of $y = 2^x$. In your notebook, sketch $y = 2^x$, showing the scale on the axes.

   b. Use the TRACE function to find the value of the y-intercept. Label the y-intercept on your sketch.

   c. Using the TRACE function, move the cursor left. Watch the y-values as the cursor moves. What do you notice about these values? The graph approaches the x-axis for small values of x. The line the graph of a function approaches is called an **asymptote.** Label the horizontal asymptote on your sketch and write its equation.

   d. What is the domain and range of $y = 2^x$?

   e. Does the graph cross the x-axis?

   Your finished sketch should look like this:

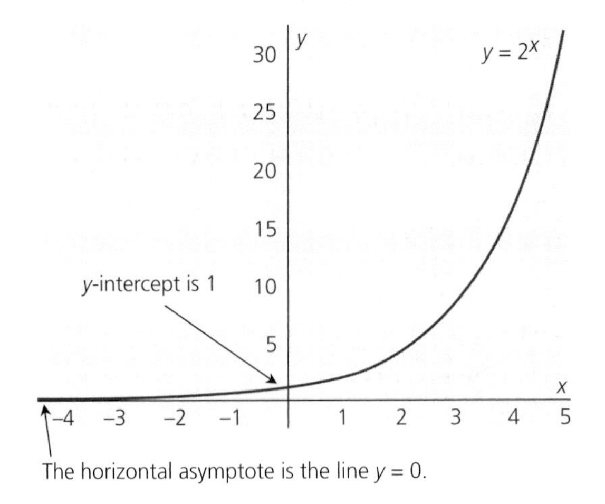

Domain is $x \in R$.
Range is $y > 0, y \in R$.

Notice that $y = 2^x$ is an **increasing function.**

2. Using your graphing calculator or graphing software, investigate the function $y = 5^x$ as you did $y = 2^x$. Draw a sketch of $y = 5^x$, showing the scale, and labelling the y-intercept and the horizontal asymptote. State the domain and range of the function.

3. Use your graphing calculator or graphing software to graph $y = 2^x$, $y = 5^x$, and $y = 10^x$. Sketch, labelling the functions carefully.

a. What are the common characteristics of these curves?
b. Predict where the graph of the curve $y = 7^x$ will lie relative to the curves graphed earlier. Check your prediction with your graphing calculator or graphing software.

4. Write a general description of the graph of the exponential curve $y = b^x$, where $b > 1$. In this description include the y-intercept, horizontal asymptote, domain, range, and a sketch.

5. Investigate the function $y = \left(\frac{1}{3}\right)^x$. Draw a sketch of $y = \left(\frac{1}{3}\right)^x$, showing the scale, and labelling the y-intercept and the horizontal asymptote. State the domain and range of the function. Note that we can express this as $y = 3^{-x}$ rather than $y = \left(\frac{1}{3}\right)^x$.

6. Graph $y = \left(\frac{1}{3}\right)^x$, $y = \left(\frac{1}{5}\right)^x$, and $y = \left(\frac{1}{10}\right)^x$. Sketch, labelling the functions carefully.
   a. What are the common characteristics of these curves?
   b. Predict where the graph of the curve $y = \left(\frac{1}{7}\right)^x$ will be relative to the curves graphed in part **a** of this question. Check your prediction with your graphing calculator or graphing software.

7. Write a general description of the graph of the exponential curve $y = b^x$, where $0 < b < 1$. In this description include the y-intercept, horizontal asymptote, domain, range, and a sketch.

8. Graph $y = 3^x$ and $y = \left(\frac{1}{3}\right)^x$. Sketch, labelling the functions carefully.
   a. What transformation on $y = 3^x$ will give $y = \left(\frac{1}{3}\right)^x$ as its image?
   b. How are the curves alike?
   c. How are they different?

9. Graph $y = 3^x$ and $y = -3^x$.
   a. What transformation on $y = 3^x$ will give $y = -3^x$ as its image?
   b. How are the curves alike?
   c. How are they different?

Properties of the Exponential Function $y = b^x$

- **The base b is positive.**
- **The y-intercept is 1.**
- **The x-axis is a horizontal asymptote.**
- **The domain is the set of real numbers, R.**
- **The range is the set of positive real numbers.**
- **The exponential function is always increasing if $b > 1$.**
- **The exponential function is always decreasing if $0 < b < 1$.**

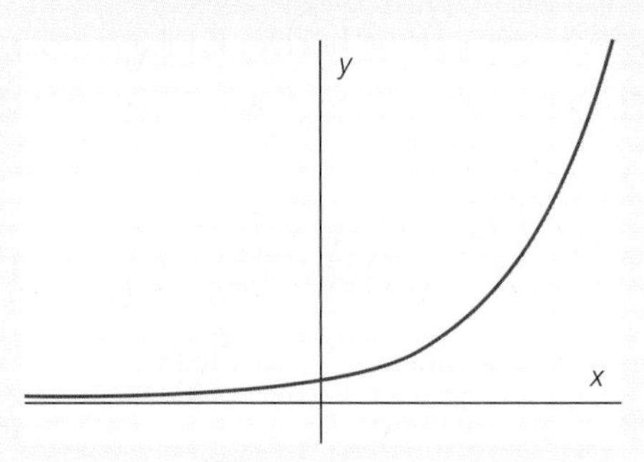

$y = b^x, b > 1$
The function is always increasing.

$y = b^x, 0 < b < 1$
The function is always decreasing.

Exercise 6.2

Part A

Knowledge/
Understanding

1. The graphs below have equations of the form $y = b^x$. Answer the following questions about each of the functions:

a.

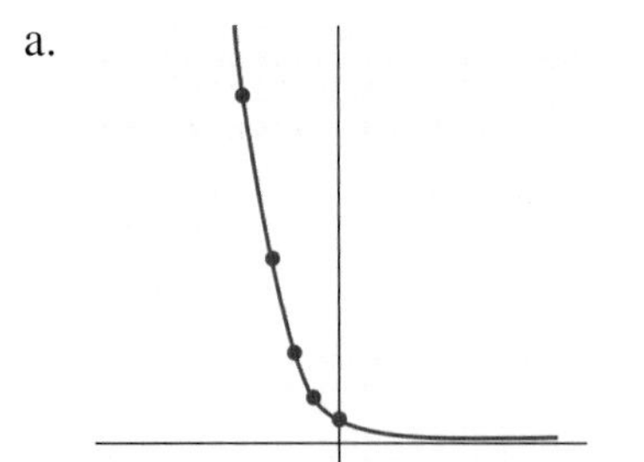

b.

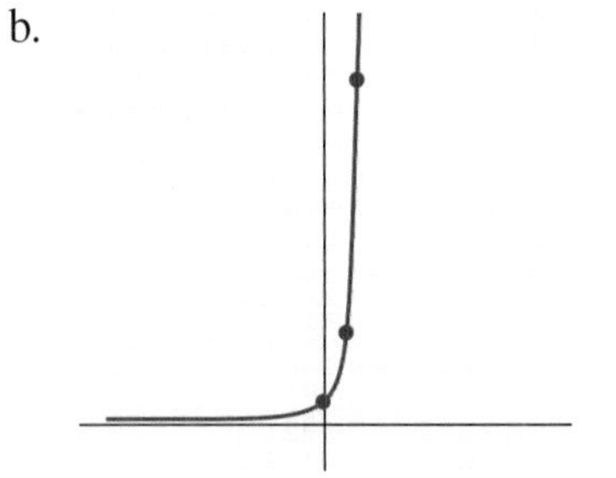

c.

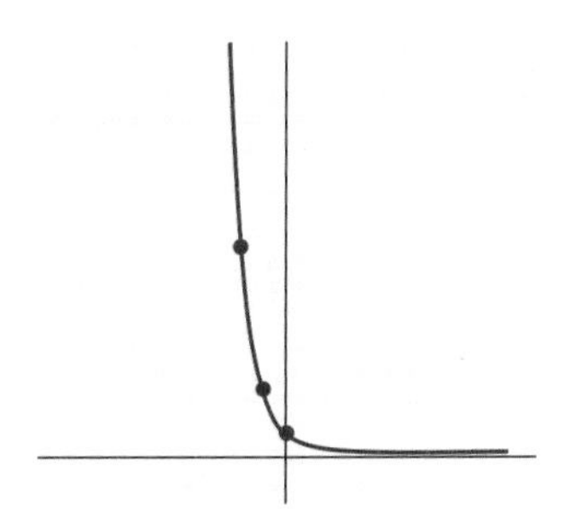

d.

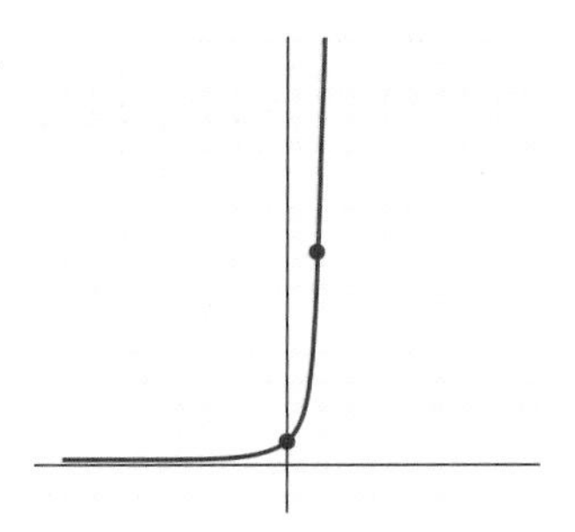

i) What is the value of the y-intercept?

ii) Is the function always increasing or always decreasing?

iii) Is $b > 1$ or is $0 < b < 1$?

iv) What is the value of y when $x = 1$ or $x = -1$?

v) Use the information you gained in parts **i** to **iv** write the equation of the function.

Part **B**

Application

2. If f is a function defined by $f(x) = b^x$, where $b > 0$, what can be stated about
   a. the sign of $f(x)$?
   b. the growth behaviour of f?
   c. $f(0)$?

Thinking/Inquiry/ Problem Solving

3. If f is a function defined by $f(x) = b^x$, where $0 < b < 1$, what can be stated about
   a. the sign of $f(x)$?
   b. the growth behaviour of f?
   c. $f(0)$?

Communication

4. Describe how you determine the equation of a function of the form $y = b^x$, $b > 0$, if you are given its graph. You can use only your knowledge of exponential functions and not your calculator. Include sketches to help you describe the procedure you use.

Section 6.3 — Investigating $f(x) = ab^x + c$

You will be investigating the effect of different transformations on the exponential function $f(x) = b^x$, $b > 0$. Since you will be drawing several curves on each grid, remember to label each curve with its equation. Some coloured pencils will also be helpful. When you are describing transformations, remember to use correct mathematical terms such as **translation, reflection,** or **dilatation.**

INVESTIGATION

technology

1. a. Using your graphing calculator or graphing software, draw the graphs of $f(x) = 2^x$, $g(x) = 2^x + 4$, and $h(x) = 2^x - 3$. Draw a sketch in your notebook and label each function.
   b. Describe the transformation of the graph of $f(x)$ to $g(x)$ and the transformation of $f(x)$ to $h(x)$. What is the effect of adding or subtracting a number from the exponential function?
   c. How is the horizontal asymptote of $g(x)$ and $h(x)$ related to the horizontal asymptote of $f(x)$?

2. a. Using your graphing calculator or graphing software, draw the graphs of $f(x) = 2^x + 4$, $g(x) = 3(2^x) + 4$, and $h(x) = 0.5(2^x) + 4$. Draw a sketch in your notebook and label each function.
   b. Describe the transformation of the graph of $f(x)$ to $g(x)$ and the transformation of $f(x)$ to $h(x)$. What is the effect of multiplying the exponential function by a positive number, where the positive number is greater than one and where the positive number is less than one?
   c. How are the horizontal asymptotes of $g(x)$ and $h(x)$ related to the horizontal asymptote of $f(x)$?

Exercise 6.3

Part A

Knowledge/Understanding

1. For each of the following, state
   i) the equation of the horizontal asymptote,
   ii) whether the function is increasing or decreasing,
   iii) the y-intercept.

   a. $y = 3^x - 5$ b. $y = 2^x + 4$ c. $y = 4\left(\frac{1}{3}\right)^x$

   d. $y = \left(\frac{1}{2}\right)^x + 2$ e. $y = 2(5^x) - 1$ f. $y = 5\left(\frac{2}{3}\right)^x + 1$

Knowledge/Understanding

2. For the curve $y = 3(4^x) + 5$,

a. determine

i) the horizontal asymptote,

ii) the y-intercept,

iii) whether the curve is increasing or decreasing,

iv) the domain and range.

Application

b. Sketch the curve.

Part B

Knowledge/Understanding

3. For the curve $y = 2\left(\frac{2}{3}\right)^x - 4$,

a. determine

i) the horizontal asymptote,

ii) the y-intercept,

iii) whether the curve is increasing or decreasing,

iv) the domain and range.

Application

b. Sketch the curve.

Communication and Thinking/Inquiry/Problem Solving

4. Describe how you can draw a quick mental picture of the graph for a function of the form $y = ab^x + c$, $b > 0$, by using your knowledge of the effect of changing the parameters a, b, and c. Use specific equations and sketches to help you describe the process.

Section 6.4 — Exponential Growth and Decay

Exponential growth occurs when quantities increase or decrease at a rate proportional to the quantity present. This growth or decay occurs in savings accounts, the size of populations, and the quantity of decay that occurs in radioactive chemicals. All situations of this type can be expressed using the exponential function.

Consider, for example, the population growth of a city. The population is currently 100 000 and is growing at the rate of 5% per year. This is exactly the same situation as the compound interest problems we dealt with in an earlier grade. Each year the population increases by a factor of 1.05, hence the population after one year is 100 000(1.05). After two years, it is (100 000(1.05))1.05 or $100\ 000(1.05)^2$. In the same way, a population of 100 000 increasing at 5% for n years grows to $1000\ 000(1.05)^n$ people, and the function that expresses the population after x years is $f(x) = 100\ 000(1.05)^x$.

EXAMPLE 1

An antique vase was purchased in 2000 for $8000. If the vase appreciates in value by 6% per year, what is its estimated value in the year 2040, to the nearest thousand dollars?

Solution

The value of the vase is given by $f(x) = 8000(1.06)^x$, where x is the time in years.

$$f(40) = 8000(1.06)^{40}$$
$$\doteq 82\ 285.7435$$

In 2040 the vase will be worth approximately $82 000.

EXAMPLE 2

A very convenient measure of population growth is a doubling period. The population of the world was 6 billion in 1999. This population is growing exponentially and doubles every 35 years.

a. Estimate the world population in 2050, to the nearest half billion.
b. When will the population be 24 billion?

Solution

a. If the population doubles, the base for the function must be 2. However, the time for doubling is 35 years, so the exponent must be of the form $\frac{t}{35}$, where t is the number of years. Then the function representing population after t years is $f(t) = 6\left(2^{\frac{t}{35}}\right)$. For the population in 2050, $t = 51$.

$$f(51) = 6\left(2^{\frac{51}{35}}\right) \doteq 16.5$$

The population in 2050 will be approximately 16.5 billion.

b. To determine t such that $f(t) = 24$, we write

$$6\left(2^{\frac{t}{35}}\right) = 24$$

$$2^{\frac{t}{35}} = 4 = 2^2.$$

Then $\frac{t}{35} = 2$

$$t = 70.$$

The population will be 24 billion in 2069.

EXAMPLE 3

We do not always know the rate of increase. In this case, we construct an exponential function with an unknown base and determine the base from the given information. The population of a town was 24 000 in 1980 and 29 000 in 1990.

a. Determine an expression for the population at the time t years after 1980.
b. Use this expression to estimate the population of the town in 2020.

Solution

a. Let the population in t years be $P(t) = P_0 b^t$, where P_0 is the population at time $t = 0$, with $t = 0$ in 1980. Then $P(0) = P_0 b^0 = P_0 = 24$, in thousands.
Now $P(t) = 24b^t$.
We are given that $P(10) = 29$.
Then $24b^{10} = 29$

$$b^{10} = \frac{29}{24}.$$

Taking roots on both sides,

$$b = \left(\frac{29}{24}\right)^{\frac{1}{10}}$$

$$\doteq 1.019.$$

Now $P(t) = 24(1.019)^t$.

b. In the year 2020, $t = 2020 - 1980 = 40$.

$$P(40) = 24(1.019)^{40}$$

$$\doteq 51.16$$

The population in 2020 will be approximately 51 000.

EXAMPLE 4

Just as population growth and inflation can be described by an exponential growth function, radioactive decay and depreciation can be described by an exponential decay function. A car depreciates by 15% per year. If you buy a car for \$15 000, find the value of the car in three years.

Solution

The car depreciates by 15% per year, so the base for the exponential function is $(1 - 0.15) = 0.85$.
The value of the car when $t = 0$ is 15 000.
The value of the car after t years is $V(t) = 15\,000(0.85)^t$.

Then $V(3) = 15\,000(0.85)^3 = 9211.88$.
After three years, the car is worth approximately \$9200.

Scientists use the term "half-life" when discussing substances that are radioactive, like polonium^{210}. Polonium^{210} has a half-life of 140 d. This means that in 140 d, half of the amount of polonium^{210} will have decayed to some other substance. If we start with 10 g of polonium^{210}, after 140 days we will have 5 g of polonium^{210} left. The other 5 g will have decayed to some other substance.

Energy is released and power is generated when a nucleus decays. Devices have been built to extract this energy in a useful form, such as electricity. When a nucleus decays, energy in the form of heat is also released. Devices that use that heat to generate electricity are useful in specialized applications, such as implantable heart pace-makers, power sources for lunar stations, and isolated automated weather stations.

EXAMPLE 5

An isotope of radium is used by a hospital for cancer radiation. The half-life of this radium is 1620 years. If the hospital initially had 10 mg, how much will they have after 50 years?

Solution

Since the radium has a half-life of 1620 years, the base for the exponential function is $\frac{1}{2}$. After time t in years, the amount of radium $A(t)$ is given by

$A(t) = A_0\left(\frac{1}{2}\right)^{\frac{t}{h}}$, where A_0 is the initial amount and h is the half-life.

The hospital initially had 10 mg of radium with a half-life of 1620 years.

Then $A(t) = 10\left(\frac{1}{2}\right)^{\frac{t}{1620}}$.

The amount left after 50 years is $A(50) = 10\left(\frac{1}{2}\right)^{\frac{50}{1620}} = 9.79$ mg.

Exercise 6.4

Part A

1. The population of a city is 810 000. If it is increasing by 4% per year, estimate the population in four years.

2. A painting, purchased for \$10 000 in 1990, increased in value by 8% per year. Find the value of the painting in the year 2000.

3. A river is stocked with 5000 salmon. The population of salmon increases by 7% per year.

   a. Write an expression for the population t years after the salmon were put into the river.

b. What will the population be in

   i) 3 years?

   ii) 15 years?

c. How many years does it take for the salmon population to double?

Knowledge/ Understanding

4. A house was bought six years ago for $175 000. If real-estate values have been increasing at the rate of 4% per year, what is the value of the house now?

5. A used-car dealer sells a five-year-old car for $4200. What was the original value of the car if the depreciation is 15% a year?

Knowledge/ Understanding

6. In the early 1990s, the Canadian dollar was declining in value due to inflation at the rate of 8.3% per year. If the situation continued, what would the dollar be worth five years later?

Part B

Application

7. To determine whether a pancreas is functioning normally, a tracer dye is injected. A normally functioning pancreas secretes 4% of the dye each minute. A doctor injects 0.50 g of the dye. Twenty minutes later, 0.35 g remain. If the pancreas were functioning normally, how much dye should remain?

8. If a bacteria population doubles in 5 d,

   a. when will it be 16 times as large?

   b. when was it $\frac{1}{2}$ of its present population?

   c. when was it $\frac{1}{4}$ of its present population?

   d. when was it $\frac{1}{32}$ of its present population?

9. Inflation is causing things to cost roughly 2% more per year.

   a. A bag of milk costs $3.75 now. Estimate its cost in five years.

   b. i) A movie ticket costs $8.50 now. If inflation continues at 2% per year, when will the ticket cost $10.00?

      ii) How long ago did the movie ticket cost $4.25?

10. An element is decaying at the rate of 12%/h. Initially we have 100 g.

   a. How much remains after 10 h?

   b. How much remains after 30 h?

   c. When will there be 40 g left?

Application **11.** A research assistant made 160 mg of radioactive sodium (Na^{24}) and found that there was only 20 mg left 45 h later.

a. What is the half-life of Na^{24}?

b. Find a function that models the amount A left after t hours.

c. If the laboratory requires 100 mg of Na^{24} 12 h from now, how much Na^{24} should the research assistant make now? (Ignore the 20 mg she currently has.)

d. How much of the original 20 mg would be left in 12 h?

12. A bacteria colony grows at the rate of 15%/h.

a. In how many hours will the colony double in size?

b. In 10 h the bacteria population grows to 1.3×10^3. How many bacteria were there initially?

Thinking/Inquiry/ Problem Solving **13.** People who work frequently in a radiation environment, such as X-ray technicians, dentists, radiologists, or nuclear reactor operations staff, are limited to a 50 mSv (milli-sievert) whole-body radiation dose in any one given year. They wear badges that measure the radiation to which they have been exposed. We all receive radiation from many sources, both naturally occuring and artificial, all the time. The North American average from all sources is approximately 2 mSv/year. We can find these levels increasing if we mountain climb or smoke.

a. Calculate your own radiation exposure in a year, using the information below.

Radiation Source	Amount of Radiation (in milli-sieverts per year)
Cosmic and terrestrial	0.8
Atmospheric fallout	0.05
Internal body	0.3
Living above sea level	0.02 for every 100 m above sea level
Chest or dental x-ray	0.1 for every x-ray
TV watching	0.003 for every 3 h/d
Housing	0.06 if house contains masonry
Flying	0.001 for every hour spent flying
Cigarette smoking (heavy smoker)	60

Communication b. How can you reduce your exposure to radiation?

Communication c. Is there anywhere that is radiation-free?

Application

14. The population of a city was estimated to be 125 000 in 1930 and 500 000 in 1998.

    a. Estimate the population of the city in 2020.

    b. If the population continues to grow at the same rate, when will the population reach 1 million?

Part C

Thinking/Inquiry/ Problem Solving

15. On the day his son is born, an excited father wants to give his new son a season's ticket to watch the father's favourite sports team. A season's ticket costs $900. The father realizes there is no point in buying tickets for a baby only a few hours old, so he decides to put the money aside until the boy is six years old. If inflation is assumed to be 3% per year, how much money should the father put aside so that he can purchase the season's ticket in six years?

Thinking/Inquiry/ Problem Solving

16. Two different strains of cold virus were isolated and put in cultures to grow. Virus A triples every 8 h while virus B doubles every 4.8 h. If each culture has 1000 viruses to start, which has more after 24 h?

Thinking/Inquiry/ Problem Solving

17. With exponential growth, a population will continue to double in equal intervals of time. However, in a finite world, one population influences the growth of another. A garden pond may have water lilies covering part of the surface. Growing conditions are ideal and the number of water lilies doubles, and doubles again. Then the gardener, realizing that the water lilies will soon cover the whole pond, introduces a chemical to kill off many of the plants. The exponential growth pattern is disrupted. But this disruption in the exponential growth pattern would occur without the intervention of the gardener. As the water lilies covered more and more of the pond surface, the plants would compete for food and light. The over-crowding of the plants would reduce the rate of expansion. This levelling off occurs in every example of natural growth.

    Below is a graph of the Canadian population between the years 1860 and 2000.

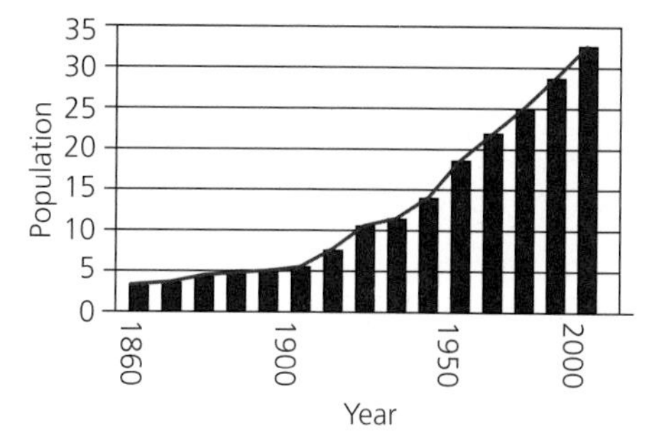

Communication

    a. Why do you think the population of Canada is not growing as fast now as it was earlier in the twentieth century?

Communication

    b. Discuss the factors that affect the population of a country.

Section 6.5 — Modelling Data Using the Exponential Function

At the turn of the last century, scientists discovered that certain naturally occurring substances emitted invisible and penetrating radiation. In such substances, the nucleus spontaneously undergoes a rearrangement that may include the ejection of some nuclear particles and possibly gamma rays. Strontium^{90} is such a substance. Below is a set of measurements for the amount of strontium^{90} remaining after several time intervals have passed. You will be using your graphing calculator to model this data.

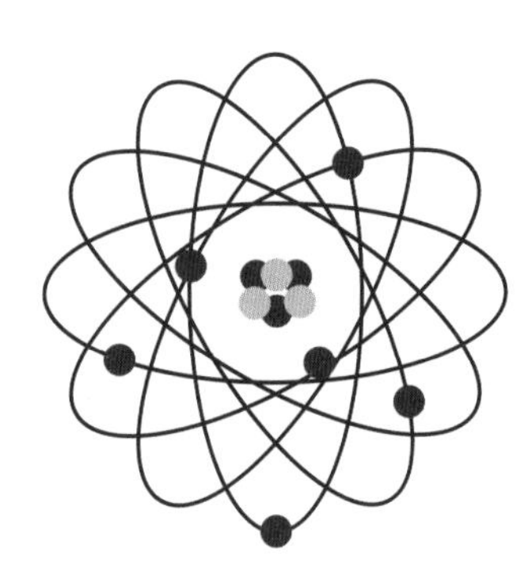

INVESTIGATION

Initially (at time zero) we have 500 mg of strontium^{90}. Here are the results of measuring the amount of strontium^{90} remaining after 6 time intervals have passed.

Number of Time Intervals	Amount of Strontium^{90} (in milligrams)
0	500
1	241
2	112
3	61
4	30
5	18
6	13

technology

a. Use your graphing calculator to draw a scatter plot of the data. Adjust your viewing window so that the graph looks similar to this. Sketch the graph in your notebook. Remember to include the scale and the labels on the axes.

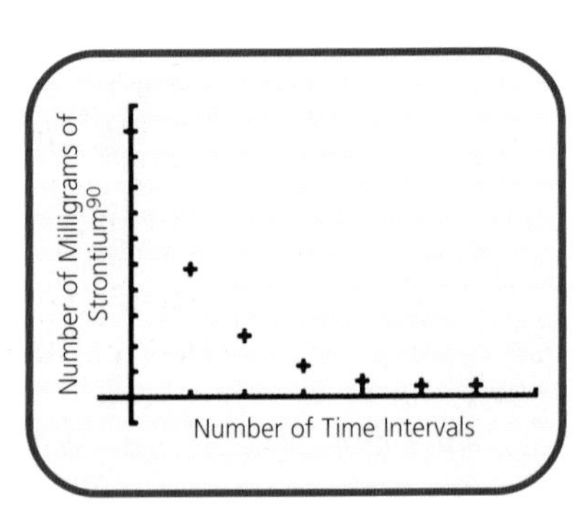

technology

Technical Help

To enter the data, press [STAT]. Under EDIT, select **1:Edit**. Enter the values in L1 and L2.

To draw the scatter plot, turn off all functions in [Y=]. Press [STATPLOT Y=] to obtain the STAT PLOT function. Select **1:Plot 1** and press [ENTER]. Turn plot 1 on, select scatter plot, and L1 and L2 for Xlist and Ylist. Press [WINDOW] to adjust the viewing window. Press [GRAPH] to see the scatter plot.

b. We now want to model this data with a function. If you pictured a curve passing through our points, it would be shaped somewhat like the exponential curve. We will find the curve of best fit determined by your calculator. Use the exponential regression calculation. To three decimal places, the equation is $y = 431.856(0.536)^x$.

technology

Technical Help

To use the exponential regression calculation, press [STAT], then under CALC, select **0:ExpReg**. Press [ENTER] twice. The coefficient and the base of the exponential regression equation are displayed.

c. Using the equation $y = 431.856(0.536)^x$, which we found as a model of the data, estimate the amount of strontium^{90} remaining after 15 time intervals.

d. Using the equation $y = 431.856(0.536)^x$, estimate when there will be 0.5 mg of strontium^{90} remaining.

Use the graphing calculator to draw the graph of $y = 0.536^x$. We can use the TRACE feature of the calculator to approximate the solution to $0.536^x = 0.0012$.

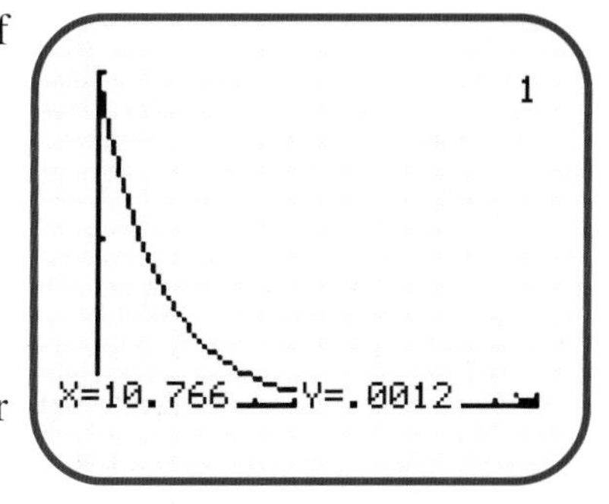

The solution to $0.536^x = 0.0012$ is approximately $x \doteq 10.766$. There will be 0.5 mg of strontium^{90} remaining after approximately 10.8 time intervals. The accuracy of your answer can be improved by using the ZOOM feature of the calculator.

Alternately, you can guess-and-check using the power key on the calculator to find the solution to $0.536^x = 0.0012$.

$$0.536^{10} = 0.0020$$
$$0.536^{11} = 0.0010$$

The value of x must be between 10 and 11. Continue to experiment with values to improve the accuracy of your approximation.

Strontium^{90} has a half-life of 26.8 years. In one half-life, half of this radioactive material will have decayed to some other substance. If we started with 10 g of strontium^{90}, after 26.8 years there should be 5 g left. In our calculations, each time interval represented 26.8 years.

As the term "half-life" indicates, our expression should be of the form $y = a\left(\frac{1}{2}\right)^x$. Since we started with 500 g of strontium^{90}, the expression should be $y = 500\left(\frac{1}{2}\right)^x$.

But things are never quite that precise when data is collected experimentally. Using experimental data allows you to get close to the theoretical equation. The more data points you have, and the more accurate the points are, the better the actual situation will fit the mathematical model.

It is unusual to obtain a good function approximation using $y = b^x$. Most data sets require an exponent of a more complicated form than x, such as $3x^2 - 2x$. Such situations are beyond the scope of this text.

Exercise 6.5

Part B

Knowledge/Understanding

1. A population of bacteria, initially 1000, is growing. The size of the population is measured every hour. The results are shown in the table below.

Number of Time Intervals	Bacteria Population
0	1000
1	1135
2	1307
3	1490
4	1696
5	1957
6	2228

technology

a. Use your graphing calculator to draw a scatter plot of the data. Sketch the scatter plot in your notebook. Include the labels and scales on the axes.

b. Using the exponential regression calculation in your calculator, determine the equation of the curve of best fit. Record this equation accurate to three decimal places.

c. Using the equation of the curve of best fit, estimate the bacteria population in 10 h.

d. Predict when there would be 10 000 bacteria. *Hint:* How many time intervals will this take?

2. Below is a table showing the population of the world. This information came from the United Nations Web site, www.un.org/popin. We will count in intervals of 50 years from 1750.

Year	Time Interval	Population (in billions)
1750	0	0.79
1800	1	0.98
1850	2	1.26
1900	3	1.65
1950	4	2.52
2000	5	6.06

Knowledge/Understanding

a. With your graphing calculator, draw a scatter plot of the data. Using the exponential regression calculation in your calculator, determine the equation of the curve of best fit accurate to three decimal places.

b. Using your mathematical model, estimate the world population in 2050.

Thinking/Inquiry/Problem Solving

c. Predict when there would be 7 billion people on the earth.

3. The table below shows the carbon dioxide concentration in the atmosphere in parts per million. We will count in intervals of 20 years from 1860.

Year	Time Interval	Carbon-Dioxide Concentration (in parts per million)
1860	0	294
1880	1	296
1900	2	300
1920	3	307
1940	4	308
1960	5	319
1980	6	340
2000	7	377

a. With your graphing calculator, draw a scatter plot of the data. Using the exponential regression calculation in your calculator, determine the equation of the curve of best fit accurate to three decimal places.

b. Using your mathematical model, estimate the carbon-dioxide concentration in 1930 and in 1990.

c. If the trend continues, predict when the concentration will be 390 parts per million.

4. The table below shows the amount of stored nuclear waste in million curies. We will count in intervals of five years from 1970.

Year	Time Intervals	Stored Nuclear Waste (in million curies)
1970	0	5
1975	1	30
1980	2	100
1985	3	210
1990	4	360
1995	5	660

a. With your graphing calculator, draw a scatter plot of the data. Using the exponential regression calculation in your calculator, determine the equation of the curve of best fit accurate to three decimal places.

b. Using your mathematical model, estimate the amount of nuclear waste stored in 1983.

c. If this trend continues, predict when the amount of nuclear waste stored will be 800 million curies.

5. Statistics Canada is a government agency that collects and analyzes data about many aspects of life in Canada. On their Web site, www.statcan.ca, you can find the population of the provinces for the last few years. Select one of the provinces. Copy and complete the chart below using the data from the Statistics Canada Web site. Count the time intervals of years from the first entry in your chart.

Year	Time Intervals	Population

a. With your graphing calculator, draw a scatter plot of the data. Using the exponential regression calculation in your calculator, determine the equation of the curve of best fit accurate to three decimal places.

b. Using your mathematical model, estimate the population of that province in 1900.

c. Predict when the population of that province will be 10% greater than its current level.

Communication

6. Given a set of data, describe how you can predict the algebraic form of a mathematical model to fit the data. Use sketches to illustrate your answer.

Part C

Thinking/Inquiry/ Problem Solving

7. You have likely observed that the models obtained by using your calculator provide a rather poor fit for the data. This is because your calculator uses only one exponential function, namely $f(x) = Ab^x$. By changing the exponent to $px^2 + qx$, a much better fit of the data can be obtained. You may be interested in using more sophisticated exponents with the data given in the problems of this section to see whether you can determine functions that better describe the situation. This will require a computer with algebraic capability.

Key Concepts Review

In Chapter 6, you learned how to identify key properties of exponential functions, and to determine intercepts and positions of the asymptotes to a graph. You should now know how to describe graphical implications of changes in parameters, as well as how to describe the significance of exponential growth or decay. You should not only be able to pose and solve problems related to models of exponential functions, but also to predict future behaviour by extrapolating from a mathematical model. Here is a brief summary of the concepts covered in this chapter.

Exponent Laws

- $a^m \times a^n = a^{m+n}$
- $\frac{a^m}{a^n} = a^{m-n}, a \neq 0$
- $(a^m)^n = a^{mn}$
- $(ab)^m = a^m b^m$
- $\left(\frac{a}{b}\right)^m = \frac{a^m}{b^m}, b \neq 0$
- $x^0 = 1$
- $x^{-n} = \frac{1}{x^n}, x \neq 0$
- $\frac{1}{x^{-n}} = x^n, x \neq 0$
- $\left(\frac{a}{b}\right)^{-n} = \left(\frac{b}{a}\right)^n, a, b \neq 0$
- $a^{\frac{p}{q}} = (\sqrt[q]{a})^p$ or $\sqrt[q]{a^p}$

Alternatively,

- $a^{\frac{p}{q}} = \left(a^{\frac{1}{q}}\right)^p$ or $(a^p)^{\frac{1}{q}}$

Properties of the Exponential Function $y = b^x$

- The base b is positive.
- The y-intercept is 1.
- The x-axis is a horizontal asymptote.
- The domain is the set of real numbers, R.
- The range is the set of positive real numbers.
- The exponential function is always increasing if $b > 1$.
- The exponential function is always decreasing if $0 < b < 1$.

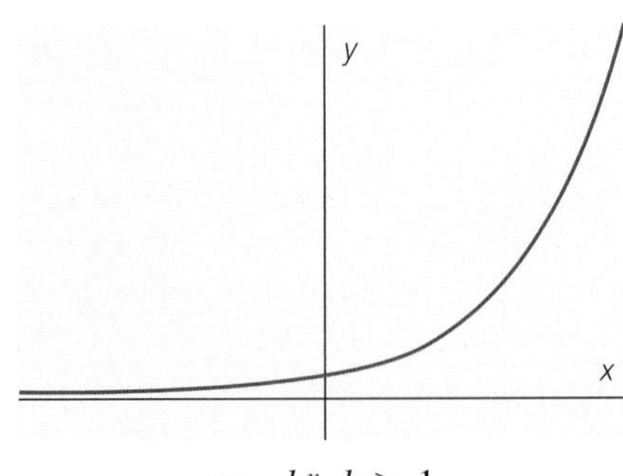

$y = b^x, b > 1$
The function is always increasing.

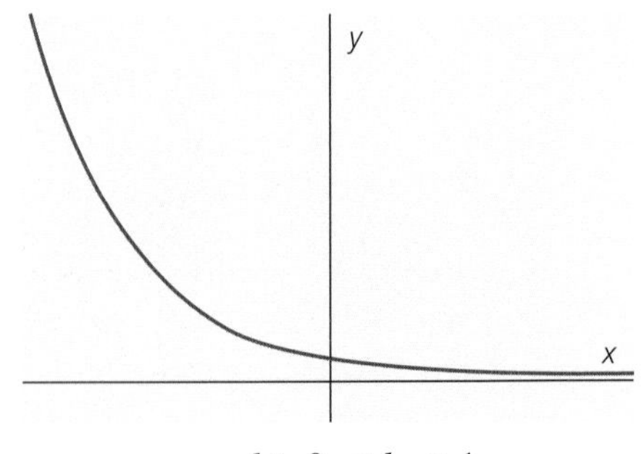

$y = b^x, 0 < b < 1$
The function is always decreasing.

Exponential Growth and Decay

Exponential growth occurs when quantities increase or decrease at a rate proportional to the quantity. This growth or decay occurs in savings accounts, the size of populations, and the quantity of decay that occurs in radioactive chemicals. All situations of this type can be expressed using the exponential function. Data on savings accounts, population growth, or radioactive decay can be modelled using an exponential function.

Career Link wrap-up investigate and apply

CHAPTER 6: DISCOVERING EXPONENTIAL GROWTH PATTERNS

An entomologist is studying the predator–prey relationship for two colonies of insects. She is investigating the possibility of introducing the predator insect in corn farming areas to control the population of the prey insect, which is a nuisance to corn crops.

a. In the experiment, the predator insect doubled in population every three days and the prey insect quadrupled in nine days. The initial population of the predator insect was 500 and the initial population of the prey insect was 1000. At what time were the two populations equal?

b. Once the populations are equal, the prey population depends on births (which would still cause a doubling every three days if there were no predator) and deaths caused by the predator, which amount to 5.0% of the population per day. The researcher needs to develop a single algebraic model to predict the population of the prey insect as a function of births and deaths:

   $P = P_o$ (Exponential Growth Due to Births)(Exponential Decay Due to Deaths)

   Expressed in doubling times format:

$$P(t) = P_o 2^{kt},$$

   where $P(t)$ is the population at time t, in days, P_o is the initial population, and k is growth rate constant.

   Hints: 1. Set $t = 0$ for the time when the populations were equal as determined in part **a.**

   2. Convert growth expression to base of 2 with exponent laws.

   3. Convert death expression to base of 2 using the graph of $y = 2^x$ and finding the value of x for $2^x = (1 - \textit{Decay Rate})$.

c. The experiment will be considered a success if the population of the prey insect is less than 6800 five days after the time the two populations were equal, and if the doubling time of the prey is now more than seven days. Use the expression developed in part **b** and the graphing calculator to judge the experiment's success. ●

Review Exercise

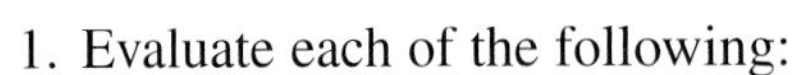

1. Evaluate each of the following:

   a. $(3^{-2} + 2^{-3})^{-1}$

   b. $\frac{3^{-3}}{3^{-1} - 3^{-2}}$

   c. $\frac{3^{-8}}{3^{-6} \times 3^{-5}}$

   d. $(5^3 - 5^2)(2^3 - 2^2)$

2. Evaluate each of the following:

   a. $32^{-\frac{3}{5}}$

   b. $\left(\frac{54}{250}\right)^{\frac{2}{3}}$

   c. $\sqrt[4]{\frac{1}{16}}$

   d. $\left(\frac{2}{3}\right)^{-3} - 4^{-1}$

3. Simplify each of the following:

   a. $a^{p^2+q^2} \div a^{p^2-q^2}$

   b. $\sqrt[3]{\frac{x^{\frac{1}{3}}\sqrt{x}}{\sqrt[3]{x^2}}}$

   c. $\frac{(x^{a-b})^{a+b}}{x^{a^2}}$

   d. $(16^{p+q})(8^{p-q})$

4. Fully factor each of the following:

   a. $1 + 8x^{-1} + 15x^{-2}$

   b. $x^{\frac{1}{2}} - x^{\frac{5}{2}}$

   c. $x^{-1} + x^{-2} - 12x^{-3}$

   d. $x^{\frac{3}{2}} - 25x^{-\frac{1}{2}}$

5. Following are the graphs of some exponential functions with equations of the form $y = b^x$, $b > 0$. Using what you have learned about exponential functions, and without the aid of your calculator, write the equation of each function. Each line on the graph represents one unit.

   a.

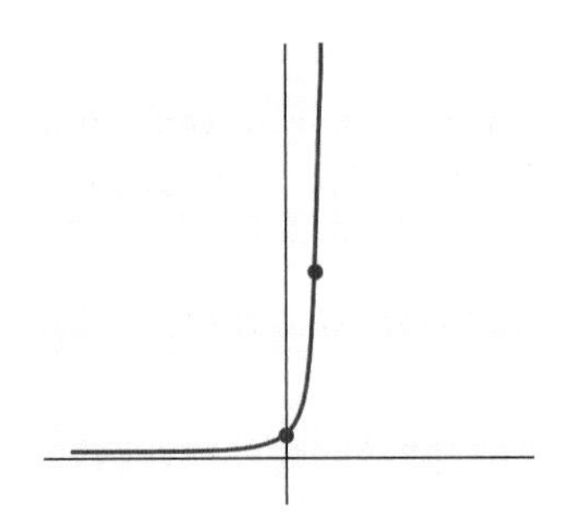

   b.

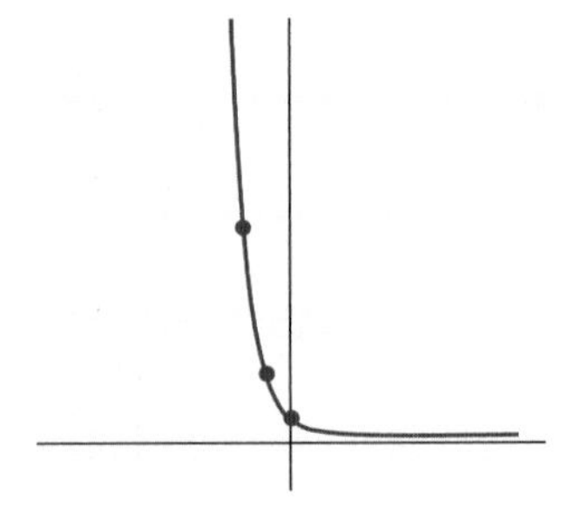

6. For the curve $y = 2(5^x) - 6$,

   a. determine

      i) the horizontal asymptote,

      ii) the y-intercept,

      iii) whether the curve is always increasing or always decreasing,

      iv) the domain and range.

b. Sketch the graph of the function.

7. For the curve $y = 5\left(\frac{1}{2}\right)^x + 3$,

   a. determine

      i) the horizontal asymptote,

      ii) the y-intercept,

      iii) whether the curve is always increasing or always decreasing,

      iv) the domain and range.

   b. Sketch the graph of the function.

8. For a biology experiment, there are 50 cells present. After 2 h there are 1600 bacteria. How many bacteria would there be in 6 h?

9. A laboratory has 40 mg of iodine 131. After 24 d there are only 5 mg remaining. What is the half-life of iodine 131?

10. The chart below shows the population of Canada. This information is from the Statistics Canada Web site at www.statcan.ca. The time intervals are in years, from 1994.

Year	Time Intervals	Population (in millions)
1994	0	29 036.0
1995	1	29 353.9
1996	2	29 671.9
1997	3	30 011.0
1998	4	30 301.2

technology

   a. Using your graphing calculator, draw a scatter plot of this data. Use the exponential regression function on your calculator to find the curve of best fit for the data.

   b. Using your mathematical model, estimate the population of Canada in 2010.

   c. Predict when there will be 35 million people in Canada.

11. The following information is from the United Nations Web site, www.un.org/popin.

   a. The following chart gives the population of Europe.

Year	Population (in millions)
1750	163
1800	203
1850	276
1900	408
1950	547
1998	729

i) Find the average rate of change in population between 1750 and 1800.

ii) Find the average rate of change in population between 1950 and 1998.

iii) Compare the answers to parts **i** and **ii**.

b. The chart below gives the population of North America.

Year	Population (in millions)
1750	2
1800	7
1850	26
1900	82
1950	172
1998	305

i) Find the average rate of change in population between 1800 and 1850.

ii) Find the average rate of change in population between 1950 and 1998.

iii) Compare the answers to parts **i** and **ii**.

c. Between 1800 and 1850, the average rate of change in population in Europe was greater than the average rate of change in population in North America. However the change in the size of the population in North America was far more dramatic. Explain.

Chapter 6 Test

Achievement Category	Questions
Knowledge/Understanding	All questions
Thinking/Inquiry/Problem Solving	10
Communication	4, 9c, 10b
Application	3, 4, 5b, 6, 7, 8, 9b

1. Evaluate each of the following:

   a. $\left(4^{\frac{1}{2}}\right)^3$ b. $(5^{\frac{1}{3}} \div 5^{\frac{1}{6}})^{12}$ c. $4^{-1} + 2^{-3} - 5^0$

   d. $(\sqrt{2})^3 \times (\sqrt{2})^5$ e. $\dfrac{2^{-1} + 2^{-2}}{2^{-3}}$ f. $(-5)^{-3} \times (5)^2$

2. Simplify each of the following:

   a. $\dfrac{a^4 \bullet a^{-3}}{a^{-2}}$ b. $(3x^2y)^2$ c. $(x^4y^{-2})^2 \bullet (x^2y^3)^{-1}$

   d. $(x^{a+b})(x^{a-b})$ e. $\dfrac{x^{p^2-q^2}}{x^{p+q}}$ f. $\sqrt{\dfrac{\sqrt{x} \bullet \sqrt[3]{x}}{x^{-1}}}$

3. Write $\dfrac{x - 16}{x^{\frac{1}{2}} - 4}$ as a polynomial expression.

4. If f is a function defined by $f(x) = b^x$, describe the growth behaviour of $f(x)$. Consider cases if required.

5. For the curve $y = 2\left(\frac{1}{3}\right)^x - 5$,

   a. determine

      i) the horizontal asymptote,

      ii) the y-intercepts,

      iii) whether the curve is increasing or decreasing,

      iv) the domain and range.

   b. Sketch the curve.

6. An antique dresser was purchased for \$3500 in 1985. The dresser increases in value by 7% per year. Find the value of the dresser in 2002.

7. The population of a fishing village is decreasing by 8% per year. In 1998 there were 4500 people living in the village. Estimate the population in 2004.

8. At the end of 14 min, $\frac{1}{16}$ of a sample of polonium remains. Determine the half-life of polonium.

technology

9. Below is a table showing the population of the world. This information came from the United Nations Web site, www.un.org/popin. The data is in intervals of 50 years from 1750, with 50 years considered as one time interval.

Year	Time Intervals	Population (in billions)
1750	0	0.79
1800	1	0.98
1850	2	1.26
1900	3	1.65
1950	4	2.52
2000	5	6.06

a. Use your graphing calculator to draw a scatter plot of the data. Using the exponential regression calculation in your calculator, determine the equation of the curve of best fit accurate to three decimal places.

b. Using your mathematical model, estimate the world population in 2300.

c. If the habitable surface area of the earth is about 20 million hectares, what will be the population density in the year 2300? (1 ha = 10 000 m^2)

d. Do you think the exponential model determined by the graphing calculator is valid over an extended period? Explain your answer.

10. This graph has an equation of the form $f(x) = b^x + c$.

a. Determine values for b and c.

b. Explain how you arrived at this answer.

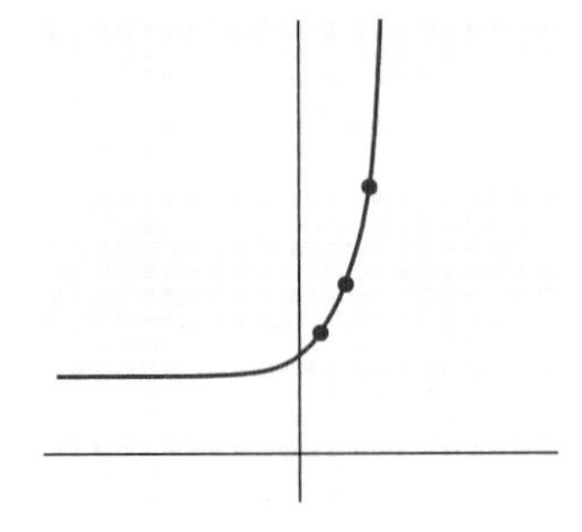

Chapter 7

THE LOGARITHMIC FUNCTION AND LOGARITHMS

Did you know that the energy in the sound of a jet aircraft engine is about one trillion times greater than the energy you exert when you whisper to your friend seated next to you on the plane that you're secretly afraid of flying? Rather than dealing with such a wide range of values, people who work with sound — whether they be broadcasters, people in the recording industry, or engineers trying to reduce engine noise inside an airplane — all measure sound levels using the more manageable decibel scale, which is an example of a logarithmic scale. Other examples of logarithmic scales include the Richter scale for measuring the intensity of earthquakes and the pH scale for measuring the acid content in a substance. These scales are used to simplify certain phenomena that might vary by large magnitudes, and the scales are all based on logarithmic functions like those that are studied in this chapter.

CHAPTER EXPECTATIONS In this chapter, you will

- define logarithmic function $\log_a x$ ($a > 1$), **Section 7.1**
- express logarithmic equations in exponential form, **Section 7.1**
- simplify and evaluate expressions containing logarithms, **Section 7.2**
- solve exponential and logarithmic equations, **Section 7.3, 7.5**
- solve simple problems involving logarithmic scales, **Section 7.4, Career Link**

Review of Prerequisite Skills

In the last chapter, we examined the exponential function and its use in solving equations. In this chapter, we will study the inverse of the exponential function. This function is the **logarithmic function**.

To begin, we will review the important facts associated with the exponential function:

- For $y = b^x$, $b > 1$, the function is increasing, the y-intercept is 1, and the x-axis is a horizontal asymptote.
- For $y = b^x$, $0 < b < 1$, the function is decreasing, the y-intercept is 1, and the x-axis is a horizontal asymptote.
- If a population is growing at the rate of $i\%$ per year, the function that expresses the population after x years is $f(x) = P_0(1 + i)^x$, where P_0 is the initial population.
- If the population doubles, the base for the exponential function is 2. The function representing the population after t years is $f(x) = P_0 2^{\frac{t}{d}}$, where P_0 is the initial population and d is the doubling time.

Exercise

1. Use your graphing calculator to sketch the graph of $y = 3^x$.
   a. State the domain and range.
   b. How is the slope of the graph of $y = 3^x$ related to the slope of the graph of $y = x^3$?
   c. How is the slope of the graph of $y = \left(\frac{1}{3}\right)^x$ related to the slope of the graph of $y = x^{\frac{1}{3}}$?
   d. Explain how the answers to parts **b** and **c** are related.
2. If f is a function defined by $f(x) = b^x$, where $b > 1$, what can be stated about
   a. the sign of $f(x)$?
   b. the growth behaviour of f?
   c. $f(0)$?

3. If f is a function defined by $f(x) = b^x$, where $0 < b < 1$, what can be stated about

   a. the sign of $f(x)$?

   b. the growth behaviour of f?

   c. $f(0)$?

4. The population of a town is 2400. If the population is predicted to grow at the rate of 6% per year, determine the predicted population in 20 years.

5. A culture initially has 2000 bacteria. If the population doubles every 4 h, determine when the population would be 512 000.

6. The half-life of radium is 1620 years.

   a. If a laboratory initially had 5 g of radium, determine how much they would have in 200 years.

   b. How many years would it take until the laboratory had only 4 g of radium?

Career Link investigate

CHAPTER 7: MEASURING ON A LOGARITHMIC SCALE

We often hear the term "order of magnitude" when people are describing the severity of an earthquake, the acidity of a solution, or the loudness of a sound. **Order of magnitude** is actually a very simple concept. One order of magnitude means 10 times larger, two orders of magnitude mean 100 times larger, and so on. Mathematically, the pattern is $10^0, 10^1, 10^2, 10^3, \ldots 10^n$ with the order of magnitude as the exponent. This exponent is also known as the **logarithm** of the pattern. On a number line, the intensity of an earthquake could be represented as follows:

Logarithm Notation	0	1	2	3	4	5	6	7	8	9
Exponential Notation	10^0	10^1	10^2	10^3	10^4	10^5	10^6	10^7	10^8	10^9
Standard Notation	1	10	100	1000	10 000	100 000	1 000 000	...		

The logarithmic notation on this number line for measuring earthquake intensity is known as the Richter Scale and indicates that an earthquake of magnitude 5 is 100 times more intense than an earthquake of magnitude 3. Other examples of log scales include the pH scale in chemistry and the bel or decibel scale for the measurement of loudness. In this chapter, you will investigate the properties of the logarithm function and its graph, utilize the rules of logarithms to solve exponential equations, and model exponential and polynomial data using logarithms.

Case Study — Seismologist (Earthquake Geologist)

Seismologists play a critical role in assisting structural engineers to design earthquake-proof buildings. Designing buildings to withstand earthquakes first requires the seismologist to model the behaviour of earthquake shockwaves (e.g., magnitude and frequency). Only then can the engineer determine how the beams and columns must be designed to withstand the tensional, compressive, shearing (tearing), and torsion (twisting) forces the earthquake will cause. While most people would identify Vancouver, B.C., as the city most prone to earthquakes in Canada, there are others that might surprise you, such as Ottawa, Ontario, which experiences earthquakes on a regular basis.

DISCUSSION QUESTIONS

1. Why do you suppose a logarithmic scale is used to model the intensity of earthquakes?
2. How much more intense would an earthquake of magnitude 7.8 be compared to an earthquake of magnitude 4.5? Write down your calculations.
3. Identify at least two other situations when it would be practical to compare events in terms of order of magnitude. Explain your reasoning with specific examples.

At the end of this chapter, you have an opportunity to demonstrate your learning in exponential and logarithmic functions by completing an analysis of a lake damaged by acid rain.

Section 7.1 — The Logarithmic Function

We have been studying the exponential function $f(x) = b^x$, in which $b > 1$. A typical example is shown.

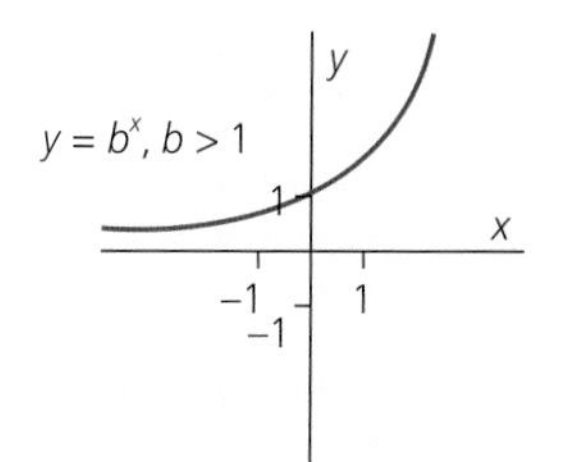

The inverse of the exponential function is obtained by interchanging the x- and y-coordinates.
The inverse of $y = b^x$ *is* $x = b^y$.
The graph of the inverse is obtained by reflection in the line $y = x$.

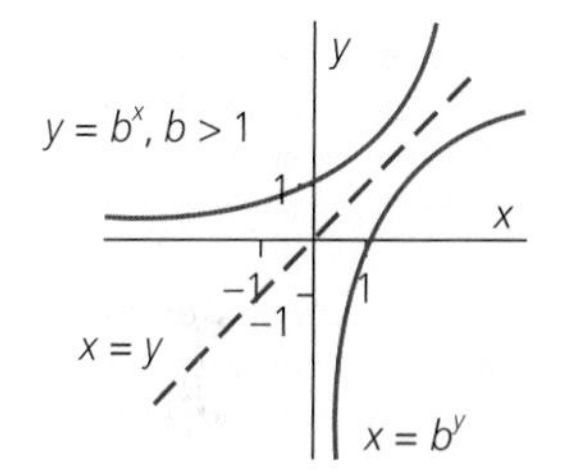

Recall that if $0 < b < 1$, the graph of $f(x) = b^x$ and its inverse, $x = b^y$, is as shown.

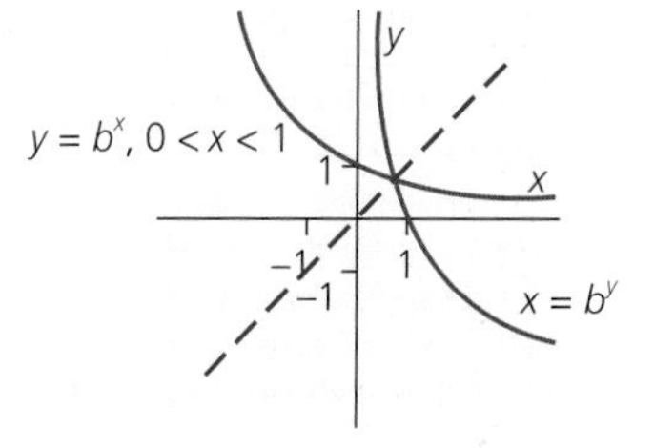

Since the exponential function $y = b^x$ is only defined for $b > 0$, it follows that the inverse function, $x = b^y$, is only defined for $b > 0$. We can also see from the graph that the domain of $x = b^y$ is $x > 0$. We will call this inverse function the **logarithmic function** and write it as $y = \log_b x$. This is read as "y equals log of x to the base b." The function $\log_b x$ is defined only for $x > 0$.

INVESTIGATION

The purpose of this investigation is to examine the shape of the graph of $f(x) = \log_b x$. To do so, follow these steps.

Step 1: Consider the function $f(x) = b^x$, where $b = 2$. Prepare a table of values using integer values for the domain $-3 \leq x \leq 4$.

Step 2: Sketch the graph.

Step 3: Using the image line $y = x$, sketch the graph of the inverse function $f(x) = \log_b x$.

Step 4: By reversing the entries in the table of values from Step 1, compile a table of values for points on the graph $f(x) = \log_b x$ and determine whether or not these points are on the graph of $f(x) = \log_b x$.

Step 5: Repeat Steps 1 to 4 using $b = 3$, $b = \frac{1}{2}$, and $b = \frac{1}{3}$.

As with the exponential function, there are two possible versions of the graph of the logarithmic function:

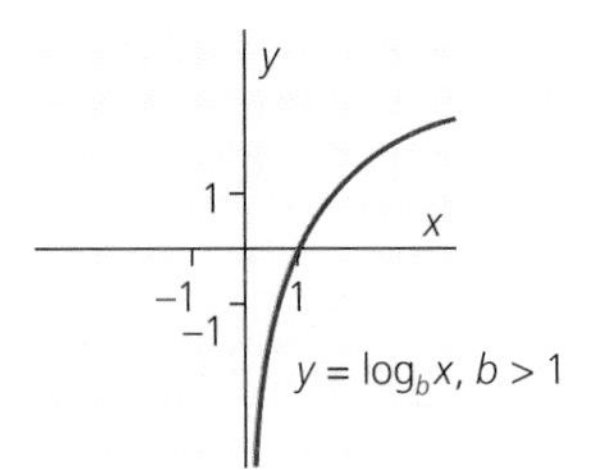

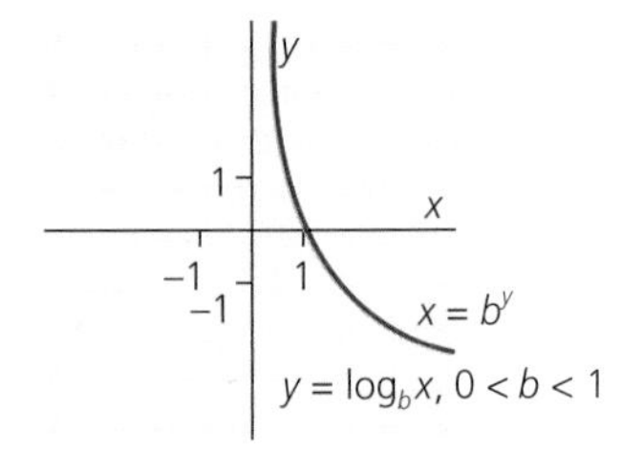

Properties of the Logarithmic Function $y = \log_b x$

- The base b is positive.
- The x-intercept is 1.
- The y-axis is a vertical asymptote.
- The domain is the set of positive real numbers.
- The range is the set of real numbers.
- The function is increasing if $b > 1$.
- The function is decreasing if $0 < b < 1$.

While any number can be used as a base, the most common base used is 10. Logarithms with base 10 are called **common logarithms**. Common logarithms were used for complicated calculations before the invention of the hand-held calculator in the 1970s. For convenience, $\log_{10} x$ is usually written as just $\log x$, and the base is understood to be 10. Calculators are programmed in base 10, and with this base we can use the calculator to sketch the graph of $y = \log x$.

Exponential Form		**Logarithmic Form**	
$x = b^y$	$\longleftrightarrow$	$y = log_b x$	$b > 0$ and $b \neq 1$

The logarithm of a number x with a given base is the exponent to which that base must be raised to yield x.

EXAMPLE 1

Change to exponential form.

a. $\log_3 81 = 4$

b. $\log_{25} 5 = \frac{1}{2}$

Solution

a. If $\log_3 81 = 4$, then $3^4 = 81$.

b. If $\log_{25} 5 = \frac{1}{2}$, then $25^{\frac{1}{2}} = 5$.

EXAMPLE 2

Change to logarithmic form.

a. $5^3 = 125$

b. $\left(\frac{1}{2}\right)^{-3} = 8$

Solution

a. If $5^3 = 125$, then $\log_5 125 = 3$.

b. If $\left(\frac{1}{2}\right)^{-3} = 8$, then $\log_{\frac{1}{2}} 8 = -3$.

EXAMPLE 3

Use your calculator to find the value of the following:

a. $\log_{10} 500$

b. $\log 4.6$

c. $\log 0.0231$

Solution

The answers are given to the accuracy of a calculator with a 10-digit display.

a. $\log_{10} 500 = 2.698\ 970\ 004$

b. $\log 4.6 = 0.662\ 757\ 831$

c. $\log 0.0231 = -1.636\ 388\ 02$

EXAMPLE 4

Our first task is to gain an understanding of the arithmetic involving logarithms. Many logarithmic expressions can be evaluated without the use of a calculator. This is particularly useful when the base of the logarithmic function is a number other than 10.

Evaluate the following:

a. $\log_5 25$

b. $\log_3 27$

c. $\log_2\left(\frac{1}{4}\right)$

d. $\log_{\frac{1}{3}} 27$

Solution

a. Let $\log_5 25 = x$.

Then, by definition, $5^x = 25$.

Then $x = 2$ and $\log_5 25 = 2$.

b. Let $\log_3 27 = x$.

Then, by definition, $3^x = 27$.

Then $x = 3$ and $\log_3 27 = 3$.

c. Let $\log_2\left(\frac{1}{4}\right) = x$.

Then $2^x = \frac{1}{4} = \frac{1}{2^2} = 2^{-2}$.

Then $x = -2$ and $\log_2\left(\frac{1}{4}\right) = -2$.

d. Let $\log_{\frac{1}{3}} 27 = x$.

Then $\left(\frac{1}{3}\right)^x = 27$ or $(3^{-1})^x = 3^{-x} = 27$.

Then $x = -3$ and $\log_{\frac{1}{3}} 27 = -3$.

Exercise 7.1

Part A

1. Write each of the following in logarithmic form.

a. $3^2 = 9$ b. $9^0 = 1$ c. $\left(\frac{1}{2}\right)^2 = \frac{1}{4}$

d. $36^{\frac{1}{2}} = 6$ e. $27^{\frac{2}{3}} = 9$ f. $2^{-3} = \frac{1}{8}$

Knowledge/ Understanding

2. Write each of the following in exponential form.

a. $\log_5 125 = 3$ b. $\log_7 1 = 0$ c. $\log 5\left(\frac{1}{25}\right) = -2$

d. $\log_7\left(\frac{1}{7}\right) = -1$ e. $\log_{\frac{1}{3}} 9 = -2$ f. $\log_9 27 = \frac{3}{2}$

3. Use your calculator to find the value of each of the following:

a. $\log_{10} 37$ b. $\log 0.24$ c. $\log 1000$

d. $\log 52$ e. $\log 1.35$ f. $\log 52648$

Part B

Application

4. On one grid, sketch the graphs of $y = 5^x$ and $y = \log_5 x$.

5. On one grid, sketch the graphs of $y = 5^{-x}$ and $y = \log_{\frac{1}{5}} x$.

Knowledge/ Understanding

6. Evaluate each of the following:

a. $\log_2 8$ b. $\log_5 25$ c. $\log_3 81$

d. $\log_7 49$ e. $\log_2\left(\frac{1}{8}\right)$ f. $\log_3\left(\frac{1}{27}\right)$

g. $\log_5 \sqrt{5}$ h. $\log_2 4^2$ i. $\log_2 \sqrt[4]{32}$

Application

7. Evaluate each of the following:

a. $\log_6 36 - \log_5 25$ b. $\log_9\left(\frac{1}{3}\right) + \log_3\left(\frac{1}{9}\right)$ c. $\log_6 \sqrt{36} - \log_{25} 5$

d. $\log_3 \sqrt[4]{27}$ e. $\log_3\left(9 \times \sqrt[5]{9}\right)$ f. $\log_2 16^{\frac{1}{3}}$

Thinking/Inquiry/ Problem Solving

8. Use your knowledge of logarithms to solve each of the following equations for x.

a. $\log_5 x = 3$ b. $\log_4 x = 2$ c. $\log_x 27 = 3$

d. $\log_4\left(\frac{1}{64}\right) = x$ e. $\log_x\left(\frac{1}{9}\right) = 2$ f. $\log_{\frac{1}{4}} x = -2$

Communication

9. Explain how you find the value of a logarithm. Give specific examples to illustrate your thought processes.

Part C

Thinking/Inquiry/ Problem Solving

10. Sketch the graph of $y = 3^x + 3^{-x}$, $-4 \leq x \leq 4$. The resulting curve is called a **catenary.**

11. For the function $y = \log_{10}x$, where $0 < x \leq 1000$, how many integer values of y are possible if $y > -20$?

The History of Logarithms

Scottish mathematician John Napier (1550–1617) was the first to define logarithms. Napier, realizing that the base of our number system is 10, used 10 as the base for his logarithms. These logarithms could then be used to make calculations easier.

Henry Briggs (1561–1630) saw the practical applications of logarithms to his investigations in trigonometry and astronomy. He spent nine years laboriously calculating a partial table of common logarithms. There was great excitement in the scientific community when this table was published. It simplified the massive calculations of the great astronomers of the day, Tycho Brahe and Johannes Kepler.

Until the mid-1970s, logarithms were used to simplify calculations. Text-books had tables of common logarithms in the back. Now the hand-held calculator is used instead of logarithms. However, the study of logarithms is still important, because logarithms appear in scientific formulas and in the study of calculus.

Section 7.2 — Properties of Logarithms

In order to simplify and evaluate expressions containing logarithms, we will start to develop an arithmetic of logarithmic expressions by considering some basic ideas.

BASIC PROPERTIES OF LOGARITHMS

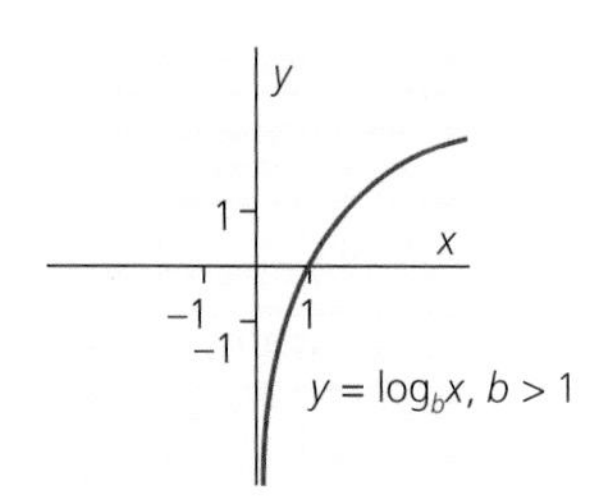

INVESTIGATION

The purpose of this investigation is to identify basic properties of logarithms.

1. In each of the following, use the definition of a logarithm as an exponent and determine the value of the expression.

a. $\log_5 5$	b. $\log_3 1$	c. $\log_7 7$
d. $\log_4 1$	e. $\log_2 2^5$	f. $\log_3 3^4$
g. $\log 10^{3.6}$	h. $\log 10^{5.78}$	i. $5^{\log_5 25}$
j. $4^{\log_4 64}$	k. $10^{\log 6}$	l. $10^{\log 97}$

2. State a possible value for $\log_b 1$.

3. State a possible value for $\log_b b$.

4. State a possible value for $\log_b b^x$.

5. State a possible value for $b^{\log_b x}$.

Basic Properties of Logarithms

$$\log_b 1 = 0$$
$$\log_b b = 1$$
$$\log_b b^x = x$$
$$b^{\log_b x} = x$$

The proofs of these four basic properties of logarithms are as follows:

1. $\log_b 1 = 0$

   Proof
   Let $\log_b 1 = y$.
   From the definition, $b^y = 1 = b^0$.
   Then $y = 0$ and $\log_b 1 = 0$.

2. $\log_b b = 1$

   Proof
   Let $\log_b b = y$.
   From the definition, $b^y = b = b^1$.
   Then $y = 1$ and $\log_b b = 1$.

3. $\log_b b^x = x$

   Proof
   Let $\log_b b^x = y$.
   From the definition, $b^y = b^x$.
   Then $y = x$ and $\log_b b^x = x$.

4. $b^{\log_b x} = x$

   Proof
   Let $b^{\log_b x} = y$.
   From our knowledge of exponentials, we can write $y = b^t$ for some value of t.
   Then $b^{\log_b x} = b^t$.
   Now $\log_b x = t$.
   From the definition, $b^t = x = y$.
   Then $b^{\log_b x} = x$.

Because logarithms are exponents, the Properties of Logarithms can be derived from the Laws of Exponents. Three properties deal with the logarithm of a product, a quotient, and a power.

1. The logarithm of a product is equal to the sum of the logarithms of the factors. That is,

$$\begin{aligned} \log_b xw &= \log_b x + \log_b w, \text{ if } x, w > 0. \\ \text{Let } \log_b x &= s \text{ and } \log_b w = t. \\ \text{Then } x &= b^s \text{ and } w = b^t. \\ \text{Therefore, } \log_b xw &= \log_b(b^s \bullet b^t) \\ &= \log_b b^{s+t} \\ &= s + t \\ &= \log_b x + \log_b w \end{aligned}$$

2. The logarithm of a quotient is equal to the logarithm of the numerator minus the logarithm of the denominator. That is,

$$\begin{aligned} \log_b\left(\frac{x}{w}\right) &= \log_b x - \log_b w. \\ \text{Let } \log_b x &= s \text{ and } \log_b w = t. \\ \text{Then } x &= b^s \text{ and } w = b^t. \\ \text{Therefore, } \log_b\left(\frac{x}{w}\right) &= \log_b\left(\frac{b^s}{b^t}\right) \\ &= \log_b b^{s-t} \\ &= s - t \\ &= \log_b x - \log_b w. \end{aligned}$$

Note that if $x = 1$, $\log_b 1 = 0$ and $\log\left(\frac{1}{w}\right) = -\log_b w$.

3. The logarithm of a number raised to a power is equal to the exponent of the power multiplied by the logarithm of the number. That is,

$$\begin{aligned} \log_b x^r &= r\log_b x, \text{ when } x > 0 \text{ and } r \text{ is a real number.} \\ \text{Let } \log_b x &= s, \text{ so } x = b^s. \\ \text{Then } \log_b x^r &= \log_b(b^s)^r \\ &= \log_b b^{rs} \\ &= rs \\ &= r\log_b x. \end{aligned}$$

Note that $\log_b \sqrt[r]{x} = \log_b x^{\frac{1}{r}} = \frac{1}{r}\log_b x$.

Properties of Logarithms
When $x > 0$, $w > 0$, and r is a real number,

$$\log_a xw = \log_a x + \log_a w$$

$$\log_a\left(\frac{x}{w}\right) = \log_a x - \log_a w$$

$$\log_a x^r = r\log_a x.$$

These properties allow us to simplify expressions that might otherwise be complicated.

EXAMPLE 1

Evaluate the following:

a. $\log_{10}(47 \times 512)$ b. $\log_3(81 \times 243)$ c. $\log_4 2 + \log_4 32$

Solution

a. $\log_{10}(47 \times 512) \doteq 4.381\ 367\ 8$ (by calculator)

b. $\log_3(81 \times 243) = \log_3 81 + \log_3(243) = 4 + 5 = 9$

c. $\log_4 2 + \log_4 32 = \log_4(2 \times 32) = \log_4 64 = 3$

EXAMPLE 2

Simplify the following:

a. $\log_3\left(\frac{27}{81}\right)$ b. $\log_2\left(\frac{75}{26}\right)$ c. $\log_2 48 - \log_2 3$ d. $\log_5 45$

Solution

a. $\log_3\left(\frac{27}{81}\right) = \log_3 27 - \log_3 81 = 3 - 4 = -1,$

or $\log_3\left(\frac{27}{81}\right) = \log_3\left(\frac{1}{3}\right) = \log_3(3^{-1}) = -1$

b. $\log_2\left(\frac{75}{26}\right) = \log_2 75 - \log_2 26$

c. $\log_2 48 - \log_2 3 = \log_2\left(\frac{48}{3}\right) = \log_2 16 = 4$

d. $\log_5 45 = \log_5(5 \times 9) = \log_5 5 + \log_5 9 = 1 + \log_5 9$

EXAMPLE 3

Write $\log_a x^3y^4$ in terms of $\log_a x$ and $\log_a y$.

Solution

$$\begin{aligned}\log_a x^3y^4 &= \log_a x^3 + \log_a y^4 \\ &= 3 \log_a x + 4 \log_a y\end{aligned}$$

EXAMPLE 4

Write $3 \log (x + 3) - 2 \log (x - 1)$ as a single logarithm.

Solution

$$\begin{aligned}3 \log (x + 3) - 2 \log (x - 1) &= \log (x + 3)^3 - \log (x - 1)^2 \\ &= \log \frac{(x + 3)^3}{(x - 1)^2}\end{aligned}$$

EXAMPLE 5 Evaluate $3^{-\frac{1}{2}\log_3 49}$.

Solution

Consider the exponent first.

$$-\frac{1}{2}\log_3 49 = \log_3(49)^{-\frac{1}{2}}$$
$$= \log_3\left(\frac{1}{7}\right)$$

Now, $3^{-\frac{1}{2}\log_3 49} = 3^{\log_3\left(\frac{1}{7}\right)}$
$$= \frac{1}{7}.$$

EXAMPLE 6 Logarithms are particularly useful in solving exponential equations.

Solve each of the following, giving answers to two decimals.

a. $7^x = 400$

b. $7(1.06^x) = 5.20$

Solution

a. $7^x = 400$

Taking logarithms of each side,

$$x \log 7 = \log 400$$
$$x = \frac{\log 400}{\log 7} = 3.08.$$

b. $7(1.06^x) = 5.20$

Taking logarithms of each side,

$$\log 7 + x \log 1.06 = \log 5.20$$
$$x \log 1.06 = \log 5.20 - \log 7$$
$$x = \frac{\log 5.20 - \log 7}{\log 1.06}$$
$$= -5.10.$$

EXAMPLE 7 Describe the relation between the graph of $y = \log_2 x$ and the graph of each of the following:

a. $y = \log_2 x^2$

b. $y = \log_2(4x)$

Solution

a. Since $\log_2 x^2 = 2 \log_2 x$, the graph of $y = \log_2 x^2$ is a vertical dilatation of $y = \log_2 x$ by a factor of 2.

b. Since $\log_2 4x = \log_2 4 + \log_2 x = 2 + \log_2 x$, the graph of $y = \log_2 4x$ is a vertical translation of the graph of $y = \log_2 x$ by 2 units upwards.

Exercise 7.2

Part A

1. Write each of the following as a sum of logarithms.

   a. $\log_a(xy)$ b. $\log_m(pq)$

2. Write each of the following as the logarithm of a product.

   a. $\log_a x + \log_a w$ b. $\log_a s + \log_a r$

3. Write each of the following as a difference of logarithms.

   a. $\log_b\left(\frac{x}{y}\right)$ b. $\log_a\left(\frac{r}{s}\right)$

Knowledge/ Understanding

4. Write each of the following in the form $m \log_a p$.

   a. $\log_6 13^4$ b. $\log_5 1.3^{-2}$ c. $\log_7 x^{\frac{1}{3}}$ d. $\log_a 6^{-\frac{3}{4}}$

5. Use the properties of logarithms to write each of the following as a sum and/or a difference of logarithms.

   a. $\log_b\left(\frac{xy}{z}\right)$ b. $\log_a\left(\frac{x}{yz}\right)$

Part B

Knowledge/ Understanding

6. On the same grid, sketch the graphs of

   a. $y = \log_3 x$ b. $y = \log_3(9x)$ c. $y = \log_3(27x)$ d. $y = \log_3\left(\frac{x}{3}\right)$

7. On the same grid, sketch the graphs of

   a. $y = \log_3 x$ b. $y = \log_3 x^2$ c. $y = \log_3 x^3$ d. $y = \log_3 \sqrt{x}$

8. Evaluate each of the following:

   a. $\log_3 135 - \log_3 5$ b. $\log_2 40 + \log_2\left(\frac{4}{5}\right)$ c. $\log_8 640 - \log_8 10$

   d. $\log_5(2.5) + \log_5 10$ e. $\log_2 224 - \log_2 7$ f. $\log_3 36 + \log_3\left(\frac{3}{4}\right)$

Application

9. Evaluate each of the following:

   a. $\log_3 3 + \log_5 1$ b. $\log_3 18 + \log_3\left(\frac{3}{2}\right)$ c. $\log_4 16 - \log_4 1$

   d. $\log_5 5^3$ e. $\log_2 40 - \log_2\left(\frac{5}{2}\right)$ f. $\log_4 4^4 + \log_3 3^3$

   g. $\log_2 14 + \log_2\left(\frac{4}{7}\right)$ h. $\log_5 200 - \log_5 8$ i. $\log_6 4 + \log_6 54$

10. Use the properties of logarithms to write each of the following in terms of $\log_a x$, $\log_a y$, and $\log_a w$.

a. $\log_a \sqrt[3]{x^2y^4}$ b. $\log_a \sqrt{\frac{x^3y^2}{w}}$ c. $\log_a \frac{x^3\,y^4}{\sqrt{x^{\frac{1}{4}}y^{\frac{2}{3}}}}$ d. $\log_a\left(\frac{x^5}{y^3}\right)^{\frac{1}{4}}$

11. Solve each of the following:

a. $10^{2x} = 495$ b. $10^{3x} = 0.473$ c. $10^{-x} = 31.46$

d. $7^x = 35.72$ e. $(0.6)^{4x} = 0.734$ f. $(3.482)^{-x} = 0.0764$

Application 12. Solve each of the following:

a. $12^{2x-3} = 144$ b. $7^{x+9} = 56$ c. $5^{3x+4} = 25$

d. $10^{2x+1} = 95$ e. $6^{x+5} = 71.4$ f. $3^{5-2x} = 875$

13. Solve each of the following. Write your answers correct to two decimal places.

a. $2 \times 3^x = 7 \times 5^x$ b. $12^x = 4 \times 8^{2x}$

c. $4.6 \times 1.06^{2x+3} = 5 \times 3^x$ d. $2.67 \times 7.38^x = 9.36^{5x-2}$

e. $12 \times 6^{2x-1} = 11^{x+3}$ f. $7 \times 0.43^{2x} = 9 \times 6^{-x}$

g. $5^x + 3^{2x} = 92$ h. $4 \times 5^x - 3(0.4)^{2x} = 11$

Application 14. Write each of the following as a single logarithm.

a. $\frac{1}{3}\log_a x + \frac{1}{4}\log_a y - \frac{2}{5}\log_a w$ b. $(4\log_5 x - 2\log_5 y) \div 3\log_5 w$

Thinking/Inquiry/ Problem Solving and Communication 15. Describe the transformation that takes the graph of the first function to that of the second.

a. $y = \log x$ and $y = \log(10x)$

b. $y = \log_2 x$ and $y = \log_2(8x^2)$

c. $y = \log_3 x$ and $y = \log_3(27x^3)$

Part C

Thinking/Inquiry/ Problem Solving 16. Evaluate each of the following:

a. $\log_3(27 \bullet \sqrt[3]{81}) + \log_5(125 \bullet \sqrt[4]{5})$ b. $\log_4(2 \bullet \sqrt{32}) + \log_{27}\sqrt{3}$

Communication 17. a. If $y = 3\log x$, what happens to the value of y if

i) x is multiplied by 2?

ii) x is divided by 2?

b. If $y = 5\log x$, what happens to the value of y if

i) x is replaced by $4x$?

ii) x is replaced by $\frac{x}{5}$?

Section 7.3 — Solving Logarithmic Equations

The properties of logarithms we learned in the last section can help us solve equations involving logarithmic expressions. We must remember that $y = \log_a x$ is defined only for $x > 0$. Some of the logarithmic equations we solve will appear to have a root that is less than zero. Such a root is inadmissible. This means that every time we solve a logarithmic equation, we must check that the roots obtained are admissible.

EXAMPLE 1

Solve $\log_6 x = 2$.

Solution

$$\log_6 x = 2$$

Then $x = 6^2$

$$x = 36.$$

The root of the equation is $x = 36$.
Checking, $\log_6 36 = 2$, therefore the root is admissible.

EXAMPLE 2

Solve $\log_6 x + \log_6(x + 1) = 1$.

Solution

Simplifying, $\log_6 x + \log_6(x + 1)$

$$= \log_6(x(x + 1))$$
$$= \log_6(x^2 + x).$$

Then $\log_6(x^2 + x) = 1$.
In exponential form, $x(x + 1) = 6^1$

$$x^2 + x - 6 = 0$$
$$(x + 3)(x - 2) = 0$$
$$x = -3 \text{ or } x = 2.$$

The logarithm of a negative number is **not** defined.
Therefore, the root $x = -3$ is inadmissible.

If $x = 2$,

L.S. $= \log_6 x + \log_6(x + 1)$ R.S. $= 1$

$$= \log_6(2) + \log_6(3)$$
$$= \log_6(2 \times 3)$$
$$= \log_6 6$$
$$= 1.$$

The only root of the equation is $x = 2$.

In the last chapter, we considered some problems involving the exponential function in which it was difficult to solve the resulting equation. Using logarithms makes this process much easier.

EXAMPLE 3 Solve $3^x = 23$.

Solution

Take the logarithm of each side.

$$\log 3^x = \log 23$$

Now use the logarithmic properties to simplify and isolate the variable x.

$$x \log 3 = \log 23$$

$$x = \frac{\log 23}{\log 3}$$

This is the exact value of x. You can use your calculator to determine an approximate value:

$$x = \frac{\log 23}{\log 3} = 2.85 \quad \text{(Correct to two decimal places)}$$

Exercise 7.3

Part B

1. Solve the following:

   a. $\log_2 x = 2 \log_2 4$
   b. $\log_3 x = 4 \log_3 3$
   c. $2 \log_5 x = \log_5 36$
   d. $2 \log x = 4 \log 7$

Knowledge/ Understanding

2. Solve the following. Give the answer correct to two decimal places.

   a. $3^x = 5$
   b. $5^x = 6$
   c. $2^x - 1 = 4$
   d. $7 = 12 - 4^x$

3. Solve for x.

   a. $\log x = 2 \log 3 + 3 \log 2$
   b. $\log x + \log 3 = \log 1 + \log 4$
   c. $\log x^2 = 3 \log 4 - 2 \log 2$
   d. $\log \sqrt{x} = \log 1 - 2 \log 3$
   e. $\log x^{\frac{1}{2}} - \log x^{\frac{1}{3}} = \log 2$
   f. $\log_4(x + 2) + \log_4(x - 3) = \log_4 9$

Knowledge/ Understanding

4. Solve the following:

   a. $\log_6(x + 1) + \log_6(x + 2) = 1$
   b. $\log_7(x + 2) + \log_7(x - 4) = 1$

c. $\log_2(x + 2) = 3 - \log_2 x$

d. $\log_4 x + \log_4(x + 6) = 2$

e. $\log_5(2x + 2) - \log_5(x - 1) = \log_5(x + 1)$

Communication

5. Explain why there are no solutions to the equations $\log_5(-125) = x$ and $\log_{-2} 16 = x$.

Application

6. A car depreciates at 15% per year. How long is it until it is worth half its original value?

7. Carbon taken from an old animal skeleton contains $\frac{3}{4}$ as much radioactive carbon^{14} (C^{14}) as carbon taken from a present-day bone. How old is the animal skeleton? (The half-life of carbon^{14} is 5760 years.)

Application

8. An isotope of cobalt, Co^{60}, is used in medical therapy. When the radioisotope activity has decreased to 45% of its initial level, the exposure times required are too long and the hospital needs to replace the cobalt. How often does the cobalt need to be replaced? (The half-life of Co^{60} is 5.24 years.)

9. A man wants to sell an old piece of wood to a museum. He claims it came from the stable in which Christ was born 2000 years ago. The museum tests the wood and finds that it contains 4.2×10^{10} atoms of C^{14} per gram. Carbon from present-day wood contains 5.0×10^{10} atoms of C^{14} per gram. Determine the approximate age of the wood. Do you think the relic is authentic? (The half-life of C^{14} is 5760 years.)

Part C

Thinking/Inquiry/ Problem Solving

10. If $\log_2(\log_3 a) = 2$, determine the value of a.

Thinking/Inquiry/ Problem Solving

11. If $\log_{2n}(1944) = \log_n(486\sqrt{2})$, determine the value of n^6.

Section 7.4 — Where We Use Logarithms

LOGARITHMS AND EARTHQUAKES

Earthquakes occur along a fault line, a line where two of the tectonic plates forming the earth's crust meet. Stress builds up between these plates. Eventually the plates slip, resulting in a violent shaking at the earth's surface.

Earthquakes can strike wherever a fault line is located, but the most severe earthquakes occur around the Pacific Rim. Areas most prone to major earthquakes are Japan, Alaska, Taiwan, Mexico, and the western coasts of the United States and Canada.

In 1935, seismologist Charles F. Richter developed a scale to compare the intensities of earthquakes. The amount of energy released in an earthquake is very large, so to avoid using large numbers, a logarithmic scale is used to compare intensities.

The formula Richter used to define the magnitude of an earthquake is
$M = \log\left(\frac{I}{I_0}\right)$,
where I is the intensity of the earthquake being measured,
I_0 is the intensity of a reference earthquake, and
M is the Richter number used to measure the intensity of earthquakes.

On the Richter scale, the energy of the earthquake increases by powers of 10 in relation to the Richter magnitude number. Earthquakes below magnitude 4 usually cause no damage, and quakes below 2 cannot be felt. A magnitude 6 earthquake is strong, while one of magnitude 7 or higher causes major damage. Below is a list of the five deadliest earthquakes of the twentieth century.

Location	Date	Magnitude	Death Toll
Tangshan, China	July 28, 1976	7.8 to 8.2	240 000
Tokyo, Japan	Sept. 1, 1923	8.3	200 000
Gansu, China	Dec. 16, 1920	8.6	100 000
Northern Peru	May 31, 1970	7.7	70 000
Northern Iran	June 21, 1990	7.3 to 7.7	50 000

EXAMPLE 1

An earthquake of magnitude 7.5 on the Richter scale struck Guatemala on February 4, 1976, killing 23 000 people. On October 2, 1993, an earthquake of magnitude 6.4 killed 20 000 in Maharashtra, India. Compare the intensities of the two earthquakes.

Solution

Let the intensity of the Guatemalan earthquake be I_G and the intensity of the Indian earthquake be I_I. We can use our formula to compare the intensity of the Guatemalan earthquake to the intensity of a reference earthquake (I_0).

$$7.5 = \log\left(\frac{I_G}{I_0}\right)$$

First we solve the expression for I_G:

$$\frac{I_G}{I_0} = 10^{7.5}$$
$$I_G = 10^{7.5}I_0.$$

We use the formula to compare the intensity of the Indian earthquake to the intensity of the reference earthquake (I_0).

$$6.4 = \log\left(\frac{I_I}{I_0}\right)$$

Then solve this expression for I_I:

$$\frac{I_I}{I_0} = 10^{6.4}$$
$$I_I = 10^{6.4}I_0.$$

Now we can compare the intensity of the Guatemalan earthquake to the intensity of the Indian earthquake.

$$\frac{I_G}{I_I} = \frac{10^{7.5}I_0}{10^{6.4}I_0}$$
$$= 10^{1.1}$$
$$= 12.6$$
$$I_G = 12.6I_I$$

The intensity of the Guatemalan earthquake was 12.6 times the intensity of the Indian earthquake.

LOGARITHMS AND SOUND

Our ear is divided into three connecting sections: the outer, middle, and inner ear. The outer ear funnels noise to the eardrum. In the middle ear, three tiny bones transmit sound to the inner ear. In the inner ear, sound waves are converted to readable nerve impulses by approximately 16 000 hair-like receptor cells, which sway with the sound waves. These cells can be severely damaged by loud sounds, resulting in permanent hearing loss. If you lose one third of these cells, your hearing will be significantly impaired. Hearing loss is progressive. Some hearing loss is inevitable with age, but we would lose much less if we protected our ears at the appropriate times.

The loudness of any sound is measured relative to the loudness of sound at the threshold of hearing. Sounds at this level are the softest that can still be heard.

The formula used to compare sounds is
$L = 10 \log(\frac{I}{I_0})$,
where I is the intensity of the sound being measured,
I_0 is the intensity of a sound at the threshold of hearing, and
L is the loudness measured in decibels $\left(\frac{1}{10}\text{ of a bel}\right)$.

At the threshold of hearing, the loudness of sound is zero decibels (0 dB).

EXAMPLE 2

A sound is 1000 times more intense than a sound you can just hear. What is the measure of its loudness in decibels?

Solution

The loudness of a sound is calculated using the formula $L = 10 \log\left(\frac{I}{I_0}\right)$.

L is the loudness of the sound.
I_0 is the intensity of a sound you can just hear.
I is the intensity of the sound being measured.
$I = 1000\ I_0$

Substituting into the formula:

$$\begin{aligned} L &= 10 \log\left(\frac{1000\ I_0}{I_0}\right) \\ &= 10 \log 1000 \\ &= 10 \times 3 \\ &= 30. \end{aligned}$$

The loudness of the sound is 30 dB.

This table shows the loudness of a selection of sounds.

30 dB	Soft whisper
60 dB	Normal conversation
80 dB	Shouting
90 dB	Subway
100 dB	Screaming child
120 dB	Rock concert
140 dB	Jet engine
180 dB	Space-shuttle launch

Exposure to sound levels of 85 dB during a 35 h work week will eventually cause damage to most ears. The 120 dB volume of the average rock concert will cause the same damage in less than half an hour. The higher the level, the less time it takes before sound-receptor cells start dying and permanent hearing damage occurs. At sound levels of 130 dB, after 75 s you are at risk of suffering permanent damage to your hearing.

EXAMPLE 3

How many more times intense is the sound of normal conversation (60 dB) than the sound of a whisper (30 dB)?

Solution

Let the intensity of the normal conversation be I_n and the intensity of the whisper be I_w. We use our formula to compare the intensity of the normal conversation to the intensity of a sound at the threshold of hearing (I_0).

$$60 = 10 \log\left(\frac{I_n}{I_0}\right)$$

Now solve the expression for I_n.

$$6 = \log\left(\frac{I_n}{I_0}\right)$$
$$\frac{I_n}{I_0} = 10^6$$
$$I_n = 10^6 I_0$$

Now we use our formula to compare the intensity of the whisper to the intensity of a sound at the threshold of hearing (I_0).

$$30 = 10 \log\left(\frac{I_w}{I_0}\right)$$

Solve the expression for I_w.

$$3 = \log\left(\frac{I_w}{I_0}\right)$$
$$\frac{I_w}{I_0} = 10^3$$
$$I_w = 10^3 I_0$$

Now we can compare the intensity of normal conversation to the intensity of a whisper.

$$\frac{I_n}{I_w} = \frac{10^6 I_0}{10^3 I_0}$$
$$= 10^3$$
$$I_n = 1000 I_w$$

The intensity of normal conversation is 1000 times the intensity of a whisper.

LOGARITHMS AND CHEMISTRY

Chemists measure the acidity of a liquid by determining the concentration of the hydrogen ion $[H^+]$ in the liquid. This concentration is measured in moles per litre. Since this is usually a very small number, a far more convenient measure uses logarithms and is called the pH of a liquid.

Chemists define the acidity of a liquid on a pH scale,
$pH = -\log[H^+]$,
where $[H^+]$ is the concentration of the hydrogen ion in moles per litre.

For distilled water, $[H^+] = 10^{-7}$ mol/L.
To find the pH of distilled water, we proceed as follows:

$$\begin{aligned} pH &= -\log[H^+] \\ &= -\log(10^{-7}) \\ &= -(-7) \\ &= 7. \end{aligned}$$

A liquid with a pH lower than 7 is called an *acid*. A substance with a pH greater than 7 is called a *base*. Chemists calculate the pH of a substance to an accuracy of two decimal places.

EXAMPLE 4

Find the pH of a swimming pool with a hydrogen ion concentration of 6.1×10^{-8} mol/L.

Solution

$$\begin{aligned} pH &= -\log[H^+] \\ &= -\log(6.1 \times 10^{-8}) \\ &= 7.21 \text{ (correct to two decimal places)} \end{aligned}$$

(pH is given to two decimal places)

Alternate Solution

$$\begin{aligned} pH &= -\log(6.1 \times 10^{-8}) \\ &= -(\log 6.1 + \log 10^{-8}) \\ &= -(.79 - 8) \\ &= 7.21 \end{aligned}$$

The pH of the pool is 7.21.

EXAMPLE 5 The pH of a fruit juice is 3.10. What is the hydrogen ion concentration of the fruit juice?

Solution

$$\begin{aligned} pH &= -\log[H^+] \\ 3.10 &= -\log[H^+] \\ \log[H^+] &= -3.10 \\ [H^+] &= 10^{-3.10} \\ &= 0.000\ 79 \end{aligned}$$

The hydrogen ion concentration is 7.9×10^{-4} mol/L.

Exercise 7.4

Part B

Communication

1. It is interesting to note the inclusion of the negative sign in the formula for pH. Discuss reasons why this makes sense.

Knowledge/Understanding

2. If one earthquake has a magnitude of 5 on the Richter scale and a second earthquake has a magnitude of 6, compare the intensities of the two earthquakes.

3. A sound is 1 000 000 times more intense than a sound you can just hear. What is the loudness of the sound?

Knowledge/Understanding

4. Find the pH of a liquid with a hydrogen ion concentration of 8.7×10^{-6} mol/L.

Application

5. An earthquake of magnitude 2 cannot be felt. An earthquake of magnitude 4 will be noticed but usually causes no damage. Compare the intensities of two such earthquakes.

Application

6. An earthquake in Gansu, China, on December 16, 1920, measured 8.6 on the Richter scale and killed 100 000 people. An earthquake that usually causes no damage measures 4 on the Richter scale. Compare the intensities of the two earthquakes.

Communication

7. An earthquake in the Quetta area of Pakistan on May 31, 1935, measured 6.8 on the Richter scale. This quake killed 50 000 people. On October 2, 1987, an earthquake of magnitude 6.1 shook Los Angeles, California, and killed six people.
   a. Compare the magnitude of the two earthquakes.
   b. Why do you think the death toll was so much higher with the earthquake in Pakistan?

8. On January 24, 1939, an earthquake measuring 8.3 occurred in Chillan, Chile, killing 28 000 people. On September 21, 1999, an earthquake in Taiwan measured 7.6 on the Richter scale and killed 2100 people. Compare the intensities of these two earthquakes.

Thinking/Inquiry/
Problem Solving

9. Sasha needs a new muffler on her car. She has been told that the sound from her car was measured at 120 dB. After installing the new muffler, the loudness of her car is 75 dB. How many times more intense was the sound from her defective muffler?

Thinking/Inquiry/
Problem Solving

10. Tania's infant daughter has colic and cries during the night. The noise level in the house at these times is 75 dB. When the baby finally falls asleep, the noise level is 35 dB. How many times more intense is the noise level in the house when the baby is crying?

11. How many times more intense is the sound of a space-shuttle launch (180 dB) than the sound of a jet engine (140 dB)?

Thinking/Inquiry/
Problem Solving

12. Jonathan lives near a busy street. He has all the windows in his home open and measures the noise level inside as 79 dB. He closes the windows and finds the noise level is 68 dB. By what factor did the intensity of the noise decrease when Jonathan closed the windows?

Application

13. Find the hydrogen ion concentration of milk, which has a pH of 6.50.

14. Find the hydrogen ion concentration of milk of magnesia, which has a pH of 10.50.

Section 7.5 — Change of Base

We have avoided two types of questions so far, and there is a very good reason for doing so. We can determine $\log_2 64$ because $2^6 = 64$; however, we cannot easily express 63 as a power of 2, which makes determining $\log_2 63$ more challenging. We cannot use a calculator because the logarithm operation only determines logarithms to base 10.

For a similar reason, we cannot easily use a calculator to obtain the graph of $y = \log_5 x$.

What is to be done? It turns out that the solution lies in our ability to use the properties of logarithms so that we can always use base 10.

EXAMPLE 1 Determine $\log_2 63$.

technology

Solution

Let $\log_2 63 = y$.
Then $2^y = 63$.

Taking logarithms of both sides,

$$\log 2^y = \log 63 \text{ (using base 10)}$$

$$y \log 2 = \log 63$$

$$y = \frac{\log 63}{\log 2}.$$

Then $\log_2 63 = \dfrac{\log 63}{\log 2} = 5.977$ (correct to three decimals).

Can this be done in any situation? Let's consider a general case and prove that $\log_b x = \dfrac{\log_a x}{\log_a b}$, where $a > 0$.

Proof

Let $\log_b x = y$.
From the definition, $b^y = x$.
Taking logarithms of both sides, using base a,

$$\log_a b^y = \log_a x$$

$$y \log_a b = \log_a x$$

$$y = \frac{\log_a x}{\log_a b}.$$

Then $\log_b x = \dfrac{\log_a x}{\log_a b}$.

Since this is true for any base a, it is certainly true for the particular base 10, and we can use this to determine logarithms given any base.

Change of Base Formula

$$\log_b x = \frac{\log_a x}{\log_a b}$$

EXAMPLE 2

Use your calculator to find the value of $\log_3 23$, correct to two decimal places.

Solution

$$\begin{aligned}\log_3 23 &= \frac{\log 23}{\log 3} \\ &= 2.8540\end{aligned}$$

Correct to two decimal places, $\log_3 23 = 2.85$.

EXAMPLE 3

Prove that $\log_t b = \frac{1}{\log_b t}$.

Proof

$$\begin{aligned}\log_t b &= \frac{\log b}{\log t} \\ &= \frac{1}{\frac{\log t}{\log b}} \\ &= \frac{1}{\log_b t}\end{aligned}$$

$$\log_t b = \frac{1}{\log_b t}$$

EXAMPLE 4

Show that $\frac{1}{\log_3 a} + \frac{1}{\log_4 a} = \frac{1}{\log_{12} a}$.

Solution

$$\begin{aligned}\frac{1}{\log_3 a} + \frac{1}{\log_4 a} &= \log_a 3 + \log_a 4 \\ &= \log_a 12 \\ &= \frac{1}{\log_{12} a}\end{aligned}$$

Therefore, $\frac{1}{\log_3 a} + \frac{1}{\log_4 a} = \frac{1}{\log_{12} a}$.

EXAMPLE 5 If $a^2 + b^2 = 14ab$, where $a > 0$, $b > 0$, show that $\log\left(\frac{a+b}{4}\right) = \frac{1}{2}(\log a + \log b)$.

Solution

Since
$$\begin{aligned} a^2 + b^2 &= 14ab \\ a^2 + 2ab + b^2 &= 16ab \\ (a+b)^2 &= 16ab \\ \left(\frac{a+b}{4}\right)^2 &= ab. \end{aligned}$$

Taking logarithms of both sides,

$$\begin{aligned} 2\log\left(\frac{a+b}{4}\right) &= \log(ab) \\ &= \log a + \log b. \end{aligned}$$

Then $\log\left(\frac{a+b}{4}\right) = \frac{1}{2}(\log a + \log b)$.

We noted at the beginning of this discussion that the graph of $y = \log_b x$ is not immediately accessible by calculator. Using the change of base formula, it is easy to use a graphing calculator to obtain such a graph.

EXAMPLE 6 Use a graphing calculator to graph each of the following:

a. $y = \log_5 x$

b. $y = \log_{0.5} x$

Solution

technology

a. $\log_5 x = \frac{\log x}{\log 5} = \frac{1}{\log 5} \log x$

Input $y = \frac{1}{\log 5} \log x$ and graph the function.

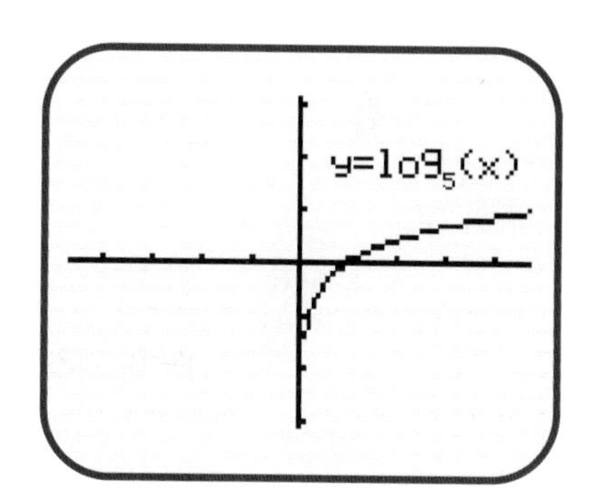

b. $\log_{0.5} x = \frac{\log x}{\log 0.5} = \frac{1}{\log 0.5} \log x$

Input $y = \frac{1}{\log 0.5} \log x$ and graph the function.

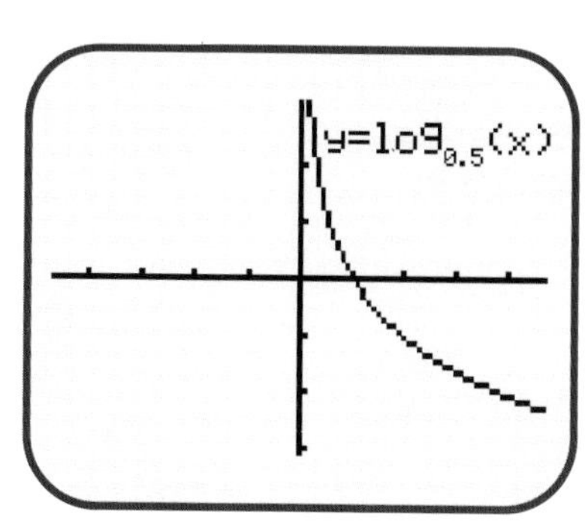

Exercise 7.5

Part B

Knowledge/Understanding

1. Use your calculator to find the value of each of the following, correct to three decimal places.

a. $\log_5 21$

b. $\log_7 124$

c. $\log_6 3.24$

d. $\log_4 4.7$

Application

2. Show that each of the following statements is true.

a. $\frac{1}{\log_5 a} + \frac{1}{\log_3 a} = \frac{1}{\log_{15} a}$

b. $\frac{1}{\log_8 a} - \frac{1}{\log_2 a} = \frac{1}{\log_4 a}$

c. $\frac{2}{\log_6 a} = \frac{1}{\log_{36} a}$

d. $\frac{2}{\log_8 a} - \frac{4}{\log_2 a} = \frac{1}{\log_4 a}$

Application

3. Sketch the graph of each of the following:

a. $y = \log_3 x$

b. $y = 4 \log_2 x$

c. $y = \log_{0.5} x$

d. $y = \log_{0.2} x^2$

Communication

4. Describe the changes to the graph of $y = \log_3 x$ when x is replaced by x^2.

Thinking/Inquiry/Problem Solving

5. For $a > 1$, $b > 1$, show that $(\log_a b)(\log_b a) = 1$.

Part C

6. If $a^2 + b^2 = 23ab$, where $a > 0$, $b > 0$, show that $\log\left(\frac{a+b}{5}\right) = \frac{1}{2}(\log a + \log b)$.

Thinking/Inquiry/Problem Solving

7. For $a > 0$, $a \neq 1$, $x > 0$, prove that $\log_a \frac{1}{x} = \log_{\frac{1}{a}} x$.

8. If $\log_a b = p^3$ and $\log_b a = \frac{4}{p^2}$, show that $p = \frac{1}{4}$.

9. If $a^3 - b^3 = 3a^2b + 5ab^2$, where $a > 0$, $b > 0$, show that $\log\left(\frac{a-b}{2}\right) = \frac{1}{3}(\log a + 2 \log b)$.

Key Concepts Review

In Chapter 7, you have learned that the logarithmic function is the inverse of the exponential function, and that the logarithmic function is usually written as $y = \log_b x$. You should now know how to solve logarithmic equations as well as where we use logarithms. You should also be familiar with Change of Base formulas. Here is a brief summary of key chapter concepts.

The Logarithmic Function

Exponential Form		**Logarithmic Form**	
$x = b^y$	$\longleftrightarrow$	$y = \log_b x$	$b > 0$ and $b \neq 1$

The logarithm of a number x with a given base is the exponent to which that base must be raised to yield x.

As with the exponential function, there are two possible versions of the graph of the logarithmic function:

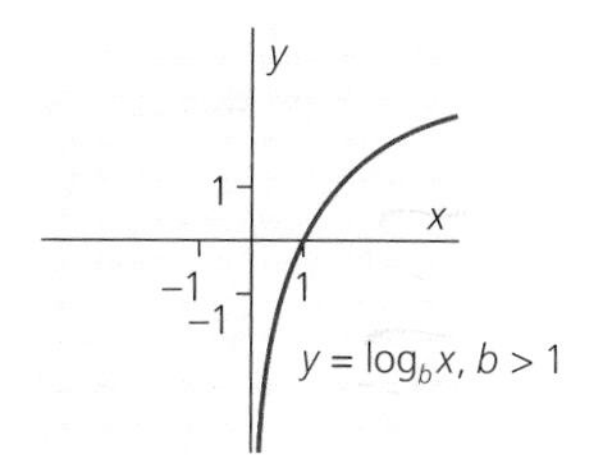

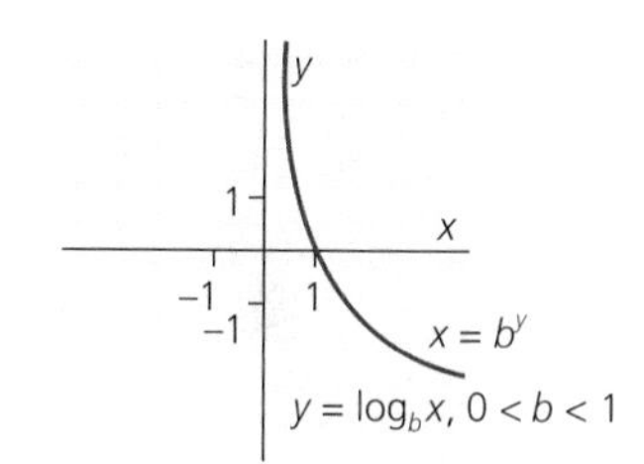

Basic Properties of Logarithms

- $\log_b 1 = 0$
- $\log_b b = 1$
- $\log_b b^x = x$
- $b^{\log_b x} = x$

Properties of Logarithms

For $x > 0$, $w > 0$, and r a real number:

- $\log_a xw = \log_a x + \log_a w$
- $\log_a\left(\frac{x}{w}\right) = \log_a x - \log_a w$
- $\log_a x^r = r \log_a x$

Change of Base Formulas

- $\log_b x = \frac{\log_a x}{\log_a b}$
- $\log_b x = \frac{1}{\log_x b}$

Career Link wrap-up

investigate and apply

CHAPTER 7: MEASURING ON A LOGARITHMIC SCALE

Many Northern Ontario communities are familiar with the devastation acid rain can bring to lake ecosystems. While the major contributors to acid rain are oxides of sulfur and nitrogen generated in industrial processes, carbon dioxide, the so-called "greenhouse gas" that is thought by many to cause global warming, also can contribute to acid rain. Carbon dioxide can acidify water in the atmosphere just as it acidifies the water used to make our favourite soft drinks when it is bubbled through liquids to make carbonated beverages.

Acidity is measured on the pH scale, which is defined as

$$\text{pH} = -\log[\text{H}^+]$$

where $[\text{H}^+]$ is the concentration of the hydrogen ion in moles per litre. The hydrogen ion, which causes acidity, is a function of the percentage of carbon dioxide in the atmosphere, an amount that can be elevated through the combustion of fossil fuels, shown by

$$\frac{[\text{H}^+]^2}{(\text{CO}_2)} = \text{K},$$

where CO_2 is the percentage of carbon dioxide in the atmosphere and K is a constant (1.52×10^{-10}).

a. Use log rules to show that $\text{pH} = -\frac{1}{2}[\log(\text{CO}_2) + \log(\text{K})]$ and determine the change in pH if the percentage of CO_2 increases from 0.03% to 0.06%. Is this a significant change? Explain.

b. Aquatic toxicologists conduct research on the response of fish and other aquatic species to the environmental contamination of their ecosystem. The data in the table was collected in a lab study to examine the effect of pH on a fish population.

   Obtain an algebraic expression for population as a function of pH by linearizing the population data in the table and obtaining an equation of the form $P = 10^{k(\text{pH})+d}$, where k is the growth rate factor and d is a constant. Verify your equation by looking at doubling patterns in the table and plotting both equations on the graphing calculator.

pH	Population
4.0	250
4.5	353
5.0	500
5.5	707
6.0	1000

c. An environmental assessment has established that a 25% decline in a population due to decreased pH is tolerable. Use your model from part **b** to determine how low the pH can drop. What percentage of carbon dioxide does this correlate to? The initial pH is 6.0 and the initial population is 1000.

Review Exercise

1. Evaluate each of the following:

   a. $\log_3 27$ b. $\log_5 \frac{1}{125}$ c. $\log_4 32$ d. $\log_6 \sqrt[3]{36}$

2. Evaluate each of the following:

   a. $\log_6 9 + \log_6 4$ b. $\log_2 3.2 + \log_2 100 - \log_2 5$

   c. $\log_5 \sqrt[3]{25} - \log_3 \sqrt[3]{27}$ d. $7^{\log_7 5}$

3. Solve each of the following equations:

   a. $3 = \log_2\left(\frac{1}{y}\right)$ b. $\log(x + 3) + \log x = 1$

   c. $\log_5(x + 2) - \log_5(x - 1) = 2 \log_5 3$ d. $\frac{\log(35 - x^3)}{\log(5 - x)} = 3$

4. Compare the intensities of an earthquake of magnitude 7.2 on the Richter scale that occurred in Kobe, Japan, on January 17, 1995, to an earthquake of magnitude 6.9 that occurred in northwest Armenia on December 7, 1988.

5. The noise in the school cafeteria is recorded at 50 dB at 10:00. At 12:00 the noise is found to be 100 dB. By what factor does the intensity of the sound increase at lunchtime?

6. A liquid has a pH of 5.62. Find the hydrogen ion concentration $[H^+]$.

7. Describe the transformation that takes the graph of $y = \log_4 x$ to the graph of $y = \log_4(16x^2)$.

technology

8. Use your calculator to find the value of each of the following, correct to three decimal places.

   a. $\log_{19} 264$ b. $\log_5 34.62$

9. Show that $\frac{2}{\log_9 a} - \frac{1}{\log_3 a} = \frac{3}{\log_3 a}$.

technology

10. Use a graphing calculator to graph each of the following:

    a. $y = \log_7 x$ b. $y = 2 \log_6(6x)$

Chapter 7 Test

Achievement Category	Questions
Knowledge/Understanding	All questions
Thinking/Inquiry/Problem Solving	8, 10, 11
Communication	3, 5
Application	2, 4, 6, 7, 9

1. Evaluate each of the following:

   a. $\log_3 27$
   b. $\log_5 125$
   c. $\log_2 \frac{1}{16}$
   d. $\log_5 \sqrt[4]{25}$
   e. $\log_2 8 + \log_3 9$
   f. $\log_3 9^{\frac{1}{3}}$

2. Evaluate each of the following:

   a. $\log_2 \frac{8}{5} + \log_2 10$
   b. $\log_6 108 - \log_6 3$

3. Describe the effect on the graph of $y = \log_5 x$ when x is replaced by $25x^2$.

4. Solve the following equations:

   a. $2 \log x = 3 \log 4$
   b. $\log x + \log 3 = \log 12$
   c. $\log_2(x + 2) + \log_2 x = 3$
   d. $\log_2(x - 2) + \log_2(x + 1) = 2$

5. Explain why there are no solutions to the equation $\log_3(-9) = x$.

6. A radioactive substance decays from 20 g to 15 g in 7 h. Determine the half-life of the substance.

7. An earthquake of magnitude 8.3 on the Richter scale killed 200 000 in Tokyo, Japan, on September 1, 1923. On February 4, 1976, an earthquake of magnitude 7.5 killed 23 000 in Guatemala. Compare the intensity of these earthquakes.

8. Kendra is talking to her friend on the subway platform, where the noise level is 60 dB. When a subway train enters the station, Kendra can no longer hear her friend. The noise level from the train is 90 dB. How many times more intense is the noise level in the station when the train enters?

9. A liquid has a pH of 8.31. Find the hydrogen ion concentration $[H^+]$.

10. Show that the following statement is true: $\frac{3}{\log_2 a} = \frac{1}{\log_8 a}$.

11. If $\log_a b = \frac{1}{x}$ and $\log_b \sqrt{a} = 3x^2$, show that $x = \frac{1}{6}$.

Cumulative Review

CHAPTERS 5–7

1. Find $\frac{dy}{dx}$ for the following:
   a. $x^2 + y^2 = 324$ b. $4x^2 - 16y^2 = 64$ c. $x^2 + 16y^2 = 5x + 4y$
   d. $2x^2 - xy + 2y = 5$ e. $\frac{1}{x} + \frac{1}{y} = 1$ f. $(2x + 3y)^2 = 10$

2. Find an equation of the tangent to the curve at the indicated point.
   a. $x^2 + y^2 = 13$ at $(-2, 3)$ b. $x^3 + y^3 = y + 21$ at $(3, -2)$
   c. $xy^2 + x^2y = 2$ at $(1, 1)$ d. $y^2 = \frac{3x^2 + 9}{7x^2 - 4}$ at $(1, 2)$

3. Find f' and f'' for the following:
   a. $f(x) = x^5 - 5x^3 + x + 12$ b. $f(x) = \frac{-2}{x^2}$
   c. $f(x) = \frac{4}{\sqrt{x}}$ d. $f(x) = x^4 - \frac{1}{x^4}$

4. Find $\frac{d^2y}{dx^2}$ for the following:
   a. $y = x^5 - 5x^4 + 7x^3 - 3x^2 + 17$ b. $y = (x^2 + 4)(1 - 3x^3)$

5. The displacement at time t of an object moving along a line is given by $s(t) = 3t^3 - 40.5t^2 + 162t$ for $0 \leq t \leq 8$.
   a. Find the position, velocity, and acceleration.
   b. When is the object stationary? advancing? retreating?
   c. At what time t is the velocity not changing?
   d. At what time t is the velocity decreasing; that is, the object is decelerating?
   e. At what time t is the velocity increasing; that is, the object is accelerating?

6. A particle moving on the x-axis has displacement $x(t) = 2t^3 + 3t^2 - 36t + 40$.
   a. Find the velocity of the particle at time t.
   b. Find the acceleration of the particle at time t.
   c. Determine the total distance travelled by the particle during the first three seconds.

7. For each of the following cost functions, in dollars, find

   a. the cost of producing 900 items.

   b. the average cost of each of the first 900 items produced.

   c. the marginal cost when $x = 900$, and the cost of producing the 901st item.

   i) $C(x) = 5x + 100$ ii) $C(x) = \sqrt{x} + 8000$

8. The total cost of producing x units of a certain commodity is given by the function $C(x) = 3x^2 + x + 48$.

   a. Determine the average cost of 3, 4, 5, and 6 units of the commodity.

   b. Using a graphing utility, show that the minimum average cost is $25 when 4 units are produced.

9. Find the indicated rate for each of the following:

   a. Find $\frac{dy}{dt}$, where $x^2 + y^2 = 36$ and $\frac{dx}{dt} = 4$, when $x = 3$.

   b. Find $\frac{dy}{dt}$, where $5x^2 - y = 100$ and $\frac{dx}{dt} = 10$, when $x = 10$.

10. An environmental study of a suburban community suggests that t years from now, the average level of carbon monoxide in the air will be $q(t) = 0.05t^2 + 0.1t + 3.4$ parts per million.

    a. At what rate will the carbon monoxide level be changing with respect to time one year from now?

    b. By how much will the carbon monoxide level change in the first year?

11. Suppose a spherical piece of ice is melting at a rate of 5 cm^3/min and retains its spherical shape at all times. How fast is the radius changing at the instant when the radius is 4 cm? How fast is the surface area of the sphere changing at the same instant?

12. Sand is being dumped on a pile in such a way that it always forms a cone whose radius equals its height. If the sand is being dumped at a rate of 10 m^3/h, at what rate is the height of the pile increasing when there are 1050 m^3 of sand in the pile?

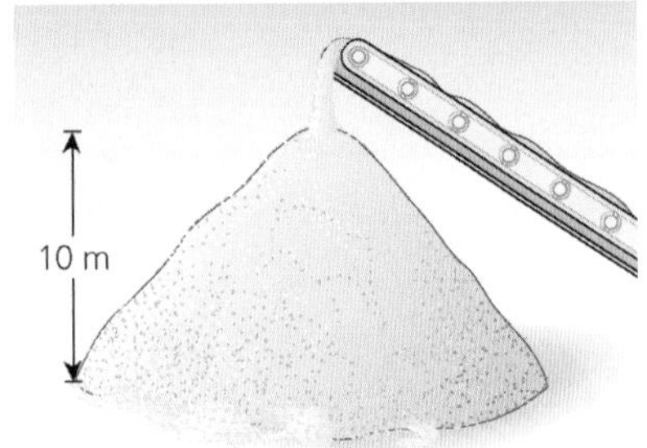

technology

13. Graph each of the following:

    a. $y = 2^x$ b. $y = 10^x + 1$ c. $y = 5^{x-2} + 3$

    d. $y = \left(\frac{1}{2}\right)^{x+3}$ e. $y = 3e^{x-1} - 2$ f. $y = 8 - e^{-x}$

14. Simplify each of the following:

a. $\frac{(27)^{\frac{1}{3}} \cdot 4^2}{48}$

b. $4 \cdot 2^{x-1}$

c. $e^{\sqrt{25}} \cdot e^{-5}$

d. $9\left(\frac{1}{3}\right)^{-3}$

e. $\frac{e^3e^{-2x}}{e^{-x}}$

f. $(e^{4x})^3$

15. Solve each equation, if possible.

a. $5^{2x+9} = 125$

b. $3^{x^2+3} = 81^x$

c. $\left(\frac{1}{4}\right)^{x+3} = \left(\frac{1}{8}\right)^{x-1}$

d. $2^{2x} - 12(2^x) + 32 = 0$

e. $e^x = 1$

f. $e^{2x} + e^x - 2 = 0$

16. Digital cable is being introduced into a certain city. The number of subscribers t months from now is expected to be $N(t) = \frac{80\ 000}{1 + 10e^{-0.2t}}$.

a. How many subscribers will there be after six months?

b. How many subscribers will there eventually be?

17. A rumour spreads through a school. After the rumour has begun, $N(t) = \frac{50}{1 + 49e^{-t}}$ people have heard the rumour where t is in hours. How many people have heard it after 4 h?

18. Assume that the annual rate of inflation will average 5% over the next ten years.

a. Write an equation to represent the approximate cost, C, of goods or services during any year in that decade.

b. If the price of a mechanical inspection for your car is presently $39.95, estimate the price ten years from now.

c. If the price of an oil change ten years from now is $40.64, determine the price of an oil change today.

19. The value of a new car depreciates at a rate of 25% per year.

a. Write an equation to represent the approximate value, V, of a car purchased for $30 000.

b. Determine the value of the car two years after it is purchased.

c. Approximately how many years will it take until the car is worth $3000?

technology

20. Find an exponential function modelled by the experimental data collected over time t.

t	0	1	2	3	4
y	1200	720	432	259.2	155.52

21. Graph each of the following:

a. $y = \log_2 x$ b. $y = \log x$ c. $y = 3\log(2 - x)$

22. Find the value of each of the following:

a. $\log 100$ b. $\log_2 16$ c. $\log_3 243$ d. $\log 0.001$
e. $\log_8 2$ f. $\log_4\left(\frac{1}{8}\right)$ g. $\log 10$ h. $\log 2.2$
i. $\log_a \frac{1}{a^2}$ j. $4^{\log_4 7}$ k. $10^{-10\log 3}$ l. $a^{8\log_a \sqrt{a}}$

23. Use the properties of logarithms to write each expression as a sum, difference, and/or multiple of logarithms.

a. $\log\frac{2}{3}$ b. $\log\frac{xy}{z}$ c. $\log\frac{1}{5}$
d. $\log\sqrt{\frac{x+1}{x-1}}$ e. $\log\left(\frac{x^2-4}{x^5}\right)^4$ f. $\log_a 4a^5$

24. Write the expression as a logarithm of a single quantity.

a. $\log(x - 4) + \log(3 - x)$ b. $3\log_2 x + 2\log_2 y - 4\log_2 z$
c. $2\log 3 - \frac{1}{2}\log(x^2 + 1)$ d. $\log x - 4\log(x - 5) + \frac{2}{3}\log\sqrt{x+1}$

25. Use the formula $\log_a x = \frac{\log x}{\log a}$ to determine the value of each of the following logarithms:

a. $\log_2 12$ b. $\log_3 \frac{1}{2}$ c. $\log_3 8$
d. $\log_8 4$ e. $\log_4 6$ f. $\log_{\frac{1}{2}} 15$

26. Solve each of the following equations:

a. $x = \log_5 125$ b. $x = \log_5 225 - \log_5 9$
c. $x - 3\log_3 243 = 4\log_2\sqrt{512}$ d. $\log_5(2x + 5) = 2$
e. $2\log_3(4x + 1) = 4$ f. $\log_{12} x - \log_{12}(x - 2) + 1 = 2$
g. $2^x = 7$ h. $\log 10^x = -1$
i. $\log(x - 4) = 1$ j. $(\log x)^2 + 3\log x - 10 = 0$

27. The level of sound in decibels is $SL = 10\log(I \times 10^{12})$ where I is the intensity of the sound in watts per square metre (W/m^2). A decibel, or dB, named for Alexander Graham Bell, is the smallest increase of the loudness of a sound that is detectable by the human ear.

a. What is the sound level when the intensity is 2.51×10^{-5} W/m^2?

b. The threshold of pain is 120 dB. A room with appliances on has an intensity of 6.31×10^{-4}. Is the sound level in the room bearable to the human ear?

c. Write the intensity of sound of normal conversation, 50 dB, in scientific notation.

d. Calculate the intensity of the sound at a rock concert where the sound level is 110 dB.

Chapter 8

DERIVATIVES OF EXPONENTIAL AND LOGARITHMIC FUNCTIONS

The world's population experiences exponential growth, which means that the rate of growth becomes more rapid as the size of the population increases. But how do we explain this in the language of calculus? Well, the rate of growth of the population is described by an exponential function, and the derivative of the population with respect to time is a constant multiple of the population. But there are other examples of growth that require not just exponential functions, but compositions of exponential functions with other functions. These examples include electronic signal transmission with amplification, the "bell curve" used in statistics, the effects of shock absorbers on car vibration, or the function describing population growth in an environment that has a maximum sustainable population. By combining the techniques in this chapter with other rules for derivatives, we can find the derivative of an exponential function that is composed with other functions. Logarithmic functions and exponential functions are inverses of each other, and in this chapter, you will see how their derivatives are also related to each other.

CHAPTER EXPECTATIONS In this chapter, you will

- identify e as $\lim_{n\to\infty}\left(1+\frac{1}{n}\right)^2$ and approximate the limit, **Section 8.1**
- define e and the derivative of $y = e^x$, **Section 8.1**
- define the logarithmic function $\log_a x$ ($a > 1$), **Section 8.2**
- determine the derivatives of exponential and logarithmic function, **Section 8.2, 8.3, Career Link**
- determine the derivatives of combinations of the basic functions, **Section 8.3**
- solve optimization problems using exponential and logarithmic functions, **Section 8.4**
- make inferences from models of applications and compare the inferences with the original hypotheses regarding the rates of change, **Section 8.1, 8.2**
- compare the key features of a mathematical model with the features of the application it represents, **Section 8.3, 8.4**

Review of Prerequisite Skills

In Chapter 8, you will be studying two classes of functions that occur frequently in calculus problems: the derivatives of logarithmic and exponential functions. To begin, we will review some properties of exponential and logarithmic functions.

Properties of Logarithms

- $\log_b(pq) = \log_b p + \log_b q$
- $\log_b\left(\frac{p}{q}\right) = \log_b p - \log_b q$
- $\log_b(p^r) = r\log_b p$
- $\log_b(b^r) = r$

Properties of Exponents

- $b^m b^n = b^{m+n}$
- $\frac{b^m}{b^n} = b^{m-n}$
- $(b^m)^n = b^{mn}$
- $b^{\log_b(m)} = m$

The Graphs of $y = \log_b x$ and $y = b^x$

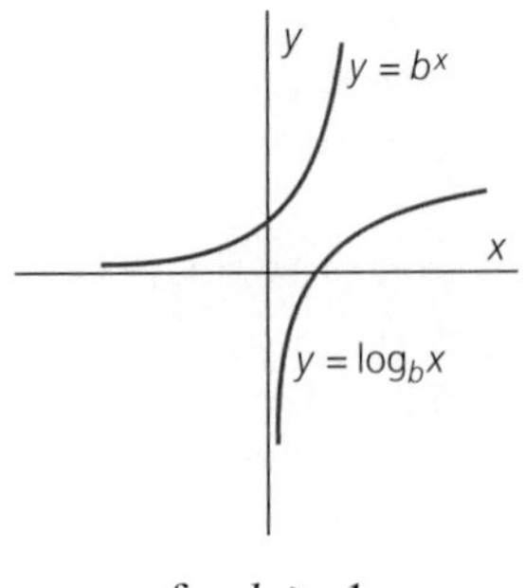

for $b > 1$

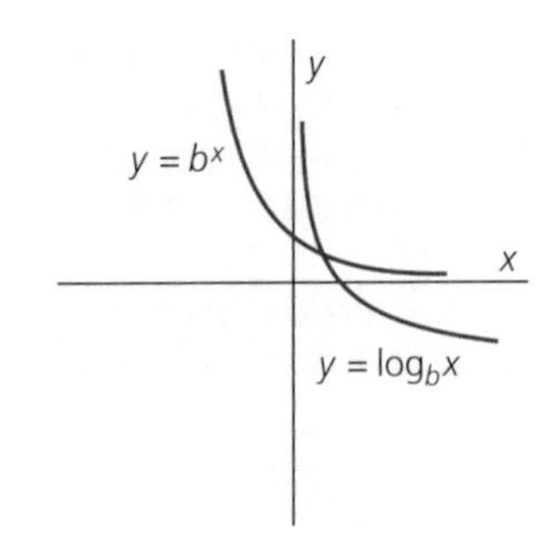

for $0 < b < 1$

- If $b^m = n$ for $b > 0$, then $\log_b n = m$.
- If $y = \log_a p$, then $y = \frac{\log_b p}{\log_b a}$ for any $a, b > 0$.

Exercise

1. Evaluate each of the following:

   a. 3^{-2} b. $32^{\frac{2}{5}}$ c. $27^{-\frac{2}{3}}$ d. $\left(\frac{2}{3}\right)^{-2}$

2. In each of the following, change to the equivalent logarithmic form.

   a. $5^4 = 625$ b. $4^{-2} = \frac{1}{16}$ c. $x^3 = 3$

   d. $10^w = 450$ e. $3^8 = z$ f. $a^b = T$

3. Express each of the following in an equivalent exponential form.

   a. $\log_{11}(121) = 2$ b. $\log_{125}(x) = \frac{1}{3}$ c. $\log_a 1296 = 4$ d. $\log_b A = W$

4. Evaluate each of the following:

   a. $\log_2 32$ b. $\log_{10} 0.0001$ c. $\log_{10} 20 + \log_{10} 5$

   d. $\log_2 20 - \log_2 5$ e. $3^{2\log_3 5}$ f. $\log_3\left(5^3 9^{-3} 25^{-\frac{3}{2}}\right)$

5. In each of the following, use the change of base formula to express the given logarithm in terms of the base b, and then use a calculator to evaluate to three decimal places.

   a. $\log_2(80)$, $b = e$ b. $3\log_5 22 - 2\log_5 15$, $b = 10$

6. Sketch the graph of each function and find its x-intercept.

   a. $y = \log_{10}(x + 2)$ b. $y = 5^{x+3}$

investigate

CHAPTER 8: RATE-OF-CHANGE MODELS IN MICROBIOLOGY

How would you find the slope of the function

$$y = \frac{(7x - 3)^{\frac{5}{2}}(3x + 2)^4}{\sqrt{-2x^3 + 6}}$$

using each of the Power, Product, Quotient, and Chain Rules? While this task would be very difficult using traditional methods of differentiation, it will be pain-free when you use the logarithmic and exponential differential calculus methods of this chapter. In addition to developing ideas and skills, you will also take the logarithmic and exponential models constructed in Chapters 6 and 7 and utilize them in rate-of-change applications.

Case Study — Microbiologist

Microbiologists contribute their expertise to many fields, including medicine, environmental science, and biotechnology. Enumerating, the process of counting bacteria, allows microbiologists to build mathematical models that predict populations. Once they can predict a population accurately, the model could be used in medicine, for example, to predict the dose of medication required to kill a certain bacterial infection. The data set in the table was used by a microbiologist to produce a polynomial-based mathematical model to predict population $p(t)$, as a function of time t, in hours, for the growth of a certain bacteria:

Time (in hours)	Population
0	1000
0.5	1649
1.0	2718
1.5	4482
2.0	7389

$$p(t) = 1000\left(1 + t + \frac{1}{2}t^2 + \frac{1}{6}t^3 + \frac{1}{24}t^4 + \frac{1}{120}t^5\right)$$

DISCUSSION QUESTIONS

1. How well does the equation fit the data set? Use the equation, a graph, and/or the graphing calculator to comment on the "goodness of fit."
2. What is the population after 0.5 h? How fast is the population growing at this time? (Use calculus to determine this.) Complete these calculations for the 1.0 h point.
3. What pattern did you notice in your calculations? Explain this pattern by examining the terms of this equation to find the reason why.

The polynomial function in this case is an approximation of the special function in mathematics, natural science, and economics, $f(x) = e^x$, where e has a value of 2.718 28.... At the end of this chapter, you will complete a task on rates of change of exponential growth in a biotechnology case study.

Section 8.1 — Derivatives of Exponential Functions

We are familiar with the properties of the exponential function $f(x) = b^x$, where $b > 0$. In trying to compute its derivative, we note that the Power Rule developed earlier does not apply, since the base of the exponential function is constant and the exponent varies. By using the definition of a derivative, we obtain

$$
\begin{aligned}
f'(x) &= \lim_{h \to 0} \frac{f(x+h) - f(x)}{h} \\
&= \lim_{h \to 0} \frac{b^{x+h} - b^x}{h} \\
&= \lim_{h \to 0} \frac{b^x \bullet b^h - b^x}{h} && \text{(Properties of the exponential function)} \\
&= \lim_{h \to 0} \frac{b^x(b^h - 1)}{h}. && \text{(Common factor)}
\end{aligned}
$$

The factor b^x is constant as $h \to 0$ and does not depend on h.

$$f'(x) = b^x \lim_{h \to 0} \frac{b^h - 1}{h}$$

In fact,

$$
\begin{aligned}
f'(0) &= b^0 \lim_{h \to 0} \frac{b^h - 1}{h} \\
&= \lim_{h \to 0} \frac{b^h - 1}{h}.
\end{aligned}
$$

Therefore if $f(x) = b^x$,

$$f'(x) = b^x \bullet f'(0)$$

or

$$f'(x) = f(x)f'(0).$$

Here we have a surprising result. The derivative at any point is the product of the value of the function at that point and a constant. This constant is the value of the slope of the function at $x = 0$, namely $f'(0)$. In other words, the slope of the tangent line at a given point is proportional to the y-coordinate at that point.

It is clear that as b changes, the value of $f'(0)$ will change. Is there any value of b that gives a particularly useful result? The following investigation addresses this question.

INVESTIGATION

The purpose of this investigation is to examine the value of $f'(0) = \lim_{h \to 0} \frac{b^h - 1}{h}$ for different values of b.

1. Using $h = 0.0001$, determine the value of $\lim_{h \to 0} \frac{b^h - 1}{h}$ for $b = 1, 2, 3, 4, 5$, and 6.
2. What happens to the value of the expression as b increases?

3. a. What is the maximum value of b so that the $\lim_{h \to 0} \frac{b^h - 1}{h} < 1$?

   b. What is the minimum value of b so that the $\lim_{h \to 0} \frac{b^h - 1}{h} > 1$?

4. What is the implication of $\lim_{h \to 0} \frac{b^h - 1}{h} = 1$ in calculating $f'(x) = f(x)f'(0)$?

5. Repeat Question 1 of this Investigation using $b = 2.5, 2.6, 2.7,$ and 2.8.

6. By further investigation, determine, correct to three decimal places, the value for b that gives a value of the limit closest to 1.

The exact number for which $f'(0) = 1$ is given the name "e," after the mathematician Euler (pronounced "oiler"). The approximate value of e is 2.718281. Its exact value cannot be determined, since e is an irrational number, as is π. With this number as base, we have the exponential function $f(x) = e^x$ with a particular property.

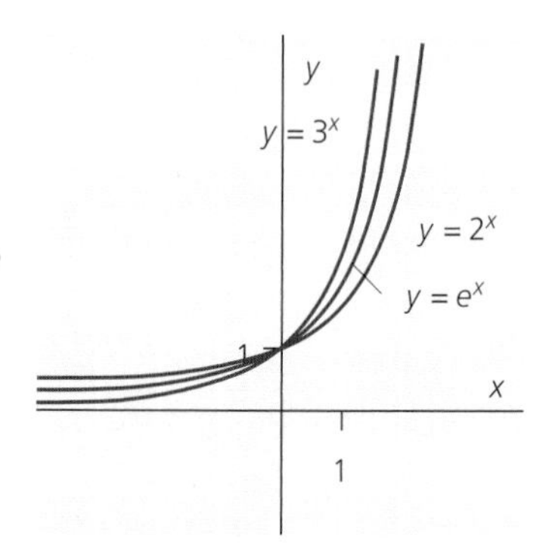

For the function $f(x) = e^x, f'(x) = e^x$.

technology

This function is its own derivative. The value of the slope of the tangent, at any point on the curve of $y = e^x$, is equal to the value of the y-coordinate at that point. There is a e^x [LN] button on your calculator. This button can be used to obtain the graph of $y = e^x$. Also note that entering e^1 yields 2.718281..., which is an approximation of the value of e. When we look at the graph of $y = e^x$, we see that the slopes of the tangents increase as x increases.

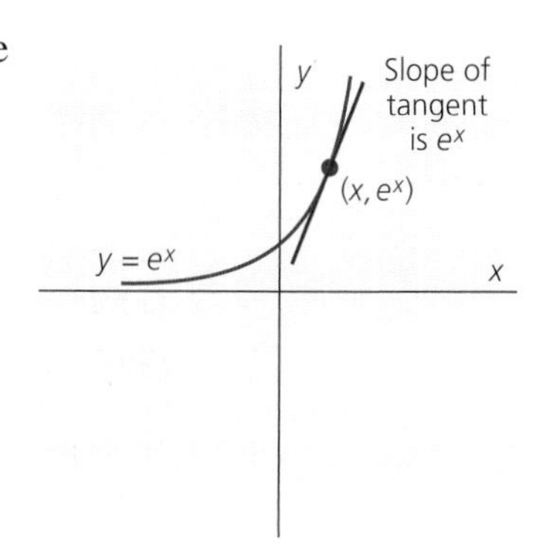

Technology Extension: Using a Spreadsheet Approach

technology
APPENDIX P. 447

To try this Investigation utilizing a spreadsheet option, please refer to page 447 of the Technical Assistance Appendix.

EXAMPLE 1

Find derivatives of the following functions:

a. $f(x) = x^2e^x$

b. $g(x) = e^{x^2 - x}$

Solution

a. Using the Product Rule,

$$f'(x) = 2xe^x + x^2e^x$$
$$= e^x(2x + x^2).$$

b. If we let $u = x^2 - x$ and use the Chain Rule,

$$g(u) = e^u$$
$$\frac{dg}{dx} = \frac{dg}{du} \bullet \frac{du}{dx}$$
$$= e^u(2x - 1)$$
$$= e^{x^2-x}(2x - 1).$$

In general, if $f(x) = e^{g(x)}$, then $f'(x) = e^{g(x)}\, g'(x)$ by the Chain Rule.

EXAMPLE 2

Given $f(x) = 3e^{x^2}$, determine $f'(-1)$.

Solution

$$f'(x) = 3e^{x^2}(2x)$$
$$= 6xe^{x^2}$$

Then $\quad f'(-1) = -6e.$

Answers are usually left in this form. If desired, numeric approximations can be obtained from a calculator. Here $f'(-1) = -16.31$ correct to two decimals.

EXAMPLE 3

Determine the equation of the line tangent to the graph of $y = xe^x$ at the point where $x = 2$.

Solution

When $x = 2$, $y = 2e^2$, so $(2, 2e^2)$ is the point of contact of the tangent.

$$y' = e^x + xe^x$$
$$= e^x(1 + x)$$

When $x = 2$, $y' = 3e^2$.

The equation of the tangent is $y - 2e^2 = 3e^2(x - 2)$

or $3e^2x - y - 4e^2 = 0$.

EXAMPLE 4

Determine the equation of the line tangent to the graph of $y = \frac{e^x}{x^2}$, $x \neq 0$, at the point where $x = 2$.

Solution

Using the Quotient Rule,

$$\frac{dy}{dx} = \frac{e^x x^2 - e^x(2x)}{(x^2)^2}$$
$$= \frac{e^x x(x-2)}{x^4}$$
$$= \frac{e^x(x-2)}{x^3},\ x \neq 0.$$

technology

When $x = 2$, $\frac{dy}{dx} = 0$, and the tangent is horizontal. Therefore, the equation of the required tangent is $y = \frac{e^2}{4}$. A calculator yields this graph for $y = \frac{e^x}{x^2}$, and we see the horizontal tangent at $x = 2$.

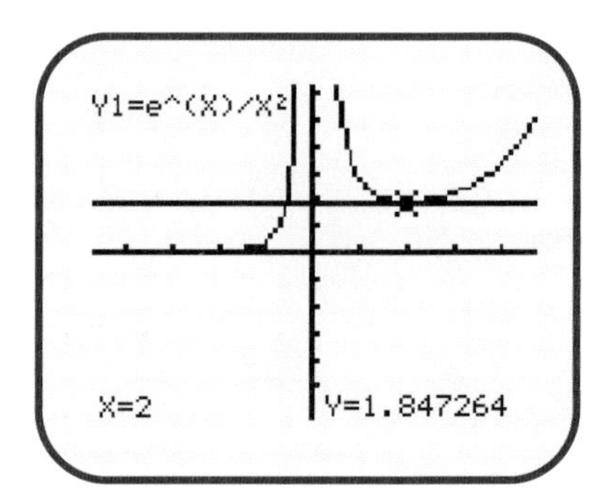

We will return to the problem of finding the derivative of the general exponential function $f(x) = b^x$ in Section 8.3.

Exercise 8.1

Part A

1. If $f(x) = e^x$, compare the graphs of $y = f(x)$ and $y = f'(x)$.

Communication

2. Why can you not use the Power Rule for derivatives to differentiate $y = 2^x$?

3. Use the Chain Rule and the new Exponential Derivative Rule to find the derivative for each of the following:

   a. $y = e^{3x}$
   b. $s = e^{3t-5}$
   c. $y = 2e^{10t}$
   d. $y = e^{-3x}$
   e. $y = e^{5-6x+x^2}$
   f. $y = e^{\sqrt{x}}$

Knowledge/Understanding

4. Use the Exponential Derivative Rule in conjunction with other appropriate derivative rules to differentiate each of the following:

   a. $y = 2e^{x^3}$
   b. $y = xe^{3x}$
   c. $f(x) = \frac{e^{-x^3}}{x}$
   d. $s = \frac{e^{3t^2}}{t^2}$
   e. $f(x) = \sqrt{x}e^x$
   f. $h(t) = e^{t^2} + 3e^{-t}$
   g. $p = e^{(w+e^w)}$
   h. $g(t) = \frac{e^{2t}}{1 + e^{2t}}$

5. a. If $f(x) = \frac{1}{3}(e^{3x} + e^{-3x})$, find $f'(1)$.
   b. If $f(x) = e^{-\left(\frac{1}{x+1}\right)}$, find $f'(0)$.
   c. If $h(z) = z^2(1 + e^{-z})$, determine $h'(-1)$.

technology

6. a. Find the equation of the tangent to the curve defined by $y = \frac{2e^x}{1 + e^x}$ at the point $(0, 1)$.
   b. Use technology to graph the function in part **a** and draw the tangent at $(0, 1)$.
   c. Compare the equation in part **a** to the computer equation.

Part B

Application

7. Find the equation of the tangent to the curve defined by $y = e^x$ that is perpendicular to the line defined by $3x + y = 1$.

8. Find the equation of the tangent to the curve defined by $y = xe^{-x}$ at the point $A(1, e^{-1})$.

9. Find all points at which the tangent to the curve defined by $y = x^2e^{-x}$ is horizontal.

10. If $y = \frac{5}{2}\left(e^{\frac{x}{5}} + e^{-\frac{x}{5}}\right)$, then prove that $y'' = \frac{y}{25}$.

11. a. For the function $y = e^{-3x}$, determine $\frac{dy}{dx}, \frac{d^2y}{dx^2}$ and $\frac{d^3y}{dx^3}$.
    b. From the pattern in part **a**, state the value for $\frac{d^ny}{dx^n}$.

12. For each of the following, determine the equation of the tangent at the given point.
    a. For the curve defined by $y - e^{xy} = 0$ at $A(0, 1)$.
    b. For the curve defined by $x^2e^y = 1$ at $B(1, 0)$.
    c. Explain why these relations cannot easily be graphed using a calculator.

Application

13. The number, N, of bacteria in a culture at time t in hours is $N = 1000\left[30 + e^{-\frac{t}{30}}\right]$.
    a. What is the initial number of bacteria in the culture?
    b. Find the rate of change of the number of bacteria at time t.
    c. How fast is the number of bacteria changing when $t = 20$ h?
    d. Find the largest number of bacteria in the culture during the interval $0 \leq t \leq 50$.

14. The distance (in metres) fallen by a skydiver t seconds after jumping (and before her parachute opens) is $s = 160\left(\frac{1}{4}t - 1 + e^{-\frac{t}{4}}\right)$.

    a. Find the skydiver's velocity, v, at time t.

    b. Show that her acceleration is given by $a = 10 - \frac{1}{4}v$.

    c. Find $v_T = \lim_{t\to\infty} v$. This is the "terminal" velocity, the constant velocity attained when the air resistance balances the force of gravity.

    d. At what time is the skydiver's velocity 95% of the terminal velocity? How far has she fallen at that time?

Part C

Thinking/Inquiry/ Problem Solving

15. Use the definition of the derivative to evaluate each limit.

    a. $\lim_{h\to 0}\frac{e^h - 1}{h}$

    b. $\lim_{h\to 0}\frac{e^{2+h} - e^2}{h}$

16. For what values of m does the function $y = Ae^{mt}$ satisfy the following equation?

    $$\frac{d^2y}{dx^2} + \frac{dy}{dx} - 6y = 0$$

17. The hyperbolic functions are defined as $\sinh x = \frac{1}{2}(e^x - e^{-x})$ and $\cosh x = \frac{1}{2}(e^x + e^{-x})$.

    a. Prove $D_x \sinh x = \cosh x$.

    b. Prove $D_x \cosh x = \sinh x$.

    c. Prove $D_x \tanh x = \frac{1}{(\cosh x)^2}$, if $\tanh x = \frac{\sinh x}{\cosh x}$.

technology

Graphing the Hyperbolic Function

1. Use a calculator or computer to graph $y = \cosh x$ by using the definition $\cosh x = \frac{1}{2}(e^x + e^{-x})$.
2. Press [2nd] [0] (CATALOG) for the list of CATALOG items and select **cosh(** to investigate if cosh is a built-in function.
3. On the same window, graph $y = 1.25x^2 + 1$ and $y = 1.05x^2 + 1$. Investigate changes in the coefficient a in the equation $y = ax^2 + 1$ to see if you can create a parabola that will approximate the hyperbolic cosine function.

Section 8.2 — The Derivative of the Natural Logarithmic Function

The logarithmic function is the inverse of the exponential function. For the particular exponential function $y = e^x$, the inverse is $x = e^y$ or $y = \log_e x$, a logarithmic function where $e \approx 2.719281$. This logarithmic function is referred to as the "natural" logarithmic function, and is usually written as $y = \ln x$ (pronounced "lon x"). The functions $y = e^x$ and $y = \ln x$ are inverses of each other. This means that the graphs of the functions are reflections of each other in the line $y = x$, as shown.

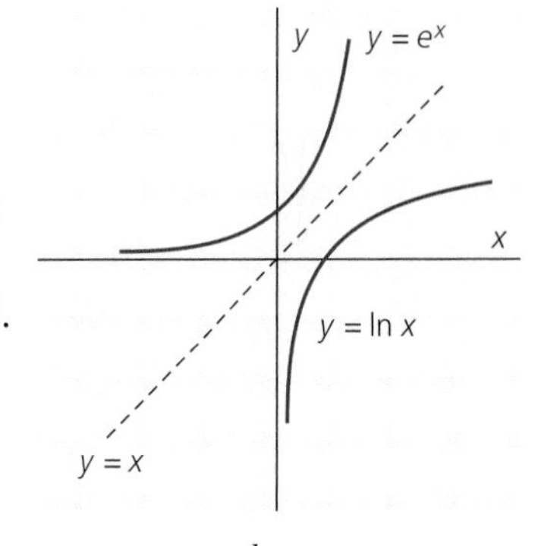

technology

There is a LN key on your calculator that is useful for sketching the graph of $y = \ln x$. This key can also be used to determine the numeric value of the natural logarithm of a number. For example, $\log 12 \approx 1.079$, while $\ln(12) \approx 2.485$.

What is the derivative of this logarithmic function? For $y = \ln x$, the definition of the derivative yields

$$\frac{dy}{dx} = \lim_{h \to 0} \frac{\ln(x + h) - \ln(x)}{h}.$$

We could investigate this limit in order to determine the value of $\frac{dy}{dx}$, an investigation we will consider later. First, we can determine the derivative of the natural logarithm function using the derivative of the exponential function we developed in the previous section.

Given $y = \ln x$, we can rewrite this as $e^y = x$. Differentiating both sides of this equation with respect to x, and using implicit differentiation on the left side, yields

$$e^y \frac{dy}{dx} = 1$$

$$\frac{dy}{dx} = \frac{1}{e^y}$$

$$= \frac{1}{x}.$$

The derivative of the natural logarithmic function $y = \ln x$ is $\frac{dy}{dx} = \frac{1}{x}$, $x > 0$.

This fits nicely with the graph of $y = \ln x$. The function is defined only for $x > 0$, and the slopes are all positive. We see that as $x \to \infty$, $\frac{dy}{dx} \to 0$. As x increases, the slope of the tangent decreases.

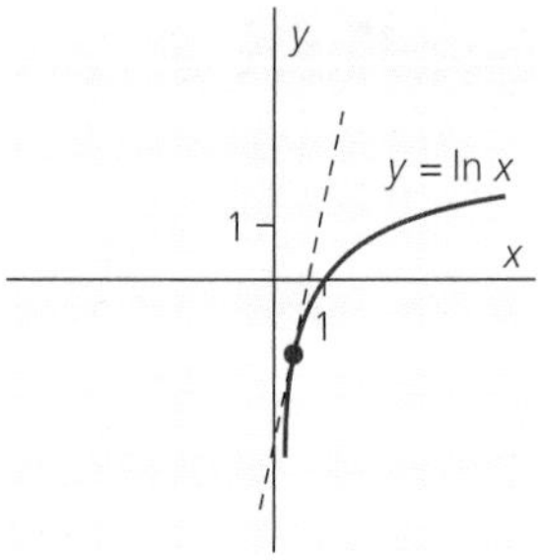

We can apply this new derivative, along with the Product, Quotient, and Chain Rules to find derivatives of fairly complicated functions.

EXAMPLE 1

Find $\frac{dy}{dx}$ for the following functions:

a. $y = \ln(5x)$

b. $y = \frac{\ln x}{x^3}$

c. $y = \ln(x^2 + e^x)$

Solution

a. $y = \ln(5x)$

Solution 1

Using the Chain Rule,

$$\frac{dy}{dx} = \frac{1}{5x}(5)$$
$$= \frac{1}{x}$$

Solution 2

$y = \ln(5x) = \ln(5) + \ln(x)$

$$\frac{dy}{dx} = 0 + \frac{1}{x}$$
$$= \frac{1}{x}$$

b. $y = \frac{\ln x}{x^3}$

Using the Quotient and Power Rules,

$$\frac{dy}{dx} = \frac{\frac{d}{dx}(\ln(x)) \cdot x^3 - \ln(x)\frac{d}{dx}(x^3)}{(x^3)^2}$$
$$= \frac{\frac{1}{x} \cdot x^3 - \ln(x) \cdot 3x^2}{x^6}$$
$$= \frac{x^2 - 3x^2\ln(x)}{x^6}$$
$$= \frac{1 - 3\ln(x)}{x^4}.$$

c. $y = \ln(x^2 + e^x)$

Using the Chain Rule,

$$\frac{dy}{dx} = \frac{1}{(x^2 + e^x)} \frac{d}{dx}(x^2 + e^x)$$
$$= \frac{2x + e^x}{(x^2 + e^x)}.$$

If $f(x) = \ln(g(x))$, then $f'(x) = \frac{1}{g(x)}g'(x)$, by the Chain Rule.

EXAMPLE 2

Determine the equation of the line tangent to $y = \frac{\ln x^2}{3x}$ at the point where $x = 1$.

Solution

$\ln 1 = 0$, so $y = 0$ when $x = 1$, and the point of contact of the tangent is $(1, 0)$.

The slope of the tangent is given by $\frac{dy}{dx}$.

$$\frac{dy}{dx} = \frac{3x\left(\frac{1}{x^2}\right)2x - 3\ln x^2}{9x^2}$$

$$= \frac{6 - 3\ln x^2}{9x^2}$$

When $x = 1$, $\frac{dy}{dx} = \frac{2}{3}$.

The equation of the tangent is $y - 0 = \frac{2}{3}(x - 1)$, or $2x - 3y - 2 = 0$.

EXAMPLE 3

a. For the function $f(x) = \sqrt{x} - \ln x$, $x > 0$, use your graphing calculator to determine the value of x at a point on the graph that minimizes the function.

b. Use calculus methods to determine the exact solution.

Solution

technology APPENDIX P. 444

a. The graph of $f(x) = \sqrt{x} - \ln x$ is shown. Use the minimum value function, **3:minimum**, in the CALCULATE mode of your calculator to find the minimum value of $f(x)$. The minimum value occurs at $x = 4$.

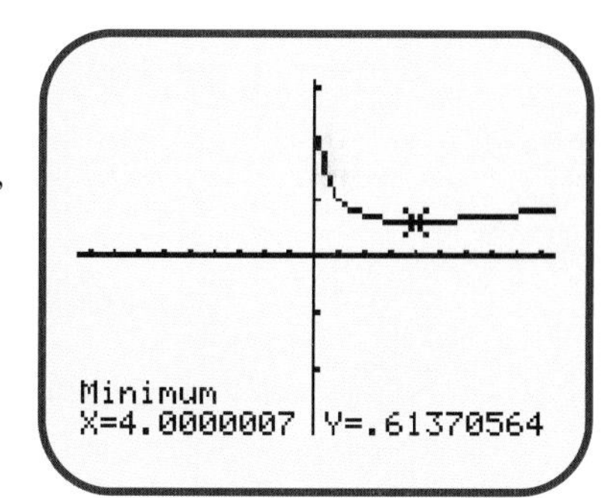

b. $f(x) = \sqrt{x} - \ln x$

To minimize $f(x)$, set the derivative equal to zero.

$$f'(x) = \frac{1}{2\sqrt{x}} - \frac{1}{x}$$

$$\frac{1}{2\sqrt{x}} - \frac{1}{x} = 0$$

$$\frac{1}{2\sqrt{x}} = \frac{1}{x}$$

$$x = 2\sqrt{x}$$

$$x^2 = 4x$$

$$x(x - 4) = 0$$

$$x = 4 \text{ or } x = 0$$

But $x = 0$ is not in the domain of the function, so $x = 4$.
Therefore, the minimum value of $f(x)$ occurs at $x = 4$.

We now look back at the derivative of the natural logarithm function using the definition.

For the function $f(x) = \ln(x)$,

$$f'(x) = \lim_{h \to 0} \frac{\ln(x + h) - \ln(x)}{h}$$

and, specifically,

$$\begin{aligned} f'(1) &= \lim_{h \to 0} \frac{\ln(1 + h) - \ln(1)}{h} \\ &= \lim_{h \to 0} \frac{\ln(1 + h)}{h} \\ &= \lim_{h \to 0} \ln(1 + h)^{\frac{1}{h}}, \text{ since } \frac{1}{h}\ln(1 + h) = \ln(1 + h)^{\frac{1}{h}}. \end{aligned}$$

However, since we know that $f'(x) = \frac{1}{x}$, $f'(1) = 1$.

Then $\lim_{h \to 0} \ln(1 + h)^{\frac{1}{h}} = 1$.

Since the natural logarithm function is a continuous and a one-to-one function, (meaning that for each acceptable value of the variable, there is exactly one function value), we can rewrite this as

$$\ln\left[\lim_{h \to 0} (1 + h)^{\frac{1}{h}}\right] = 1.$$

Since $\ln e = 1$,

$$\ln\left[\lim_{h \to 0} (1 + h)^{\frac{1}{h}}\right] = \ln e.$$

Therefore, $\lim_{h \to 0} (1 + h)^{\frac{1}{h}} = e$.

Earlier in this chapter, the value of e was presented as $e \approx 2.718281$. We now have a means of approximating the value of e using the above limit.

h	0.1	0.01	0.001	0.0001
$(1 + h)^{\frac{1}{h}}$	2.59374246	2.704813829	2.71692393	2.7181459268

From the table, it appears that $e \approx 2.718281$ is a good approximation as h approaches zero.

Exercise 8.2

Part A

Communication

1. Distinguish between natural logarithms and common logarithms.

2. At the end of this section, we found that we could approximate the value of e, Euler's constant, using $e = \lim_{h \to 0}(1 + h)^{\frac{1}{h}}$. By substituting $h = \frac{1}{n}$, we can express e as $e = \lim_{n \to \infty}\left(1 + \frac{1}{n}\right)^n$. Justify the definition by evaluating the limit for increasing values of n.

3. Use the Chain Rule in conjunction with the Logarithm Derivative Rule to find the derivative for each of the following:

   a. $y = \ln(5x + 8)$ b. $y = \ln(x^2 + 1)$ c. $s = 5\ln t^3$

   d. $y = \ln\sqrt{x + 1}$ e. $s = \ln(t^3 - 2t^2 + 5)$ f. $w = \ln\sqrt{z^2 + 3z}$

Knowledge/Understanding

4. Use the Logarithm Derivative Rule in conjunction with other appropriate derivative rules to differentiate each of the following:

   a. $f(x) = x\ln x$ b. $y = \frac{\ln x}{x^2}$ c. $y = e^{\ln(x)}$

   d. $y = [\ln x]^3$ e. $v = e^t\ln t$ f. $g(z) = \ln(e^{-z} + ze^{-z})$

   g. $s = \frac{e^t}{\ln t}$ h. $h(u) = e^{\sqrt{u}}\ln\sqrt{u}$ i. $f(x) = \ln\left(\frac{x^2 + 1}{x - 1}\right)$

technology

5. a. If $g(x) = e^{2x-1}\ln(2x - 1)$, evaluate $g'(1)$.

   b. If $f(t) = \ln\left(\frac{t - 1}{3t + 5}\right)$, evaluate $f'(5)$.

   c. Check the above calculations using either a calculator or a computer.

6. For each of the following functions, solve the equation $f'(x) = 0$.

   a. $f(x) = \ln(x^2 + 1)$

   b. $f(x) = (\ln x + 2x)^{\frac{1}{3}}$

   c. $f(x) = (x^2 + 1)^{-1}\ln(x^2 + 1)$

technology

7. a. Find the equation of the tangent to the curve defined by $f(x) = \frac{\ln\sqrt[3]{x}}{x}$ at the point where $x = 1$.

   b. Use technology to graph the function in part **a**, and then draw the tangent at the point where $x = 1$.

   c. Compare the equation in part **a** to the equation obtained on the calculator or computer.

Part B

Application

8. Find the equation of the tangent to the curve defined by $y = \ln x - 1$ that is parallel to the straight line with equation $3x - 6y - 1 = 0$.

9. a. If $f(x) = (x\ln x)^2$, then find all points at which the graph of $f(x)$ has a horizontal tangent line.

technology

b. Use a calculator or a computer to check your work in part **a**.

c. Comment on the efficiency of the two solutions.

10. Find the equation of the tangent to the curve defined by $y = \ln(1 + e^{-x})$ at the point where $x = 0$.

Application

11. The velocity in kilometres per hour of a car as it begins to slow down is given by the equation $v(t) = 90 - 30\ln(3t + 1)$, where t is in seconds.

a. What is the velocity of the car as the driver begins to brake?

b. What is the acceleration of the car?

c. What is the acceleration at $t = 2$?

d. How long does it take the car to stop?

12. The pH value of a chemical solution measures the acidity or alkalinity of the solution. The formula is

$$pH = -\log_{10}(H)$$

$$= -\frac{\ln(H)}{\ln(10)} \quad \text{(Using the Change of Base identity)}$$

where H is the concentration of hydrogen ions in the solution (in moles per litre).

a. Tomatoes have $H = 6.3 \times 10^{-5}$. Find the pH value.

b. Recipe ingredients are being added to a bowl of tomatoes, so that the concentration of hydrogen ions in the whole mixture is given by $H(t) = 30 - 5t - 25\left(e^{-\frac{t}{5}} - 1\right)$ moles per litre, where t is measured in seconds. Determine the rate of change of the pH value with respect to time after 10 s.

13. If a force F is defined by $F = k(e^{-S} - 6e^{-2S})$, where S is the distance between two objects, then prove $\frac{d^2F}{dS^2} = F - 18ke^{-2S}$.

14. For each of the following, find the slope of the tangent.

a. For the curve defined by $xe^y + y\ln x = 2$, at $(1, \ln 2)$.

b. For the curve defined by $\ln\sqrt{xy} = 0$, at the point $\left(\frac{1}{3}, 3\right)$.

Part C

Thinking/Inquiry/ Problem Solving

15. Use the definition of the derivative to evaluate $\lim_{h \to 0} \frac{\ln(2 + h) - \ln(2)}{h}$.

16. One definition for e is $e = \lim_{n \to \infty} \left(1 + \frac{1}{n}\right)^n$.

    a. Use the Binomial Theorem to expand $\left(1 + \frac{1}{n}\right)^n$ and then evaluate the limit.

    Show that the value of e can be calculated from the series
    $e = 1 + 1 + \frac{1}{2!} + \frac{1}{3!} + \frac{1}{4!} + \frac{1}{5!} + \ldots.$

    b. For the above series calculate the following partial sums: S_3, S_4, S_5, S_6, and S_7.

17. Recall that $|x| = x$ if $x \geq 0$ and $|x| = -x$ if $x < 0$.

    a. Find the derivative of $y = \ln|x|$.

    b. Find the derivative of $y = \ln|2x + 1|$.

    c. Find the derivative of $y = x^2 \ln|x|$.

Section 8.3 — Derivatives of General Exponential and Logarithmic Functions

In finding the derivative of the general exponential function $f(x) = b^x$ in Section 8.1, we obtained the expression $f'(x) = b^x f'(0)$. We saw that there is a problem in determining $f'(0)$ for different values of the base b. We can avoid this problem by using the fact that $\frac{d}{dx}e^x = e^x$ together with the properties of logarithmic and exponential functions.

First, note that $e^{\ln(p)} = p$. Then for $f(x) = b^x$, we can write

$$\begin{aligned} f(x) &= b^x \\ &= e^{\ln(b^x)} \\ &= e^{x\ln b}. \quad \text{(Property of Logarithmic Functions)} \end{aligned}$$

Since $\ln b$ is a constant for any value of b, we differentiate $f(x) = e^{x\ln b}$ using the Chain Rule and get

$$\begin{aligned} f'(x) &= e^{x\ln(b)}\frac{d}{dx}(x\ln b) \\ &= e^{x\ln(b)}\ln b \\ &= e^{\ln(b^x)}\ln b \\ &= b^x\ln b. \end{aligned}$$

What happens if the exponent is $g(x)$? Then we have $f(x) = b^{g(x)}$. Now we let $u = g(x)$ and use the Chain Rule on $f(u) = b^u$, as follows:

$$\frac{df}{dx} = \frac{df}{du} \bullet \frac{du}{dx}.$$

Then $\frac{df}{du} = b^u\ln b$ and $\frac{du}{dx} = g'(x)$.

$$\frac{df}{dx} = b^{g(x)}\ln b[g'(x)]$$

For $f(x) = b^{g(x)}$, $f'(x) = b^{g(x)}\ln b(g'(x))$.
If $g(x) = x$ and $f(x) = b^x$, then $f'(x) = b^x\ln b$.

The derivative of $f(x) = 2^x$ is $f'(x) = 2^x\ln(2)$, and the derivative of $g(x) = 3^x$ is $g'(x) = 3^x\ln(3)$. (Check on your calculator to verify that $\ln 2 \approx 0.69$ and $\ln 3 \approx 1.09$, which match the values estimated in Section 8.1.)

Note that the derivative of $f(x) = e^x$ is a special case of this general derivative. If we apply the general formula, we get $f'(x) = e^x\ln(e) = e^x$, since $\ln e = 1$.

EXAMPLE 1

Find the derivative of the function $f(x) = 3^{x^2+2}$.

Solution

We have $f(x) = 3^{g(x)}$ with $g(x) = x^2 + 2$.
Then $g'(x) = 2x$.
Now, $f'(x) = 3^{x^2+2} (\ln 3)2x$.

We can use these derivatives to solve problems.

EXAMPLE 2

On January 1, 1850, the population of Goldrushtown was 50 000. Since then the size of the population has been modelled by the function $P(t) = 50\,000(0.98)^t$, where t is the number of years since January 1, 1850.

a. What was the population of Goldrushtown on January 1, 1900?
b. At what rate was the population of Goldrushtown changing on January 1, 1900? Was it increasing or decreasing at that time?

Solution

a. January 1, 1900 is exactly 50 years after January 1, 1850, so we let $t = 50$.

$$\begin{aligned} P(50) &= 50\,000(0.98)^{50} \\ &= 18\,208.484 \end{aligned}$$

The population on January 1, 1900 was approximately 18 208.

b. To determine the rate of change of the population, we require the derivative of P.

$$\begin{aligned} P'(t) &= 50\,000(0.98)^t \ln(0.98) \\ P'(50) &= 50\,000(0.98)^{50} \ln(0.98) \\ &\approx -367.861 \end{aligned}$$

Hence, after 50 years, the population was decreasing at a rate of approximately 368 people per year. (We expected the rate of change to be negative, as the original population function was a decaying exponential function with a base less than 1.)

We can now determine the derivative of the general logarithmic function, that is $y = \log_b x$, for any base $b > 0$. We use the fact that this logarithmic function can be written as $b^y = x$. Differentiating both sides implicitly with respect to x yields

$$\begin{aligned} b^y \ln b \frac{dy}{dx} &= 1 \\ \frac{dy}{dx} &= \frac{1}{b^y \ln b} \\ &= \frac{1}{x \ln b}. \end{aligned}$$

For the special case of the natural logarithm function, that is, $y = \log_e x = \ln x$, this becomes $\frac{dy}{dx} = \frac{1}{x \ln e} = \frac{1}{x}$.

In the general case, for $y = \log_b g(x)$, $b^y = g(x)$, from the definition of logarithms.

Taking derivatives $b^y \ln b \dfrac{dy}{dx} = g'(x)$,

$$\frac{dy}{dx} = \frac{g'(x)}{b^y \ln b} = \frac{g'(x)}{g(x)\ln b}.$$

For $y = \log_b x$, $\dfrac{dy}{dx} = \dfrac{1}{x\ln b}$.

For $y = \log_e x$, $\dfrac{dy}{dx} = \dfrac{1}{x}$.

For $y = \log_b g(x)$, $\dfrac{dy}{dx} = \dfrac{g'x}{g(x)\ln b}$.

EXAMPLE 3

Find the value of $g'(2)$ for the function $g(x) = x^3\log_2\left(\sqrt{x^2 + 4}\right)$.

Solution

Using the Product and Chain Rules,

$$g'(x) = 3x^2\log_2\left(\sqrt{x^2 + 4}\right) + x^3 \frac{1}{\sqrt{x^2 + 4}\ln(2)} \frac{2x}{2\sqrt{x^2 + 4}}$$

$$= 3x^2\log_2\left(\sqrt{x^2 + 4}\right) + \frac{x^4}{(x^2 + 4)\ln 2}.$$

Then

$$g'(2) = 12 \log_2\sqrt{4 + 4} + \frac{16}{(4 + 4)\ln(2)}$$

$$= 12 \log_2\sqrt{8} + \frac{16}{8\ln 2}$$

$$= 12 \log_2 2^{\frac{3}{2}} + \frac{2}{\ln 2}$$

$$= 12 \times \frac{3}{2} + \frac{2}{\ln 2} = 18 + \frac{2}{\ln 2}.$$

EXAMPLE 4

If I_0 is the intensity of barely audible sound, then the decibel (dB) measure of the loudness, L, of a sound of intensity I is given by $L = \log_{10}\left(\frac{I}{I_0}\right)$.

a. What is the loudness, in dB, of a sound of intensity I_0? $100\ I_0$?

b. If the intensity of a siren is 7000 units and is increasing at 100 000 units per second, what is the accompanying rate of change of the loudness of the sound?

Solution

a. A sound of intensity I_0 has loudness

$$L = \log_{10}\left(\frac{I_0}{I_0}\right)$$

$$= \log_{10} 1$$

$$= 0 \text{ dB}.$$

A sound of intensity 100 I_0 has loudness

$$L = \log_{10}\left(\frac{100I_0}{I_0}\right)$$
$$= \log_{10}(100)$$
$$= 2 \text{ dB}.$$

b. We know that $\frac{dI}{dt} = 100\,000$ and we wish to find $\frac{dL}{dt}$.

$$L = \log_{10}\left(\frac{I}{I_0}\right)$$

Differentiate both sides of the equation implicitly with respect to time, t, and get

$$\frac{dL}{dt} = \frac{1}{\frac{I}{I_0}\ln 10}\left(\frac{1}{I_0}\frac{dI}{dt}\right) \qquad \textit{Note: } \frac{d}{dt}\left(\frac{I}{I_0}\right) = \frac{1}{I_0}\frac{dI}{dt}$$
$$= \frac{I_0}{I\ln 10}\left(\frac{1}{I_0}\frac{dI}{dt}\right)$$
$$= \frac{1}{I\ln(10)}\frac{dI}{dt}.$$

When $I = 7000$ and $\frac{dI}{dt} = 100\,000$, we get

$$\frac{dL}{dt} = \frac{1}{7000\ln(10)}(100\,000)$$
$$\approx 6.2.$$

Therefore, the loudness of the siren is increasing at approximately 6.2 dB per second.

In this section, we learned the derivatives for the general exponential and logarithmic functions $y = b^x$ and $y = \log_b(x)$. Many students will wish to compile a list of formulas and memorize them. However, there is no need to do so. You can always use identities to convert general exponential and logarithmic functions to exponential and logarithmic functions with base e, and then use the specific derivatives of $y = e^x$ and $y = \ln(x)$ along with the Chain Rule.

Exercise 8.3

Part A

Knowledge/Understanding

1. Use the Chain Rule in conjunction with the Exponential or Logarithm Derivative Rule to find the derivative for each of the following:

a. $y = 2^{3x}$

b. $y = 3.1^x + x^3$

c. $s = 10^{3t-5}$

d. $w = 10^{(5-6n+n^2)}$

e. $y = \log_5(x^3 - 2x^2 + 10)$

f. $y = \log_{10}\left(\frac{1+x}{1-x}\right)$

g. $f(x) = 7^{x^2}$

h. $v = \log_2\sqrt{t^2 + 3t}$

i. $y = 3^{x^2+3}$

2. Find the derivative function for each of the following:

a. $v = \frac{2^t}{t}$
b. $y = 2^x\log_2(x^4)$
c. $p = 2\log_3(5^s) - \log_3(4^s)$
d. $s = t^2\log_{10}(1 - t)$
e. $f(x) = \frac{\sqrt{3^x}}{x^2}$
f. $y = \frac{\log_5(3x^2)}{\sqrt{x + 1}}$

3. a. If $f(t) = \log_2\left(\frac{t + 1}{2t + 7}\right)$, evaluate $f'(3)$.

b. If $h(t) = \log_3[\log_2(t)]$, determine $h'(8)$.

4. If $f(t) = 10^{3t-5} \bullet e^{2t^2}$, then find the values of t so that $f'(t) = 0$.

Communication

5. a. Find the equation of the tangent to the curve defined by $y = 10^{2x-9}\log_{10}(x^2 - 3x)$ at the point where $x = 5$.

b. Use technology to graph the function and the tangent defined in part **a**.

technology

c. Compare the equation determined by the calculator with the theoretical result. If you did not have the theoretical equation, explain how you would know when the equation provided by the calculator (or computer) is accurate to three decimal places.

Part B

6. Find the equation of the tangent to the curve defined by $y = 20 \times 10^{\left(\frac{t-5}{10}\right)}$ at the point where the curve crosses the y-axis.

Communication

7. Let $f(x) = \log_2(\log_2(x))$.

a. Find the domain of $f(x)$.

b. Find the slope of the tangent to the graph of $f(x)$ at its x-intercept.

c. Explain why it is extremely difficult to check this result on a calculator.

8. A particle moves according to the formula $s = 40 + 3t + 0.01t^2 + \ln t$, where t is measured in minutes and s in centimetres from an initial point I.

a. Find the velocity after 20 min.

b. Determine how long it takes before the acceleration of the particle is 0.01 cm/min^2.

9. Historical data shows that the amount of money sent out of Canada for interest and dividend payments during the period 1967 to 1979 can be approximated by the model $P = 0.5(10^9)e^{0.20015t}$, where t is measured in years, ($t = 0$ in 1967) and P is the total payment in Canadian dollars.

a. Determine and compare the rates of increase for the years 1968 and 1978.

b. Assume the model remained accurate until the year 2002. Compare the rate of increase for 1988 to the increase in 1998.

c. Investigate: Check the Web site of Statistics Canada to see if the rates of increase predicted by this model were accurate for 1988 and 1998.

Part C

Thinking/Inquiry/ Problem Solving

10. An earthquake of minimal intensity, I_0, is given a value 0 on the Richter scale. An earthquake of intensity I has a magnitude $R = \log_{10}\left(\frac{I}{I_0}\right)$ on the Richter scale.

    a. Show that increasing the intensity of the earthquake by a factor of 10 will increase the Richter magnitude by 1.

    b. If the intensity I of a large earthquake is increasing at a rate of 100 units per second, at what rate is the Richter magnitude increasing when $I = 35$?

11. In this section, we used an identity property to rewrite b^x as $e^{x\ln(b)}$. This allowed us to easily determine the derivative of b^x using the known derivative of e^x. This alternate expression for b^x is also useful when we are asked to sketch a graph of $y = b^x$. Since our calculator does not have exponential keys for a general base b, we rewrite $y = e^{x\ln(b)}$ and use the e^x key to sketch the graph.

    a. On your calculator, sketch the graph of $y = e^x$.

    b. On the same set of axes, use your calculator to sketch the graph of $y = 7^x$.

    c. Give a graphical interpretation of the factor $\ln 7$ in the expression $7^x = e^{x\ln(7)}$.

12. The change of base formula allows us to rewrite $\log_b x$ as $\frac{\ln x}{\ln b}$. Again, this is useful when graphing $y = \log_b(x)$ on a calculator, since calculators do not have logarithmic keys for a general base b.

    a. On your calculator, sketch the graph of $y = \ln x$.

    b. On the same set of axes, use your calculator to sketch the graph of $y = \log_5 x$.

    c. Give a graphical interpretation of the factor $\frac{1}{\ln 5}$ in the expression $\log_5(x) = \frac{\ln x}{\ln 5}$.

Section 8.4 — Optimization Problems

In earlier chapters, you considered numerous situations in which you were asked to optimize a given situation. Recall that to optimize means to determine values of variables so that a function that represents cost, area, number of objects, or other quantities can be minimized or maximized.

Here we will consider further optimization problems, using exponential and logarithmic functions.

EXAMPLE 1

The effectiveness of studying for a test depends on how many hours a student studies. Some experiments showed that if the effectiveness, E, is put on a scale of 0 to 10, then $E(t) = 0.5\left[10 + te^{-\frac{t}{20}}\right]$, where t is the number of hours spent studying for an examination. If a student has up to 30 h that he can spend studying, how many hours should he study for maximum effectiveness?

Solution

We wish to find the maximum value for the function $E(t) = 0.5\left[10 + te^{-\frac{t}{20}}\right]$ on the interval $0 \le t \le 30$.

First find critical points by determining $E'(t)$.

$$E'(t) = 0.5\left(e^{-\frac{t}{20}} + t\left(-\frac{1}{20}e^{-\frac{t}{20}}\right)\right) \qquad \text{(Using the Product and Chain Rules)}$$

$$= 0.5e^{-\frac{t}{20}}\left(1 - \frac{t}{20}\right)$$

E' is never undefined, and $e^{-\frac{t}{20}} > 0$ for all values of t. Then, $E'(t) = 0$ when

$$1 - \frac{t}{20} = 0$$

$$t = 20.$$

To determine the maximum effectiveness, we use the algorithm for extreme values.

$$E(0) = 0.5\left(10 + 0e^{0}\right) = 5$$

$$E(20) = 0.5\left(10 + 20e^{-1}\right) \doteq 8.7$$

$$E(30) = 0.5\left(10 + 30e^{-1.5}\right) \doteq 8.3$$

Therefore, the maximum effectiveness measure of 8.7 is achieved when a student studies 20 h for the exam.

EXAMPLE 2 A mathematical consultant determines that the proportion of people who will have responded to the advertisement of a new product after it has been marketed for t days is given by $f(t) = 0.7\left(1 - e^{-0.2t}\right)$. The area covered by the advertisement contains 10 million potential customers, and each response to the advertisement results in revenue to the company of \$0.70 (on average), excluding the cost of advertising. The advertising costs \$30 000 to produce and a further \$5000 per day to run.

a. Find $\lim_{t \to \infty} f(t)$ and interpret the result.

b. What percentage of potential customers have responded after seven days of advertising?

c. Write the function $P(t)$ that represents the profit after t days of advertising. What is the profit after seven days?

d. For how many full days should the advertising campaign be run in order to maximize the profit? Assume an advertising budget of \$180 000.

Solution

a. As $t \to \infty$, $e^{-0.2t} \to 0$, so $\lim_{t \to \infty} f(t) = \lim_{t \to \infty} 0.7\left(1 - e^{-0.2t}\right) = 0.7$. This result means that if the advertising is left in place indefinitely (forever), 70% of the population will respond.

b. $f(7) = 0.7\left(1 - e^{-0.2(7)}\right) \approx 0.53$
After seven days of advertising, 53% of the population has responded.

c. The profit is the difference between the revenue received from all customers responding to the ad minus the advertising costs. Since the area covered by the ad contains 10 million potential customers, the number of customers responding to the ad after t days is
$10^7\left[0.7\left(1 - e^{-0.2t}\right)\right] = 7 \times 10^6\left(1 - e^{-0.2t}\right)$.
The revenue to the company from these respondents is
$R(t) = 0.7\left[7 \times 10^6\left(1 - e^{-0.2t}\right)\right] = 4.9 \times 10^6\left(1 - e^{-0.2t}\right)$.
The advertising costs for t days are $C(t) = 30\,000 + 5000t$.
Therefore, the profit to the company after t days of advertising is given by

$$\begin{aligned} P(t) &= R(t) - C(t) \\ &= 4.9 \times 10^6\left(1 - e^{-0.2t}\right) - 30\,000 - 5000t. \end{aligned}$$

After seven days of advertising, the profit is

$$\begin{aligned} P(7) &= 4.9 \times 10^6\left(1 - e^{-0.2(7)}\right) - 30\,000 - 5000(7) \\ &\approx 3\,627\,000. \end{aligned}$$

d. If the total advertising budget is \$180 000, then we require that

$$\begin{aligned} 30\,000 + 5000t &\leq 180\,000 \\ 5000t &\leq 150\,000 \\ t &\leq 30. \end{aligned}$$

We wish to maximize the profit function $P(t)$ on the interval $0 \leq t \leq 30$.
For critical points, determine $P'(t)$.

$$P'(t) = 4.9 \times 10^6\left(0.2e^{-0.2t}\right) - 5000$$
$$= 9.8 \times 10^5 e^{-0.2t} - 5000$$

$P'(t)$ is never undefined. Let $P'(t) = 0$.

$$9.8 \times 10^5 e^{-0.2t} - 5000 = 0$$

$$e^{-0.2t} = \frac{5000}{9.8 \times 10^5}$$
$$e^{-0.2t} \doteq 0.005102041$$
$$-0.2t = \ln(0.005102041)$$
$$t \doteq 26$$

To determine the maximum profit, we evaluate

$$P(26) = 4.9 \times 10^6\left(1 - e^{-0.2(26)}\right) - 30\,000 - 5000(26)$$
$$\doteq 4\,713\,000$$
$$P(0) = 4.9 \times 10^6\left(1 - e^0\right) - 30\,000 - 0$$
$$= -30\,000 \text{ (they're losing money!)}$$
$$P(30) = 4.9 \times 10^6\left(1 - e^{-0.2(30)}\right) - 30\,000 - 5000(30)$$
$$\doteq 4\,708\,000.$$

The maximum profit of \$4 713 000 occurs when the ad campaign runs for 26 days.

Exercise 8.4

Part A

technology

1. Use your calculator to graph each of the following functions. From the graph, find the absolute maximum and absolute minimum values of the given functions on the indicated intervals.

   a. $f(x) = e^{-x} - e^{-3x}$ on $0 \leq x \leq 10$

   b. $g(t) = \dfrac{e^t}{1 + \ln t}$ on $1 \leq t \leq 12$

   c. $m(x) = (x + 2)e^{-2x}$ on $-4 \leq x \leq 4$

   d. $s(t) = \ln\left(\dfrac{t^2 + 1}{t^2 - 1}\right) + 6\ln t$ on $1.1 \leq t \leq 10$

2. a. Use the maximum and minimum algorithm to determine the absolute maximum and minimum values for the functions in Question 1.

   b. Explain which approach is easier to use for the functions that were given in Question 1.

3. A small self-contained forest was studied for squirrel population by a biologist. It was found that the forest population, P, was a function of time, t, where t was measured in weeks. The function was $P = \frac{20}{1 + 3e^{-0.02t}}$.

   a. Find the population at the start of the study when $t = 0$.

   b. The largest population the forest can sustain is represented mathematically by the limit as $t \to \infty$. Determine this limit.

   c. Determine the point of inflection.

   d. Graph the function.

   e. Explain the meaning of the point of inflection in terms of squirrel population growth.

Part B

4. The net monthly profit from the sale of a certain product is given (in dollars) by the formula $P(x) = 10^6\left[1 + (x - 1)e^{-0.001x}\right]$, where x is the number of items sold.

   a. Find the number of items that yield the maximum profit. At full capacity, the factory can produce 2000 items per month.

   b. Repeat part **a**, assuming that, at most, 500 items can be produced per month.

5. Suppose the revenue (in thousands of dollars) for sales of x hundred units of an electronic item is given by the function $R(x) = 40x^2e^{-0.4x} + 30$, where the maximum capacity of the plant is eight hundred units. Determine the number of units to produce so the revenue is a maximum.

6. In a telegraph cable, the speed of the signal is proportional to $v(x) = x^2 \ln\left(\frac{1}{x}\right)$, where x is the ratio of the radius r of the cable's core to the overall radius R. Find the value of x that maximizes the speed of the signal. For technical reasons, it is required that $\frac{R}{10} \leq r \leq \frac{9R}{10}$.

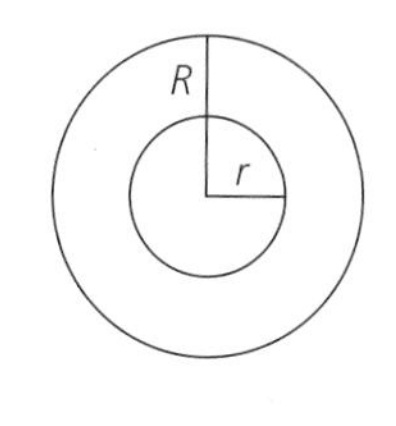

7. A student's intensity of concentration, on a scale of 0 to 1, is given by $C(h) = 1 + h(\ln h)^2$, where h is the time of the study session in hours, and where $0 \leq h \leq 1$. For a student involved in a 45-minute study session, at what time is the intensity of study at its lowest level?

8. A rumour spreads through a population in such a way that t hours after its beginning, the percentage of people involved in passing on the rumour is given by $P(t) = 100(e^{-1} - e^{-4t})$. What is the highest percentage of people involved in spreading the rumour within the first 3 h? When does this occur?

9. Small countries trying to rapidly develop an industrial economy often try to achieve their objectives by importing foreign capital and technology. Statistics Canada data shows that when Canada attempted this strategy from 1867 to 1967, the amount of U.S. investment in Canada increased from about $\$15 \times 10^6$ to $\$280\ 305 \times 10^6$. This increase in foreign investment can be represented by the simple mathematical model $C = 0.015 \times 10^9 e^{0.07533t}$, where t represents the number of years starting with 1867 as zero and C represents the total capital investment from U.S. sources.

   a. Graph the curve for the 100-year period.

   b. Compare the growth rate of U.S. investment in 1947 to 1967.

   c. Find the growth rate of investment in 1967 as a percentage of the amount invested.

technology

   d. If this model is used up to 1977, calculate the total U.S. investment and the growth rate.

   e. Use the Internet to determine the actual amount of total U.S. investment in 1977, and calculate the error in the model.

   f. If the model is used up to 2007, calculate the expected U.S. investment and the expected growth rate.

10. If a drug is injected into the body, the concentration C in the blood at time t is given by the function $C(t) = \frac{k}{b - a}\left(e^{-at} - e^{-bt}\right)$, where a, $b(b > a)$, and k are positive constants that depend on the drug. At what time does the largest concentration occur?

11. A colony of bacteria in a culture grows at a rate given by $N = 2^{\frac{t}{5}}$, where N is the number of bacteria t minutes from time of starting. The colony is allowed to grow for 60 min, at which time a drug is introduced that kills the bacteria. The number of bacteria killed is given by $K = e^{\frac{t}{3}}$, where K bacteria are killed at time t minutes.

   a. Determine the maximum number of bacteria present and the time at which this occurs.

   b. Determine the time at which the bacteria colony is obliterated.

12. A student is studying for two different exams. Because of the nature of the courses, the measure of study effectiveness for the first course is $0.5\left(10 + te^{-\frac{t}{10}}\right)$ while the measure for the second course is $0.6\left(9 + te^{-\frac{t}{20}}\right)$. The student is prepared to spend 30 h in total in preparing for the exams. If E_1 is the first measure and E_2 is the second, then $f(t) = E_1 + E_2$, where $E_1 = 0.6\left(9 + te^{-\frac{t}{20}}\right)$ and $E_2 = 0.5\left(10 + te^{-\frac{t}{10}}\right)$. How should this time be allocated so as to maximize total effectiveness?

Part C

13. Suppose that in Question 12 the student has only 25 h to study for the two exams. Is it possible to determine the time to be allocated to each exam? If so, how?

14. Although it is true that many animal populations grow exponentially for a period of time, it must be remembered that eventually the food available to sustain the population will run out and at that point the population will decrease through starvation. Over a period of time, the population will level out to the maximum attainable value, L. One mathematical model that will describe a population that grows exponentially at the beginning and then levels off to a limiting value L is the **logistic model**. The equation for this model is $P = \frac{aL}{a + (L - a)e^{-kLt}}$, where the independent variable t represents the time and P represents the size of the population. The constant a is the size of the population at time $t = 0$, L is the limiting value of the population, and k is a mathematical constant.

    a. Suppose a biologist starts a cell colony with 100 cells and finds that the limiting size of the colony is 10 000 cells. If the constant $k = 0.0001$, draw a graph to illustrate this population, where t is in days.

    b. At what point in time does the cell colony stop growing exponentially? How large is the colony at this point?

    c. Compare the growth rate of the colony at the end of day 3 to the end of day 8. Explain what is happening.

Section 8.5 — Logarithmic Differentiation

The derivatives of most functions involving exponential and logarithmic expressions can be determined with the techniques we have developed. However, a function such as $y = x^x$ poses new problems. The Power Rule cannot be used because the exponent is not a constant.

The method of determining the derivative of an exponential function also can't be used because the base isn't a constant. What can be done?

It is frequently possible in functions presenting special difficulties to simplify the situation by employing the properties of logarithms. We say that we are using *logarithmic differentiation.*

EXAMPLE 1

Determine $\frac{dy}{dx}$ for the function $y = x^x$, $x > 0$.

Solution

Take natural logarithms of each side: $\ln y = x \ln x$.

Differentiate each side: $\frac{1}{y}\frac{dy}{dx} = x\frac{1}{x} + \ln x = 1 + \ln x$.

Then $\frac{dy}{dx} = y(1 + \ln x)$

$= x^x(1 + \ln x)$.

This technique of logarithmic differentiation also works well to help simplify a function with many factors and powers before the differentiation takes place.

We can use logarithmic differentiation to prove the Power Rule, $\frac{d}{dx}(x^n) = nx^{n-1}$, for all real values of n. (In previous chapters, we proved this rule for positive integer values of n and we have been cheating a bit in using the rule for other values of n.)

Given the function $y = x^n$, for any real values of n, determine $\frac{dy}{dx}$. To solve this, we take the natural logarithm of both sides of this expression and get

$$\begin{aligned}\ln y &= \ln x^n \\ &= n \ln x.\end{aligned}$$

Differentiating both sides with respect to x, using implicit differentiation and remembering that n is a constant, we get

$$\begin{aligned}\frac{1}{y}\frac{dy}{dx} &= n\frac{1}{x} \\ \frac{dy}{dx} &= ny\frac{1}{x} \\ &= nx^n\frac{1}{x} \\ &= nx^{n-1}.\end{aligned}$$

Therefore, $\frac{d}{dx}(x^n) = nx^{n-1}$ for any real value of n.

EXAMPLE 2 For $y = (x^2 + 3)^x$, find $\frac{dy}{dx}$.

Solution

Here we can use logarithmic differentiation again. Take the natural logarithm of both sides of the equation:

$$\begin{aligned} y &= (x^2 + 3)^x \\ \ln y &= \ln(x^2 + 3)^x \\ &= x \ln(x^2 + 3). \end{aligned}$$

Differentiate both sides of the equation with respect to x, using implicit differentiation on the left side and the Product and Chain Rules on the right side.

Therefore,
$$\begin{aligned} \frac{1}{y}\frac{dy}{dx} &= 1 \bullet \ln(x^2 + 3) + x\left(\frac{1}{x^2 + 3}(2x)\right) \\ \frac{dy}{dx} &= y\left[\ln(x^2 + 3) + x\left(\frac{2x}{x^2 + 3}\right)\right] \\ &= (x^2 + 3)^x\left[\ln(x^2 + 3) + x\left(\frac{2x}{x^2 + 3}\right)\right]. \end{aligned}$$

Logarithmic differentiation is useful when the function that we wish to differentiate contains a power with variables in both the base and the exponent.

You will recognize logarithmic differentiation as the method used in the previous section, and its use makes memorization of many formulas unnecessary. It also allows for complicated functions to be handled much more easily.

EXAMPLE 3 Given $y = \frac{(x^4 + 1)\sqrt{x + 2}}{(2x^2 + 2x + 1)}$, determine $\frac{dy}{dx}$ at $x = -1$.

Solution

While it is possible to find $\frac{dy}{dx}$ using a combination of the Product, Quotient, and Chain Rules, this process is awkward and time-consuming. Instead, before differentiating, we take the natural logarithm of both sides of the equation.

Since $y = \frac{(x^4 + 1)\sqrt{x + 2}}{(2x^2 + 2x + 1)}$,

$$\begin{aligned} \ln y &= \ln\left[\frac{(x^4 + 1)\sqrt{x + 2}}{(2x^2 + 2x + 1)}\right] \\ &= \ln(x^4 + 1) + \ln\sqrt{x + 2} - \ln(2x^2 + 2x + 1) \\ &= \ln(x^4 + 1) + \frac{1}{2}\ln(x + 2) - \ln(2x^2 + 2x + 1). \end{aligned}$$

The right side of this equation looks much simpler. We can now differentiate both sides with respect to x, using implicit differentiation on the left side.

$$\begin{aligned} \frac{1}{y}\frac{dy}{dx} &= \frac{1}{x^4 + 1}(4x^3) + \frac{1}{2}\frac{1}{x + 2} - \frac{1}{2x^2 + 2x + 1}(4x + 2) \\ \frac{dy}{dx} &= y\left[\frac{4x^3}{x^4 + 1} + \frac{1}{2(x + 2)} - \frac{4x + 2}{2x^2 + 2x + 1}\right] \\ &= \frac{(x^4 + 1)\sqrt{x + 2}}{(2x^2 + 2x + 1)}\left[\frac{4x^3}{x^4 + 1} + \frac{1}{2(x + 2)} - \frac{4x + 2}{2x^2 + 2x + 1}\right] \end{aligned}$$

While this derivative is a very complicated function, the process of finding the derivative is straightforward, using only the derivative of the natural logarithm function and the Chain Rule.

We do not need to simplify this in order to determine the value of the derivative at $x = -1$.

For $x = -1$, $\frac{dy}{dx} = \frac{(1+1)\sqrt{1}}{(2-2+1)}\left[\frac{-4}{1+1} + \frac{1}{2(-1+2)} - \frac{-4+2}{2-2+1}\right]$

$= 2\left[-2 + \frac{1}{2} + 2\right]$

$= 1.$

Exercise 8.5

Part A

1. Differentiate each of the following.

   a. $y = x^{\sqrt{10}} - 3$ b. $f(x) = 5x^{3\sqrt{2}}$ c. $s = t^{\pi}$ d. $f(x) = x^e + e^x$

Knowledge/Understanding

2. Use the technique of Logarithmic Differentiation to find the derivative for each of the following:

   a. $y = x^{\ln x}$

   b. $y = \frac{(x+1)(x-3)^2}{(x+2)^3}$

   c. $y = x^{\sqrt{x}}$

   d. $s = \left(\frac{1}{t}\right)^t$

3. a. If $y = f(x) = x^x$, evaluate $f'(e)$.

   b. If $s = e^t + t^e$, find $\frac{ds}{dt}$ when $t = 2$.

   c. If $f(x) = \frac{(x-3)^2\sqrt[3]{x+1}}{(x-4)^5}$, determine $f'(7)$.

4. Find the equation of the tangent to the curve defined by $y = x^{(x^2)}$ at the point where $x = 2$.

Part B

5. If $y = \frac{1}{(x+1)(x+2)(x+3)}$, find the slope of the tangent to the curve at the point where $x = 0$.

Application

6. Determine the points on the curve defined by $y = x^{\frac{1}{x}}$, $x > 0$, where the slope of the tangent is zero.

7. If tangents to the curve defined by $y = x^2 + 4 \ln x$ are parallel to the line defined by $y - 6x + 3 = 0$, find the points where the tangents touch the curve.

Thinking/Inquiry/
Problem Solving

8. The tangent at point A (4, 16) to the curve defined by $y = x^{\sqrt{x}}$ is extended to cut the x-axis at B and the y-axis at C. Determine the area of ΔOBC where O is the origin.

Part C

9. The position of a particle that moves on a straight line is given by $s(t) = t^{\frac{1}{t}}$ for $t > 0$.

   a. Find the velocity and acceleration.

   b. At what time, t, is the velocity zero? What is the acceleration at that time?

Thinking/Inquiry/
Problem Solving

10. Without using a calculator, determine which number is larger, e^{π} or π^{e}. (*Hint:* Question 9 can help.) Verify your work with a calculator.

Key Concepts Review

In this chapter, we introduced a new base for exponential and logarithmic functions, namely e, where $e \approx 2.718281$. Approximations to the value of e can be calculated using one of the following two limits:

- $e = \lim_{h \to 0} (1 + h)^{\frac{1}{h}}$
- $e = \lim_{n \to \infty} \left(1 + \frac{1}{n}\right)^n$

New Derivative Rules for Exponential and Logarithmic Functions

- $\frac{d}{dx}(e^x) = e^x$
- $\frac{d}{dx}\ln x = \frac{1}{x}, x > 0$
- $\frac{d}{dx}(b^x) = b^x \ln b$
- $\frac{d}{dx}\left(b^{g(x)}\right) = b^{g(x)}(\ln b)g'(x)$
- $\frac{d}{dx}(\log_b x) = \frac{1}{x \ln b}$
- $\frac{d}{dx}(\log_b g(x)) = \frac{g'(x)}{g(x) \ln b}$

The only rules that need to be memorized are those in the shaded area. The other rules can be determined from the first two, using properties of exponential and logarithmic functions along with logarithmic differentiation.

CHAPTER 8: RATE-OF-CHANGE MODELS IN MICROBIOLOGY

To combat the widespread problem of soil and groundwater contamination, scientists and engineers have investigated and engineered bacteria capable of destroying environmental toxicants. The use of bacteria in environmental clean-ups, known as bioremediation, has been proven effective in destroying toxic compounds ranging from PCBs to gasoline additives such as benzene. An environmental engineer conducting a lab study found the growth in mass of a quantity of bioremediation bacteria follows a "logistic" growth pattern. The logistic model is characterized by the familiar "S"-shaped graph and equation as follows:

$$m_b(t) = \frac{L}{1 + \left(\frac{L - m_0}{m_0}\right)e^{-Lkt}}$$

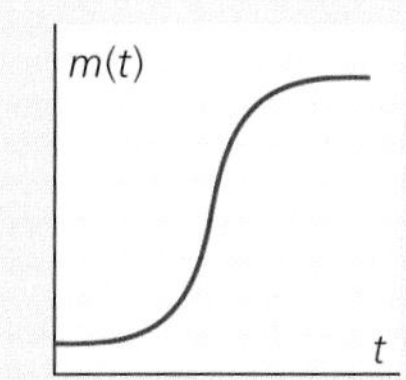

where $m_b(t)$ is the mass of bacteria at time t, L is bounded/maximum mass, k is the growth constant, and m_0 is the initial mass. The model can be constructed by substituting values of m_0, L, and a known ordered pair for (t, m_b) into the equation and solving for k.

The engineer conducting the study found that starting from an initial mass of 0.2 kg, the bacteria grow to a maximum mass of 2.6 kg following a logistic growth pattern. The mass after five days for this experiment was 1.5 kg. The engineer has modelled the mass of contaminant remaining in kilograms as

$$m_c(t) = -\log_3(\sqrt{t} + 1) + 2.5$$

where $m_c(t)$ is the mass of contaminant remaining (kilograms) in t days.

a. Develop the logistic growth function model for the bacterial mass.

b. Like humans, many bacteria also need oxygen to survive. The oxygen demand for bacteria is

$$D_{O_2} = 10(m_c)\left(\frac{dm_b}{dt}\right) \text{ [litres per hour]}$$

What is the oxygen demand after five days?

c. The experiment is re-inoculated (new bacteria added) when the amount of contamination has reached 50% of the initial mass. When must the new bacteria be added, and how quickly is the contamination being destroyed at this time?

Review Exercise

1. Use the Chain Rule and the appropriate derivative rule for a logarithmic or exponential function to find the derivative for each of the following:

   a. $y = e^{2x+3}$ b. $s = \ln(t^3 + 1)$ c. $f(x) = \ln(x^3 - 3x^2 + 6x)$

   d. $y = e^{-3x^2+5x}$ e. $y = \ln(e^x + e^{-x})$ f. $y = 2e^{e^x}$

2. Use the appropriate derivative rules to find the derivative for each of the following. If necessary, use logarithmic differentiation.

   a. $y = xe^x$ b. $y = \dfrac{x\ln x}{e^x}$

   c. $s = \sqrt{t^4 + 2} \bullet \ln(3t)$ d. $y = \dfrac{(x + 2)(x - 4)^5}{(2x^3 - 1)^2}$

   e. $s = \dfrac{e^t - 1}{e^t + 1}$ f. $y = \left(\sqrt{x^2 + 3}\right)^{e^x}$

   g. $y = \left(\dfrac{30}{x}\right)^{2x}$ h. $e^{xy} = \ln(x + y)$

3. For each of the following functions, solve the equation $f'(x) = 0$.

   a. $f(x) = \dfrac{e^x}{x}$ b. $f(x) = \left[\ln(3x^2 - 6x)\right]^4$

4. a. If $g(t) = 10^t \log_{10} t$, then evaluate $g'(10)$.

   b. If $f(x) = xe^{-2x}$, then find $f'\left(\dfrac{1}{2}\right)$.

5. Find the second derivative for each of the following:

   a. $s = t\ln t$ b. $y = xe^{10x}$

6. Find the equation of the tangent to the curve defined by $y = \dfrac{\ln x^2}{x}$ at the point where $x = 4$.

7. If $y = \dfrac{e^{2x} - 1}{e^{2x} + 1}$, prove that $\dfrac{dy}{dx} = 1 - y^2$.

8. Find the value of k in the equation $y = e^{kx}$ so that y is a solution of

   a. $y' - 7y = 0$. b. $y'' - 16y = 0$.

   c. $y''' - y'' - 12y' = 0$.

9. Find the equation of the tangent to the curve defined by $y = x - e^{-x}$ that is parallel to the line represented by $3x - y - 9 = 0$.

10. Find an equation for the normal line to the curve defined by $y = \frac{e^x}{1 + \ln x}$ at the point where $x = 1$.

11. The number, N, of bacteria in a culture at time t is given by $N = 2000\left[30 + te^{-\frac{t}{20}}\right]$.

    a. When is the rate of change of the number of bacteria equal to zero?

    b. If the bacterial culture is placed into a colony of mice, the number of mice, M, that become infected is related to the number of bacteria present by the equation $M = \sqrt[3]{N + 1000}$. After ten days, how many mice are becoming infected per day?

12. The measure of effectiveness of a medicine on a scale of 0 to 1 is given by $g(t) = \frac{\ln(t^3)}{2t}$, where t is the time in hours after administering the medicine and $t > 1$. Determine the maximum measure of effectiveness of this medicine and the time at which it is reached.

13. Some psychologists model a child's ability to memorize by a function of the form $m(t) = t\ln(t) + 1$ for $0 < t \leq 4$, where t is time, measured in years. Determine when a child's ability to memorize is highest and when it is lowest.

14. The concentrations of two medicines in the blood stream t hours after injection are $c_1(t) = te^{-t}$ and $c_2(t) = t^2e^{-t}$.

    a. Which medicine has the larger maximum concentration?

    b. Within the first half-hour, which medicine has the larger maximum concentration?

15. One model of a computer disk storage system uses the function $T(x) = N\left(k + \frac{c}{x}\right)p^{-x}$ for the average time needed to send a file correctly by modem (including all re-transmission of messages in which errors were detected), where x is the number of information bits, p is the (fixed) probability that any particular file will be received correctly, and N, k, and c are positive constants. Use the values $p = 0.9$, $N = 10$, and $c = 1$ to answer the following questions:

    a. Find $T'(x)$.

    b. For what value of x is $T(x)$ minimized?

16. In a telegraph cable, the speed of the signal is given by $v(x) = kx^2 \ln\left(\frac{1}{x}\right)$, where k is a positive constant and x is the ratio of the radius r of the cable's core to the overall radius R.

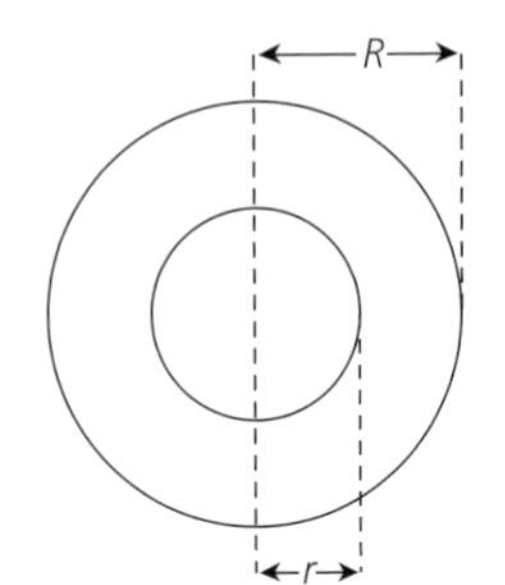

    a. For $k = 2$, determine the speed of the signal if $x = \frac{1}{2}$.

    b. For $k = 2$, at what rate is the speed changing when $x = \frac{1}{2}$?

17. The function $C(t) = K\left(e^{-2t} - e^{-5t}\right)$, where K is a positive constant, can be used to model the concentration at time t, in days, of a drug injected into the bloodstream.

    a. Evaluate $\lim_{t \to \infty} C(t)$.

    b. Find $C'(t)$, the rate at which the drug is cleared from circulation.

    c. When is this rate equal to zero?

Chapter 8 Test

Achievement Category	Questions
Knowledge/Understanding	All questions
Thinking/Inquiry/Problem Solving	8, 9
Communication	8
Application	3, 5, 6, 7, 8

1. Find the derivative $\frac{dy}{dx}$ for each of the following:

   a. $y = e^{-2x^2}$
   b. $y = \ln(x^2 - 6)$
   c. $y = 3^{x^2+3x}$
   d. $y = \frac{e^{3x} + e^{-3x}}{2}$
   e. $y = (4x^3 - x)\log_{10}(2x - 1)$
   f. $y = \frac{\ln(x + 4)}{x^3}$

2. If $f(t) = \ln(3t^2 + t)$, determine $f'(2)$.

3. If $y = x^{\ln x}$, $x > 0$, find the slope of the tangent when $x = e$.

4. Determine $\frac{dy}{dx}$ for the relation $x^2y + x\ln x = 3y$, where $x > 0$.

5. If $e^{xy} = x$, determine $\frac{dy}{dx}$ at $x = 1$.

6. For what values of A does the function $y = e^{Ax}$ satisfy the equation $y'' + 3y' + 2y = 0$?

7. Find the equation of the straight line that is normal to the curve defined by $y = 3^x + x\ln x$ at point $A(1, 3)$.

8. The velocity of a particular particle that moves in a straight line under the influence of forces is given by $v(t) = 10e^{-kt}$, where k is a positive constant and $v(t)$ is in cm/s.

   a. Show that the acceleration of this particle is proportional to (a constant multiple of) its velocity. Explain what is happening to this particle.

   b. At time $t = 0$, what is the initial velocity of the particle?

c. At what time is the velocity equal to half of the initial velocity? What is the acceleration at this time?

9. A manufacturer can produce jackets at a cost of $50 per jacket. If he produces p jackets weekly and all the jackets are sold, the revenue is $R(p) = 4000[e^{0.01(p-100)} + 1]$. Weekly production must be at least 100 and cannot exceed 250.

   a. At what price should the manufacturer sell the jackets to maximize profit?

   b. What is the maximum weekly profit?

Chapter 9

CURVE SKETCHING

If you are having trouble figuring out a mathematical relationship, what do you do? Many people find that visualizing mathematical problems is the best way to understand them and communicate them more meaningfully. Graphing calculators and computers are powerful tools for producing visual information about functions. Similarly, since the derivative of a function at a point is the slope of the tangent to the function at that point, the derivative is also a powerful tool for providing information about the graph of a function. It should come as no surprise then that the Cartesian coordinate system in which we graph functions, and the calculus that we use to analyze functions were invented in close succession, in the seventeenth century. In this chapter, you will see how to draw the graph of a function using the methods of calculus, including the first and second derivatives of the function.

CHAPTER EXPECTATIONS In this chapter, you will

- compare rates of change of graphs of functions, **Section 9.1**
- determine properties of the graphs of polynomial functions, **Section 9.1, 9.5**
- describe key features of a given graph of a function, **Section 9.1, 9.2, 9.4**
- determine intercepts and positions of the asymptotes to a graph, **Section 9.3**
- sketch the graph of a function, **Section 9.4**
- determine key features of the graph of a function, **Section 9.5, Career Link**
- sketch, by hand, the graph of the derivative of a given graph, **Section 9.2**
- determine from the equation of a simple combination of polynomial, rational, or exponential functions $\left(\text{e.g., } f(x) = x^2 + \frac{1}{x}\right)$ the key features of the graph of the combination of functions, using the techniques of differential calculus, and sketch the graph by hand, **Section 9.4**

Review of Prerequisite Skills

When we are sketching the graph of a function, there are many features that we can analyze in order to help us create the sketch. For example, we can try to determine the x- and y-intercepts for the graph, we can test for horizontal and vertical asymptotes using limits, and we can use our knowledge of certain kinds of functions to help us determine ranges, domains, and possible symmetries.

In this chapter, we will use what we have learned about the derivatives of functions, in conjunction with all the things mentioned above, to learn more about functions and their graphs. In approaching these concepts, you should first

- be able to solve simple equations and inequalities.
- know how to sketch graphs of basic functions and simple transformations of these graphs (including parabolas, and logarithmic and exponential functions).
- understand the intuitive concept of a limit of a function and be able to evaluate simple limits.
- be able to find the derivatives of functions using all known rules.
- understand the intuitive concept of a limit of a function and be able to evaluate simple limits.

Exercise

1. In the following, solve the given equation.
   a. $2y^2 + y - 3 = 0$
   b. $x^2 - 5x + 3 = 17$
   c. $4x^2 + 20x + 25 = 0$
   d. $y^3 + 4y^2 + y - 6 = 0$

2. In the following, solve the given inequality.
   a. $3x + 9 < 2$
   b. $5(3 - x) \geq 3x - 1$
   c. $t^2 - 2t < 3$
   d. $x^2 + 3x - 4 > 0$

3. In the following, sketch the graph of the given function.
   a. $f(x) = (x + 1)^2 - 3$
   b. $f(x) = x^2 - 5x - 6$
   c. $f(x) = 1 - 2^x$
   d. $f(x) = \log_{10}(x + 4)$

4. In the following, evaluate the given limits.

a. $\lim_{x \to 2^-} (x^2 - 4)$

b. $\lim_{x \to 2} \frac{x^2 + 3x - 10}{x - 2}$

c. $\lim_{x \to 0} x^2 3^{-x}$

d. $\lim_{x \to 2} \log_5(x - 1)$

5. In the following, find the derivative of the given function.

a. $f(x) = \frac{1}{4}x^4 + 2x^3 - \frac{1}{x}$

b. $f(x) = \frac{x + 1}{x^2 - 3}$

c. $f(x) = e^{-x^2}$

d. $f(x) = x^5 \ln(x)$

6. Divide each of the following and write your answer in the form $ax + b + \frac{r}{q(x)}$. For example, $(x^2 + 4x - 5) \div (x - 2) = x + 6 + \frac{7}{x - 2}$.

a. $(x^2 - 5x + 4) \div (x + 3)$

b. $(x^2 + 6x - 9) \div (x - 1)$

Career Link investigate

CHAPTER 9: PREDICTING STOCK VALUES

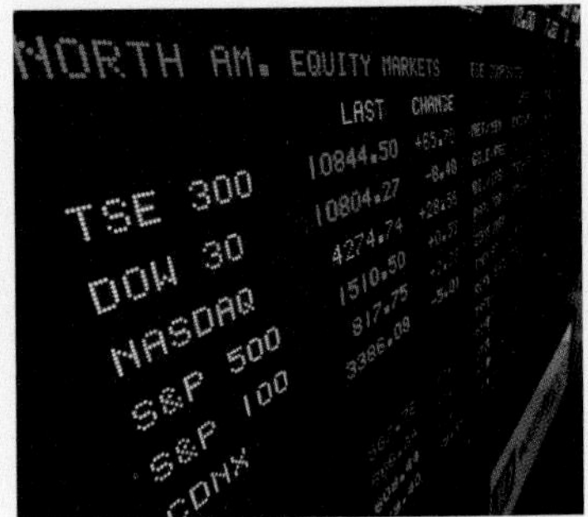

Stock-market analysts collect and interpret vast amounts of information and then predict trends in stock values. Stock analysts are broken down into two main groups, the fundamentalists who predict stock values based on analysis of the companies' economic situations, and the technical analysts who predict stock values based on trends and patterns in the market. Technical analysts spend a significant amount of their time constructing and interpreting graphical models that are used to find undervalued stocks that will give returns in excess of what the market predicts. In this chapter, your skills in producing and analyzing graphical models will be extended through the use of differential calculus.

Case Study: Technical Stock Analyst

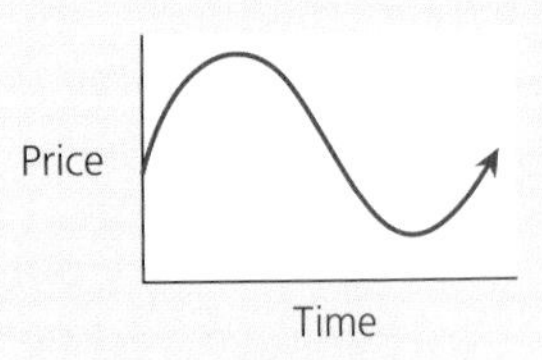

In order to raise money to expand operations, many privately owned companies give the public a chance to own a part of their company through purchasing stock. Those who buy ownership anticipate obtaining a share in future profits of the company. Some technical analysts believe that the greatest profits to be had in the stock market are through buying brand new stocks and selling them quickly. A technical analyst predicts that a stock's price over its first several weeks on the market will follow the pattern shown on the graph. The technical analyst is advising a person who purchased the stock the day it went on sale.

DISCUSSION QUESTIONS

Make a rough sketch of the graph and answer the following questions:

1. When would you recommend the owner sell her shares? Mark this point on your graph with an "S." What do you notice about the slope, or instantaneous rate of change, of the graph at this point?
2. When would you recommend the owner get back into the company and buy shares again? Mark this point on your graph with a "B." What do you notice about the slope, or instantaneous rate of change, of the graph at this point?
3. A concave-down section of a graph is one that opens down, and similarly, concave up opens up. Mark a "C" on the graph when the concavity changes from concave down to concave up. A fellow analyst says that a change in concavity from concave down to concave up is a signal that a selling opportunity will soon occur. Do you agree with your fellow analyst? Explain.

At the end of this chapter, you will have an opportunity to apply the tools of graph sketching to create, evaluate, and apply a model that will be used to provide advice to clients on when to buy, sell, and hold new stocks. ●

Section 9.1 — Increasing and Decreasing Functions

The graph of the function $f(x) = x^2$ is a parabola. If we imagine a particle moving along this parabola from left to right, we can see that while the x-coordinates of the ordered pairs steadily increase, the y-coordinates of the ordered pairs along the particle's path first decrease then increase. Determining intervals in which a function increases or decreases is of great use in understanding the behaviour of the function. The following statements give a clear picture:

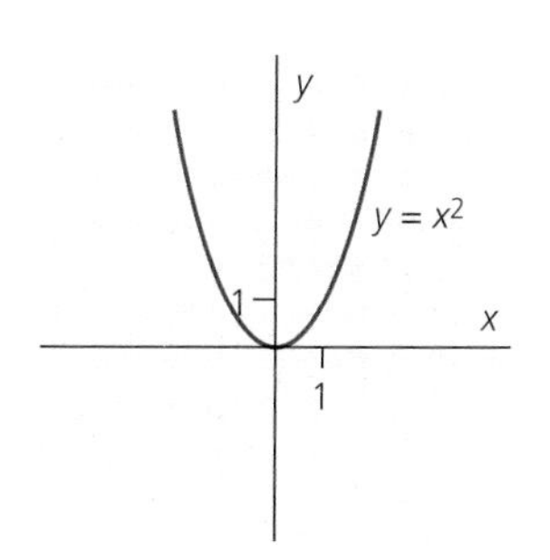

We say that a function, f, *is decreasing on an interval* if, for any $x_1 < x_2$ in the interval, $f(x_1) > f(x_2)$.

Similarly, we say that a function, f, *is increasing on an interval* if, for any $x_1 < x_2$ in the interval, $f(x_1) < f(x_2)$.

For the parabola with equation $y = x^2$, the change from decreasing y-values to increasing y-values occurs at the vertex of the parabola, which is (0, 0). The function $f(x) = x^2$ is decreasing on the interval $x < 0$ and is increasing on the interval $x > 0$.

If we examine a line tangent to the parabola anywhere on the interval where the y-values are decreasing (i.e., on $x < 0$), we see that all of these tangents have negative slopes. Similarly, the slopes of lines tangent to the increasing portion of the graph are all positive.

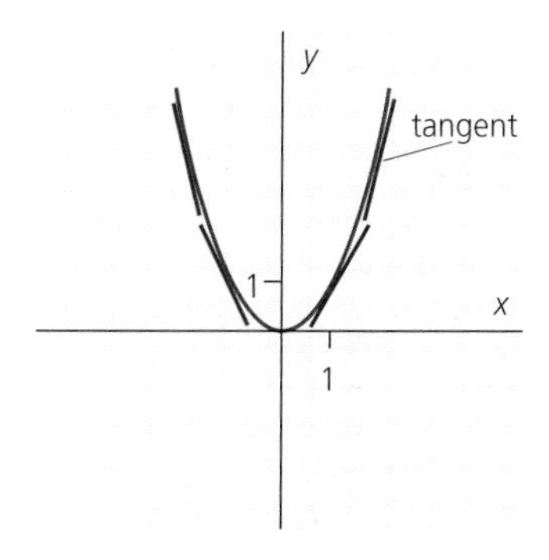

For functions that are both continuous and differentiable, we can determine intervals of increasing and decreasing y-values using the derivative of the function. In the case of $y = x^2$, $\frac{dy}{dx} = 2x$. For $x < 0$, $\frac{dy}{dx} < 0$, and the slopes of the tangents are negative. The interval $x < 0$ corresponds to the decreasing portion of the graph of the parabola. For $x > 0$, $\frac{dy}{dx} > 0$ and the slopes of the tangents are positive on the interval where the graph is increasing.

We summarize this as follows:

For a continuous and differentiable function f, the function values (y-values) are increasing for all x-values where $f'(x) > 0$, and the function values (y-values) are decreasing for all x-values where $f'(x) < 0$.

EXAMPLE

Use your calculator to obtain graphs of the following functions. Use the graph to estimate the values of x for which the function (y-values) is increasing, and for which values of x the function is decreasing. Verify your estimates with an analytic solution.

a. $y = x^3 + 3x^2 - 2$

b. $y = x^2e^{-x}$

Solution

technology

a. Using a calculator, we obtain the graph of $y = x^3 + 3x^2 - 2$. Using the TRACE key on the calculator, we estimate that the function values are increasing on $x < -2$, decreasing on $-2 < x < 0$, and increasing again on $x > 0$. To verify these estimates with an analytic solution, we consider the slopes of the tangents.

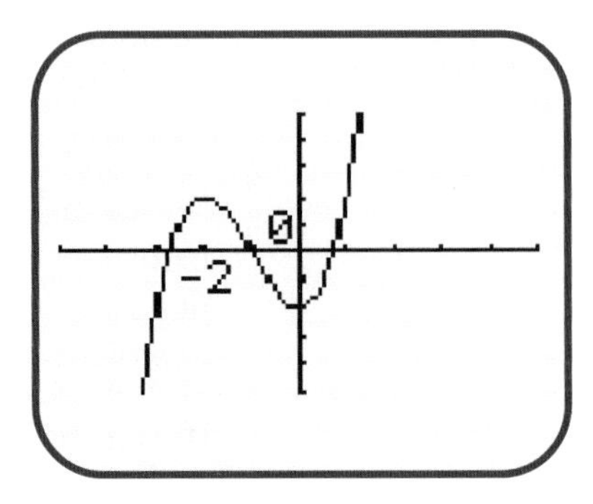

The slope of a general tangent to the graph of $y = x^3 + 3x^2 - 2$ is given by $\frac{dy}{dx} = 3x^2 + 6x$. We first determine values of x for which $\frac{dy}{dx} = 0$. These values tell us where the function has a maximum or minimum value.

Setting $\frac{dy}{dx} = 0$, we obtain $3x^2 + 6x = 0$

$$3x(x + 2) = 0$$

$$x = 0, x = -2$$

These values of x locate points on the graph at which the slope of the tangent is zero (i.e., horizontal).

Since $\frac{dy}{dx}$ is defined for all values of x, and since $\frac{dy}{dx} = 0$ only at $x = -2$ and $x = 0$, it must be either positive or negative for all other values of x. We consider the intervals $x < -2$, $-2 < x < 0$, and $x > 0$.

Value of x	Value of $\frac{dy}{dx} = 3x(x + 2)$	Slope of Tangent	y-Values Increasing or Decreasing
$x < -2$	$\frac{dy}{dx} > 0$	positive	increasing
$-2 < x < 0$	$\frac{dy}{dx} < 0$	negative	decreasing
$x > 0$	$\frac{dy}{dx} > 0$	positive	increasing

Then $y = x^3 + 3x^2 - 2$ is increasing on the intervals $x < -2$ and $x > 0$ and is decreasing on the interval $-2 < x < 0$.

b. Using a calculator, we obtain the graph of $y = x^2e^{-x}$. Using the TRACE key on the calculator, we estimate that the function values (y-values) are decreasing on $x < 0$, increasing on $0 < x < 2$, and decreasing again on $x > 2$.

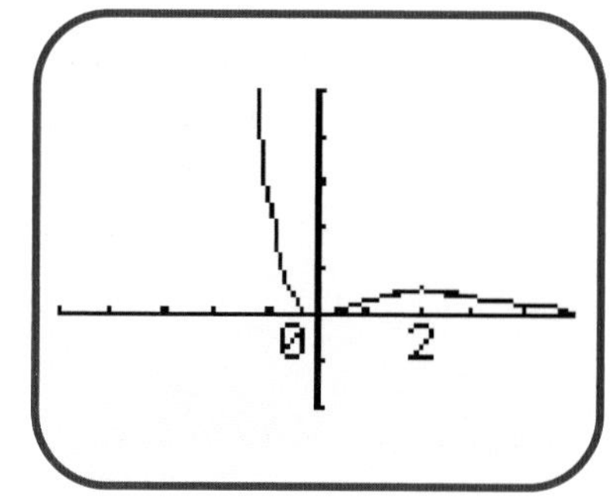

We analyze the intervals of increasing/decreasing y-values for the function by determining where $\frac{dy}{dx}$ is positive and where it is negative.

$$\begin{aligned}\frac{dy}{dx} &= 2xe^{-x} + x^2e^{-x}(-1)\\ &= xe^{-x}(2 - x)\end{aligned}$$

Since $e^{-x} > 0$ for all values of x, $\frac{dy}{dx} = 0$ when $x = 0$ or $x = 2$, and we consider intervals $x < 0$, $0 < x < 2$, and $x > 2$.

Value of x	Value of $\frac{dy}{dx} = xe^{-x}(2 - x)$	Graph Increasing or Decreasing
$x < 0$	$\frac{dy}{dx} < 0$	decreasing
$0 < x < 2$	$\frac{dy}{dx} > 0$	increasing
$x > 2$	$\frac{dy}{dx} < 0$	decreasing

Then $y = x^2e^{-x}$ is increasing on the interval $0 < x < 2$ and is decreasing on the intervals $x < 0$ and $x > 2$.

Exercise 9.1

Part **A**

Knowledge/ Understanding

1. Determine the points at which $f'(x) = 0$ for each of the following functions:

   a. $f(x) = x^3 + 6x^2 + 1$
   b. $f(x) = \sqrt{x^2 + 4}$
   c. $f(x) = (2x - 1)^2(x^2 - 9)$
   d. $f(x) = x^{\frac{2}{3}}(2x - 5)$

Communication

2. Explain how you would determine when a function is increasing or decreasing.

3. For each of the following functions, determine the direction of the curve by evaluating the derivative for a suitably large positive value of x.

   a. $y = x^7 - 430x^6 - 150x^3$
   b. $s = \frac{3t}{1 - t^2}$
   c. $y = x\ln x - x^4$
   d. $y = 10xe^{-x} + x^2\ln x$

4. For each of the following graphs, state:

   i) the intervals where the function is increasing.

   ii) the intervals where the function is decreasing.

   iii) the points where the tangent to the function is horizontal.

a.

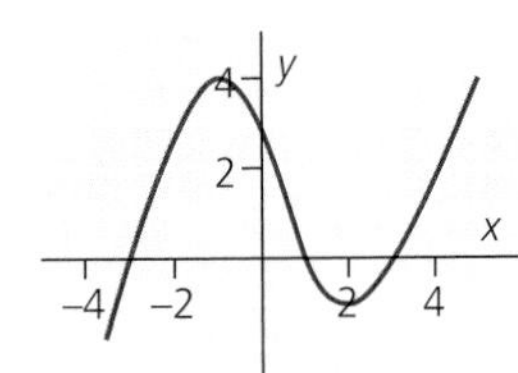

b.

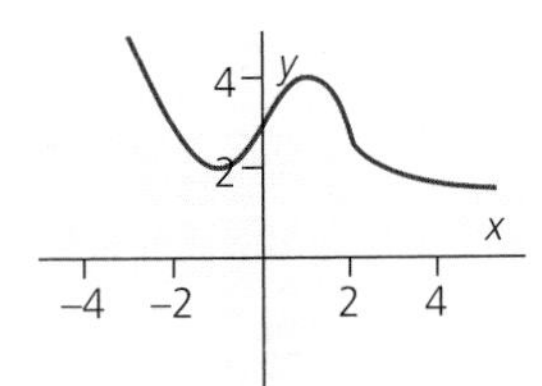

c.

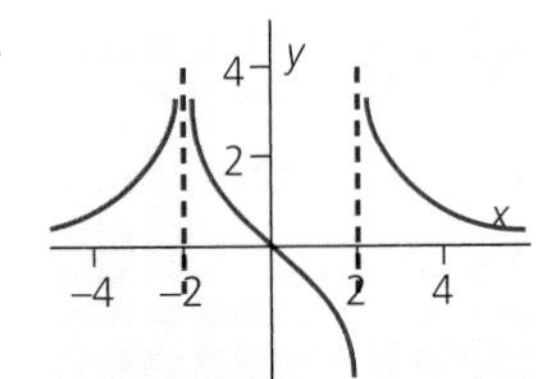

d.

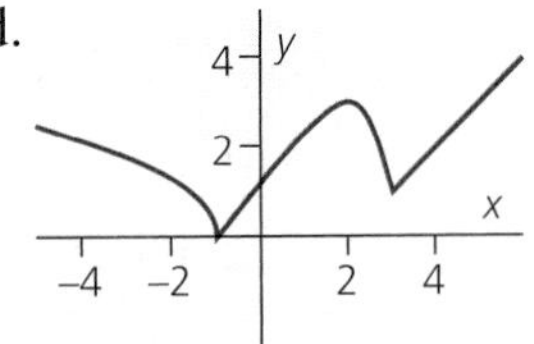

technology

5. Use a calculator to graph each of the following functions. Inspect the graph to estimate where the function is increasing and where it is decreasing. Verify your estimates with an analytic solution.

   a. $f(x) = x^3 + 3x^2 + 1$
   b. $f(x) = x^5 - 5x^4 + 100$
   c. $f(x) = x + \frac{1}{x}$
   d. $f(x) = \frac{x - 1}{x^2 + 3}$
   e. $f(x) = x\ln(x)$
   f. $f(x) = xe^{-x}$

Part B

6. Suppose that f is a differentiable function with derivative $f'(x) = (x - 1)(x + 2)(x + 3)$. Determine where the function values of f are increasing and where they are decreasing.

Application

7. Suppose that g is a differentiable function with derivative $g'(x) = (3x - 2)\ln(2x^2 - 3x + 2)$. Determine where the function values of f are increasing and where they are decreasing.

Application

8. Sketch a graph of a function that is differentiable on the interval $-2 \leq x \leq 3$ and that satisfies the following conditions:
   - The graph of f passes through points $(-1, 0)$ and $(2, 5)$.
   - The function f is decreasing on $-2 < x < -1$, increasing on $-1 < x < 2$, and decreasing again on $2 < x < 5$.

9. Find constants a, b, and c that guarantee that the graph of $f(x) = x^3 + ax^2 + bx + c$ will increase to the point $(-3, 18)$, then decrease to the point $(1, -14)$, then continue increasing.

10. Sketch a graph of a function f that is differentiable and that satisfies the following conditions:
    - $f'(x) > 0$, when $x < -5$.
    - $f'(x) < 0$, when $-5 < x < 1$ and when $x > 1$.
    - $f'(-5) = 0$ and $f'(1) = 0$.
    - $f(-5) = 6$ and $f(1) = 2$.

11. Each of the following graphs represents the derivative function $f'(x)$ of a function $f(x)$. Determine
    i) the intervals where $f(x)$ is increasing.
    ii) the intervals where $f(x)$ is decreasing.
    iii) the x-coordinate for all local extrema of $f(x)$.
    iv) Assuming that $f(0) = 2$, make a rough sketch of the graph of each function.

a.

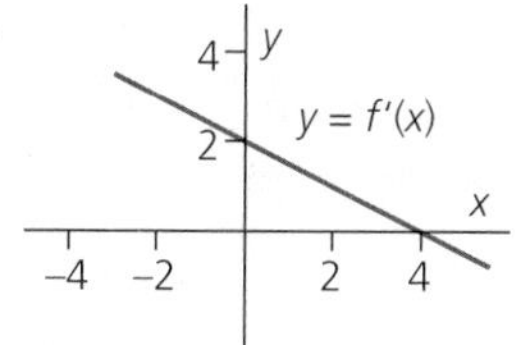

b.

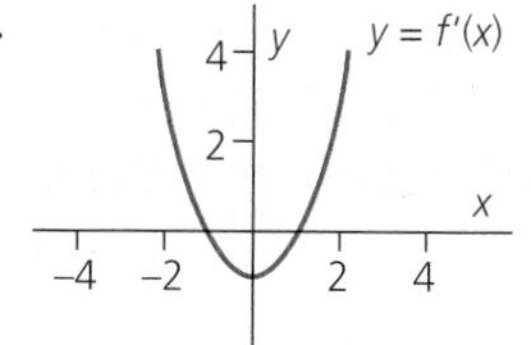

$f'(x)$ is a quadratic function

c.

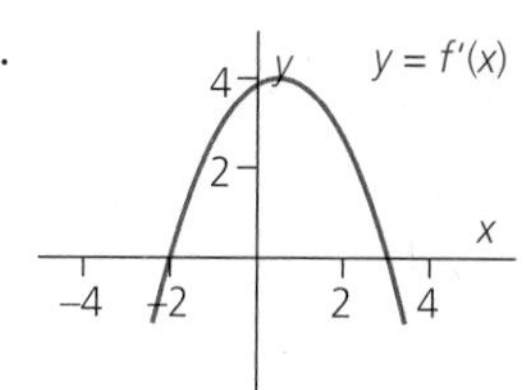

$f'(x)$ is a quadratic function

12. Use calculus techniques to show that the graph of the quadratic function $f(x) = ax^2 + bx + c$, $a > 0$, is decreasing on the interval $x < -\frac{b}{2a}$ and increasing on the interval $x > -\frac{b}{2a}$.

Part C

Thinking/Inquiry/ Problem Solving

13. Let f and g be continuous and differentiable functions on the interval $a \leq x \leq b$. If f and g are both strictly increasing on $a \leq x \leq b$, and if $f(x) > 0$ and $g(x) > 0$ on $a \leq x \leq b$, show that the product fg is also strictly increasing on $a \leq x \leq b$.

14. Let f and g be continuous and differentiable functions on the interval $a \leq x \leq b$. If f and g are both strictly increasing on $a \leq x \leq b$, and if $f(x) < 0$ and $g(x) < 0$ on $a \leq x \leq b$, is the product fg strictly increasing on $a \leq x \leq b$, strictly decreasing, or neither?

Section 9.2 — Critical Points, Relative Maxima, and Relative Minima

We saw in an earlier chapter that a maximum or minimum function value might be determined at a point $(c, f(c))$ if $f'(c) = 0$. Combining this with the properties of increasing and decreasing functions, we have a First Derivative Test for local extrema.

Test for local minimum and local maximum points. Suppose $f'(c) = 0$.

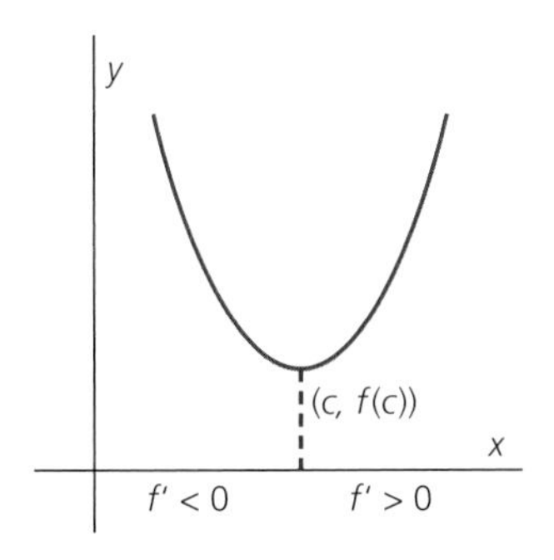

If $f'(x)$ changes sign from negative to positive at $x = c$, then $f(x)$ has a local minimum at this point.

If $f'(x)$ changes sign from positive to negative at $x = c$, then $f(x)$ has a local maximum at this point.

There are possible implications of $f'(c) = 0$ other than the determination of maxima or minima. There are also simple functions for which the derivative does not exist at certain points. In Chapter 4, we demonstrated three different ways that this could happen.

EXAMPLE 1

For the function $y = x^4 - 8x^3 + 18x^2$, determine all values of x such that $f'(x) = 0$. For each of these values of x, determine whether it gives a relative maximum, a relative minimum, or neither for the function.

Solution

First determine $\frac{dy}{dx}$.

$$\begin{aligned}\frac{dy}{dx} &= 4x^3 - 24x^2 + 36x \\ &= 4x(x^2 - 6x + 9) \\ &= 4x(x - 3)^2\end{aligned}$$

For a relative maximum or minimum, let $\frac{dy}{dx} = 0$.

$$4x(x - 3)^2 = 0$$

$$x = 0 \quad \text{or} \quad x = 3$$

Both values of x are in the domain of the function. There is a horizontal tangent at each of these values of x. To determine which of the values of x yield relative maximum or minimum values of the function, we use a table to analyze the behaviour of $\frac{dy}{dx}$ and $y = x^4 - 8x^3 + 18x^2$.

	$x < 0$	$0 < x < 3$	$x > 3$
$\frac{dy}{dx}$	<0	>0	>0
$y = x^4 - 8x^3 + 18x^2$	decreasing	increasing	increasing
Shape of the Curve	╲	╱	╱

Using the information from the table, we see that at $x = 0$, there is a relative minimum value of the function, since the function values are decreasing before $x = 0$ and increasing after $x = 0$. We can also tell that at $x = 3$ there is neither a relative maximum nor minimum value, since the function values increase towards this point and increase away from it.

technology

A calculator gives this graph for $y = x^4 - 8x^3 + 18x^2$, which verifies our analysis.

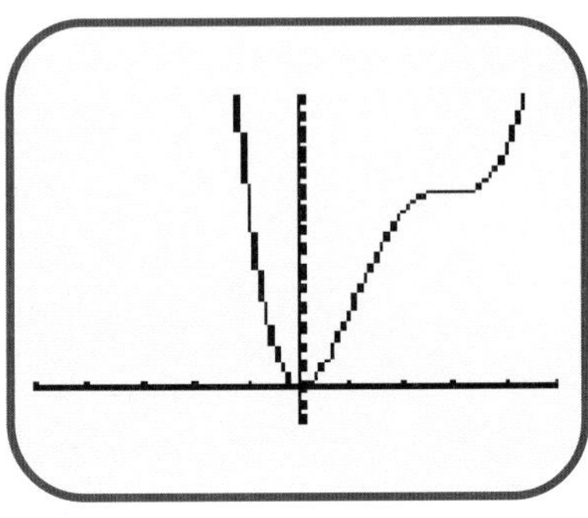

EXAMPLE 2

Determine whether or not the function $f(x) = x^3$ has a maximum or minimum at $(c, f(c))$ where $f'(c) = 0$.

Solution

The derivative is $f'(x) = 3x^2$.
Setting $f'(x) = 0$ gives

$$3x^2 = 0$$
$$x = 0.$$

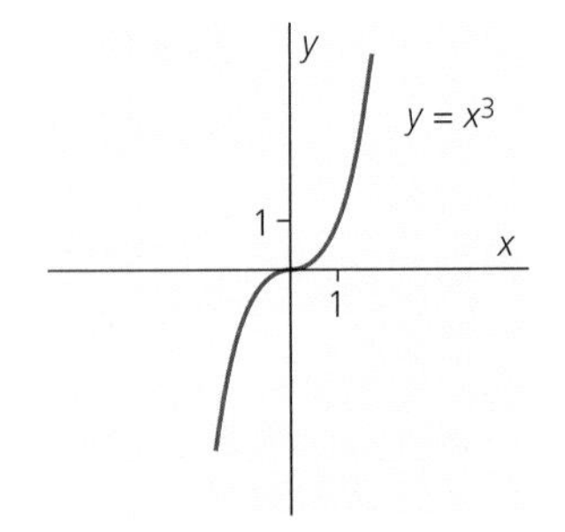

From the graph, it is clear that $(0, 0)$ is neither a maximum nor a minimum value of the function. Note that $f'(x) > 0$ for all values of x other than 0.

From this example, we can see that it is possible $f'(c) = 0$, but there is no maximum or minimum point at $(c, f(c))$. It is also possible for a maximum or minimum to occur at a point at which the derivative does not exist.

EXAMPLE 3

For the function $f(x) = (x + 2)^{\frac{2}{3}}$, determine values of x such that $f'(x) = 0$. Use your calculator to sketch a graph of the function.

technology

Solution

First determine $f'(x)$.

$$f'(x) = \frac{2}{3}(x + 2)^{-\frac{1}{3}}$$

$$= \frac{2}{3(x + 2)^{\frac{1}{3}}}$$

Note that there is no value of x for which $f'(x) = 0$, and $f'(x)$ is undefined for $x = -2$.

However, $x = -2$ is in the domain of $y = (x + 2)^{\frac{2}{3}}$, since $y = (-2 + 2)^{\frac{2}{3}} = 0$. Therefore, this function has one critical point, when $x = -2$. The slope of the tangent is undefined at this point. We determine the slopes of tangents for x values close to -2.

x	$f'(x) = \frac{2}{3(x + 2)^{\frac{1}{3}}}$	x	$f'(x) = \frac{2}{3(x + 2)^{\frac{2}{3}}}$
−2.1	−1.43629	−1.9	1.43629
−2.01	−3.09439	−1.99	3.09439
−2.001	−6.6667	−1.999	6.66667
−2.00001	−66.6667	−1.99999	66.6667

In this example, the slopes of the tangents to the left of $x = -2$ are approaching $-\infty$, while the slopes to the right of $x = -2$ are approaching $+\infty$. Since the slopes on opposite sides of $x = -2$ are not tending towards the same value, there is no tangent at $x = -2$ even though there is a point on the graph.

A calculator gives the following graph of $y = (x + 2)^{\frac{2}{3}}$. There is a cusp at $(-2, 0)$.

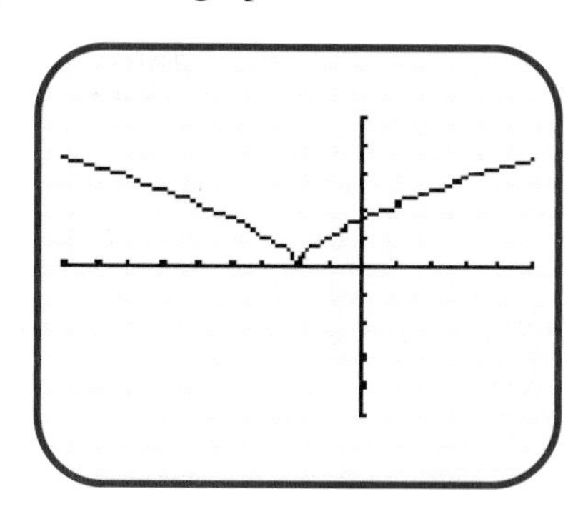

If a value c is *in the domain* of a function $f(x)$, and if this value is such that $f'(c) = 0$ or $f'(c)$ is undefined, then $(c, f(c))$ is called a *critical point* of the function f.

Notice that in the case of $f'(x) = 0$ at a critical point, the slope of the tangent is zero at that point and the tangent to the graph of $y = f(x)$ is horizontal.

In summary, critical points that occur when $\frac{dy}{dx} = 0$ give the locations of horizontal tangents on the graph of a function. Critical points that occur when $\frac{dy}{dx}$ is undefined give the locations of either vertical tangents or cusps (where we say that no tangent exists). Besides giving the location of interesting tangents, critical points also determine other interesting features for the graph of a function.

The value c determines the location of a relative (or local) minimum value for a function f if $f(c) < f(x)$ for all x near c.

Similarly, the value c determines the location of a relative (or local) maximum value for a function f if $f(c) > f(x)$ for all x near c.

Together, relative maximum and minimum values of a function are called relative (or local) extrema.

Note that a relative minimum value of a function does not have to be the smallest value on the entire domain, just the smallest value in its neighbourhood. Similarly, a relative maximum value of a function does not have to be the largest value on the entire domain, just the largest value in its neighbourhood. Relative extrema occur graphically as peaks or valleys. The peaks can be either smooth or sharp.

Let's now reconsider the graphs of two of the functions that we have already analyzed in applying this reasoning.

Here is the graph of $y = x^2e^{-x}$:

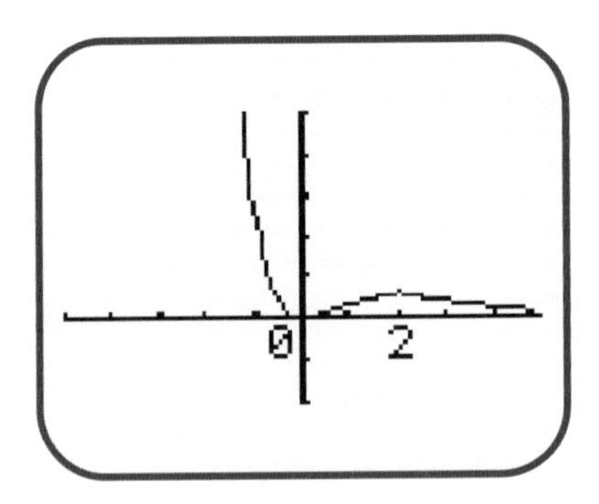

The function $f(x) = x^2e^{-x}$ has a relative maximum value at $x = 2$, since $f(2) = \frac{4}{e^2}$ is the largest value in its neighbourhood. However, $f(2) = \frac{4}{e^2}$ is not the largest function value on the entire domain. The function $f(x) = x^2e^{-x}$ also has a relative minimum value at $x = 0$, since $f(0) = 0$ is the smallest value in its neighbourhood. This value also happens to be the smallest on the entire domain.

Here is the graph of $y = (x + 2)^{\frac{2}{3}}$:

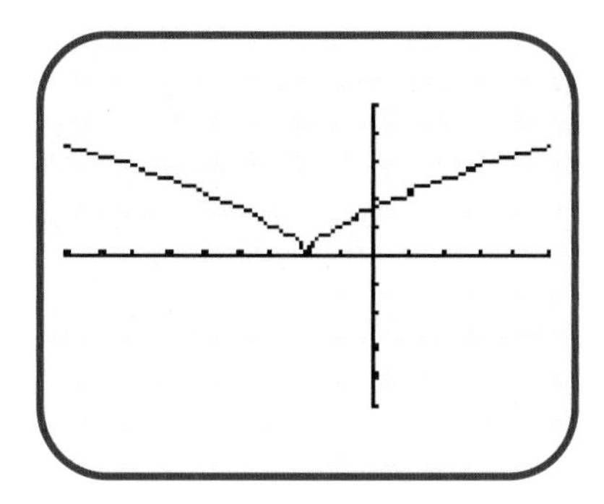

The function $f(x) = (x + 2)^{\frac{2}{3}}$ has a relative minimum value at $x = -2$, which also happens to be a critical value of the function.

Every relative maximum or minimum value of a function occurs at a critical point of the function.

In simple terms, peaks or valleys occur on the graph of a function at places where the tangent to the graph is horizontal, vertical, or does not exist.

How do we determine whether a critical point yields a relative maximum or minimum value of a function without examining the graph of the function? We use the first derivative to analyze whether the function is increasing or decreasing on either side of the critical point.

Algorithm for finding relative maximum and minimum values of a function f:

1. **Find critical points of the function; that is, determine where $f'(x) = 0$ and where $f'(x)$ is undefined, for x values in the domain of f.**
2. **Use the first derivative to analyze whether f is increasing or decreasing on either side of each critical point.**
3. **Conclude that each critical point locates either a relative maximum value of the function f, a relative minimum value, or neither.**

Exercise 9.2

Part A

Communication

1. Explain what it means to determine the critical points of the graph of a given function.

Knowledge/Understanding

2. a. For the function $y = x^3 - 6x^2$, explain how you would find the critical points.

   b. Determine the critical points for $y = x^3 - 6x^2$ and then sketch the graph.

3. For each of the following, find the critical points. Use the first derivative test to determine whether the critical point is a local maximum, local minimum, or neither.

   a. $y = x^4 - 8x^2$
   b. $f(x) = \frac{2x}{x^2 + 9}$
   c. $y = xe^{-4x}$
   d. $y = \ln(x^2 - 3x + 4)$

4. For each of the parts in Question 3, find the x- and y-intercepts and then sketch the curve.

5. Find the critical points for each of the following. Determine whether the critical point is a local maximum or minimum and whether or not the tangent is parallel to the horizontal axis.

   a. $h(x) = -6x^3 + 18x^2 + 3$
   b. $s = -t^2e^{-3t}$
   c. $y = (x - 5)^{\frac{1}{3}}$
   d. $f(x) = (x^2 - 1)^{\frac{1}{3}}$
   e. $g(t) = t^5 + t^3$
   f. $y = x^2 - 12x^{\frac{1}{3}}$

technology

6. Use a technology of your choice to graph the functions in Question 5.

Part B

Knowledge/Understanding

7. Find the critical points for each of the following functions, and determine whether the function has a relative maximum value, a relative minimum value, or neither at the critical points. Sketch the graph of each function.

   a. $f(x) = -2x^2 + 8x + 13$
   b. $f(x) = \frac{1}{3}x^3 - 9x + 2$
   c. $f(x) = 2x^3 + 9x^2 + 12x$
   d. $f(x) = -3x^3 - 5x$
   e. $f(x) = \sqrt{x^2 - 2x + 2}$
   f. $f(x) = 3x^4 - 4x^3$
   g. $f(x) = e^{-x^2}$
   h. $f(x) = x^2\ln x$

8. Suppose f is a differentiable function with derivative $f'(x) = (x + 1)(x - 2)(x + 6)$. Find all critical numbers of f and determine whether each corresponds to a relative maximum, a relative minimum, or neither.

Application

9. Sketch a graph of a function f that is differentiable on the interval $-3 \leq x \leq 4$ and that satisfies the following conditions:

   - The function f is decreasing on $-1 < x < 3$ and increasing elsewhere on $-3 \leq x \leq 4$.

- The largest value of f is 6 and the smallest is 0.
- The graph of f has relative extrema at $(-1, 6)$ and $(3, 1)$.

10. Find values for a, b, and c such that the graph of $y = ax^2 + bx + c$ has a relative maximum at $(3, 12)$ and crosses the y-axis at $(0, 1)$.

11. For each of the following graphs of the function $y = f(x)$, make a rough sketch of the derivative function $f'(x)$. By comparing the graphs of $f(x)$ and $f'(x)$, show that the intervals for which $f(x)$ is increasing correspond to the intervals where $f'(x)$ is positive. Also show that the intervals where $f(x)$ is decreasing correspond to the intervals for which $f'(x)$ is negative.

a.

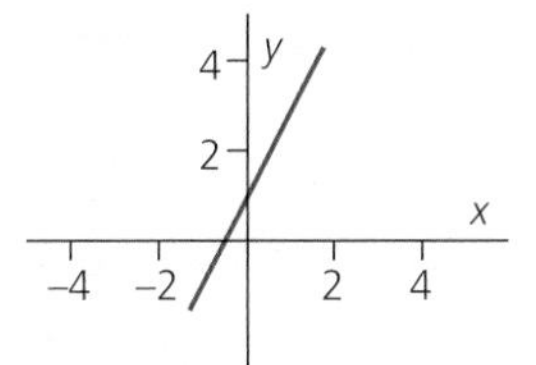

$f(x)$ is a linear function.

b.

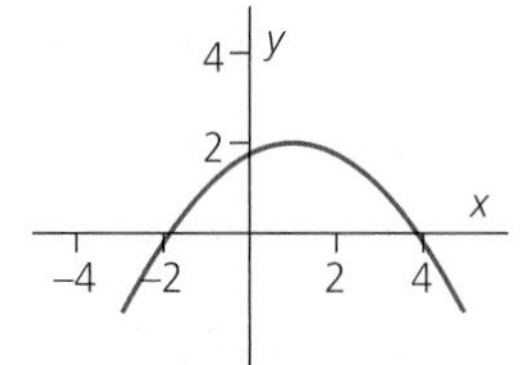

$f(x)$ is a quadratic function.

c.

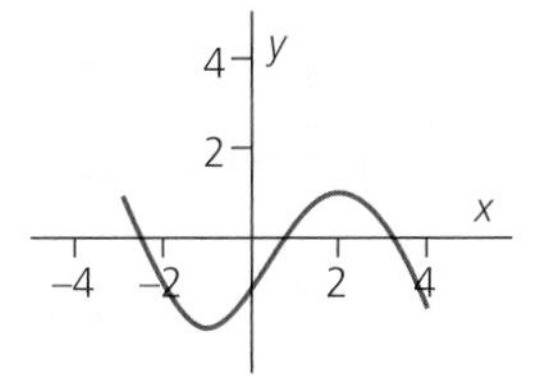

$f(x)$ is a cubic function.

d.

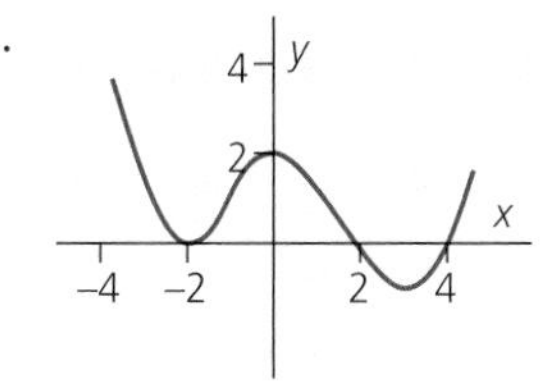

$f(x)$ is a quartic function.

12. For the function $f(x) = 3x^4 + ax^3 + bx^2 + cx + d$,

    a. find constants a, b, c, and d that guarantee that the graph of f will have horizontal tangents at $(-2, -73)$ and $(0, -9)$.

    b. there is a third point that has a horizontal tangent. Find this point.

    c. For all three points, determine whether each corresponds to a relative maximum, a relative minimum, or neither.

Part C

13. For each of the following polynomials, find the local extrema and the direction the curve is opening for $x = 100$. Use this information to make a quick sketch of the curve.

    a. $y = 4 - 3x^2 - x^4$

    b. $y = 3x^5 - 5x^3 - 30x$

14. Suppose that $f(x)$ and $g(x)$ are positive functions such that $f(x)$ has a local maximum and $g(x)$ has a local minimum at $x = c$. Show that $h(x) = \dfrac{f(x)}{g(x)}$ has a local maximum at $x = c$.

Section 9.3 — Vertical and Horizontal Asymptotes

In sketching the graph of the exponential function $y = e^x$, you saw that the x-axis is a horizontal asymptote. In graphing $y = \ln x$, you saw that the y-axis is a vertical asymptote.

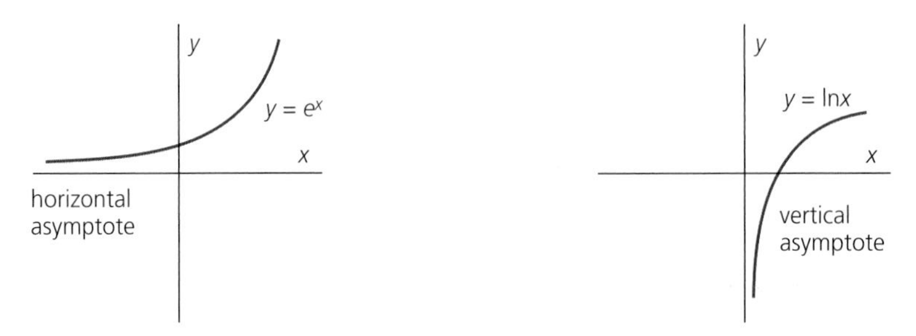

Asymptotes play a significant role in curve sketching. In this section, we will consider vertical and horizontal asymptotes of rational functions and expand our understanding of asymptotes of exponential and logarithmic functions.

Vertical Asymptotes and Rational Functions

INVESTIGATION

The purpose of this investigation is to examine the occurrence of vertical asymptotes for rational functions.

1. Use your graphing calculator to obtain the graph of $f(x) = \frac{1}{x - k}$ and the table of values for each of the following: $k = 3, 1, 0, -2, -4$, and -5.

2. Describe the behaviour of each graph as x approaches k from the right and from the left.

3. Repeat Questions 1 and 2 for the function $f(x) = \frac{x + 3}{x - k}$, using the same values of k.

4. Repeat Questions 1 and 2 for the function $f(x) = \frac{1}{x^2 + x - k}$, using the following values: $k = 2, 6$, and 12.

5. Make a general statement about the existence of a vertical asymptote for a rational function of the form $y = \frac{p(x)}{q(x)}$ if there is a value c such that $q(c) = 0$ and $p(c) \neq 0$.

We use the notation $x \to c^+$ to indicate that x approaches c from the right. Similarly, $x \to c^-$ means that x approaches c from the left.

You can see from this investigation that as $x \to c$ from either side, the function values get increasingly large and positive or negative depending on the value of $p(c)$. We say that the function values approach $+\infty$ (positive infinity) or $-\infty$ (negative infinity). These are not numbers. They are symbols that represent the value of a function that increases or decreases without limits.

Because the symbol ∞ is not a number, the limits

$$\lim_{x \to c^+} \frac{1}{x - c} \quad \text{and} \quad \lim_{x \to c^-} \frac{1}{x - c}$$

do not exist. However, for convenience, we use the notation

$$\lim_{x \to c^+} \frac{1}{x - c} = +\infty \quad \text{and} \quad \lim_{x \to c^-} \frac{1}{x - c} = -\infty.$$

In similar fashion, and for the same reason, we also write

$$\lim_{x \to 0^+} \ln x = -\infty.$$

These three limits form the basis for determining asymptotes to simple functions.

A rational function of the form $f(x) = \frac{p(x)}{q(x)}$ has a vertical asymptote $x = c$ if $q(c) = 0$ and $p(c) \neq 0$.

EXAMPLE 1

Determine any vertical asymptotes of the function $f(x) = \frac{x}{x^2 + x - 2}$, and describe the behaviour of the graph of the function for values of x near the asymptotes.

Solution

First determine the values of x for which $f(x)$ is undefined by solving

$$\begin{aligned} x^2 + x - 2 &= 0 \\ (x + 2)(x - 1) &= 0 \\ x = -2 \text{ or } x &= 1. \end{aligned}$$

Neither of these values for x makes the numerator zero, so both of these values for x give vertical asymptotes. The asymptotes are $x = -2$ and $x = 1$.

To determine the behaviour of the graph near the asymptotes, it can be helpful to use a chart.

x-values	x	$x + 2$	$x - 1$	$f(x)$	$\lim_{x \to c} f(x)$
$x \to -2^-$	<0	<0	<0	<0	$-\infty$
$x \to -2^+$	<0	>0	<0	>0	$+\infty$
$x \to 1^-$	>0	>0	<0	<0	$-\infty$
$x \to 1^+$	>0	>0	>0	>0	$+\infty$

The behaviour of the graph can be illustrated as follows:

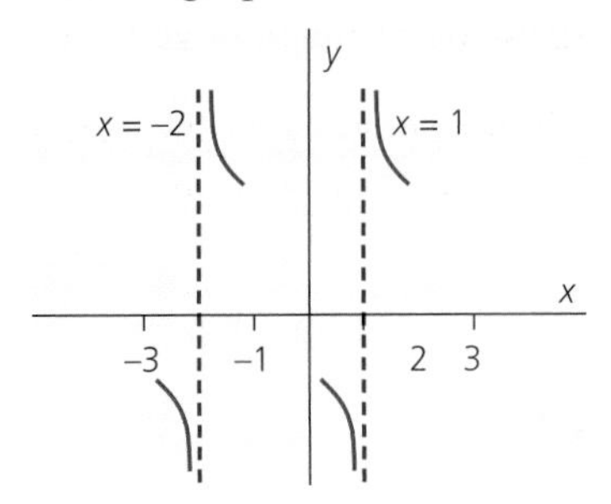

To proceed beyond this point, we require additional information.

Vertical Asymptotes
The graph of $f(x)$ has a vertical asymptote $x = c$ if one of the following limit statements is true:

$$\lim_{x \to c^-} f(x) = +\infty \qquad \lim_{x \to c^-} f(x) = -\infty \qquad \lim_{x \to c^+} f(x) = +\infty \qquad \lim_{x \to c^+} f(x) = -\infty$$

The following graphs correspond to each limit statement.

$\lim_{x \to c^-} f(x) = +\infty$ $\qquad$ $\lim_{x \to c^-} f(x) = -\infty$

$\lim_{x \to c^+} f(x) = +\infty$ $\qquad$ $\lim_{x \to c^+} f(x) = -\infty$

Horizontal Asymptotes

Consider the behaviour of rational functions $f(x) = \frac{p(x)}{q(x)}$ as x increases without bound, in both the positive and negative directions. The following notation is used to describe this behaviour:

$$\lim_{x \to +\infty} f(x) \quad \text{and} \quad \lim_{x \to -\infty} f(x).$$

The notation $x \to +\infty$ is read as "x tends to positive infinity" and means that the values of x are positive and growing without bound. Similarly, the notation

$x \to -\infty$ is read as "x tends to negative infinity" and means that the values of x are negative and growing in magnitude without bound.

The value of these limits can be determined by making two observations. The first is a list of simple limits parallel to those used in determining vertical asymptotes.

$$\lim_{x\to+\infty} \frac{1}{x} = 0 \quad \text{and} \quad \lim_{x\to-\infty} \frac{1}{x} = 0$$

As observed earlier, for the exponential function $f(x) = e^x$,

$$\lim_{x\to-\infty} e^x = 0.$$

The second observation is that a polynomial can always be written so that the term of highest degree is a factor.

EXAMPLE 2

Write each of the following so that the term of highest degree is a factor.

a. $p(x) = x^2 + 4x + 1$

b. $q(x) = 3x^2 - 4x + 5$

Solution

a.
$$\begin{aligned} p(x) &= x^2 + 4x + 1 \\ &= x^2\left(1 + \frac{4}{x} + \frac{1}{x^2}\right) \end{aligned}$$

b.
$$\begin{aligned} q(x) &= 3x^2 - 4x + 5 \\ &= 3x^2\left(1 - \frac{4}{3x} + \frac{5}{3x^2}\right) \end{aligned}$$

The value of writing a polynomial in this form is clear. It is easy to see that as x becomes large, either positive or negative, the value of the second factor always approaches 1.

We can now determine the limit of a rational function in which the degree of $p(x)$ is equal to or less than the degree of $q(x)$.

EXAMPLE 3

Determine the value of each of the following:

a. $\displaystyle\lim_{x\to+\infty} \frac{2x - 3}{x + 1}$

b. $\displaystyle\lim_{x\to-\infty} \frac{x}{x^2 + 1}$

c. $\displaystyle\lim_{x\to+\infty} \frac{2x^2 + 3}{3x^2 - x + 4}$

Solution

a.
$$\begin{aligned} f(x) &= \frac{2x - 3}{x + 1} = \frac{2x\left(1 - \frac{3}{2x}\right)}{x\left(1 + \frac{1}{x}\right)} \\ &= \frac{2\left(1 - \frac{3}{2x}\right)}{1 + \frac{1}{x}} \\ \lim_{x\to+\infty} f(x) &= \frac{2\left[\lim_{x\to+\infty}\left(1 - \frac{3}{2x}\right)\right]}{\lim_{x\to+\infty}\left(1 + \frac{1}{x}\right)} \\ &= \frac{2(1 - 0)}{1 + 0} \\ &= 2 \end{aligned}$$

b.
$$\begin{aligned} g(x) &= \frac{x}{x^2 + 1} \\ &= \frac{x(1)}{x^2\left(1 + \frac{1}{x^2}\right)} \\ \lim_{x\to-\infty} g(x) &= \frac{1}{\lim_{x\to-\infty} x \bullet \lim_{x\to-\infty}\left(1 + \frac{1}{x^2}\right)} \\ &= \lim_{x\to-\infty} \frac{1}{x} \\ &= 0 \end{aligned}$$

c. $p(x) = \dfrac{2x^2 + 3}{3x^2 - x + 4}$

$$= \frac{2x^2\left(1 + \frac{3}{2x^2}\right)}{3x^2\left(1 - \frac{1}{3x} + \frac{4}{3x^2}\right)}$$

$$= \frac{2\left(1 + \frac{3}{2x^2}\right)}{3\left(1 - \frac{1}{3x} + \frac{4}{3x^2}\right)}$$

$$\lim_{x \to +\infty} p(x) = \frac{2}{3} \frac{\lim_{x \to +\infty}\left(1 + \frac{3}{2x^2}\right)}{\lim_{x \to +\infty}\left(1 - \frac{1}{3x} + \frac{4}{3x^2}\right)}$$

$$= \frac{2}{3} \frac{(1 + 0)}{(1 - 0 + 0)}$$

$$= \frac{2}{3}$$

Alternate Solution

Divide the numerator and denominator by the largest power of x, that is, x^2.

$$p(x) = \frac{2 + \frac{3}{x^2}}{3 - \frac{1}{x} + \frac{4}{x^2}}$$

$$\lim_{x \to +\infty} p(x) = \frac{\lim_{x \to +\infty}\left(2 + \frac{3}{x^2}\right)}{\lim_{x \to +\infty}\left(3 - \frac{1}{x} + \frac{4}{x^2}\right)}$$

$$= \frac{2}{3}$$

When $\lim_{x \to +\infty} f(x) = k$ or $\lim_{x \to -\infty} f(x) = k$, the graph of the function is approaching the line $y = k$. This line is a horizontal asymptote of the function. In Example 3, $y = 2$ is a horizontal asymptote of $f(x) = \dfrac{2x - 3}{x + 1}$.

From the solution above, you can see that

$$\lim_{x \to -\infty} \frac{2x - 3}{x + 1} = \frac{2\left(\lim_{x \to -\infty}\left(1 - \frac{3}{x}\right)\right)}{\lim_{x \to -\infty}\left(1 + \frac{1}{x}\right)}$$

$$= 2$$

and, therefore, $y = 2$ is an asymptote for large positive x-values and also for large negative x-values.

In order to use this knowledge in sketching the graph for this function, we need to know whether the curve approaches the asymptote from above or from below. This is answered by considering $f(x) - k$ where k is the limit determined. This is illustrated in the following examples.

EXAMPLE 4

Determine the equations of any horizontal asymptotes of the function $f(x) = \dfrac{3x + 5}{2x - 1}$, and state whether the graph approaches the asymptote from above or below.

Solution

$$f(x) = \frac{3x + 5}{2x - 1} = \frac{3x\left(1 + \frac{5}{3x}\right)}{2x\left(1 - \frac{1}{2x}\right)}$$

$$= \frac{3\left(1 + \frac{5}{3x}\right)}{2\left(1 - \frac{1}{2x}\right)}$$

$$\lim_{x \to +\infty} f(x) = \frac{3 \lim_{x \to +\infty}\left(1 + \frac{5}{3x}\right)}{2 \lim_{x \to +\infty}\left(1 - \frac{1}{2x}\right)}$$

$$= \frac{3}{2}$$

Similiarly, we can show $\lim_{x \to -\infty} f(x) = \frac{3}{2}$. Then $y = \frac{3}{2}$ is a horizontal asymptote of the graph $f(x)$ for both large positive and negative values of x. To determine whether the graph approaches the asymptote from above or below, we consider very large positive and negative values for x.

If x is large and positive, for example, if $x = 1000, f(x) = \frac{3005}{1999}$, which is greater than $\frac{3}{2}$. Therefore, the graph approaches the asymptote $y = \frac{3}{2}$ from above.

If x is large and negative, for example, if $x = -1000, f(x) = \frac{-2995}{-2000}$, which is less than $\frac{3}{2}$. This graph approaches the asymptote $y = \frac{3}{2}$ from below, as illustrated in the diagram.

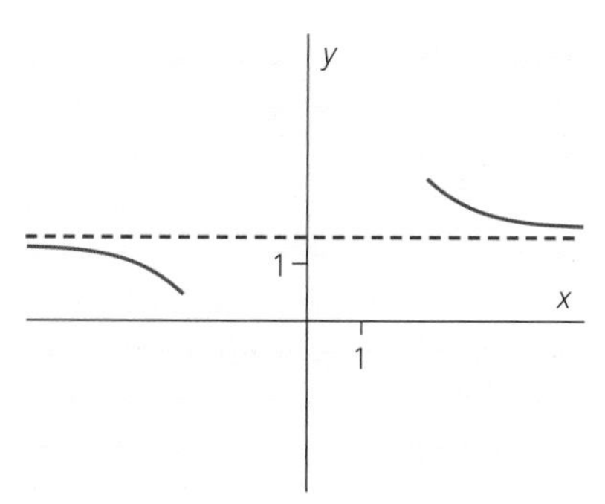

EXAMPLE 5

For the function $f(x) = \frac{3x}{x^2 - x - 6}$, determine the equations of all horizontal or vertical asymptotes and illustrate the behaviour of the graph as it approaches the asymptotes.

Solution

For vertical asymptotes

$$x^2 - x - 6 = 0$$
$$(x - 3)(x + 2) = 0$$
$$x = 3 \text{ or } x = -2$$

There are two vertical asymptotes at $x = 3$ and $x = -2$.

x-values	x	$x-3$	$x+2$	$f(x)$	$\lim_{x \to c} f(x)$
$x \to 3^-$	>0	<0	>0	<0	$-\infty$
$x \to 3^+$	>0	>0	>0	>0	$+\infty$
$x \to -2^-$	<0	<0	<0	<0	$-\infty$
$x \to -2^+$	<0	<0	>0	>0	$+\infty$

For horizontal asymptotes,

$$f(x) = \frac{3x}{x^2 - x - 6}$$

$$= \frac{3x}{x^2\left(1 - \frac{1}{x} - \frac{6}{x^2}\right)}$$

$$= \frac{3}{x\left(1 - \frac{1}{x} - \frac{6}{x^2}\right)}$$

$$\lim_{x \to +\infty} f(x) = \lim_{x \to \infty} \frac{3}{x} = 0.$$

Similarly, we can show $\lim_{x \to -\infty} f(x) = 0$. Therefore, $y = 0$ is a horizontal asymptote of the graph of $f(x)$ for both large positive and negative values of x.
As x becomes large positively, $f(x) > 0$, so the graph is above the asymptote.
As x becomes large negatively, $f(x) < 0$, so the graph is below the asymptote.

This diagram illustrates the behaviour of the graph as it nears the asymptotes:

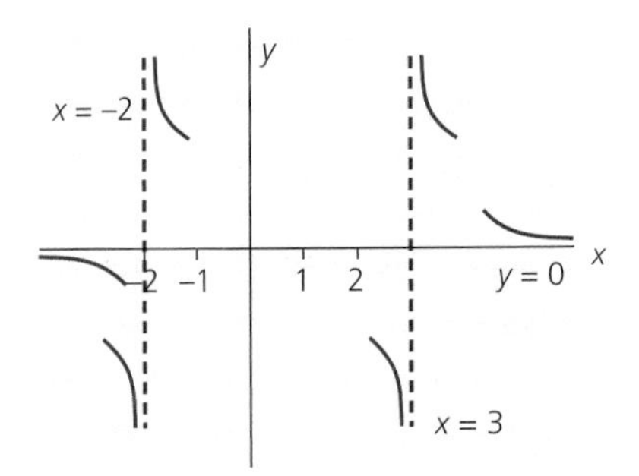

Horizontal Asymptotes
If $\lim_{x \to +\infty} f(x) = L$ or $\lim_{x \to -\infty} f(x) = L$, we say that the line $y = L$ is a horizontal asymptote of the graph of $f(x)$.

The following graphs illustrate some typical situations:

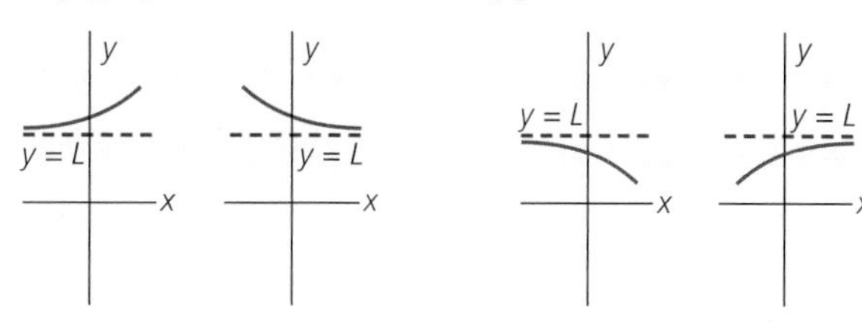

$f(x) > L$ for large x $\qquad$ $f(x) < L$ for large x

In addition to vertical and horizontal asymptotes, it is possible for a graph to have **oblique asymptotes**. These are straight lines that are not parallel to the axes and that the curve approaches infinitely closely. They occur with rational functions in which the degree of the numerator polynomial exceeds the degree of the denominator polynomial by exactly one. This is illustrated in the following example.

EXAMPLE 6 Determine the equations of all asymptotes of the graph of $f(x) = \frac{2x^2 + 3x - 1}{x + 1}$.

Solution

Since $x + 1 = 0$ for $x = -1$ and $2x^2 + 3x - 1 \neq 0$ for $x = -1$, then $x = -1$ is a vertical asymptote.

$$\text{Now } \lim_{x\to\infty} \frac{2x^2 + 3x - 1}{x + 1} = \lim_{x\to\infty} \frac{2x^2\left(1 + \frac{3}{2x} - \frac{1}{2x^2}\right)}{x(1 + x)}$$

$$= \lim_{x\to\infty} 2x.$$

This limit does not exist, and by a similar calculation, $\lim_{x\to-\infty} f(x)$ does not exist, so there is no horizontal asymptote.

After dividing the numerator by the denominator,

$$\begin{array}{r@{}l} & 2x + 1 \\ x + 1 \,\big)\!\!\!\! & \overline{2x^2 + 3x - 1} \\ & \underline{2x^2 + 2x} \\ & x - 1 \\ & \underline{x + 1} \\ & -2 \end{array}$$

we can write $f(x)$ in the form $f(x) = 2x + 1 - \frac{2}{x + 1}$.

Now consider the straight line $y = 2x + 1$ and the graph of $y = f(x)$. For any value of x, we determine point $P(x, 2x + 1)$ on the line and $Q\left(x, 2x + 1 - \frac{2}{x + 1}\right)$ on the curve.

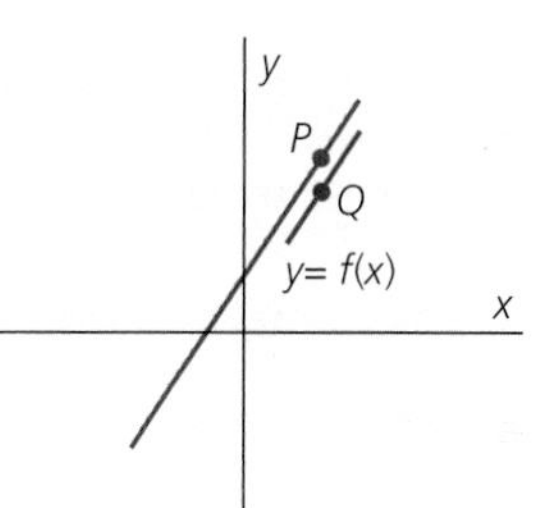

Then the vertical distance QP from the curve to the line is $QP = 2x + 1 - \left(2x + 1 - \frac{2}{x + 1}\right)$

$$= \frac{2}{x + 1}.$$

$$\text{Then } \lim_{x\to\infty} QP = \lim_{x\to\infty} \frac{2}{x+1}$$
$$= 0.$$

That is, as x gets very large, the curve approaches the line but never touches it. Therefore, the line $y = 2x + 1$ is an asymptote of the curve.

Since $\lim_{x\to-\infty} \frac{2}{x+1} = 0$, the line is also an asymptote for large negative values of x.

In conclusion, there are two asymptotes of the graph of $f(x) = \frac{2x^2 + 3x - 1}{x + 1}$. They are $y = 2x + 1$ and $x = -1$.

technology

Use the graphing calculator to obtain the graph of $f(x) = \frac{2x^2 + 3x - 1}{x + 1}$.

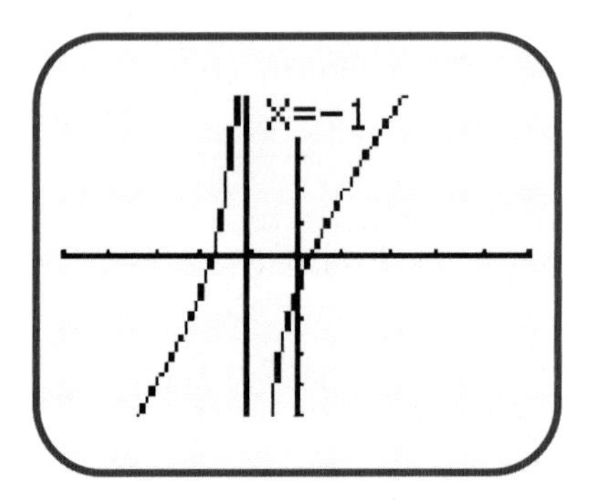

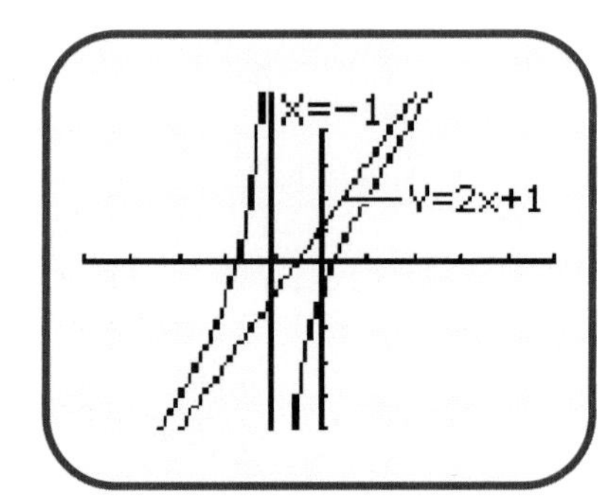

Note that the vertical asymptote $x = -1$ appears on the graph on the left, but the oblique asymptote $y = 2x + 1$ does not. Use the Y_2 function to graph the oblique asymptote $y = 2x + 1$.

The techniques for curve sketching developed to this point are described in the following algorithm. As we develop new ideas, the algorithm will be extended.

Algorithm for Curve Sketching

To sketch a curve, apply the following in the order shown. Add the information to the diagram step by step.

Step 1: Check for any discontinuities in the domain. Determine if there are vertical asymptotes and the direction at which the curve approaches these asymptotes.

Step 2: Find the y-intercept.

Step 3: Find any critical points.

Step 4: Use the first derivative test to determine the type of critical points that may be present.

Step 5: Extremity tests: Determine $\lim_{x\to\infty} f(x)$, $\lim_{x\to-\infty} f(x)$.

Exercise 9.3

Part A

Knowledge/ Understanding

1. State the equations of the vertical and horizontal asymptotes of the curves shown.

a.

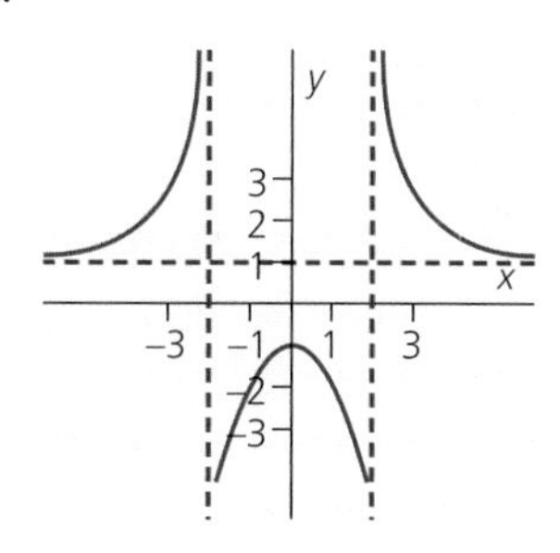

b.

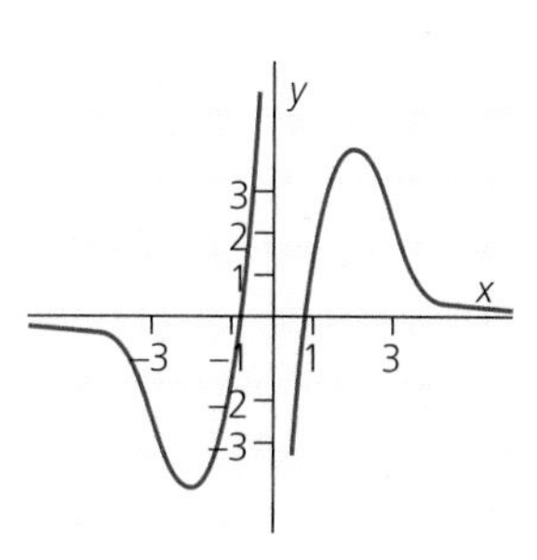

Communication

2. Under what condition does a rational function have vertical, horizontal, and oblique asymptotes?

3. Evaluate $\lim_{x \to \infty} f(x)$ and $\lim_{x \to -\infty} f(x)$, using the symbol "$\infty$" when appropriate.

a. $f(x) = \dfrac{2x + 3}{x - 1}$ b. $f(x) = \dfrac{5x^2 - 3}{x^2 + 2}$

c. $f(x) = \dfrac{-5x^2 + 3x}{2x^2 - 5}$ d. $f(x) = \dfrac{2x^5 - 3x^2 + 5}{3x^4 + 5x - 4}$

4. For each of the following, check for discontinuities and state the equation of any vertical asymptotes. Conduct a limit test to determine the behaviour of the curve on either side of the asymptote.

a. $y = \dfrac{x}{x + 5}$ b. $f(x) = \dfrac{x + 2}{x - 2}$ c. $s = \dfrac{1}{(t - 3)^2}$

d. $y = \dfrac{x^2 - x - 6}{x - 3}$ e. $g(x) = \dfrac{1}{e^x - 2}$ f. $y = x\ln x$

5. For each of the following, determine the equations of any horizontal asymptotes and state whether the curve approaches the asymptote from above or below.

a. $y = \dfrac{x}{x + 4}$ b. $f(x) = \dfrac{2x}{x^2 - 1}$

c. $g(t) = \dfrac{3t^2 + 4}{t^2 - 1}$ d. $y = \dfrac{3x^2 - 8x - 7}{x - 4}$

Part B

technology

6. For each of the following, check for discontinuities and then use at least two other tests to make a rough sketch of the curve. Verify on a calculator.

a. $y = \dfrac{x - 3}{x + 5}$ b. $f(x) = \dfrac{5}{(x + 2)^2}$ c. $g(t) = \dfrac{t^2 - 2t - 15}{t - 5}$

d. $p(x) = \frac{15}{6 - 2e^x}$ e. $y = \frac{(2 + x)(3 - 2x)}{(x^2 - 3x)}$ f. $P = \frac{10}{n^2 + 4}$

7. Find the equation of the oblique asymptote for each of the following:

a. $f(x) = \frac{3x^2 - 2x - 17}{x - 3}$ b. $f(x) = \frac{2x^2 + 9x + 2}{2x + 3}$

c. $f(x) = \frac{x^3 - 1}{x^2 + 2x}$ d. $f(x) = \frac{x^3 - x^2 - 9x + 15}{x^2 - 4x + 3}$

8. a. In Question 7 **a,** determine whether the curve approaches the asymptote from above or below.

b. In Question 7 **b,** determine the direction from which the curve approaches the asymptote.

Application

9. Use the algorithm for curve sketching to sketch the following:

a. $f(x) = \frac{3 - x}{2x + 5}$ b. $h(t) = 2t^3 - 15t^2 + 36t - 10$

c. $y = \frac{20}{x^2 + 4}$ d. $s(t) = t + \frac{1}{t}$

e. $g(x) = \frac{2x^2 + 5x + 2}{x + 3}$ f. $s(t) = \frac{t^2 + 4t - 21}{t - 3}, t \geq -7$

10. For the function $y = \frac{ax + b}{cx + d}$, where a, b, c, and d are constants, $a \neq 0$, $c \neq 0$,

a. determine the horizontal asymptote of the graph.

b. determine the vertical asymptote of the graph.

Part C

Thinking/Inquiry/ Problem Solving

11. Find constants a and b that guarantee that the graph of the function defined by $f(x) = \frac{ax + 5}{3 - bx}$ will have a vertical asymptote at $x = 5$ and a horizontal asymptote at $y = -3$.

12. This question will illustrate that we cannot work with the symbol "∞" as though it were a real number. Consider the functions $f(x) = \frac{x^2 + 1}{x + 1}$ and $g(x) = \frac{x^2 + 2x + 1}{x + 1}$.

a. Show that $\lim_{x \to +\infty} f(x) = +\infty$ and $\lim_{x \to +\infty} g(x) = +\infty$.

b. Evaluate $\lim_{x \to +\infty} [f(x) - g(x)]$ and show that the limit is not zero.

13. Use the algorithm for curve sketching to sketch the function $f(x) = \frac{2x^2 - 2x}{x^2 - 9}$.

14. Determine the oblique asymptote of the graph of $y = \frac{x^2 + 3x + 7}{x + 2}$.

Section 9.4 — Concavity and Points of Inflection

In Chapter 5, you saw that the second derivative of a function has applications in problems involving velocity and acceleration, or in general rates of change problems. Here we examine the use of the second derivative of a function in curve sketching.

INVESTIGATION 1

The purpose of this investigation is to examine the relationship between tangent slopes and the second derivative of a function.

1. Sketch the graph of $f(x) = x^2$.
2. Determine the slope of the tangent to the curve at each of the points having $x = -4, -3, -2, -1, 0, 1, 2, 3, 4$, and sketch each of these tangents.
3. Are the tangents above or below the graph of $y = f(x)$?
4. Describe the change in the slopes as x increases.
5. Determine $f''(x)$ and compare it with your answer in Question 3.
6. Repeat Questions 2, 3, and 4 for the graph of $f(x) = -x^2$.
7. How does the value of $f''(x)$ relate to the way in which the curve opens?

INVESTIGATION 2

The purpose of this investigation is to extend the results of Investigation 1 to other functions.

1. Sketch the graph of $f(x) = x^3$.
2. Determine all values of x for which $f'(x) = 0$.
3. Determine intervals of the domain of the function such that $f''(x) < 0$, $f''(x) = 0$, and $f''(x) > 0$.
4. For values of x such that $f''(x) < 0$, how does the shape of the curve compare to your conclusions in Investigation 1?
5. Repeat Question 4 for values of x such that $f''(x) > 0$.
6. What happens when $f''(x) = 0$?
7. Using your observations from this investigation, sketch the graph of $y = x^3 - 12x$.

From these investigations, we can make a summary of the behaviour of the graphs.

1. The graph of $y = f(x)$ is *concave up* on an interval $a \leq x \leq b$ in which its slopes are increasing. On this interval, $f''(x)$ exists and $f''(x) > 0$. The graph of the function is above the tangent at every point in the interval.

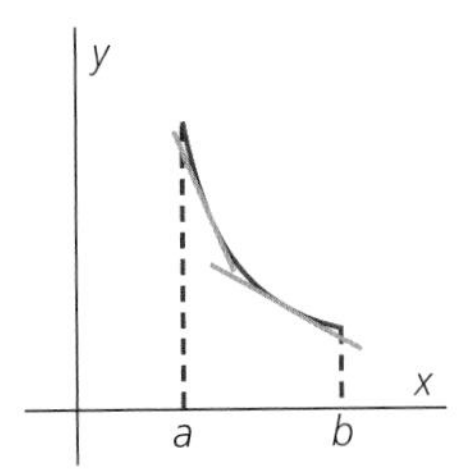

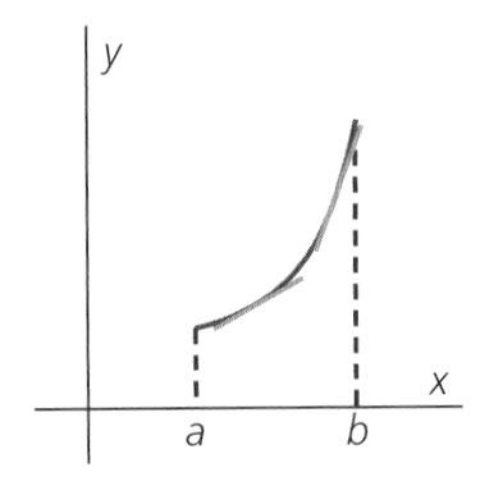

2. The graph of $y = f(x)$ is *concave down* on an interval $a \leq x \leq b$ in which its slopes are decreasing. On this interval, $f''(x)$ exists and $f''(x) < 0$. The graph of the function is below the tangent at every point in the interval.

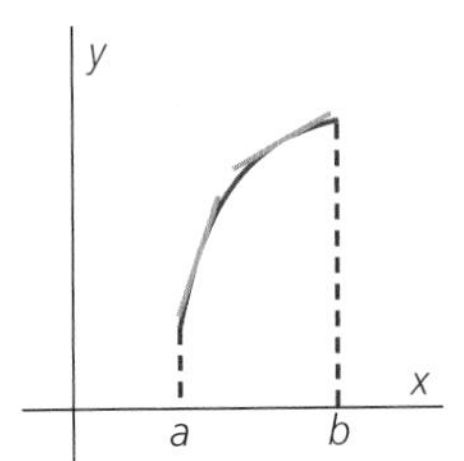

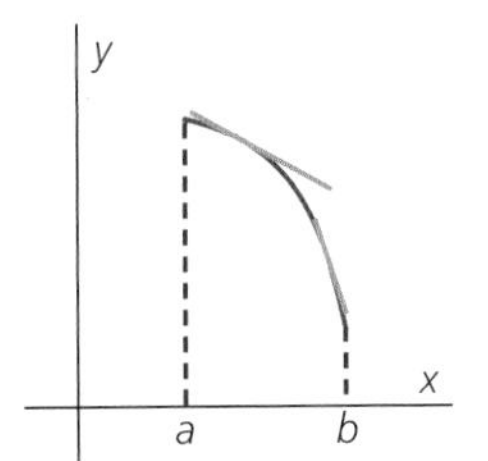

3. If $y = f(x)$ has a critical point at $x = c$, with $f'(c) = 0$, then:

   a. the graph is concave up and $x = c$ is the location of a relative minimum value of the function if $f''(c) > 0$.

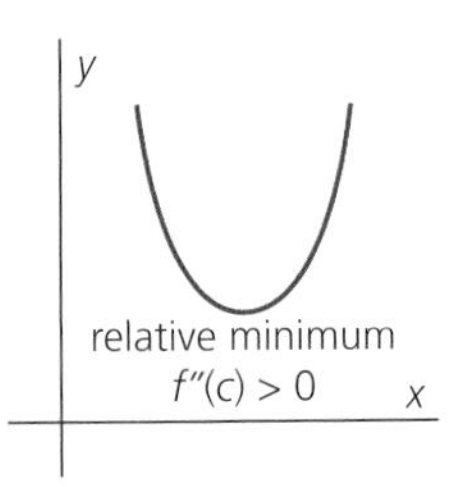

   b. the graph is concave down and $x = c$ is the location of a relative maximum value of the function if $f''(c) < 0$.

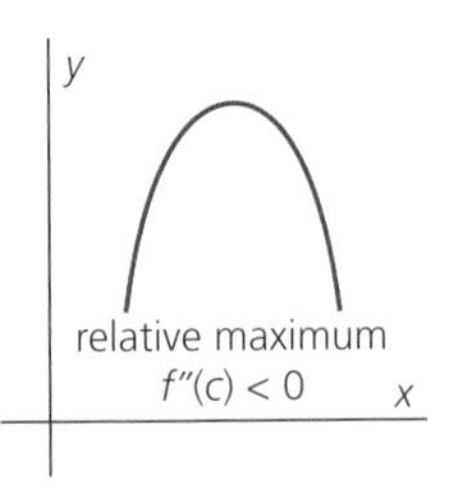

   c. the nature of the critical point cannot be determined if $f''(c) = 0$ without further work.

4. A point of inflection occurs at $(c, f(c))$ on the graph of $y = f(x)$ if $f''(x)$ changes sign at $x = c$. That is, the curve changes from concave down to concave up, or vice versa.

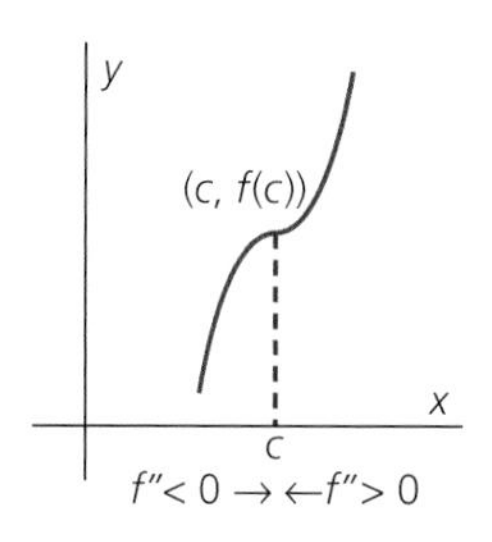

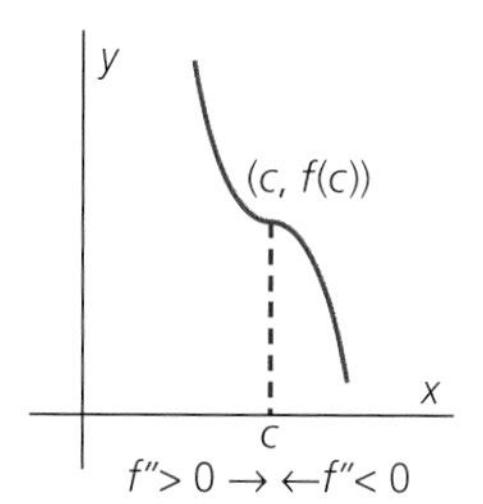

5. All points of inflection of the graph of $y = f(x)$ must occur either for $\frac{d^2y}{dx^2} = 0$ or $\frac{d^2y}{dx^2}$, undefined.

In the following examples, we can use these properties to sketch graphs of other functions.

EXAMPLE 1 Sketch the graph of $y = x^3 - 3x^2 - 9x + 10$.

Solution

$\frac{dy}{dx} = 3x^2 - 6x - 9$

Setting $\frac{dy}{dx} = 0$, we obtain $3(x^2 - 2x - 3) = 0$

$$(x - 3)(x + 1) = 0$$

$$x = 3 \text{ or } x = -1.$$

$\frac{d^2y}{dx^2} = 6x - 6$

Setting $\frac{d^2y}{dx^2} = 0$, we obtain $6x - 6 = 0$

$$x = 1.$$

Now determine the sign of $f''(x)$ in the intervals determined by $x = 1$.

Interval	$x < 1$	$x = 1$	$x > 1$
$f''(x)$	< 0	0	> 0
Graph of $f(x)$	concave down	point of inflection	concave up
Sketch of $f(x)$	∩	⌣	∪

Using $x = 3$, we obtain the local minimum point, $(3, -17)$.
Using $x = -1$, we obtain the local maximum point, $(-1, 15)$.
The graph can now be sketched.

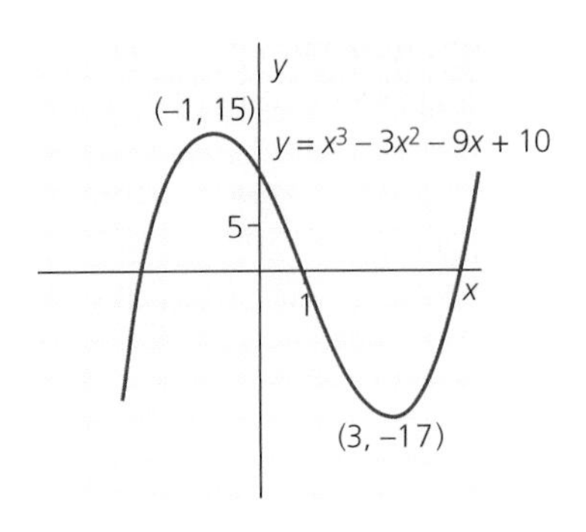

EXAMPLE 2

Sketch the graph of $f(x) = x^4$.

technology

Solution

The first and second derivatives of $f(x)$ are $f'(x) = 4x^3$ and $f''(x) = 12x^2$.
Setting $f''(x) = 0$, we obtain $12x^2 = 0$

$$x = 0.$$

But $x = 0$ is also obtained from $f'(x) = 0$.
Now determine the sign of $f''(x)$ in the intervals determined by $x = 0$.

Interval	$x < 0$	$x = 0$	$x > 0$
$f''(x)$	> 0	$= 0$	> 0
Graph of $f(x)$	concave up	?	concave up
Sketch of $f(x)$	∪		∪

We conclude that the point (0, 0) is *not* an inflection point because $f''(x)$ does not change sign at $x = 0$.

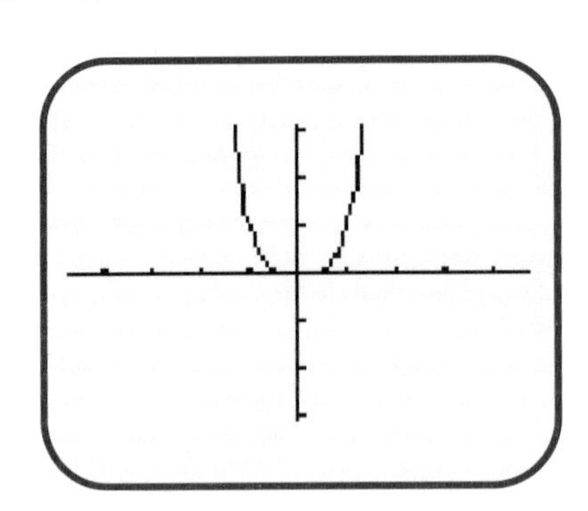

EXAMPLE 3

Sketch the graph of the function $f(x) = x^{\frac{1}{3}}$.

technology

Solution

The derivative of $f(x)$ is

$$f'(x) = \frac{1}{3}x^{-\frac{2}{3}}$$
$$= \frac{1}{3x^{\frac{2}{3}}}.$$

Note that $f'(0)$ does not exist, so that $x = 0$ is a critical value of $f(x)$. It is important to determine the behaviour of $f'(x)$ as $x \to 0$. Since $f'(x) > 0$ for all $x \neq 0$ and the denominator of $f'(x)$ is zero when $x = 0$, we have

$$\lim_{x \to 0} f'(x) = +\infty.$$

This means that there is a *vertical tangent* at $x = 0$. In addition, $f(x)$ is increasing for $x < 0$ and $x > 0$.

The second derivative of $f(x)$ is

$$f''(x) = -\frac{2}{9}x^{-\frac{5}{3}}.$$

Since $x^{\frac{5}{3}} > 0$ if $x > 0$ and $x^{\frac{5}{3}} < 0$ for $x < 0$, we obtain the following table:

Interval	$x < 0$	$x = 0$	$x > 0$
$f''(x)$	+	does not exist	−
$f(x)$	∪	∫	∩

The graph has a point of inflection when $x = 0$, even though $f'(0)$ and $f''(0)$ do not exist. Note that the curve crosses its tangent at $x = 0$.

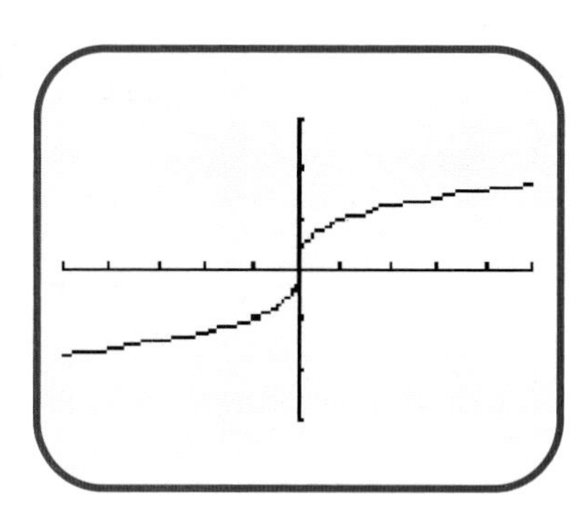

EXAMPLE 4

Determine any points of inflection in the graph of $f(x) = \frac{1}{x^2 + 3}$.

Solution

The derivative of $f(x) = \frac{1}{x^2 + 3} = (x^2 + 3)^{-1}$ is

$$f'(x) = -2x(x^2 + 3)^{-2}.$$

The second derivative is

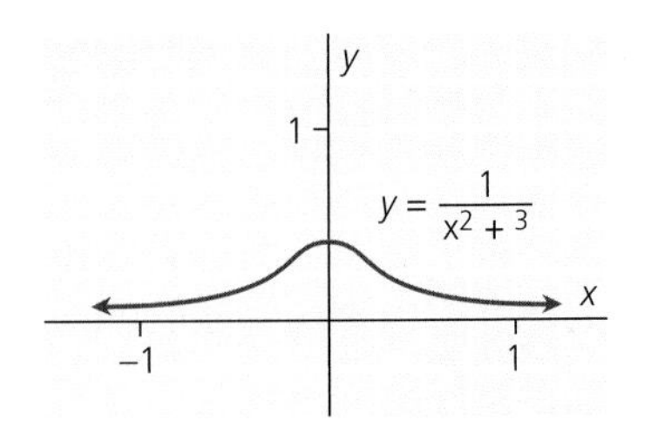

$$\begin{aligned} f''(x) &= -2(x^2+3)^{-2} + 4x(x^2+3)^{-3}(2x) \\ &= \frac{-2}{(x^2+3)^2} + \frac{8x^2}{(x^2+3)^3} \\ &= \frac{-2(x^2+3) + 8x^2}{(x^2+3)^3} \\ &= \frac{6x^2-6}{(x^2+3)^3}. \end{aligned}$$

Setting $f''(x) = 0$ gives $6x^2 - 6 = 0$

$$x = \pm 1.$$

Determine the sign of $f''(x)$ in the intervals determined by $x = -1$ and $x = 1$.

Interval	$x < -1$	$x = -1$	$-1 < x < 1$	$x = 1$	$x > 1$
$f''(x)$	> 0	$= 0$	< 0	$= 0$	> 0
Graph of $f(x)$	concave up	point of inflection	concave down	point of inflection	concave up

Therefore, $\left(-1, \frac{1}{4}\right)$ and $\left(1, \frac{1}{4}\right)$ are points of inflection in the graph of $f(x)$.

EXAMPLE 5 Determine any points of inflection in the graph of $f(x) = xe^x$.

Solution

The derivative of $f(x) = xe^x$ is

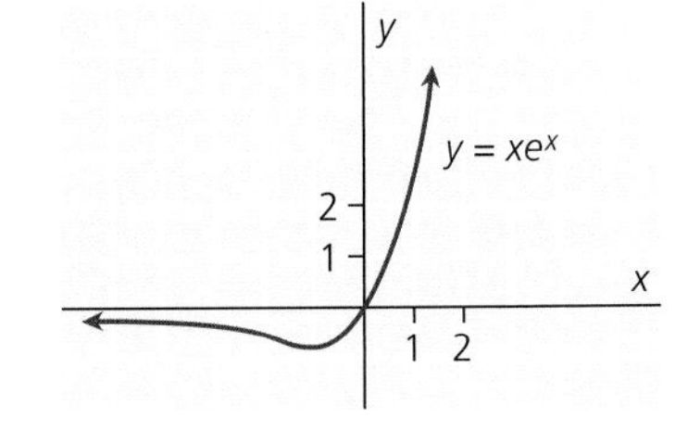

$$f'(x) = e^x + xe^x.$$

The second derivative is

$$\begin{aligned} f''(x) &= e^x + e^x + xe^x \\ &= e^x(2 + x). \end{aligned}$$

Setting $f''(x) = 0$ gives $e^x(2 + x) = 0$

$$x + 2 = 0 \quad (\text{since } e^x \neq 0 \text{ for any } x)$$

$$x = -2.$$

Determine the sign of $f''(x)$ in intervals determined by $x = -2$.

Interval	$x < -2$	$x = -2$	$x > -2$
$f''(x)$	< 0	$= 0$	> 0
Graph of $f(x)$	concave down	point of inflection	concave up

Therefore, $\left(-2, -\frac{2}{e^2}\right)$ is a point of inflection in the graph of $f(x)$.

Exercise 9.4

Part A

Knowledge/ Understanding

1. For each of the following functions, state whether the value of the second derivative is positive or negative at each of points A, B, C, and D.

a.

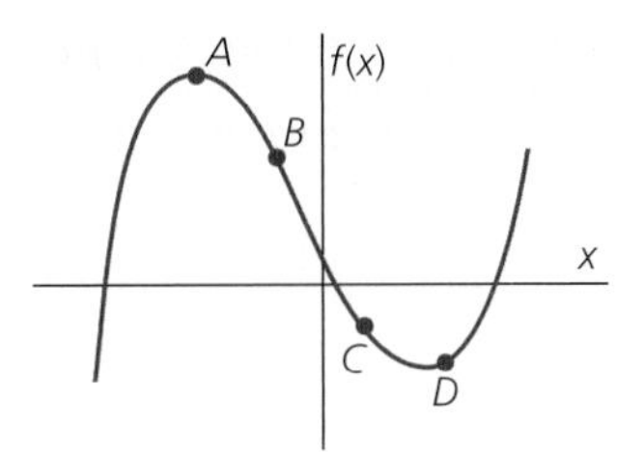

b.

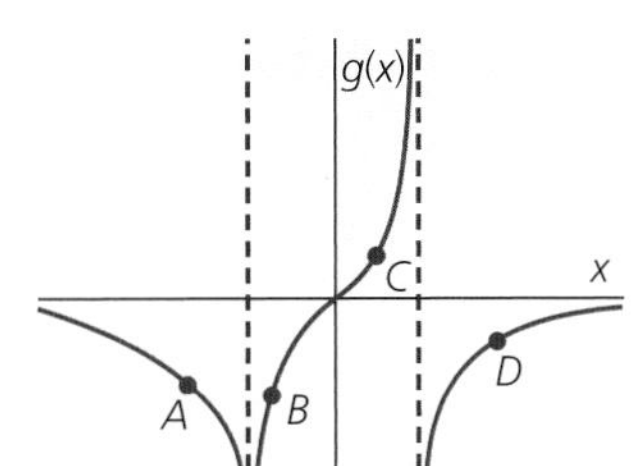

c.

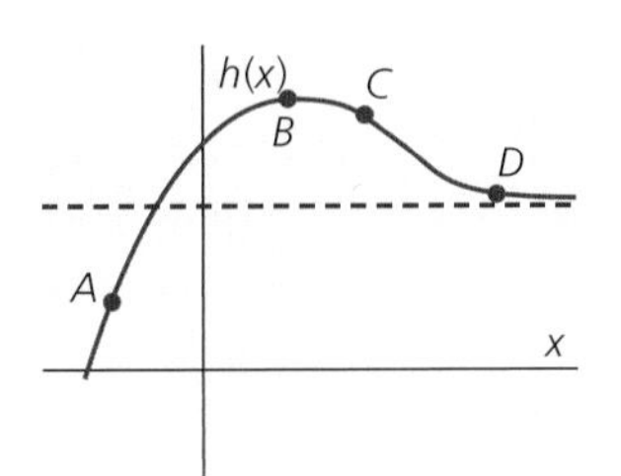

d.

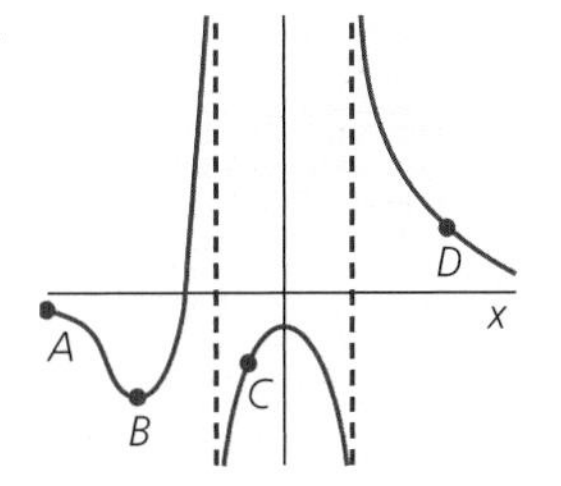

2. Find the critical points for each of the following, and use a second derivative test to decide if the point is a local maximum, a local minimum, or neither.

a. $y = x^3 - 6x^2 - 15x + 10$

b. $y = \dfrac{25}{x^2 + 48}$

c. $s = t + t^{-1}$

d. $y = (x - 3)^3 + 8$

3. For Question 2, determine the points of inflection for each of the given functions. In each case, conduct a test to determine the change of sign in the second derivative.

4. Find the value of the second derivative at the value indicated. Determine whether the curve lies above or below the tangent at this point.

a. $f(x) = 2x^3 - 10x + 3$ at $x = 2$

b. $g(x) = x^2 - \dfrac{1}{x}$ at $x = -1$

c. $s = e^t \ln t$ at $t = 1$

d. $p = \dfrac{w}{\sqrt{w^2 + 1}}$ at $w = 3$

Part B

5. Each of the following graphs represents the second derivative, $f''(x)$, of a function $f(x)$.

i) 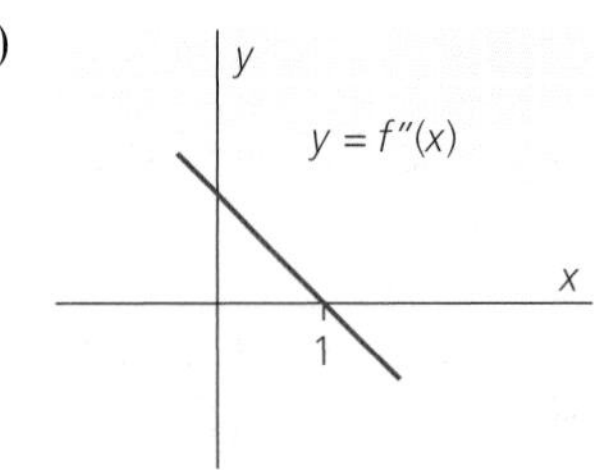

ii) 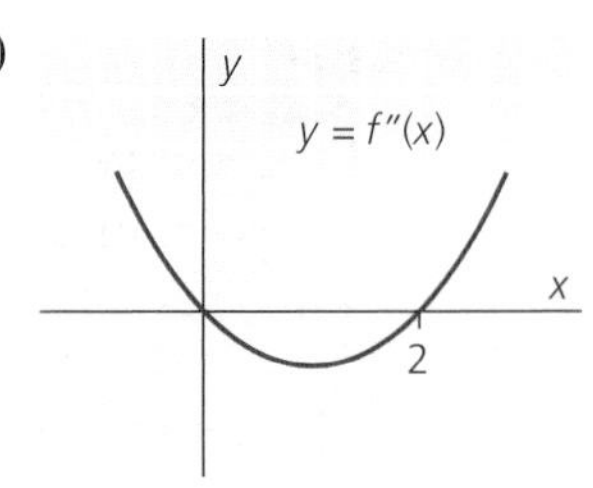

$f''(x)$ is a linear function $\qquad$ $f''(x)$ is a quadratic function

a. On which intervals is the graph of $f(x)$ concave up, and on which is the graph concave down?

b. List the x-coordinates of all points of inflection.

c. Make a rough sketch of a possible graph of $f(x)$, assuming that $f(0) = 2$.

Communication

6. Describe how you would use the second derivative to determine the local minimum or maximum.

7. In the algorithm for curve sketching on page 360, reword Step 4 to include the use of the second derivative to test for local minimum or maximum values.

8. For each of the following functions,

   i) determine any points of inflection, and

   ii) use the results of part **i** along with the revised algorithm to sketch each function.

   a. $f(x) = x^4 + 4x^3$ $\qquad$ b. $y = x - \ln x$

   c. $y = e^x + e^{-x}$ $\qquad$ d. $g(w) = \dfrac{4w^2 - 3}{w^3}$

9. Sketch the graph of a function with the following properties:

   - $f'(x) > 0$ when $x < 2$ and when $2 < x < 5$
   - $f'(x) < 0$ when $x > 5$
   - $f'(2) = 0$ and $f'(5) = 0$
   - $f''(x) < 0$ when $x < 2$ and when $4 < x < 7$
   - $f''(x) > 0$ when $2 < x < 4$ and when $x > 7$
   - $f(0) = -4$

10. Find constants a, b, and c so that the function $f(x) = ax^3 + bx^2 + c$ will have a relative extremum at $(2, 11)$ and a point of inflection at $(1, 5)$. Sketch the graph of $y = f(x)$.

Part C

11. Find the value of the constant b so that the function $f(x) = \sqrt{x + 1} + \frac{b}{x}$ has a point of inflection at $x = 3$.

Thinking/Inquiry/ Problem Solving

12. Show that the graph of $f(x) = ax^4 + bx^3$ has two points of inflection. Show that the x-coordinate of one of these points lies midway between the x-intercepts.

13. a. Use the algorithm for curve sketching to sketch the function $y = \frac{x^3 - 2x^2 + 4x}{x^2 - 4}$.

    b. Explain why it is difficult to determine the oblique asymptote using a graphing calculator.

Section 9.5 — An Algorithm for Graph Sketching

You now have the necessary skills to sketch the graphs of most elementary functions. However, you might be wondering why you should spend time developing techniques for sketching graphs when you have a graphing calculator. The answer is that, in doing so, you develop an understanding of the qualitative features of the functions you are analyzing. In this section, you will combine the skills you have developed. Some of them use the calculus properties. Others were learned earlier. Putting them all together allows you to develop an approach that leads to simple, yet accurate, sketches of the graphs of functions.

The algorithm for curve sketching now reads:

An Algorithm for Sketching the Graph of $y = f(x)$

Note: As each piece of information is obtained, make use of it in building the sketch.

Step 1: Determine any discontinuities or limitations in the domain. For discontinuities, investigate function values on either side of the discontinuity.

Step 2: Determine any vertical asymptotes.

Step 3: Determine any intercepts.

Step 4: Determine any critical points using $\frac{dy}{dx} = 0$.

Step 5: Test critical points to see whether they are local maxima, local minima, or neither.

Step 6: Determine the behaviour of the function for large positive and large negative values of x. This will identify horizontal asymptotes if they exist.

Step 7: Test for points of inflection.

Step 8: Determine any oblique asymptotes.

Step 9: Complete the sketch.

In using this algorithm, keep two things in mind:

1. You will not use all steps in every situation. Use only those that are essential.
2. You are familiar with the basic shapes of many functions. Use this knowledge when possible.

INVESTIGATION

Use the algorithm for curve sketching to sketch the graphs of $y = -3x^3 - 2x^2 + 5x$ and $y = x^4 - 3x^2 + 2x$.

EXAMPLE 1 Sketch the graph of $f(x) = \dfrac{x-4}{x^2-x-2}$.

Solution

The function is not defined if $x^2 - x - 2 = 0$.

$$\text{or } (x-2)(x+1) = 0$$
$$\text{or } x = 2 \text{ or } x = -1.$$

There are vertical asymptotes at $x = 2$ and $x = -1$.

Using $f(x) = \dfrac{x-4}{(x-2)(x+1)}$, we examine function values near the asymptotes.

$$\lim_{x\to -1^-} f(x) = -\infty \qquad \lim_{x\to -1^+} f(x) = +\infty$$
$$\lim_{x\to 2^-} f(x) = +\infty \qquad \lim_{x\to 2^+} f(x) = -\infty$$

The x-intercept is 4 and the y-intercept is 2.

Sketch the information you have to this point, as shown.
Now determine the critical points.

$$f'(x) = \frac{(1)(x^2-x-2)-(x-4)(2x-1)}{(x^2-x-2)^2}$$
$$= \frac{-x^2+8x-6}{(x^2-x-2)^2}$$

$$f'(x) = 0 \quad \text{if} \quad -x^2+8x-6 = 0$$
$$x = \frac{8 \pm 2\sqrt{10}}{2}$$
$$= 4 \pm \sqrt{10}$$

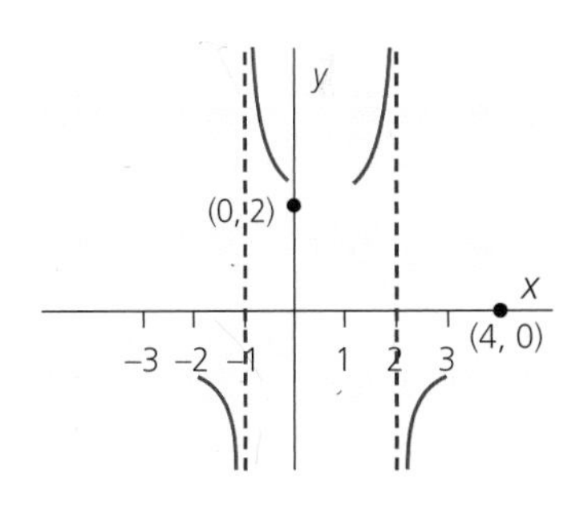

Since we are sketching, approximate values 7.2 and 0.8 are acceptable. These values give the points (7.2, 0.1) and (0.8, 1.5).

From the information we already have, we can see that (7.2, 0.1) is probably a local maximum and (0.8, 1.5) is probably a local minimum. Using the second derivative test to verify this is a difficult computational task. Instead, we can verify using the first derivative test, as in the following chart:

x	0	0.8	1	7	7.2	8
$f'(x)$	< 0	0	> 1	> 0	0	< 0

$x = 0.8$ gives the local minimum. $x = 7.2$ gives the local maximum.

Now check for large values of x.

$$\lim_{x\to\infty} \frac{x-4}{x^2-x-2} = 0, \text{ but } y > 0 \text{ always;}$$
$$\lim_{x\to -\infty} \frac{x-4}{x^2-x-2} = 0, \text{ but } y < 0 \text{ always.}$$

Therefore, $y = 0$ is a horizontal asymptote. The curve approaches $y = 0$ from above on the right and below on the left.

There is a point of inflection beyond $x = 7.2$ since the curve opens down at that point but changes as x becomes very large. The amount of work necessary to determine the point is greater than the information we gain, so we leave it undone here. (If you wish to check it, it occurs for $x \cong 10.4$). The finished sketch is given below, and because it is a sketch, it is not to scale.

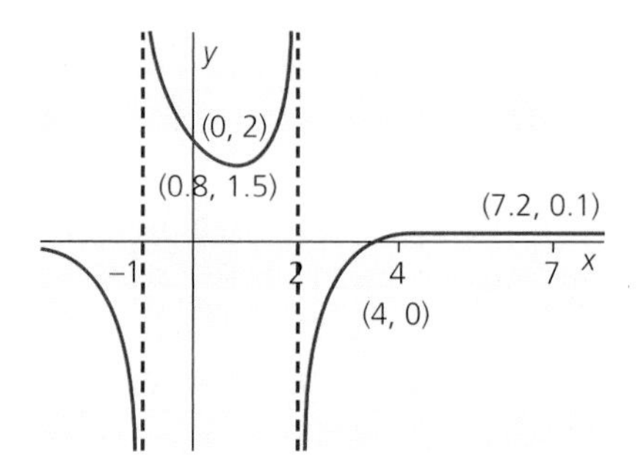

EXAMPLE 2 Sketch the graph of $y = \frac{x^2 - 2}{x}$, showing all asymptotes of the curve.

Solution

Since y is undefined for $x = 0$, there is a vertical asymptote at $x = 0$.

Checking values near $x = 0$, we rewrite the function as $y = x - \frac{2}{x}$.

$$\lim_{x \to 0^-} \left(x - \frac{2}{x}\right) = +\infty \qquad \lim_{x \to 0^+} \left(x - \frac{2}{x}\right) = -\infty$$

If $y = 0$, $x^2 - 2 = 0$ and $x = \pm\sqrt{2}$, so the x-intercepts are $\sqrt{2}$ and $-\sqrt{2}$. There is no y-intercept.

Now determine the critical points.

$$\frac{dy}{dx} = 1 + \frac{2}{x^2} = \frac{x^2 + 2}{x^2}$$

$$\frac{dy}{dx} = 0 \quad \text{if} \quad x^2 + 2 = 0.$$

There are no real solutions of x, and therefore no critical values.

For large values of x, we examine $y = x - \frac{2}{x}$.

$$\lim_{x \to \infty} \frac{2}{x} = 0 \quad \text{but} \quad \frac{2}{x} > 0.$$

Hence $y = x - \frac{2}{x}$ approaches $y = x$ but is below the line.

$$\lim_{x \to -\infty} \frac{2}{x} = 0 \quad \text{but} \quad \frac{2}{x} < 0.$$

Hence $y = x - \frac{2}{x}$ approaches $y = x$ but is above the line.

Therefore, $y = x$ is an oblique asymptote.

The sketch can now be completed as shown.

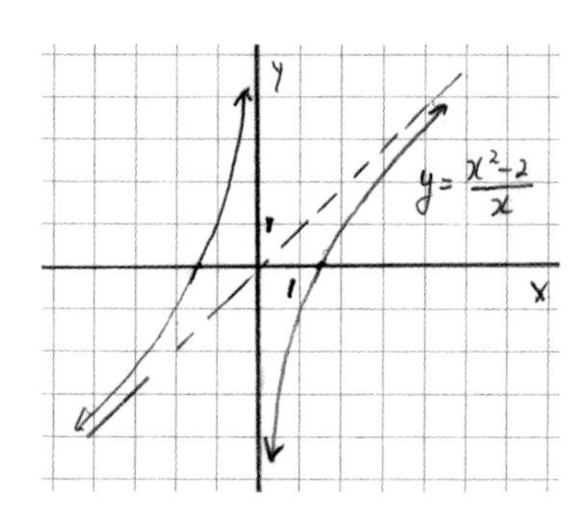

Exercise 9.5

Part B

Knowledge/ Understanding

1. Use the algorithm for curve sketching to sketch the following:

a. $y = x^3 - 9x^2 + 15x + 30$

b. $f(x) = -4x^3 + 18x^2 + 3$

c. $y = 3 + \frac{1}{(x+2)^2}$

d. $f(x) = x^4 - 4x^3 - 8x^2 + 48x$

e. $y = \frac{2x}{x^2 - 25}$

f. $y = \frac{1}{\sqrt{2\pi}}e^{-\frac{x^2}{2}}$

g. $y = \frac{6x^2 - 2}{x^3}$

h. $s = \frac{50}{1 + 5e^{-0.01t}}, t \geq 0$

i. $y = \frac{x+3}{x^2 - 4}$

j. $y = \frac{x^2 - 3x + 6}{x - 1}$

k. $c = te^{-t} + 5$

l. $y = x(\ln x)^3$

Application

2. Determine the constants a, b, c, and d so that the curve defined by $y = ax^3 + bx^2 + cx + d$ has a local maximum at the point (2, 4) and a point of inflection at the origin. Sketch the curve.

3. Sketch the function defined by $g(x) = \frac{8e^x}{e^{2x} + 4}$.

4. Sketch the graph of $y = e^x + \frac{1}{x}$.

Part C

5. Sketch the graph of $f(x) = \frac{k - x}{k^2 + x^2}$, where k is any positive constant.

6. Sketch the curve defined by $g(x) = x^{\frac{1}{3}}(x + 3)^{\frac{2}{3}}$.

7. Find the horizontal asymptotes for each of the following:

a. $f(x) = \frac{x}{\sqrt{x^2 + 1}}$

b. $g(t) = \sqrt{t^2 + 4t} - \sqrt{t^2 + t}$

Thinking/Inquiry/ Problem Solving

8. Show that for any cubic function of the form $y = ax^3 + bx^2 + cx + d$, there is a single point of inflection where the slope of the curve at that point is $c - \frac{b^2}{3a}$.

Key Concepts Review

In this chapter, you saw that calculus can aid in sketching graphs. Remember that things learned in earlier studies are useful and that calculus techniques help in sketching. Basic shapes should always be kept in mind. Use these together with the algorithm for curve sketching, and always use accumulated knowledge.

Basic Shapes to Remember

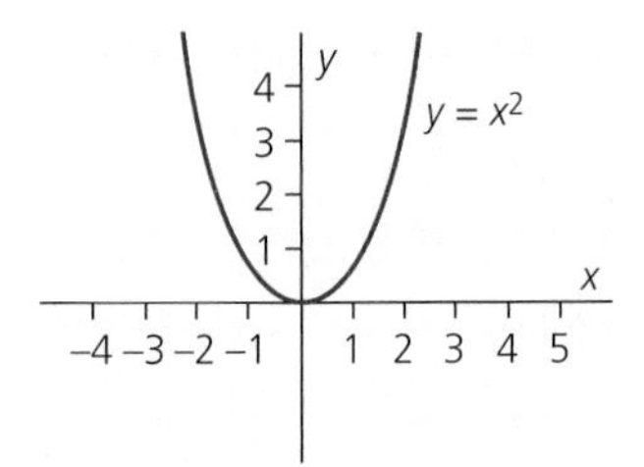

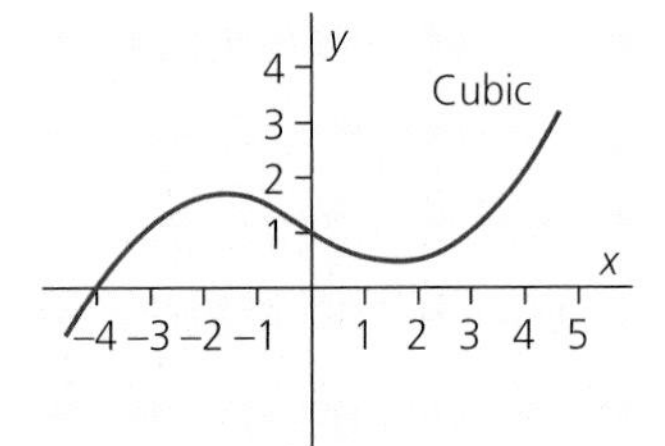

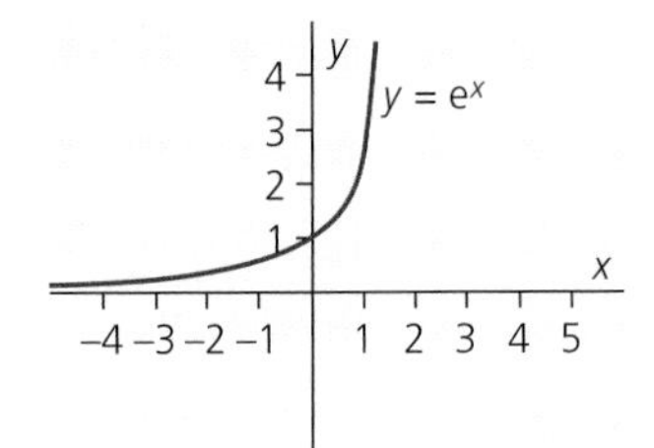

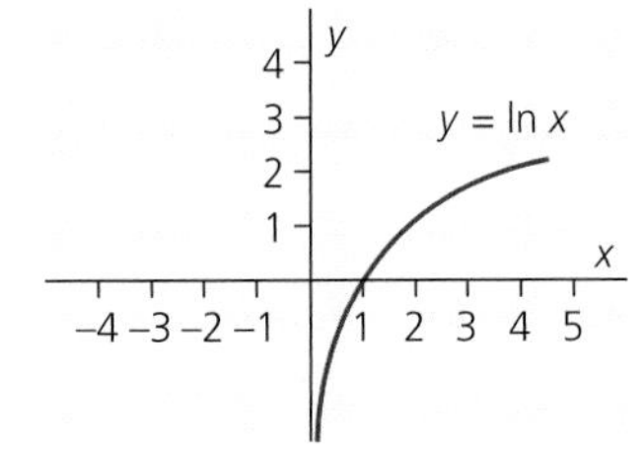

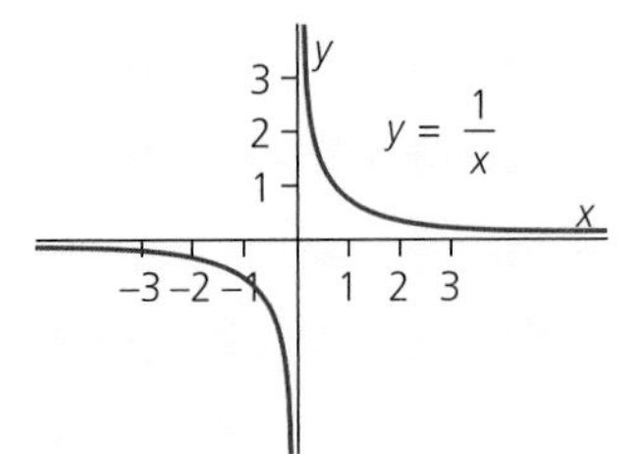

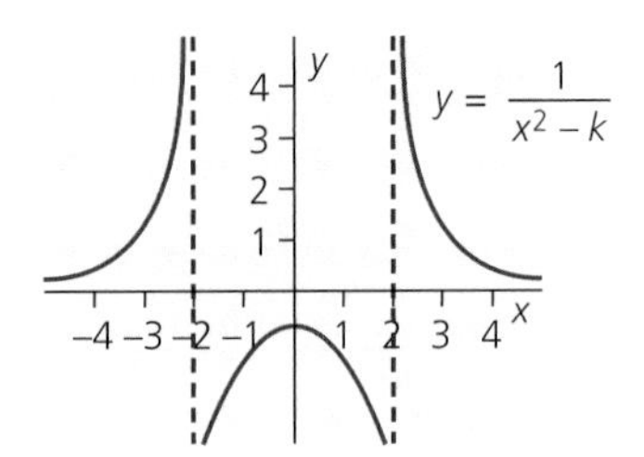

Career Link wrap-up investigate and apply

CHAPTER 9: PREDICTING STOCK VALUES

In the Career Link earlier in the chapter, you investigated a graphical model used to predict stock values for a new stock. A brand new stock is also called an Initial Public Offering, or IPO. Remember that in this model, the period immediately after the stock is issued offers excess returns on the stock (i.e., the stock is selling for more than it is really worth). One such model for a class of Internet IPOs predicts the percentage overvaluation of a stock as a function of time, as

$$R(t) = 250\frac{t^2}{e^{3t}},$$

where $R(t)$ is the overvaluation in percent and t is the time in months after issue.

Use the information provided by the first derivative, second derivative, and asymptotes to prepare advice for clients as to when they should expect a signal to prepare to buy or sell (inflection point), the exact time when they should buy or sell (max/min), and any false signals prior to an asymptote. Explain your reasoning. Make a sketch of the function without using a graphing calculator.

Review Exercise

1. Determine the derivative and the second derivative for each of the following:

   a. $y = e^{nx}$
   b. $f(x) = \ln(x + 4)^{\frac{1}{2}}$
   c. $s = \dfrac{e^t - 1}{e^t + 1}$
   d. $g(t) = \ln(t + \sqrt{1 + t^2})$

2. For each of the following graphs, state:

   i) the intervals where the function is increasing,
   ii) the intervals where the function is decreasing,
   iii) the points where the tangent to the function is horizontal.

   a.

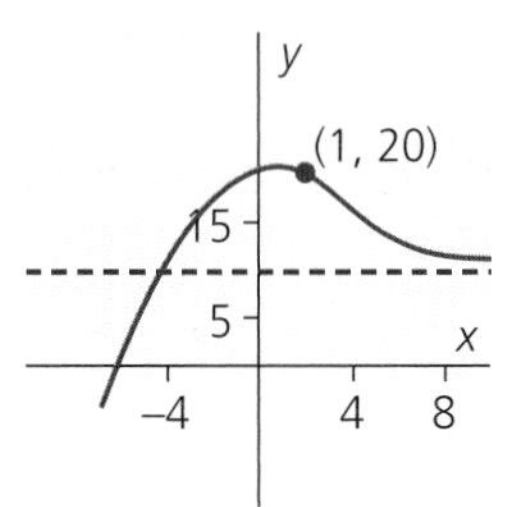

   b.

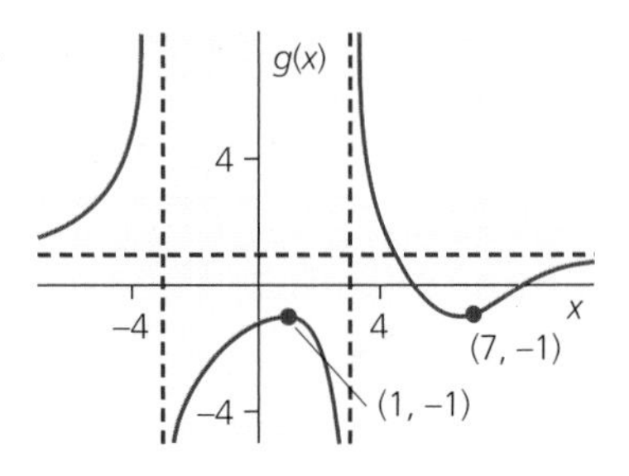

3. Is it always true that an increasing function is concave up in shape? Explain.

4. Find the critical points for each of the following. Determine whether the critical point is a local maximum or local minimum and whether or not the tangent is parallel to the horizontal axis.

   a. $f(x) = -2x^3 + 9x^2 + 20$
   b. $g(t) = \dfrac{e^{-2t}}{t^2}$
   c. $h(x) = \dfrac{x - 3}{x^2 + 7}$
   d. $k(x) = \ln(x^3 - 3x^2 - 9x)$

5. The graph for the function $y = f(x)$ has relative extrema at points A, C, and E and points of inflection at B and D. If a, b, c, d, and e are the x-coordinates for the points, then state the intervals in which each of the following conditions are true:

   a. $f'(x) > 0$ and $f''(x) > 0$
   b. $f'(x) > 0$ and $f''(x) < 0$
   c. $f'(x) < 0$ and $f''(x) > 0$
   d. $f'(x) < 0$ and $f''(x) < 0$

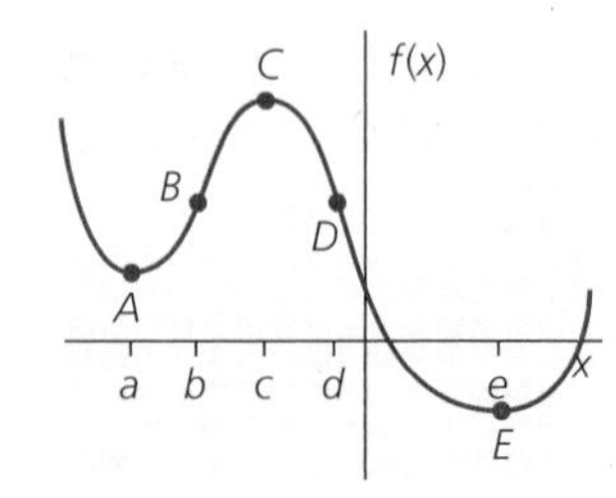

6. For each of the following, check for discontinuities and state the equation of any vertical asymptotes. Conduct a limit test to determine the behaviour of the curve on either side of the asymptote.

a. $y = \frac{2x}{x - 3}$

b. $g(x) = \frac{x - 5}{x + 5}$

c. $s = \frac{5}{2e^x - 8}$

d. $f(x) = \frac{x^2 - 2x - 15}{x + 3}$

7. Determine the points of inflection for each of the following:

a. $f(w) = \frac{\ln w^2}{w}$

b. $g(t) = te^t$

8. Sketch a graph of a function that is differentiable on the interval $-3 \leq x \leq 5$ and satisfies the following conditions:

- local maxima at $(-2, 10)$ and $(3, 4)$,
- the function f is decreasing on the intervals $-2 < x < 1$ and $3 \leq x \leq 5$,
- the derivative $f'(x)$ is positive for $-3 \leq x < -2$ and for $1 < x < 3$,
- $f(1) = -6$.

9. Each of the graphs below represents the second derivative $g''(x)$ of a function $g(x)$.

i)

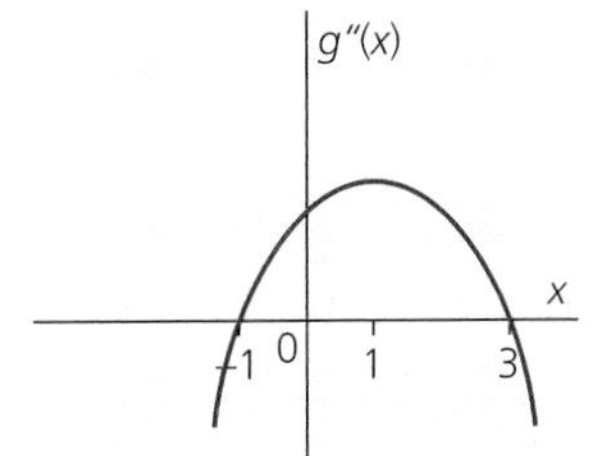

$g''(x)$ is a quadratic function

ii)

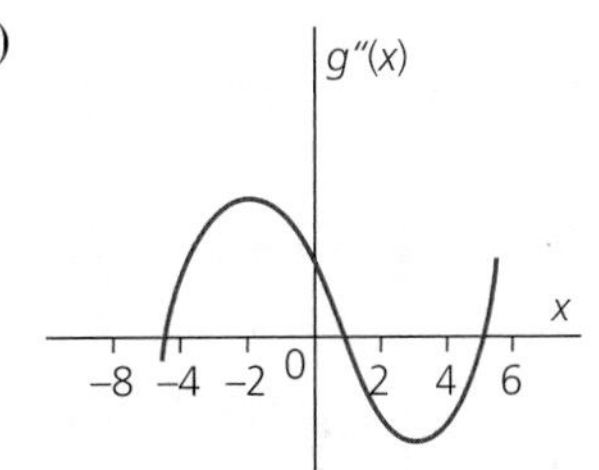

$g''(x)$ is a cubic function

a. On what intervals is the graph of $g(x)$ concave up and on what intervals is the graph concave down?

b. List the x-coordinates of the points of inflection.

c. Make a rough sketch of a possible graph for $g(x)$, assuming that $g(0) = -3$.

10. a. If the graph of the function $g(x) = \frac{ax + b}{(x - 1)(x - 4)}$ has a horizontal tangent at point $(2, -1)$, then determine the values of a and b.

b. Sketch the function g.

11. Find the equation of the oblique asymptote in the form $y = mx + b$ for each of the following, and then show that $\lim_{x \to +\infty} [y - f(x)] = 0$ for each of the functions given.

a. $f(x) = \frac{2x^2 - 7x + 5}{2x - 1}$

b. $f(x) = \frac{4x^3 - x^2 - 15x - 50}{x^2 - 3x}$

12. Sketch the following using suitable techniques.

a. $y = x^4 - 8x^2 + 7$

b. $f(x) = \frac{3x - 1}{x + 1}$

c. $g(x) = \frac{x^2 + 1}{4x^2 - 9}$

d. $y = 3x^2 \ln x$

e. $h(x) = \frac{x}{x^2 - 4x + 4}$

f. $f(t) = \frac{t^2 - 3t + 2}{t - 3}$

g. $s = te^{-3t} + 10$

h. $P = \frac{100}{1 + 50e^{-0.2t}}$

13. The population, P, of a laboratory colony of bacteria is given by the formula $P = 10^4 te^{-0.2t} + 100$ where t is the time in days since the creation of the colony.

a. Find the maximum number of bacteria the colony will sustain and when this maximum is reached.

b. Find the time when the rate of change of the growth rate of the colony starts to increase.

c. Sketch the curve for the first 15 days.

14. Prove the second derivative of the function $y = \ln\left[\frac{x^2 + 1}{x^2 - 1}\right]$ is positive for all real values of x except $|x| \leq 1$.

15. a. Find the conditions on parameter k so that the function $f(x) = \frac{2x + 4}{x^2 - k^2}$ will have critical points.

b. Select a value for k that satisfies the constraint established in part **a** and sketch the section of the curve that lies in the domain $|x| \leq k$.

Chapter 9 Test

Achievement Category	Questions
Knowledge/Understanding	1, 2, 4, 8, 10
Thinking/Inquiry/Problem Solving	2, 3, 5, 7, 8, 10
Communication	1, 9
Application	3, 6, 9

1. A function $y = f(x)$ is defined in the following graph.
   a. State the intervals where the function is increasing.
   b. State the intervals where $f'(x) < 0$.
   c. Write the coordinates for the critical points.
   d. Write the equations for any vertical asymptotes.
   e. What is the value of $f''(x)$ on the interval $-3 < x < 3$?
   f. If $x \geq -6$, state the intervals where $f'(x) < 0$ and $f''(x) > 0$.
   g. Identify a point of inflection and state the approximate ordered pair for the point.

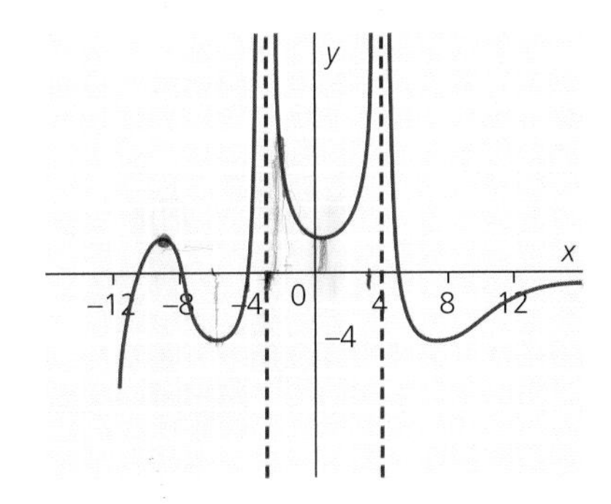

2. a. Find the critical points for the function $g(x) = 2x^4 - 8x^3 - x^2 + 6x$.
   b. Determine the type of each critical point in part **a.**

3. Sketch the graph of a function with the following properties:
   - There are relative extrema at $(-1, 7)$ and $(3, 2)$.
   - There is a point of inflection at $(1, 4)$.

- The graph is concave down only when $x < 1$.
- The x-intercept is -4 and the y-intercept is 6.

4. Check the function $g(x) = \frac{x^2 + 7x + 10}{(x - 3)(x + 2)}$ for discontinuities. Conduct appropriate tests to determine if asymptotes exist at the discontinuity values. State the equations of any asymptotes.

5. Find the critical points for the function $g(x) = e^{2x}(x^2 - 2)$, and determine the type of critical point by using an appropriate test.

6. Use at least five curve-sketching techniques to explain how to sketch the graph of the function $f(x) = \frac{2x + 10}{x^2 - 9}$. Sketch the graph on squared paper.

7. The function $y = kx^2 + \ln(kx)$ has $\frac{d^2y}{dx^2} = -\frac{33}{16}$ when $x = \frac{4}{11}$. Determine the value of k.

8. The function $f(x) = x^3 + bx^2 + c$ has a critical point at $(-2, 6)$.
   a. Find the constants b and c.
   b. Sketch the graph of $f(x)$ using only the critical points and the second derivative test.

9. Use appropriate techniques to sketch the function $y = x^{\frac{2}{3}}(x - 5)$. Explain your work.

10. For the function $y = x^2 e^{kx} + p$, the slope of the tangent is zero when $x = \frac{2}{3}$ (k and p are parameters).
    a. Determine the value of k.
    b. Describe the role of p in this function.

Cumulative Review

CHAPTERS 3–9

1. Write the first four terms for the sequences defined by the given function and then find the limit for term t_n in the sequence as $n \to \infty$.

   a. $f(n) = 2 - \frac{1}{5^n}$
   b. $g(k) = \frac{1}{k(k+1)}$

2. Evaluate each of the following limits:

   a. $\lim_{x \to 1} \frac{x^2 - 4x + 3}{x^2 - 5x + 4}$
   b. $\lim_{x \to 0} \frac{x}{2x - x^2}$
   c. $\lim_{x \to 2} \frac{x^3 - 8}{x - 2}$

   d. $\lim_{x \to \infty} \frac{5 - 2x^2}{3x + 5x^2}$
   e. $\lim_{x \to \infty} \frac{2^{\frac{1}{n}} - 3^{-n}}{2^n}$
   f. $\lim_{x \to 0} \frac{\sqrt{2 + x} - \sqrt{2}}{\sqrt{2x}}$

   g. $\lim_{t \to 0} \frac{4t^2 + 3t + 2}{t^3 + 2t - 6}$
   h. $\lim_{h \to 0} \frac{\sqrt{x + h} - \sqrt{x}}{h}$
   i. $\lim_{h \to 0} \frac{x^2h + 3xh^2 + h^3}{2xh + 5h^2}$

3. If $f(x) = x^3 - 5x^2 + 10x$, find $\lim_{h \to 0} \frac{f(x + h) - f(x)}{h}$.

4. Use the method of first principles to find the derivative function of each of the following:

   a. $s = t^2 + 10t$
   b. $y = \frac{2 - x}{x^2}$

5. Use either the Product Rule or the Quotient Rule to find the derivative of each of the following:

   a. $s = (t^2 - 5t)(5t^3 - 2t + 7)$
   b. $y = \frac{x^3 - 3x}{x^2 + 2x + 5}$

   c. $v = e^w(1 + w)$
   d. $s = \frac{e^t - e^{-t}}{e^t + e^{-t}}$

   e. $y = (e^x)(\ln x)$
   f. $s = (\ln t + e^t)t$

6. Use the Chain Rule to find the derivative of each of the following:

   a. $s(t) = e^{t^2 - 5t}$
   b. $y = \ln(x^2 + x + 1)$

   c. $w = \sqrt{3x + \frac{1}{x}}$
   d. $g(t) = 3e^{(2t + \ln t)}$

   e. $p = \log_a(2r) + 3\ln(5r)$
   f. $e^{x+y} = xy$

   g. $y = (a^2 - x^2)^{-\frac{1}{2}}$
   h. $\ln(x^2y) = 2y$

7. Find the slope of the tangent to the circle defined by $x^2 + y^2 = 100$ at the point $(-6, -8)$.

8. Use the appropriate derivative rule to find the derivative of each of the following. In all cases, the values a, b, and c are constants.

a. $w = r(2^r) - r^2e^{2r}$

b. $z = w\sqrt{a + bw}$

c. $s = 3\sqrt{\dfrac{2 + 3t}{2 - 3t}}$

d. $y = e^x - 2e^{-x}$

e. Find $\dfrac{dy}{dx}$ for $b^2x^2 + a^2y^2 = a^2b^2$.

f. Find $\dfrac{dy}{dx}$ for $x^3 + 3x^2y + y^3 = c^3$.

9. Find the equation of the tangent to the curve defined by $s = te^{t^2}$ at the point where $t = \pi$.

10. Find the value of k in the equation $y = e^{kx}$ so that y is a solution of each of the following:

a. $y'' - 3y' + 2y = 0$

b. $y''' - y'' - 4y' + 4y = 0$

11. Use implicit differentiation to find the second derivative of the relation $x^2 + 6xy - y^2 = 10$.

12. Find the slope of the tangents to the curve defined by $y^2 = e^{2x} + 2y - e$ at the point where $y = 2$.

13. Find the equation of any tangent to the curve represented by $x^2 - xy + 3y^2 = 132$ that is parallel to the straight line defined by $x - y = 2$.

14. Find the equations of the straight lines through point $A(3, -2)$ that are tangent to the curve defined by $y = x^2 - 7$.

15. Find the equation of the tangent to the curve defined by $y = x + \ln x$ that is perpendicular to the line defined by $3x + 9y = 8$.

16. A parachutist jumps out of an airplane. The distance, s, (in metres), through which she falls in t seconds is given by $s(t) = 10t - \dfrac{6t}{t + 1}$. Determine

a. the distance through which she falls in the first second.

b. the velocity of the parachutist at $t = 1$ and $t = 2$.

c. the acceleration of the parachutist at $t = 1$ and $t = 2$.

d. Find the limit of the velocity as $t \to \infty$. This limit is known as the "terminal velocity."

17. As a particle travels in a linear direction, the distance s from the origin is given by $s = 8 - 7t + t^2$, where t is in seconds and s is in millimetres.

a. Find the velocity after 3 s.

b. Find the average velocity in the fourth second.

c. Find the acceleration after 3 s.

18. a. The radius of spherical soap bubble is expanding at the rate of 2 mm/s. At what rate is the surface of the soap bubble increasing when the radius is 7 mm?

b. Repeat part **a** for the situation where the rate of expansion is 1 mm/s.

19. A kite 50 m high is being blown parallel to the ground at a rate of 3 m/s. The person flying the kite is standing still. How fast is the kite string running out at the instant when exactly 100 m of string are out?

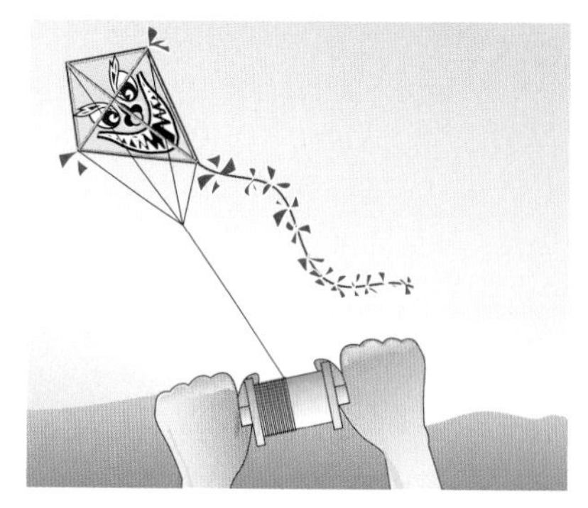

20. A conical cistern 5 m deep and 8 m across the top is being filled with water flowing in at a rate of 10 000 cm^3/min.

a. Explain the significance of the derivatives $\frac{dv}{dt}$, $\frac{dr}{dt}$, and $\frac{dh}{dt}$.

b. Use the geometry of the configuration to find a formula for the volume of the water in terms of the radius of the surface of the water, r.

c. At what rate is the water rising in the cistern when the depth is 3 m?

21. The equation of motion of a particle moving in a straight line is $s = kv^2 \ln v$, where k is a constant and v is the velocity. Find an equation that expresses the acceleration in terms of velocity.

22. A car leaves a small town at 13:00 and travels due south at a speed of 80 km/h. Another car has been heading due west at 100 km/h and reaches the same town at 15:00. At what time were the two cars closest together?

23. Find the local extreme points and the points of inflection for each of the following:

a. $y = 2x^3 + 3x^2 - 36x + 10$

b. $w = 4 - \frac{100}{z^2 + 25}$

c. $f(x) = x^2 \ln x$

d. $y = x^3 e^{-2x}$

e. $y = 5xe^{-\frac{x^2}{4}}$

f. $n = 10pe^{-p} + 2$

24. For each of the following, determine the equations of any horizontal, vertical, or oblique asymptotes and find any local extremes.

a. $y = \frac{8}{x^2 - 9}$

b. $y = \frac{4x^3}{x^2 - 1}$

25. Use the curve-sketching techniques that you think are appropriate to sketch each of the following:

a. $p = \frac{10n^2}{n^2 + 25}$

b. $y = x \ln(3x)$

c. $y = \frac{3x}{x^2 - 4}$

d. $y = 10^{-\frac{x^2}{4}}$

26. A farmer has 750 m of fencing and wants to enclose a rectangular area on all four sides, then divide it into four pens with fencing parallel to one side of the rectangle. What is the largest possible area of the four pens?

27. A metal can is made to hold 500 mL of soup. Find the dimensions of the can that will minimize the amount of metal required. (Assume that the top and sides of the can are made from metal of the same thickness.)

28. A cylindrical box of volume 4000 cm^3 is being constructed to hold Christmas candies. The cost of the base and lid is \$0.005/cm^2 and the cost of the side walls is \$0.0025/cm^2. Find the dimensions for the cheapest possible box.

29. An open rectangular box has a square base with each side x cm.

a. If the length, width, and depth have a sum of 140 cm, find the depth.

b. Find the maximum possible volume you could have when constructing a box with these proportions, and find the dimensions to make this maximum volume.

30. The price of x items of a certain type of product is $p(x) = 50 - x^2$, where $x \in N$. If the total revenue $R(x)$ is given by $R(x) = xp(x)$, find the value of x that corresponds to the maximum possible total revenue.

31. A fish biologist introduced a new species of fish into a northern lake and studied the growth of the population over a period of ten years. The mathematical model that best described the size of the fish population was $p = \frac{4000}{1 + 3e^{-0.1373t}}$, where t is in years.

a. Find the maximum population that the biologist expects in the lake.

b. Find the year when the rate of change of the growth rate started to decrease.

c. Sketch the curve for the ten-year period.

d. For how many more years must the biologist collect data to be sure the mathematical model is valid?

32. Determine values for a, b, c, and d that guarantee that the function $f(x) = ax^3 + bx^2 + cx + d$ will have a relative maximum at $(1, -7)$ and a point of inflection at $(2, -11)$.

33. Sketch a graph of a function f that has the following properties:

- $f'(x) > 0$, when $x < 2$
- $f'(x) < 0$, when $x > 2$
- $f''(x) > 0$, when $x < 2$
- $f''(x) < 0$, when $x > 2$

34. Determine the extreme values of each function on the given interval.

a. $f(x) = 1 + (x + 3)^2, -2 \leq x \leq 6$
b. $f(x) = x + \frac{1}{\sqrt{x}}, 1 \leq x \leq 9$
c. $f(x) = \frac{e^x}{1 + e^x}, 0 \leq x \leq 4$
d. $f(x) = x + \ln(x), 1 \leq x \leq 5$

35. A travel agent booking a tour currently has 80 people signed up. The price of a ticket is \$5000 per person. The agency has chartered a plane seating 150 people at a cost of \$250 000. Additional costs to the agency are incidental fees of \$300 per person. For each \$30 that the price is lowered, one new person will sign up. How much should the price per person be lowered in order to maximize the profit to the travel agent?

36. Find the equations of the tangents to the curve defined by $x^2 + xy + y^2 = 19$ at the points on the curve where $y = 2$.

37. Use the techniques of curve sketching that you think are appropriate to sketch the curve defined by $y = \frac{4}{x^2 - 4}$.

38. The Coast Guard is monitoring a giant iceberg in the approximate shape of a rectangular solid that is five times as long as the width across the front face. As the iceberg drifts south, the height above water is observed to decrease at the rate of two metres per week, and the width across the front is shrinking at three metres per week. Find the rate of loss of volume above water when the height is 60 m and the width of the face is 300 m.

39. Determine values for a, b, c, and d that guarantee that the function $f(x) = ax^3 + bx^2 + cx + d$ has a relative maximum value of 3 when $x = -2$ and a relative minimum value of 0 when $x = 1$.

40. Find the equation of the normal to each of the curves defined below, at the point specified.

a. $y = x^3 + 2x^2 + 5x + 2$, when $x = -1$

b. $y = x^{\frac{1}{2}} + x^{-\frac{1}{2}}$ at $(4, 2.5)$

Appendix A

DERIVATIVES OF TRIGONOMETRIC FUNCTIONS

So far in our study of calculus, we have worked with polynomial, rational, power, exponential, and logarithmic functions. Trigonometric functions are central in modelling oscillatory phenomena and periodic motion, such as planetary orbits, the rise and fall of tides, and the current in electrical circuits. In this appendix, we will develop the derivatives of the trigonometric functions and apply them in various problems.

Review of Basic Properties

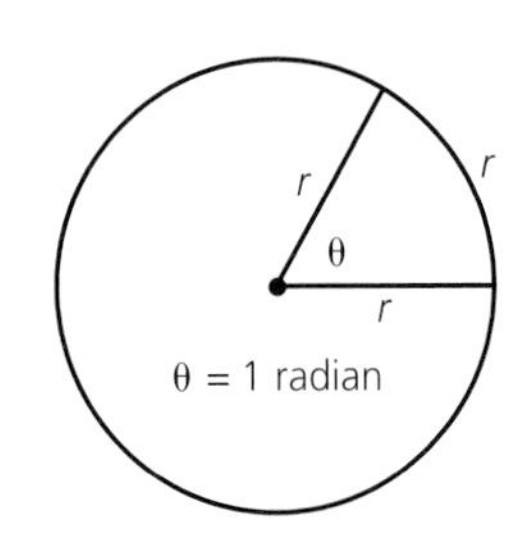

Radian Measure

A radian is the measure of an angle subtended at the centre of a circle by an arc equal in length to the radius of the circle.

π radians $= 180°$

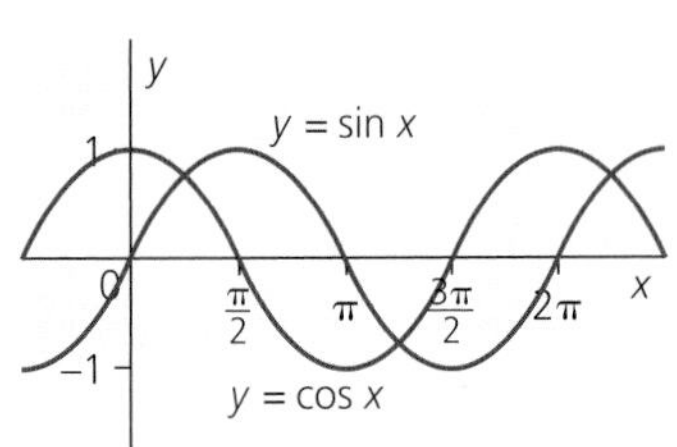

The Sine and Cosine Functions

Domain	$x \in R$
Range	$-1 \leq \sin x \leq 1$ $-1 \leq \cos x \leq 1$
Periodicity	$\sin(x + 2\pi) = \sin x$ $\cos(x + 2\pi) = \cos x$

Transformations of Sine and Cosine Functions

For $y = a \sin k(x - p) + d$ and $y = a \cos k(x - p) + d$,

the amplitude is $|a|$,

the period is $\frac{2\pi}{k}$,

the phase shift is p, and

the vertical translation is d.

Trigonometric Identities

Reciprocal Identities

$\csc \theta = \frac{1}{\sin \theta}$

$\sec \theta = \frac{1}{\cos \theta}$

$\cot \theta = \frac{1}{\tan \theta}$

Pythagorean Identities

$\sin^2 \theta + \cos^2 \theta = 1$

$\tan^2 \theta + 1 = \sec^2 \theta$

$1 + \cot^2 \theta = \csc^2 \theta$

Quotient Identities

$\tan \theta = \frac{\sin \theta}{\cos \theta}$

$\cot \theta = \frac{\cos \theta}{\sin \theta}$

Reflection Identities

$\sin(-\theta) = -\sin \theta$

$\cos(-\theta) = \cos \theta$

Exercise

1. With reference to the diagram, state the values of
   a. $\sin \theta$.
   b. $\cos \theta$.
   c. $\tan \theta$.

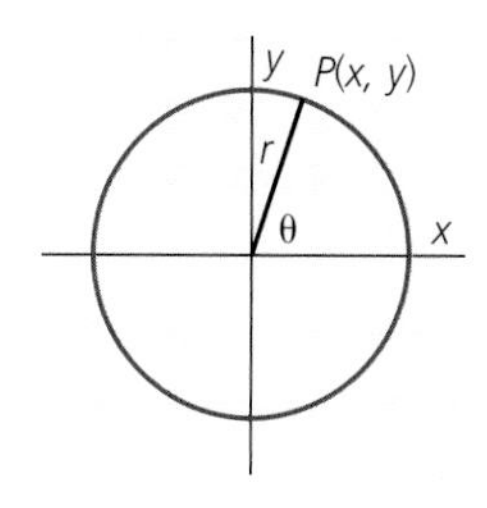

2. Convert the following angles to radian measure.

   a. 360° b. 45° c. −90° d. 30°
   e. 270° f. −120° g. 225° h. 330°

3. With reference to the diagram, state the values of
   a. $\sin \theta$.
   b. $\tan \theta$.
   c. $\cos \theta$.
   d. $\sin\left(\frac{\pi}{2} - \theta\right)$.
   e. $\cos\left(\frac{\pi}{2} - \theta\right)$.
   f. $\sin(-\theta)$.

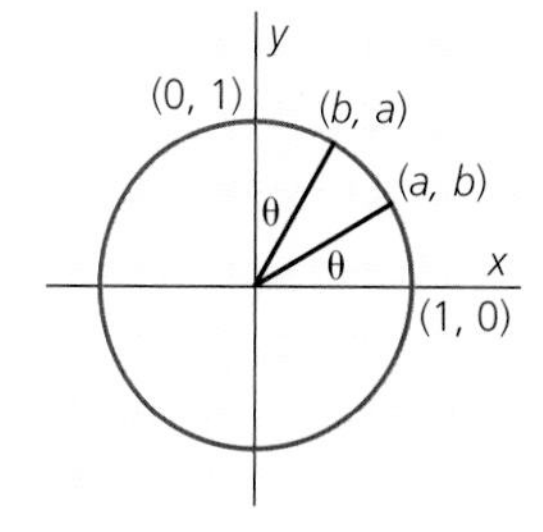

4. The value of $\sin \theta$, $\cos \theta$, or $\tan \theta$ is given. Find the values of the other two functions if θ lies in the given interval.
   a. $\sin \theta = \frac{5}{13}, \frac{\pi}{2} \leq \theta \leq \pi$
   b. $\cos \theta = -\frac{2}{3}, \pi \leq \theta \leq \frac{3\pi}{2}$
   c. $\tan \theta = -2, \frac{3\pi}{2} \leq \theta \leq 2\pi$
   d. $\sin \theta = 1, 0 \leq \theta \leq \pi$

5. State the period and amplitude for each of the following:

a. $y = \cos 2x$ b. $y = 2\sin \frac{x}{2}$ c. $y = -3\sin(\pi x) + 1$

d. $y = \frac{2}{7}\cos(12x)$ e. $y = 5\sin\left(\theta - \frac{\pi}{6}\right)$ f. $y = |3\sin x|$

6. Sketch the graph of each function over two complete periods.

a. $y = \sin 2x + 1$ b. $y = 3\cos\left(x + \frac{\pi}{2}\right)$

7. Prove the following identities:

a. $\tan x + \cot x = \sec x \csc x$ b. $\frac{\sin x}{1 - \sin^2 x} = \tan x \sec x$

c. $\sin^4 x - \cos^4 x = 1 - 2\cos^2 x$ d. $\frac{1}{1 + \sin x} = \sec^2 x - \frac{\tan x}{\cos x}$

8. Solve each of the following equations, where $0 \leq x \leq 2\pi$.

a. $6 \sin x - 3 = 1 - 2 \sin x$ b. $\cos^2 x - \cos x = 0$

c. $2 \sin x \cos x = 0$ d. $2 \sin^2 x - \sin x - 1 = 0$

e. $\sin x + \sqrt{3} \cos x = 0$ f. $2\sin^2 x - 3 \cos x = 0$

SECTION A1 — COMPOUND ANGLE IDENTITIES

Our goal is to find the derivatives of the trigonometric functions. Since none of the differentiation rules apply, we must use the definition of the derivative. For $f(x) = \sin x$,

$$f'(x) = \lim_{h \to 0} \frac{f(x+h) - f(x)}{h}$$
$$= \lim_{h \to 0} \frac{\sin(x+h) - \sin x}{h},$$

and for $f(x) = \cos x$,

$$f'(x) = \lim_{h \to 0} \frac{\cos(x+h) - \cos x}{h}.$$

In order to simplify these limits, we need to derive expansions for $\sin(x + h)$ and $\cos(x + h)$. After doing so, we will establish the derivatives in the next section.

Our intuition is of no help in finding an expansion for $\cos(A + B)$. A check with values for A and B shows that

$$\cos(A + B) \neq \cos A + \cos B.$$

For example, if $A = \frac{\pi}{4}$ and $B = \frac{\pi}{6}$, the left side is $\cos\left(\frac{5\pi}{12}\right) \doteq 0.2588$, whereas the right side is $\cos\frac{\pi}{4} + \cos\frac{\pi}{6} \doteq 0.7071 + 0.5 = 1.2071$.

Theorem $\cos(A + B) = \cos A \cos B - \sin A \sin B$

Proof

Consider a circle, with centre (0, 0) and radius 1, containing angles of measure A, $A + B$, and $-B$, as drawn. By the definition of sine and cosine, the points M, N, P, and Q have coordinates as shown in the diagram. Since $\angle MOP$ and $\angle NOQ$ have equal measure $(A + B)$ by construction, and

$OM = OP = ON = OQ = 1$,

ΔNOQ is congruent to ΔMOP.

Then $|MP| = |NQ|$.

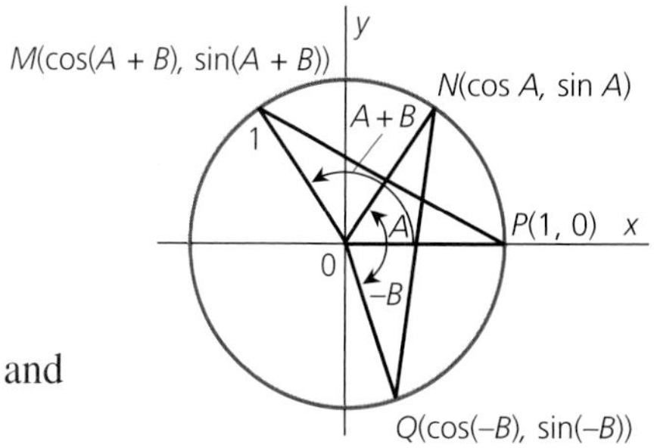

Using the distance formula,

$$\sqrt{[\cos(A+B) - 1]^2 + \sin^2(A+B)} = \sqrt{[\cos A - \cos(-B)]^2 + [\sin A - \sin(-B)]^2}.$$

On squaring both sides and expanding the brackets, we obtain

$$\cos^2(A+B) - 2\cos(A+B) + 1 + \sin^2(A+B)$$
$$= \cos^2 A - 2\cos A\cos(-B) + \cos^2(-B) + \sin^2 A - 2\sin A\sin(-B) + \sin^2(-B).$$

Since $\sin^2 x + \cos^2 x = 1$, $\cos(-x) = \cos x$, and $\sin(-x) = -\sin x$, the equation can be simplified to

$$1 - 2\cos(A+B) + 1 = 1 - 2\cos A\cos B + 1 + 2\sin A\sin B.$$

Therefore, $\cos(A+B) = \cos A\cos B - \sin A\sin B$.

Using the same method and Addition Identities, others follow easily. In the following examples, proofs are provided for some. Once you have seen how one or two are developed, you will see how others can be done.

Addition Identities

$\cos(A+B) = \cos A\cos B - \sin A\sin B$

$\cos(A-B) = \cos A\cos B + \sin A\sin B$

$\sin(A+B) = \sin A\cos B + \cos A\sin B$

$\sin(A-B) = \sin A\cos B - \cos A\sin B$

$\tan(A+B) = \dfrac{\tan A + \tan B}{1 - \tan A\tan B}$

Complementary Identities

$\cos\left(\frac{\pi}{2} - A\right) = \sin A$

$\sin\left(\frac{\pi}{2} - A\right) = \cos A$

Double-Angle Identities

$\cos 2A = \cos^2 A - \sin^2 A$

$\sin 2A = 2\sin A\cos A$

$\tan 2A = \dfrac{2\tan A}{1 - \tan^2 A}$

Example 1

Show that $\cos(A - B) = \cos A \cos B + \sin A \sin B$.

Solution

$$\cos(A - B) = \cos(A + (-B))$$
$$= \cos A \cos(-B) - \sin A \sin(-B)$$
$$= \cos A \cos B + \sin A \sin B$$

Example 2

Show that $\cos\left(\frac{\pi}{2} - A\right) = \sin A$.

Solution

$$\cos\left(\frac{\pi}{2} - A\right) = \cos\frac{\pi}{2}\cos A + \sin\frac{\pi}{2}\sin A$$
$$= 0.\cos A + 1.\sin A$$
$$= \sin A$$

Example 3

Show that $\sin(A + B) = \sin A \cos B + \cos A \sin B$.

Solution

We know that $\sin A = \cos\left(\frac{\pi}{2} - A\right)$.

Then $\sin(A + B) = \cos\left(\frac{\pi}{2} - (A + B)\right)$

$$= \cos\left(\frac{\pi}{2} - A - B\right)$$
$$= \cos\left(\left(\frac{\pi}{2} - A\right) - B\right)$$
$$= \cos\left(\frac{\pi}{2} - A\right)\cos B + \sin\left(\frac{\pi}{2} - A\right)\sin B$$
$$= \sin A \cos B + \cos A \sin B.$$

Example 4

Show that $\tan(A + B) = \frac{\tan A + \tan B}{1 - \tan A \tan B}$.

Solution

$$\text{L.S.} = \tan(A + B)$$
$$= \frac{\sin(A + B)}{\cos(A + B)}$$
$$= \frac{\sin A \cos B + \cos A \sin B}{\cos A \cos B - \sin A \sin B}$$

$$\text{R.S.} = \frac{\tan A + \tan B}{1 - \tan A \tan B}$$
$$= \frac{\frac{\sin A}{\cos A} + \frac{\sin B}{\cos B}}{1 - \frac{\sin A}{\cos A}\frac{\sin B}{\cos B}}$$
$$= \frac{\frac{\sin A \cos B + \cos A \sin B}{\cos A \cos B}}{\frac{\cos A \cos B - \sin A \sin B}{\cos A \cos B}}$$
$$= \frac{\sin A \cos B + \cos A \sin B}{\cos A \cos B - \sin A \sin B}$$
$$= \text{L.S.}$$

Therefore, L.S. = R.S., and the identity is true.

Example 5 If $\tan A = \frac{3}{2}$, where $0° < A < 90°$, and $\cos B = -\frac{3}{5}$, where $180° < B < 270°$, determine the exact value of $\sin(A + B)$ without finding the measures of $\angle A$ and $\angle B$.

Solution

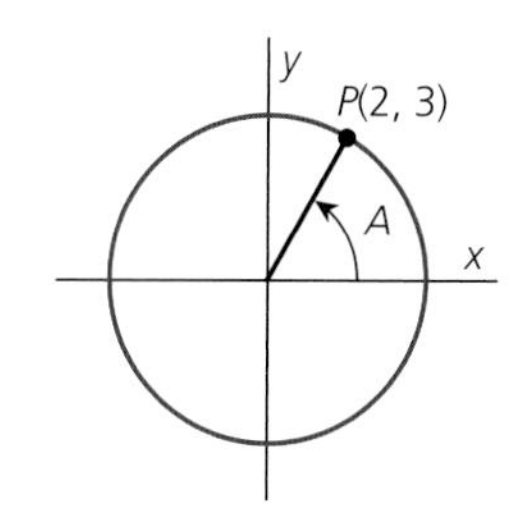

Since $\tan A = \frac{y}{x} = \frac{3}{2}$, let point P be $(2, 3)$.
Then $OP = \sqrt{4 + 9} = \sqrt{13}$.
Therefore, $\sin A = \frac{3}{\sqrt{13}}$ and $\cos A = \frac{2}{\sqrt{13}}$.
Since $\cos B = \frac{x}{r} = \frac{-3}{5}$,

$$9 + y^2 = 25$$
$$y = \pm 4.$$

Since $180° < B < 270°$, Q is $(-3, -4)$.
Then $\sin B = \frac{-4}{5}$.

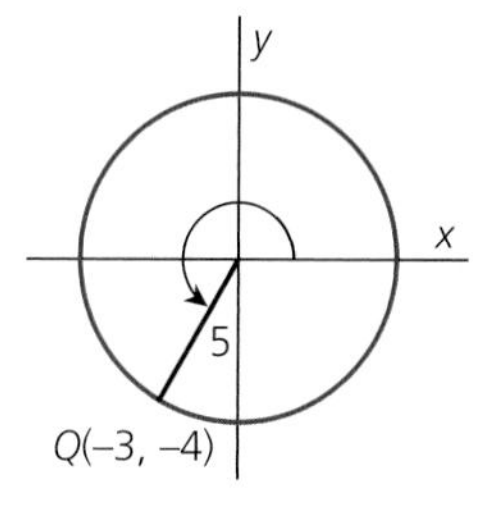

Using the addition identity, $\sin(A + B) = \sin A \cos B + \cos A \sin B$,

$$= \left(\frac{3}{\sqrt{13}}\right)\left(\frac{-3}{5}\right) + \left(\frac{2}{\sqrt{13}}\right)\left(\frac{-4}{5}\right)$$
$$= \frac{-9 - 8}{5\sqrt{13}}$$
$$= \frac{-17}{5\sqrt{13}}$$

Example 6 Prove $\tan \frac{\theta}{2} + \cot \frac{\theta}{2} = 2\csc \theta$.

Solution

Whenever half angles appear in a problem, it is a good strategy to use a substitution to remove them. In this case, let $\frac{\theta}{2} = W$ and separate the problem into two parts, as shown:

$$\text{L.S.} = \tan W + \cot W$$
$$= \frac{\sin W}{\cos W} + \frac{\cos W}{\sin W}$$
$$= \frac{\sin^2 W + \cos^2 W}{\sin W \cos W}$$
$$= \frac{1}{\sin W \cos W}$$

$$\text{R.S.} = 2\csc 2W$$
$$= \frac{2}{\sin 2W}$$
$$= \frac{2}{2\sin W \cos W}$$
$$= \frac{1}{\sin W \cos W} = \text{L.S.}$$

Since L.S. = R.S., the statement is true.

Exercise A1

Part A

1. a. Show that $\sin(90^\circ + W) = \cos W$.

   b. Prove $\cos(90^\circ + W) = -\sin W$.

2. a. Expand and simplify $\cos\left(\frac{3\pi}{2} - R\right)$.

   b. Show that $\sin(270^\circ + R) = -\cos R$.

3. If $\sin W = \frac{3}{5}$ and $\cos T = \frac{12}{13}$, where both W and T are acute angles, then

   a. find the exact value of $\sin(W + T)$.

   b. show that $\cos(W - T) < \sin(W + T)$.

Part B

4. Prove that $\sin(A - B) = \sin A \cos B - \cos A \sin B$ by replacing B by $-B$ in the expression for $\sin(A + B)$.

5. a. Prove $\cos 2A = \cos^2 A - \sin^2 A$.

   b. Prove $\cos 2A = 2\cos^2 A - 1$.

   c. Show that $\cos 2A$ can be expressed as an identity in terms of $\sin A$.

6. Show that $\sin(45^\circ + x) + \cos(45^\circ + x) = \sqrt{2}\cos x$.

7. Determine the exact value for each of the following:

   a. $\cos 75^\circ$ b. $\sin 15^\circ$ c. $\cos 105^\circ$ d. $\sin 255^\circ$

8. Express each quantity in terms of $\sin x$ and $\cos x$.

   a. $\sin\left(\frac{\pi}{3} + x\right)$ b. $\cos\left(x + \frac{3\pi}{4}\right)$ c. $\cos\left(\frac{\pi}{4} - x\right)$ d. $\sin(2\pi - x)$

9. If $\cos A = \frac{1}{3}$, with $0 < A < \frac{\pi}{2}$, and $\sin B = \frac{1}{4}$, with $\frac{\pi}{2} < B < \pi$, calculate each quantity.

   a. $\cos(A + B)$ b. $\sin(A + B)$ c. $\cos 2A$ d. $\sin 2B$

10. If $\tan A = \frac{1}{3}$ and $\pi < A < \frac{3\pi}{2}$, calculate each quantity. In what quadrant does the angle $2A$ lie?

    a. $\sin 2A$ b. $\cos 2A$

11. Prove that each of the following is an identity.

a. $\cos^4 A - \sin^4 A = \cos 2A$

b. $1 + \sin 2\alpha = (\sin \alpha + \cos \alpha)^2$

c. $\sin(A + B) \bullet \sin(A - B) = \sin^2 A - \sin^2 B$

d. $\dfrac{\cos W - \sin 2W}{\cos 2W + \sin W - 1} = \cot W$

e. $\dfrac{\sin 2\theta}{1 - \cos 2\theta} = 2\csc 2\theta - \tan\theta$

f. $\tan\dfrac{\theta}{2} = \dfrac{\sin\theta}{1 + \cos\theta}$

12. Simplify the function $f(x) = \sin 3x \csc x - \cos 3x \sec x$.

13. Prove that each of the following is an identity.

a. $\dfrac{1 + \sin \theta - \cos \theta}{1 + \sin \theta + \cos \theta} = \tan\dfrac{\theta}{2}$

b. $\dfrac{\cos 2W}{1 + \sin 2W} = \dfrac{\cot W - 1}{\cot W + 1}$

c. $\sin 3\theta = 3\sin\theta - 4\sin^3\theta$

d. $\cos 3\theta = 4\cos^3\theta - 3\cos\theta$

Part C

14. For $0 \le \beta \le 2\pi$, determine all solutions of $\sin \beta + \cos \beta = \sin \beta \cos \beta$.

15. In any acute-angled ΔABC, prove that $b^2 \sin 2C + c^2 \sin 2B = 2bc \sin A$.

16. a. Use the identity $\tan Q = \dfrac{\sin Q}{\cos Q}$ to help prove the identity

$\tan(A - B) = \dfrac{\tan A - \tan B}{1 + \tan A \tan B}$.

b. Prove that $\dfrac{1 + \tan \frac{\theta}{2}}{1 - \tan \frac{\theta}{2}} = \sec \theta + \tan \theta$.

c. Find an identity for $\tan (2A)$.

17. Use the identities for $\sin(A + B)$ and $\sin(A - B)$ to help prove each of the following:

a. $\sin x + \sin y = 2\sin\left(\dfrac{x + y}{2}\right)\cos\left(\dfrac{x - y}{2}\right)$

b. $\sin x - \sin y = 2\cos\left(\dfrac{x + y}{2}\right)\sin\left(\dfrac{x - y}{2}\right)$

18. In any ΔABC, prove that $\dfrac{a - b}{b} = \dfrac{2\sin\left(\frac{C}{2}\right)\sin\left(\frac{A - B}{2}\right)}{\sin B}$.

SECTION A2 — THE DERIVATIVES OF THE SINE AND COSINE FUNCTIONS

INVESTIGATION 1

technology

1. Using your graphing calculator, draw a graph of $y = \sin x$ with the following WINDOW settings: **Xmin** = 0, **Xmax** = 9.4, **Ymin** = −3.1, **Ymax** = 3.1.
2. Use the CALC function (with $\frac{dy}{dx}$ selected) to compute y and $\frac{dy}{dx}$, respectively, for $y = \sin x$, and record these values in a table such as the following (correct to four decimal places):

x	$\sin x$	$\frac{d}{dx} \sin x$
0		
.5		
1.0		
⋮		
⋮		
⋮		
6.5		

3. Using your graphing calculator, draw a graph of $y = \cos x$ with the following WINDOW settings: **Xmin** = 0, **Xmax** = 9.4, **Ymin** = –3.1, **Ymax**= 3.1.
4. Use the TRACE or CALC function to compute the values of $\cos x$ for $x = 0, 0.5, 1.0, \ldots\ldots.., 6.5$, correct to four decimal places, and record them in a table.
5. Compare the tables that you have computed and make a conclusion.

INVESTIGATION 2

technology

1. Using your graphing calculator, draw a graph of $y = \cos x$ with the following WINDOW settings: **Xmin** = 0, **Xmax** = 9.4, **Ymin** = –3.1, **Ymax** = 3.1.
2. Use the CALC function (with $\frac{dy}{dx}$ selected) to compute y and $\frac{dy}{dx}$, respectively, for $y = \cos x$, and record these values, correct to four decimal places, in a table such as the following:

x	$\cos x$	$\frac{d}{dx} \cos x$
0		
.5		
1.0		
⋮		
⋮		
⋮		
6.5		

3. Using your graphing calculator, draw a graph of $y = -\sin x$ with the following WINDOW settings: **Xmin** = 0, **Xmax** = 9.4, **Ymin** = –3.1, **Ymax** = 3.1.
4. Use the TRACE function to compute the values of $-\sin x$ for $x = 0, 0.5, 1.0, \ldots, 6.5$, correct to four decimal places, and record them in a table of values.
5. Compare the tables that you have computed and make a conclusion.

We will now confirm the conjectures made in the Investigations using the definition of the derivative. For $f(x) = \sin x$,

$$f'(x) = \lim_{h\to 0}\frac{f(x+h) - f(x)}{h}$$

$$= \lim_{h\to 0}\frac{\sin(x+h) - \sin x}{h}$$

$$= \lim_{h\to 0}\frac{\sin x\cos h + \cos x\sin h - \sin x}{h}$$

(Using the addition identity $\sin(A + B)$ with $A = x$ and $B = h$)

$$= \lim_{h\to 0}\frac{\cos x\sin h + \sin x(\cos h - 1)}{h}$$

$$= \lim_{h\to 0}\left[\cos x\left(\frac{\sin h}{h}\right) + \sin x\left(\frac{\cos h - 1}{h}\right)\right]$$

$$= \cos x\lim_{h\to 0}\frac{\sin h}{h} + \sin x\lim_{h\to 0}\frac{\cos h - 1}{h}.$$

(Properties of limits $\sin x$ and $\cos x$ are constants since x does not vary as $h\to 0$)

To proceed further, we need the values of the limits $\lim_{h\to 0}\frac{\sin h}{h}$ and $\lim_{h\to 0}\frac{\cos h - 1}{h}$.

INVESTIGATION 3

technology

1. On your graphing calculator, graph $y = \frac{\sin x}{x}$ from $x = -1$ to $x = 1$. (Let **Ymin** = 0.8 and **Ymax** = 1.1.)
2. Using the TRACE function, determine what happens to the value of the function as x gets closer and closer to zero (approaching from the negative and positive sides). Confirm your conclusion by using the TRACE function.
3. What appears to be the value of $\lim_{x\to 0}\frac{\sin x}{x}$?
4. On your graphing calculator, graph $y = \frac{\cos x - 1}{x}$ from $x = -1$ to $x = 1$. (Let **Ymin** = – 0.5 and **Ymax** = 0.5.)
5. Using the TRACE function, determine what happens to the value of the function as x gets closer and closer to zero (approaching from the negative and positive side). Confirm your conclusion by using the TABLE function.
6. What appears to be the value of $\lim_{x\to 0}\frac{\cos x - 1}{x}$?

From Investigation 3, it appears that

$$\lim_{x\to 0}\frac{\sin x}{x} = 1 \text{ and } \lim_{x\to 0}\frac{\cos x - 1}{x} = 0.$$

By substituting these limits in the expression for the derivative of $f(x) = \sin x$, we obtain

$$\begin{aligned} f'(x) &= (\cos x)(1) + (\sin x)(0) \\ &= \cos x. \end{aligned}$$

$$\frac{d}{dx}(\sin x) = \cos x$$

Example 1

Find $\frac{dy}{dx}$ for each function.

a. $y = \sin x^2$

b. $y = \sin^2 x$

Solution

a. To differentiate this composite function, we use the Chain Rule with $y = \sin u$, where $u = x^2$.

Then $$\begin{aligned} \frac{dy}{dx} &= \frac{dy}{du}\frac{du}{dx} \\ &= (\cos u)(2x) \\ &= 2x \cos x^2. \end{aligned}$$

b. Since $y = \sin^2 x = (\sin x)^2$, we use the Chain Rule with $y = u^2$, where $u = \sin x$.

Then $$\begin{aligned} \frac{dy}{dx} &= \frac{dy}{du}\frac{du}{dx} \\ &= (2u)(\cos x) \\ &= 2\sin x \cos x. \end{aligned}$$

With practice, you can learn to apply the Chain Rule without the intermediate step of introducing the variable u. For $y = \sin x^2$, for example, you can skip this step and immediately write

$$\frac{dy}{dx} = (\cos x^2)(2x).$$

We now use the identities

$$\sin\left(\frac{\pi}{2} - x\right) = \cos x \text{ and } \cos\left(\frac{\pi}{2} - x\right) = \sin x$$

to find the derivative of $f(x) = \cos x$.

$$\begin{aligned} f(x) &= \cos x \\ &= \sin\left(\frac{\pi}{2} - x\right) \end{aligned}$$

Using the Chain Rule,

$$\begin{aligned} f'(x) &= \cos\left(\frac{\pi}{2} - x\right)\frac{d}{dx}\left(\frac{\pi}{2} - x\right) \\ &= (\sin x)(-1) \\ &= -\sin x. \end{aligned}$$

$$\frac{d}{dx}(\cos x) = -\sin x$$

Example 2

Find the equation of the tangent to the graph of $y = x\cos 2x$ at $x = \frac{\pi}{2}$.

Solution

When $x = \frac{\pi}{2}$, $y = \frac{\pi}{2}\cos\pi = -\frac{\pi}{2}$.

The point of tangency is $\left(\frac{\pi}{2}, -\frac{\pi}{2}\right)$.

The slope of the tangent at any point on the graph is given by

$$\frac{dy}{dx} = (1)(\cos 2x) + x(-\sin 2x)(2). \qquad \text{(Product and Chain Rules)}$$

At $x = \frac{\pi}{2}$, $\frac{dy}{dx} = \cos\pi - \pi(\sin\pi)$

$= -1.$

The equation of the tangent is

$$y - \frac{\pi}{2} = -\left(x - \frac{\pi}{2}\right) \text{ or } y = -x.$$

Example 3

Find $\frac{dy}{dx}$ for $y = \tan x$.

Solution

$$\begin{aligned} y &= \tan x \\ &= \frac{\sin x}{\cos x} \end{aligned}$$

$$\begin{aligned} \frac{dy}{dx} &= \frac{(\cos x)(\cos x) - (\sin x)(-\sin x)}{(\cos x)^2} \qquad \text{(Using the Quotient Rule)} \\ &= \frac{\cos^2 x + \sin^2 x}{\cos^2 x} \\ &= \frac{1}{\cos^2 x} \\ &= \sec^2 x \end{aligned}$$

Example 4

Find $\frac{dy}{dx}$ for $y = (\sin x + \tan x)^4$.

Solution

$y = (\sin x + \tan x)^4$

$$\frac{dy}{dx} = 4(\sin x + \tan x)^3(\cos x + \sec^2 x) \qquad \text{(Using the Chain Rule)}$$

Exercise A2

Part A

1. Determine $\frac{dy}{dx}$ for each of the following:

a. $y = \sin 2x$

b. $y = x^2 + \cos x + \sin\frac{\pi}{4}$

c. $y = \cos^2 x$

d. $y = \sin(x^3 - 2x + 4)$

e. $y = 2\cos(-4x)$

f. $y = x \cos x$

g. $y = \tan 3x$

h. $y = 3\sin(3x + 2\pi)$

i. $y = \sin^2 x + \cos^2 x$

j. $y = \sin\frac{1}{x}$

k. $y = \cos\sqrt{x}$

l. $y = 2x^3 \sin x - 3x \cos x$

m. $y = 2\sin x \cos x$

n. $y = \frac{\cos 2x}{x}$

o. $y = \cos(\sin 2x)$

p. $y = \frac{\sin x}{1 + \cos x}$

q. $y = \tan^2(x^3)$

r. $y = e^x(\cos x + \sin x)$

Part B

2. Find an equation for the tangent at the given point for each of the following functions:

a. $f(x) = \sin x,\ x = \frac{\pi}{3}$

b. $f(x) = \tan x,\ x = \frac{\pi}{4}$

c. $f(x) = x + \sin x,\ x = 0$

d. $f(x) = \sin 2x + \cos x,\ x = \frac{\pi}{2}$

e. $f(x) = \cos\left(2x + \frac{\pi}{3}\right),\ x = \frac{\pi}{4}$

3. Find $\frac{dy}{dx}$ for each of the following implicitly defined functions:

a. $x = \sin y$

b. $\sin(x + y) = 1$

c. $\tan 2x = \cos 3y$

d. $y = \cos(xy)$

e. $x \sin y - \cos(x + y) = 0$

4. Derive the result that $\frac{d}{dx}\cos x = -\sin x$ using the definition of a derivative.

5. Find expressions for the derivatives of $\csc x$, $\sec x$, and $\cot x$ by first using identities to write them in terms of sine or cosine or both.

6. a. Repeat Investigation 3 of this section with the measure of the angle in degrees rather than radians.

   b. What modifications would have to be made to the derivatives $\frac{d}{dx}\sin x = \cos x$ and $\frac{d}{dx}\cos x = -\sin x$ if x were the measure of an angle in degrees instead of radians?

SECTION A3 – APPLICATIONS OF TRIGONOMETRIC FUNCTIONS

In the previous section, we learned how to differentiate trigonometric functions. In this section, we will apply this knowledge.

Example 1

Find the maximum and minimum values of the function $f(x) = \cos^2 x$ on the interval $0 \leq x \leq 2\pi$.

Solution

By the Algorithm for Extreme Values, the maximum and minimum values occur at a point on the graph where $f'(x) = 0$, or at an end point of the interval. The derivative of $f(x)$ is

$$\begin{aligned} f'(x) &= 2(\cos x)(-\sin x) \\ &= -2\sin x \cos x \\ &= -\sin 2x. \end{aligned}$$

Solving $f'(x) = 0$ yields

$$\sin 2x = 0$$

$$2x = 0, \pi, 2\pi, 3\pi, \text{ or } 4\pi$$

and $x = 0, \frac{\pi}{2}, \pi, \frac{3\pi}{2}, \text{ or } 2\pi.$

We evaluate $f(x)$ at the critical numbers and at the end points of the interval.

x	0	$\frac{\pi}{2}$	π	$\frac{3\pi}{2}$	2π
$f(x)$	1	0	1	0	1

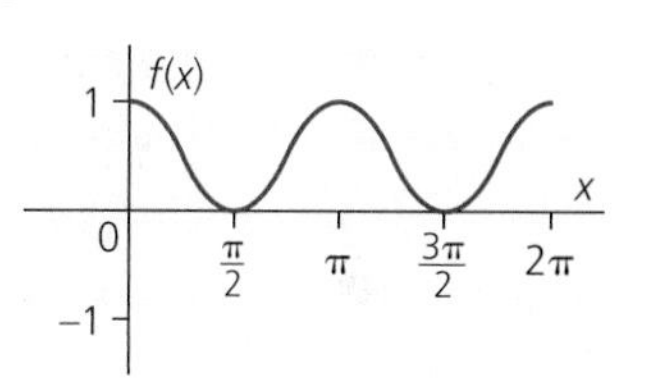

The maximum value is 1 when $x = 0, \pi, \text{ or } 2\pi$, and the minimum value is 0 when $x = \frac{\pi}{2}$ or $\frac{3\pi}{2}$.

Example 2

The top end of a 4 m ladder is sliding down a vertical wall at a rate of 0.25 m/s. If θ is the angle formed by the ladder and the floor, what is the rate of change of θ, in radians per second, at the instant the top of the ladder is 3 m above the floor?

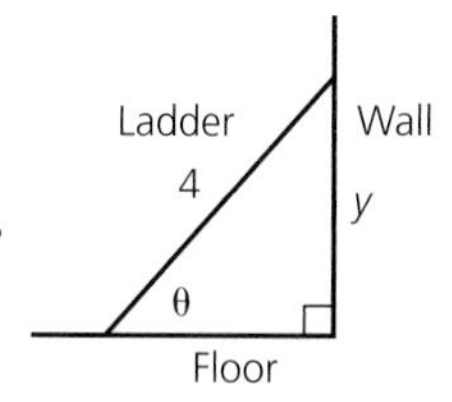

Solution

Let the distance from the top of the ladder to the floor at any time t seconds be y metres.

We are given that $\frac{dy}{dt} = -0.25$ m/s

$= -\frac{1}{4}$ m/s.

We want to determine the value of $\frac{d\theta}{dt}$ when $y = 3$. From the diagram we get

$$\frac{y}{4} = \sin\theta,$$

so $y = 4\sin\theta$.

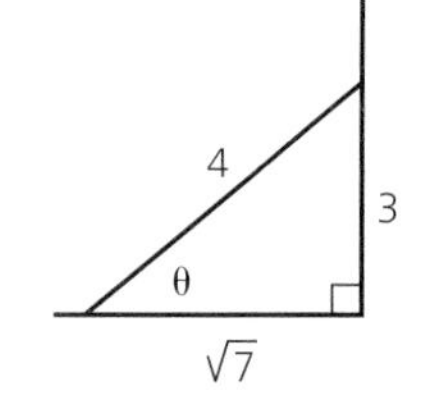

Differentiating implicitly with respect to t,

$$\frac{dy}{dt} = 4\cos\theta\,\frac{d\theta}{dt}.$$

When $y = 3$, $\cos\theta = \frac{\sqrt{7}}{4}$, and $\frac{dy}{dt} = -\frac{1}{4}$.

$$\text{Therefore, } -\frac{1}{4} = 4\left(\frac{\sqrt{7}}{4}\right)\frac{d\theta}{dt}$$

$$\frac{d\theta}{dt} = -\frac{1}{4\sqrt{7}}.$$

Therefore, the angle is decreasing at the rate of $\frac{1}{4\sqrt{7}}$ rad/s.

Example 3

The hypotenuse of a right-angled triangle is 12 cm in length. Find the measures of the remaining angles in the triangle that maximize its perimeter.

Solution

Let the base angle be θ, $0 < \theta < \frac{\pi}{2}$, and let the sides of the triangle have lengths x and y, as shown. Let the perimeter of the triangle be P cm.

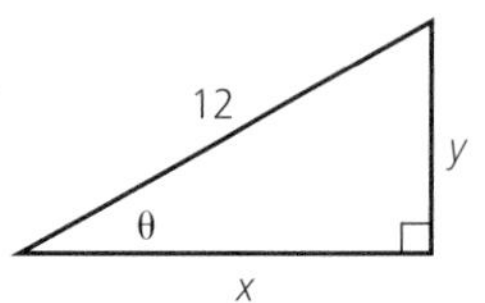

Now, $\frac{x}{12} = \cos\theta$ and $\frac{y}{12} = \sin\theta$

so $\quad x = 12\cos\theta$ and $y = 12\sin\theta$.

Therefore, $P = 12 + 12\cos\theta + 12\sin\theta$

and $\frac{dP}{d\theta} = -12\sin\theta + 12\cos\theta$.

For critical values, $-12\sin\theta + 12\cos\theta = 0$

$$\sin\theta = \cos\theta$$

$$\tan\theta = 1$$

$$\theta = \frac{\pi}{4}, \text{ since } 0 < \theta < \frac{\pi}{2}.$$

$$\text{When } \theta = \frac{\pi}{4},\ P = 12 + \frac{12}{\sqrt{2}} + \frac{12}{\sqrt{2}}$$

$$= 12 + \frac{24}{\sqrt{2}}$$

$$= 12 + 12\sqrt{2}.$$

As $\theta \to 0^+$, $\cos\theta \to 1$, $\sin\theta \to 0$, and $P \to 12 + 12 + 0 = 24$.

As $\theta \to \frac{\pi}{2}^-$, $\cos\theta \to 0$, $\sin\theta \to 1$ and $P \to 12 + 0 + 12 = 24$.

Therefore, the maximum value of the perimeter is $12 + 12\sqrt{2}$ cm, and occurs when the other two angles are each $\frac{\pi}{4}$ rad, or 45°.

Example 4

A line, L, through point $(0, 1)$ is rotating about point $(0, 1)$ at the rate of one revolution per minute in a clockwise direction. At what rate is the point of intersection of L and the x-axis moving along the x-axis when $x = 5$?

Solution

Let θ, in radians, be the angle between the line L and the y-axis, and x be the distance from the origin to the point of intersection of L and the x-axis, P, at any time t minutes, as shown.

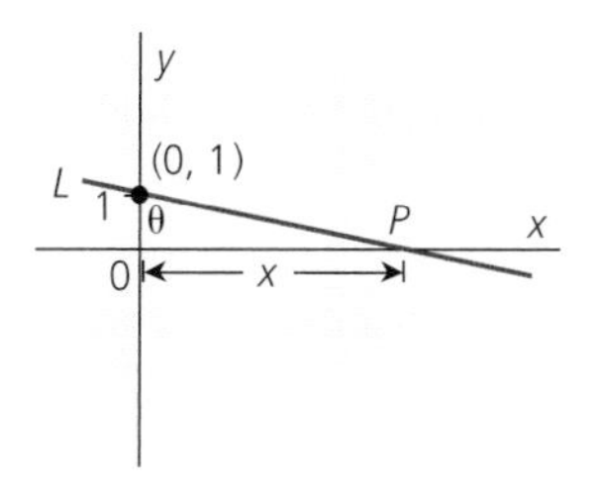

By convention, since rotation in a counter-clockwise direction is positive, we are given that $\frac{d\theta}{dt} = -1$ revolution/min or -2π rad/min.

We want to determine $\frac{dx}{dt}$ when $x = 5$.

From the diagram,

$$\tan\theta = \frac{x}{1} = x.$$

We differentiate this implicitly with respect to t as follows:

$$(\sec^2\theta)\frac{d\theta}{dt} = \frac{dx}{dt}.$$

When $x = 5$, $\sec\theta = \frac{1}{\cos\theta}$

$$= \frac{1}{\frac{1}{\sqrt{26}}}$$

$$= \sqrt{26}.$$

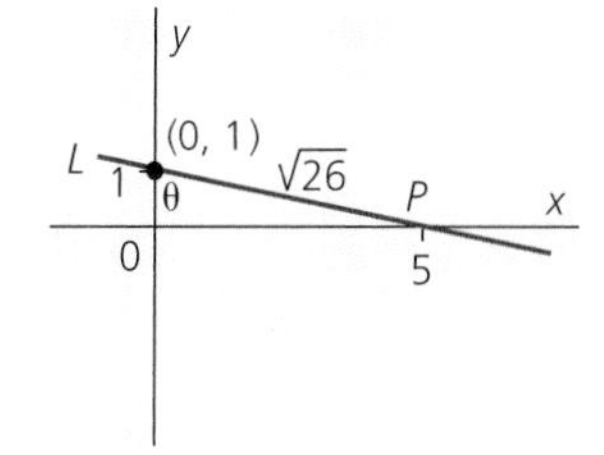

Upon substitution in $(\sec^2\theta)\frac{d\theta}{dt} = \frac{dx}{dt}$,

$$(\sqrt{26})^2(-2\pi) = \frac{dx}{dt}$$

$$-52\pi = \frac{dx}{dt}.$$

When P is 5 units to the right of the origin, it is approaching the origin at the rate of 52π units/min.

Exercise A3

Part B

1. Find the equation of the tangent to the curve $y = \cos x$ at $\left(\frac{\pi}{2}, 0\right)$.

2. Find the equation of the tangent to the curve $\cos x + \sin y = 1$ at the point $\left(\frac{\pi}{3}, \frac{5\pi}{6}\right)$.

3. Find the local maximum and minimum value of each function on the given interval. (Verify your results by graphing the functions on a graphing calculator.)

   a. $y = \cos x + \sin x,\ 0 \le x \le 2\pi$ b. $y = x + 2\cos x,\ -\pi \le x \le \pi$

4. An object is suspended from the end of a spring. Its displacement from the equilibrium position is $s = 8\sin(10\pi t)$. Calculate the velocity and acceleration of the object at any time t, and show that $\frac{d^2s}{dt^2} + 100\pi^2 s = 0$.

5. The motion of a particle is given by $s = 5\cos\left(2t + \frac{\pi}{4}\right)$. What are the maximum values of the displacement, the velocity, and the acceleration?

6. An irrigation channel is constructed by bending a sheet of metal that is 3 m wide, as shown in the diagram. What angle θ will maximize the cross-sectional area (and thus the capacity) of the channel?

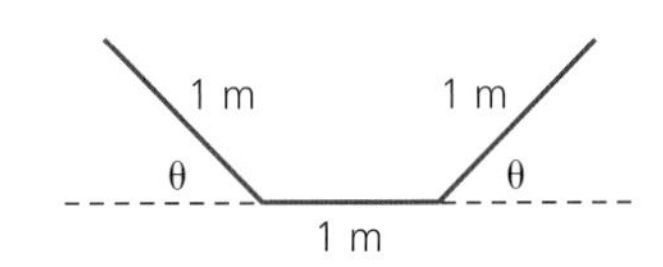

7. A fence is 1.5 m high and is 1 m from a wall. A ladder must start from the ground, touch the top of the fence, and rest somewhere on the wall. Find the minimum length of such a ladder.

8. A lighthouse is 1 km off shore. A marathoner is running along the shore. The search light on the lighthouse is rotating at a rate of $\frac{1}{6}$ revolution per minute when the runner is 3 km from the point on the shore that is closest to the lighthouse. The runner is illuminated by the beam. How fast is the beam of light moving along the shore at this moment?

9. An isosceles triangle is inscribed in a circle of radius R. Find the value of θ that maximizes the area of the triangle.

Part C

10. A man 2 m tall is watching a street light 6 m high as he jogs toward it at a rate of 2 m/s. How fast is the angle of elevation of the man's line of sight increasing at the instant that he is 3 m from the base of the light?

11. A thin rigid pole is to be carried horizontally around a corner joining two corridors of width 1 m and 0.8 m, respectively. Find the length of the longest pole that can be transported in this manner.

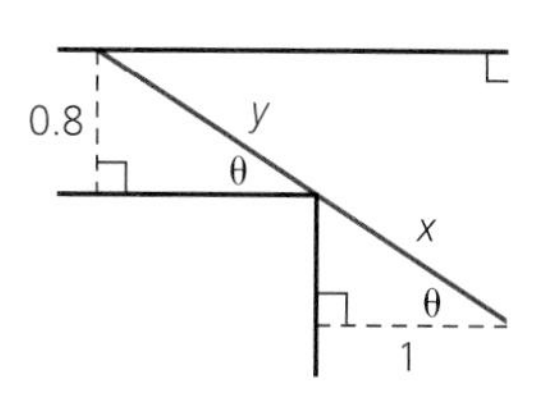

12. When the rules of hockey were developed, Canada didn't use the metric system. Thus the distance between the goal posts was designated to be six feet (slightly less than two metres). If Paul Kariya is on the goal line, three feet outside one of the goal posts, how far should he go out (perpendicular to the goal line) in order to maximize the angle in which he can shoot at the goal? *Hint:* Find the values of x that maximize θ.

Appendix B

ANTIDERIVATIVES

Throughout the text, we have studied the derivatives of functions—how they are defined, their geometric interpretation, how they are calculated, and how they are applied—to help solve different types of problems. In this appendix, we are going to reverse the process. If we were to give an alternative title for this appendix, it could be called "Working Backwards."

SECTION B1 – FINDING ANTIDERIVATIVES

Example 1

Find a function whose derivative is $f(x) = 3x^2 - 4x$.

Solution

If we let F be the name of the function that we are trying to find, then we require $F'(x) = f(x)$ or $F'(x) = 3x^2 - 4x$. Using the rules that we learned for derivatives and thinking backwards, we know that the derivative of x^3 is $3x^2$, and the derivative of $2x^2$ is $2(2x) = 4x$. So if $F'(x) = 3x^2 - 4x$, then $F(x) = x^3 - 2x^2$.

Note: We can check our answer by differentiating F to get $F'(x) = 3x^2 - 4x$.

For a function f, if we can find a function F such that $F'(x) = f(x)$, we say that F is an antiderivative of f.

From the example above, $F(x) = x^3 - 2x^2$ is an antiderivative of $f(x) = 3x^2 - 4x$. Is $F(x) = x^3 - 2x^2$ the only antiderivative of $f(x) = 3x^2 - 4x$? No, we can construct another antiderivative of $f(x) = 3x^2 - 4x$, say G, as follows: $G(x) = x^3 - 2x^2 + 1$. We know that the derivative of a constant is zero, so $G'(x) = 3x^2 - 4x = f(x)$, and G is another antiderivative of f. In fact, we see that there are an infinite number of antiderivatives of $f(x) = 3x^2 - 4x$ that can be found simply by adding (or subtracting) different constants to $x^3 - 2x^2$.

If F is an antiderivative of f (i.e., $F'(x) = f(x)$), we say that $F(x) + C$ is the general antiderivative of f, where C is any constant.

Basic Antiderivatives

- $F'(x) = x^n$, then $F(x) = \frac{x^{n+1}}{n+1} + C, n \neq -1$
- $F'(x) = e^{kx}$, then $F(x) = \frac{e^{kx}}{k} + C, k \neq 0$
- $F'(x) = \frac{1}{x}$, then $F(x) = \ln x + C, x > 0$
- $F'(x) = \cos x$, then $F(x) = \sin x + C$
- $F'(x) = \sin x$, then $F(x) = -\cos x + C$

Finding antiderivatives is mainly a process of taking the rules for derivatives and using them backwards.

Example 2

Find the general antiderivative for each of the following functions:

a. $f(x) = e^x + 2x^5$

b. $g(x) = -4 + \frac{1}{x^2}$

Solution

a. Since $\frac{d}{dx}(e^x) = e^x$, it follows that the function e^x is its own antiderivative. Also, since $\frac{d}{dx}(x^6) = 6x^5$, the antiderivative of $2x^5$ is $\frac{1}{3}x^6$. Hence, the general antiderivative of $f(x) = e^x + 2x^5$ is $F(x) = e^x + \frac{1}{3}x^6 + C$.

We check our answer using derivative rules. If $F(x) = e^x + \frac{1}{3}x^6 + C$, then

$$\begin{aligned} F'(x) &= e^x + \frac{1}{3}(6x^5) \\ &= e^x + 2x^5 \\ &= f(x). \end{aligned}$$

b. The antiderivative of -4 is $-4x$. To determine the antiderivative of $\frac{1}{x^2}$, it is easier to rewrite this term as x^{-2}. Working backwards using the Power Rule for derivatives, the antiderivative of x^{-2} must be $-x^{-1}$, or $\frac{-1}{x}$. Hence, the general antiderivative of $g(x) = -4 + \frac{1}{x^2}$ is $G(x) = -4x - \frac{1}{x} + C$.

Again, we can check our answer using the derivative rules.
If $G(x) = -4x - \frac{1}{x} + C$, then

$$\begin{aligned} G'(x) &= -4 - \left(\frac{-1}{x^2}\right) \\ &= -4 + \frac{1}{x^2} \\ &= g(x). \end{aligned}$$

The general antiderivative of a function f contains a constant, C. To determine the graphical significance of this constant, consider the function $f(x) = 3x^2$. The general antiderivative is $F(x) = x^3 + C$.

If we sketch the general antiderivative for some specific values of C, we notice that these graphs are simply vertical translations of one another. The graphs of $y = x^3$, $y = x^3 + 3$, and $y = x^3 - 1$ are shown here.

Since these graphs are vertical translations of one another, then, for any value of x, the slope of the tangent to each of these graphs will be the same.

Sometimes a question arises from a context that requires us to determine not just the general antiderivative, but a specific antiderivative. In such cases, an extra piece of information is required.

Example 3

The graph of a function f passes through point (0, 4), and the slope of the tangent at any point on the graph is given by $f'(x) = x + e^x$. Determine the function f.

Solution

We first determine the general antiderivative of $f'(x) = x + e^x$, which would be

$$f(x) = \frac{x^2}{2} + e^x + C.$$

This function must pass through point (0, 4), so $f(0) = 4$. This gives

$$4 = \frac{0^2}{2} + e^0 + C$$
$$C = 3.$$

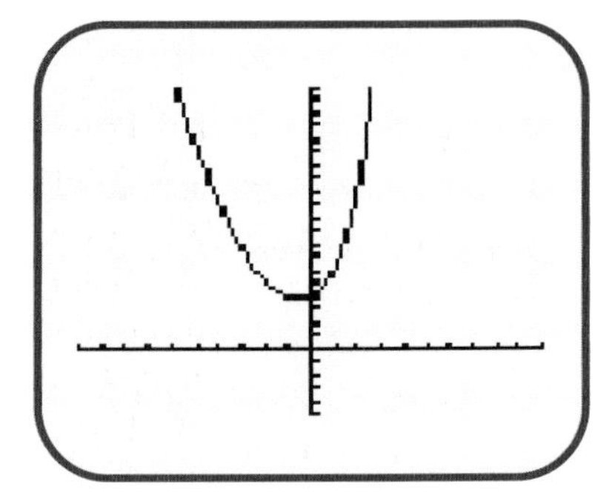

The required function is $f(x) = \frac{x^2}{2} + e^x + 3$. The graph is shown.

Example 4

The rate of change of the cost per metre of drilling a well x metres deep is given by the expression $400 + \frac{5}{4}x^{\frac{2}{3}}$. If it costs \$5000 to drill a well that is 8 m deep, determine the cost of drilling a well that is 27 m deep.

Solution

We wish to determine a function $C(x)$ that relates the cost, C, to the depth of the well, x. We are given information that relates the rate of change of the cost (the cost per metre) to the depth of the well. The function $C(x)$ relates cost to depth, while $C'(x)$ relates the rate of change of cost to depth.

Using $C'(x) = 400 + \frac{5}{4}x^{\frac{2}{3}}$, we can determine $C(x)$, the general antiderivative.

$$C(x) = 400x + \frac{5}{4}\left(\frac{3}{5}\right)x^{\frac{5}{3}} + D$$
$$= 400x + \frac{3}{4}x^{\frac{5}{3}} + D$$

Note: We use D to represent the constant in the general antiderivative, so as not to confuse this quantity with the C used for cost in this example.

In order to find the specific cost function, we use the fact that it costs \$5000 to drill a well that is 8 m deep.

$$C(8) = 5000$$
$$400(8) + \frac{3}{4}(8)^{\frac{5}{3}} + D = 5000$$
$$3200 + \frac{3}{4}(32) + D = 5000$$
$$D = 1776$$

Hence, the cost of drilling a well that is x m deep is given by the function

$$C(x) = 400x + \frac{3}{4}x^{\frac{5}{3}} + 1776,$$

and the cost of drilling a well 27 m deep is

$$C(27) = 400(27) + \frac{3}{4}(27)^{\frac{5}{3}} + 1776$$
$$= \$12\ 758.25.$$

The process of finding antiderivatives is often quite complicated. Many antiderivatives are not recognizable simply by a backward application of the rules for differentiation. In future courses in calculus, you will learn techniques that can be used to find the antiderivatives of complicated functions. For now, we will stick to functions whose antiderivatives can be found using a backward application of the derivative rules with which you are familiar. You should always remember to check your answer by differentiating, to make sure that you have found the correct antiderivative.

Example 5

Find antiderivatives for the following functions:

a. $f(x) = \frac{2x}{x^2 + 5}$

b. $g(x) = \frac{x}{\sqrt{x^2 + 1}} + \cos x$

Solution

a. To find the antiderivative of $f(x) = \frac{2x}{x^2 + 5}$, we note that the numerator of this fraction is the derivative of the denominator. We know that when we differentiate the natural logarithm function using the Chain Rule, we obtain a similar type of fraction.

Therefore, the antiderivative is $F(x) = \ln(x^2 + 5) + C$.

We check our answer and find: $F'(x) = \frac{1}{x^2 + 5}(2x) = \frac{2x}{x^2 + 5} = f(x)$.

b. To find the antiderivative of $g(x) = \frac{x}{\sqrt{x^2 + 1}} + \cos x$, we note that this function can be rewritten as

$$g(x) = \frac{2x}{2\sqrt{x^2 + 1}} + \cos x = \frac{1}{2}(x^2 + 1)^{-\frac{1}{2}}(2x) + \cos x.$$

The antiderivative G is

$$G(x) = (x^2 + 1)^{\frac{1}{2}} + \sin x + C = \sqrt{x^2 + 1} + \sin x + C.$$

Now we differentiate to check our answer:

$$G'(x) = \frac{1}{2}(x^2 + 1)^{-\frac{1}{2}}(2x) + \cos x = \frac{x}{\sqrt{x^2 + 1}} + \cos x = g(x).$$

Finally, we prove that any two different antiderivatives of the same function differ at most by a constant. From our earlier examples, we know that $y = x^3$ and $y = x^3 + 4$ are both antiderivatives of the function $f(x) = 3x^2$. We see that these two antiderivatives differ by a constant of 4. We now prove this result for a general function f.

Given a function f and two different antiderivatives, say F and G, show that F and G differ only by a constant.

Proof

Since F and G are both antiderivatives of f, we know that $F'(x) = f(x)$ and $G'(x) = f(x)$. Subtracting these two equations gives $F'(x) - G'(x) = 0$. Using our rules for derivatives, we know that $F'(x) - G'(x) = (F(x) - G(x))'$. However, if $(F(x) - G(x))' = 0$, we have a function $F(x) - G(x)$ whose derivative is always zero. This function must be a constant. Thus, $F(x) - G(x) = C$, or $F(x) = G(x) + C$, and these two antiderivatives of f differ by only a constant.

Exercise B1

Part A

1. In the following, determine the general antiderivative of the given function.

   a. $f(x) = 2$

   b. $f(x) = 3x - 4$

   c. $f(x) = 4x^3 + x^2$

   d. $f(x) = \frac{2}{x}$

   e. $f(x) = 6x^3 - \sqrt{x}$

   f. $f(x) = \frac{1}{x^2} - \frac{1}{x^3} + \frac{1}{x^4}$

g. $f(x) = 2\sin(2x)$

h. $f(x) = xe^{x^2}$

i. $f(x) = x^2\sqrt{x^3 + 1}$

j. $f(x) = \frac{\cos x}{\sin x}$

2. In the following, determine the specific antiderivative of the given function.

   a. $f(x) = 12x^2 - 24x + 1,\ F(1) = -2$

   b. $f(x) = 3\sqrt{x} - \sin x,\ F(0) = 0$

   c. $f(x) = 4 - \sqrt[3]{x},\ F(8) = 12$

   d. $f(x) = e^{3x} - \frac{1}{2x},\ F(1) = e^3$

   e. $f(x) = \frac{x^2}{\sqrt{x^3 + 1}},\ F(0) = 4$

   f. $f(x) = \cos x \sin^4 x,\ F(0) = -1$

Part B

3. It is estimated that t months from now, the population of a certain small town will be changing at the rate of $3 + 4t^{\frac{1}{3}}$ people per month. If the current population is 10 000, what will the population be six months from now?

4. Water leaks out of a tank at a rate of $\frac{t}{50}$ L/min. If the tank contains 400 L at time $t = 0$, when will the tank be empty?

5. If the water supply in a house is unsoftened, calcium compounds are deposited on the inner walls of water pipes, thereby reducing the flow of water. Suppose that the inner radius of a water pipe decreases at a rate of $0.02e^{-0.002t}$ cm per year owing to this process.

   a. Find the inner radius at time t of a pipe whose inner radius is initially (at $t = 0$) 1 cm.

   b. Find the inner radius of the pipe after three years.

   c. When will the pipe be completely blocked?

6. A certain type of tree grows at a rate of $\frac{20}{t + 30}$ m per year, starting from a height of 3 m when it was planted. Find its height ten years later.

SECTION B2 – MOTION WITH GIVEN VELOCITY OR ACCELERATION

In an earlier chapter, we saw that if we had an object moving in a straight line and we knew its position as a function of time, $s(t)$, then the velocity of the object at any time is $v(t) = \frac{ds}{dt}$, and the acceleration of the object at any time is

$a(t) = \frac{dv}{dt} = \frac{d^2s}{dt^2}$. In many situations, it is more likely that we know the acceleration and we wish to determine velocity and position as functions of time.

Given an acceleration function with respect to time, we know that velocity is an antiderivative of acceleration, and position is an antiderivative of velocity. Usually there is enough physical information known in the context of the problem for us to determine specific values of the constants at each stage, so we are able to find specific velocity and position functions. We apply these principles in the next example.

Example 1

An object moves along the x-axis with velocity $v(t) = 6t - 3t^2$, for $t \geq 0$. If it starts at the origin, determine its position when $t = 2$ and when it returns to its initial position.

Solution

Let the position of the object at any time $t \geq$ be $s(t)$.
We are given $v(t) = s'(t) = 6t - 3t^2$,

so $$s(t) = 3t^2 - t^3 + c.$$

Since the object starts at the origin, $s = 0$ when $t = 0$.

Thus,
$$\begin{aligned} s(0) &= 0 \\ 0 + 0 + c &= 0 \\ c &= 0. \end{aligned}$$

The position of the object at any time $t \geq 0$ is

$$s(t) = 3t^2 - t^3.$$

When $t = 2$, $s(2) = 3(2)^2 - 2^3$
$$= 4.$$

To determine when the object returns to the origin, we solve

$$\begin{aligned} s(t) &= 0 \\ 3t^2 - t^3 &= 0 \\ t^2(3 - t) &= 0 \\ t = 0 \quad &\text{or} \quad t = 3. \end{aligned}$$

The object returns to the origin when $t = 3$.

Example 2

Two rocks fall straight to the earth. If air resistance is ignored, the only acceleration is due to the force of gravity and is equal to -9.81 m/s^2. If the first rock is dropped from a height of 45 m and the second rock is thrown down from a height of 60 m with an initial velocity of 20 m/s, which rock hits the ground first?

Solution

Let $s_1(t)$ and $s_2(t)$ be the positions of the rocks above the ground at any time t seconds, where $t = 0$ when both rocks are released. We need to determine the time at which each rock has reached ground level: $s_1(t) = 0$ and $s_2(t) = 0$. We will consider the behaviour of each rock separately and compare the times.

Since the only acceleration is due to the force of gravity, we know that $a_1(t) = -9.81 = v_1'(t)$.

The velocity, v_1, of the first rock is the antiderivative of its acceleration, so $v_1(t) = -9.81t + C$.

We are told that the first rock is dropped, not thrown, so we know that the initial velocity is 0 m/s.

$$\begin{aligned} v_1(0) &= 0 \\ -9.81(0) + C &= 0 \\ C &= 0 \end{aligned}$$

Hence, the velocity of the first rock, at any time t, is $v_1(t) = -9.81t$.

The position, s_1, of the first rock is the antiderivative of its velocity, so

$$\begin{aligned} s_1(t) &= -9.81\left(\frac{t^2}{2}\right) + D \\ &= -4.905t^2 + D. \end{aligned}$$

We know that the first rock is initially located 45 m above the ground, so

$$\begin{aligned} s_1(0) &= 45 \\ -4.905(0)^2 + D &= 45 \\ D &= 45. \end{aligned}$$

Thus, the position of the first rock at any time t is $s_1(t) = -4.905t^2 + 45$. To determine when the first rock hits the ground, solve $s_1(t) = 0$.

$$\begin{aligned} -4.905t^2 + 45 &= 0 \\ t^2 &= 9.174 \\ t &= \pm\ 3.03 \end{aligned}$$

Therefore, the first rock hits the ground approximately 3 s after it is dropped.

Now let's consider the second rock. We know that $a_2(t) = -9.81$, so the velocity of the second rock is $v_2(t) = -9.81t + K$. Since the second rock is thrown downwards with an initial velocity of 20 m/s, we know that $v_2(0) = -20$, so $-20 = -9.81(0) + K$ and $K = -20$. Therefore $v_2(t) = -9.81t - 20$. (If the second rock had been thrown upwards with an initial velocity of 20 m/s, we would have $v_2(0) = 20$.)

The position function of the second rock is $s_2(t) = -4.905t^2 - 20t + M$. Using the fact that $s_2(0) = 60$, we find $M = 60$, so the position function is $s_2(t) = -4.905t^2 - 20t + 60$.

This second rock hits the ground when

$$-4.905t^2 - 20t + 60 = 0$$

$$t = \frac{20 \pm \sqrt{(-20)^2 - 4(-4.905)60}}{2(-4.905)}$$

$$t \doteq -6.09 \text{ or } 2.01$$

The second rock hits the ground after approximately 2 s. Even though the second rock was initially farther from the ground, it reaches the ground first.

In this question, we ignored any air resistance that might affect the acceleration of the rocks. It is possible to include a factor for air resistance when setting up the initial acceleration function, but in such cases the antiderivative becomes much more difficult to find. These antiderivatives for velocity and position are often solved using a **differential equation.** The solving and application of differential equations is a very large branch of calculus. We cover one basic type of differential equation in the next section of this appendix, but we will barely scratch the surface of this important branch of mathematics.

Example 3

A boat is anchored near the shoreline on a breezy day, bobbing up and down on the waves. Its vertical acceleration at any time, t, is $a(t) = 2\cos(\pi t)$ m/s^2.

a. Determine the velocity, v, and position, s, of the boat at any time, t. (The position is measured from sea level on a calm day, with positive positions above sea level and negative positions below sea level.) Assume that the initial velocity of the boat is 0 m/s and the initial position of the boat is $\frac{2}{\pi^2}$ m below sea level.

b. Determine the position of the boat after 2 s and after 3.5 s.

c. How long does it take for the boat to go from the crest (top) of a wave to the trough (bottom) of a wave?

Solution

a. Velocity is an antiderivative of acceleration, so the velocity of the boat is $v(t) = \frac{2}{\pi}\sin(\pi t) + C$. We know that $v(0) = 0$, so

$$0 = \frac{2}{\pi}\sin(0) + C$$

$$C = 0.$$

Hence, the velocity function is $v(t) = \frac{2}{\pi}\sin(\pi t)$.

Similarly, position is an antiderivative of velocity, so the position of the boat is $s(t) = -\frac{2}{\pi^2}\cos(\pi t) + D$. We know that $s(0) = \frac{-2}{\pi^2}$, so

$$\frac{-2}{\pi^2} = -\frac{2}{\pi^2}\cos(0) + D$$

$$D = 0.$$

Hence, the position function is $s(t) = -\frac{2}{\pi^2}\cos(\pi t)$.

b. The boat's position is determined as follows:

$$s(2) = \frac{-2}{\pi^2}\cos(2\pi)$$
$$= \frac{-2}{\pi^2}$$
$$\approx -0.20264.$$

After 2 s, the boat is approximately 20 cm below sea level.

$$s(3.5) = \frac{-2}{\pi^2}\cos(3.5\pi)$$
$$= 0$$

After 3.5 s, the boat is at sea level.

c. The position function $s(t) = \frac{-2}{\pi^2}\cos(\pi t)$ is periodic, with period 2. Hence, it takes 2 s for the boat to go from crest to crest and 1 s for the boat to go from crest to trough.

Exercise B2

Part A

1. In the following, find the position function of an object moving with the given velocity. The initial position is given. (Assume that the object is moving in a straight line.)

   a. $v(t) = 4\sqrt{t}$, $s(0) = 4$

   b. $v(t) = 3e^t - \frac{1}{t+1}$, $s(0) = 2$

   c. $v(t) = 2\left[1 - \frac{1}{(t+1)^2}\right]$, $s(0) = 0$

   d. $v(t) = 3\cos(\pi t)$, $s(0) = -1$

2. In the following, find the velocity and position functions of an object moving with the given acceleration. The initial velocity and position are given. (Assume that the object is moving in a straight line.)

   a. $a(t) = -2$, $v(0) = 10$, $s(0) = 0$

   b. $a(t) = \sqrt{3t + 1}$, $v(0) = 0$, $s(0) = 0$

   c. $a(t) = \cos(t) + \sin(t)$, $v(0) = 3$, $s(0) = 0$

   d. $a(t) = \frac{4}{(1 + 2t)^2}$, $v(0) = 0$, $s(0) = 8$

Part B

3. The upper observation deck of the CN Tower is 450 m above the ground. If a stone is dropped from this upper deck,

a. determine the position of the stone above ground level at time t.

b. how long does it take the stone to reach the ground?

c. what is the velocity of the stone when it strikes the ground?

4. Repeat Question 3 assuming that the stone is thrown downward with an initial velocity of 10 m/s.

5. Repeat Question 3 assuming that the stone is thrown upward with an initial velocity of 10 m/s.

6. During take-off, an airplane has a constant acceleration while moving down the runway from its initial resting position. What is the acceleration of the plane at lift-off if the plane requires 300 m of runway before lifting off at 28 m/s (approximately 100 km/h)?

7. What constant acceleration is required to increase the speed of a car from 80 km/h to 100 km/h in 5 s?

8. A car brakes with constant deceleration of 10 m/s^2 before coming to a stop, producing skid marks that are 50 m long. How fast was the car travelling when the brakes were first applied?

9. A stone is dropped off a building and hits the ground with a speed of 50 m/s. What is the height of the building?

SECTION B3 – EXPONENTIAL GROWTH AND DECAY MODELLING POPULATION GROWTH

There are many naturally occurring quantities that grow (or decay) at a rate that is proportional to their size. For example, if $y = f(t)$ is the number of humans in a population (or animals, or bacteria in a culture, etc.), it seems reasonable to expect the relative rate of change of the population to be constant. That is,

$$\frac{\frac{dy}{dx}}{y} = k$$

for some constant k. Another way to say this is that the rate of growth (or decay) of the population is proportional to the population itself, or

$$\frac{dy}{dt} = ky.$$

If the constant k is positive, then the population is increasing, since $\frac{dy}{dt} > 0$ (we assume that $y > 0$ for a population). If the constant k is negative, then the population is decreasing, since $\frac{dy}{dt} < 0$. The equation above is called a differential equation because it involves an unknown function y and its derivative $\frac{dy}{dt}$. Differential equations (DEs) often occur when describing natural phenomena. The DEs do not always take the same form as the one above. For example, the equation $\frac{d^2y}{dt^2} + 2\frac{dy}{dt} - 3y = 0$ is another DE, where the solution $y = f(t)$ is an unknown function. Large branches of calculus have come about as people use DEs to describe situations and then search for the function that is a solution of the equation. It is not our purpose here to learn techniques for solving DEs. The only DE that we will study has a solution that is fairly easy to guess.

What function $y = f(t)$ is a solution to the differential equation $\frac{dy}{dt} = ky$? That is, what function $y = f(t)$ has a derivative that is a constant multiple k of itself? We know that the exponential function occurs as part of its own derivative, so we guess that $y = e^{kt}$ is a solution to the differential equation $\frac{dy}{dt} = ky$. We verify our guess by finding $\frac{dy}{dt} = ke^{kt} = ky$. Hence, $y = e^{kt}$ is a function whose derivative is proportional to itself.

However, $y = e^{kt}$ is not the only possible solution to the differential equation $\frac{dy}{dt} = ky$. We note that $y = Ce^{kt}$ is also a solution, for any constant C, since $\frac{dy}{dt} = kCe^{kt} = ky$. Hence, the general function whose derivative is k times itself is $y = Ce^{kt}$. Further study on solving differential equations will prove that this general function is the only solution to the differential equation $\frac{dy}{dt} = ky$.

If $k > 0$, the function $y = Ce^{kt}$ models a population with exponential growth.
If $k < 0$, the function $y = Ce^{kt}$ models a population with exponential decay.

Example 1

A bacterial culture starts with 2000 bacteria, and after three hours there are 7500 bacteria. Assuming that the culture grows at a rate proportional to its size,

a. find the population at any time t.

b. find the number of bacteria present after ten hours.

Solution

Let P represent the population of the bacterial culture after t hours. We are told that $\frac{dP}{dt} = kP$, where k is positive (the culture is growing).

a. The population at any time, t, is given by the function $P(t) = Ce^{kt}$. There are two unknown constants in this equation, k and C. However, we are given some information about the population at various times. We know $P(0) = 2000$, so

$2000 = Ce^{k(0)} = C$, and the population function becomes $P(t) = 2000e^{kt}$. We also know that $P(3) = 7500$, so

$$7500 = 2000e^{k(3)}$$
$$e^{3k} = 3.75$$
$$3k = \ln(3.75)$$
$$k = \frac{\ln(3.75)}{3} \doteq 0.44.$$

Therefore the population at any time t is given by the function $P(t) = 2000e^{0.44t}$.

b. The number of bacteria present after ten hours is $P(10) = 2000e^{0.44(10)} \doteq 162\,900$.

Example 2

After three days, a sample of radon-222 has decayed to 60% of its original amount. If radon-222 decays at a rate proportional to its size,

a. find an expression for the amount of radon-222 present at any time t.

b. what is the half-life of radon-222? (That is, how long does it take a sample of radon-222 to decay to 50% of its original amount?)

Solution

a. If R is the amount of radon-222 present at any time t, then we know that $\frac{dR}{dt} = kR$, where k will be negative (since the sample is decaying). The general solution to this differential equation is $R(t) = Ce^{kt}$, where both C and k must be determined. We are not told the amount of radon-222 that is present initially; we will call this quantity R_0. Hence, we know that $R(0) = R_0$, so

$$R_0 = Ce^{k(0)} = C$$

and the function becomes $R(t) = R_0e^{kt}$.

We also know that after three days, the radon-222 has decayed to 60% of its original quantity. This means $R(3) = 0.6R_0$, and

$$0.6R_0 = R_0e^{k(3)}$$
$$0.6 = e^{3k}$$
$$3k = \ln(0.6)$$
$$k = \frac{\ln(0.6)}{3} \doteq -0.17$$

Therefore, the amount of radon-222 present at any time, t, is $R(t) = R_0e^{-0.17t}$. Notice that we were not able to calculate the exact amount of radon-222 present without knowing the initial amount (R_0), but we were able to determine the value of k without knowing R_0.

b. The half-life of radon-222 (or any radioactive element) is the amount of time that it takes for a sample to decay to half of its original amount. Since we do not know the initial amount, R_0, we wish to find t so that $R(t) = 0.5R_0$.

$$0.5R_0 = R_0e^{-0.17t}$$
$$0.5 = e^{-0.17t}$$
$$-0.17t = \ln(0.5)$$
$$t = \frac{\ln(0.5)}{-0.17} \doteq 4.077$$

Therefore, the half-life of radon-222 is approximately four days. Notice that we were able to calculate the half-life without knowing the value of R_0.

Newton's Law of Temperature Change

According to Newton's law of temperature change, the rate of cooling (or heating) of an object is proportional to the difference between the temperature of the object and the temperature of the surrounding medium. If T is the temperature of an object in degrees Celsius at any time t, and the temperature of the surrounding medium is S°C, then we write the following differential equation to describe the situation:

$$\frac{dT}{dt} = k(T - S).$$

The general solution for this differential equation is $T(t) = S + Ce^{kt}$. We can verify the general solution as follows:

$$\text{L.S.} = \frac{dT}{dt} = Cke^{kt}$$

$$\text{R.S.} = k(T - S) = k(S + Ce^{kt} - S) = kCe^{kt} = \text{L.S.}$$

When we use exponential growth to model the growth of a population of humans, bacteria, etc., we are assuming that the population has enough food and living space to continue to grow unchecked. However, in practice, food and living space are often factors that restrict the expansion of a population. If this occurs, the growth of the population is not purely exponential.

The Logistic Model

To construct a population model that takes into account the effect of limited resources and space, we assume that the population has an upper bound of M, called the *carrying capacity*. If this is true, then the relative rate of change in a population is proportional to the difference between the carrying capacity and the population, or

$$\frac{\frac{dy}{dt}}{y} = k(M - y).$$

We rearrange this expression to get the differential equation $\frac{dy}{dt} = ky(M - y)$.

The general solution to this differential equation is $y = \frac{M}{1 + Ce^{Mkt}}$, where C is an unknown constant, M is the limiting value of the population, and k is the constant of proportionality. (Further study in calculus will teach you how to find this solution to the differential equation yourself.)

Example 3

A population of animals on Pelee Island is limited by the amount of food available. Studies show that there were 2000 animals present in 1990 and 2500 in 1997, suggesting that a maximum of 6000 animals can be supported by the conditions present on the island. Use the logistic model to predict the animal population in the year 2005.

Solution

Using the given information, we construct the differential equation

$$\frac{dP}{dt} = kP(6000 - P),$$

where P is the number of animals present on the island after t years. For convenience, we begin measuring time in 1990; that is, $t = 0$ in 1990. (As an exercise, redo this question with $t = 0$ for any year of your choosing. Verify that the choice of year for $t = 0$ does not affect the calculations.)

The solution to this differential equation has the general form

$$P(t) = \frac{6000}{1 + Ce^{6000kt}},$$

where we must determine the values of C and k. We know that $P(0) = 2000$, so

$$2000 = \frac{6000}{1 + Ce^{6000k(0)}}$$

$$1 + C = 3$$

$$C = 2.$$

The population equation becomes $P(t) = \frac{6000}{1 + 2e^{6000kt}}$. We also know that $P(7) = 2500$, so

$$2500 = \frac{6000}{1 + 2e^{6000k(7)}}$$

$$1 + 2e^{42\,000k} = 2.4$$

$$e^{42\,000k} = 0.7$$

$$42\,000k = \ln(0.7)$$

$$k = \frac{\ln(0.7)}{42\,000} \doteq -8.492\,261 \times 10^{-6}.$$

Therefore, the population equation is

$$P(t) = \frac{6000}{1 + 2e^{6000(-8.492\,261 \times 10^{-6})t}}$$

$$= \frac{6000}{1 + 2e^{-0.051t}}.$$

In the year 2005, $t = 15$ and the animal population on Pelee Island will be

$$P(15) = \frac{6000}{1 + 2e^{-0.051(15)}} \doteq 3108.$$

Example 4

A thermometer is taken from a room where the temperature is 22°C to the outdoors, where the temperature is 8°C. After one minute, the thermometer reads 15°C.

a. What is the temperature T shown on the thermometer as a function of time t?

b. What will the reading on the thermometer be after one more minute?

c. When will the thermometer read 10°C?

Solution

a. Using the given information, we can write the differential equation $\frac{dT}{dt} = k(T - 8)$, where 8°C is the temperature of the air surrounding the thermometer. The general solution to this differential equation is $T(t) = 8 + Ce^{kt}$. We must determine the values of C and k. We know that $T(0) = 22$, since the thermometer was taken from a room where the temperature was 22°C, so

$$22 = 8 + Ce^{k(0)}$$

$$22 = 8 + C$$

$$C = 14.$$

The temperature function becomes $T(t) = 8 + 14e^{kt}$. We also know that $T(1) = 15$, so

$$15 = 8 + 14e^{k(1)}$$

$$e^k = 0.5$$

$$k = \ln(0.5) \doteq -0.69.$$

Therefore, the temperature function is $T(t) = 8 + 14e^{-0.69t}$. Notice that the value of k is negative, which corresponds to the fact that the temperature is decreasing over time.

b. After one more minute, the reading on the thermometer will be

$$T(2) = 8 + 14e^{-0.69(2)} \doteq 11.5°\text{C}.$$

c. We wish to find t so that $T(t) = 10$.

$$\begin{aligned} 8 + 14e^{-0.69t} &= 10 \\ e^{-0.69t} &= \frac{1}{7} \\ -0.69t &= \ln\left(\frac{1}{7}\right) \\ t &= \frac{\ln\left(\frac{1}{7}\right)}{-0.69} \\ &\doteq 2.8 \end{aligned}$$

Therefore, the temperature on the thermometer will read 10°C after approximately 2.8 min.

Exercise B3

Part A

1. A bacterial culture starts with 200 bacteria and the population triples every half-hour. Assuming that the rate of increase is proportional to the number of bacteria present,
   a. find an expression for the number of bacteria present after t hours.
   b. find the number of bacteria present after 20 min.
   c. when will the bacteria population reach 10 000?

2. A city had a population of 150 000 in 1980 and 250 000 in 2000. Assuming that the rate of increase is proportional to the population,
   a. find an expression for the population of the city after t years.
   b. what will the population of the city be in 2010?

3. Polonium-210 has a half-life of 140 days and eventually decays into lead. If a sample has a mass of 200 mg and we assume that the rate of decay is proportional to the amount of polonium present,
   a. find a formula for the mass that remains after t days.
   b. find the mass after 50 days.
   c. when will the mass be reduced to 5 mg?

Part B

4. The growth rate of the population of Central America is 3.5% per year (one of the highest in the world). How long does it take the population to double in size?

5. The population of a small town was 10 000 in 1950 and 12 000 in 1970. Assuming a lack of housing and services will allow a maximum population of 16 000, what will the population be in 2005?

6. The number of rabbits on Easter Island was estimated to be 20 000 in 1995 and 22 000 in 1998. Assuming that the rabbit population can grow no larger than 25 000 due to the scarcity of food and abundance of predators, find an equation for the population of rabbits at any time t.

7. A hot potato at a temperature of 80°C cools to 40°C in 15 min when the room temperature is 20°C. If hot food tastes best when its temperature remains above 50°C, how long does a restaurant server have to get the potato to a customer's table? Use Newton's law of temperature change.

8. When a coil of steel is removed from an annealing furnace, its temperature is 684°C. Four minutes later, its temperature is 246°C. How long will it take to reach 100°C? Apply Newton's law of temperature change, given that the temperature of the surrounding medium is 27°C.

Appendix C

TECHNICAL ASSISTANCE

OVERVIEW

This appendix provides an overview of the instructions for using a graphing calculator. Use this appendix whenever you are not sure of the next step to take with your calculator. For more detailed information on using a graphing calculator, you may wish to refer to a more comprehensive graphing calculator guidebook.

Contents

INSTRUCTIONS FOR THE TI-83 PLUS GRAPHING CALCULATOR

The TI-83 Plus has a colour-coded keyboard.

The secondary function on each key is printed in yellow above the key. When you press the yellow [2nd] key, the character, abbreviation, or word printed in yellow above the other keys becomes active.

For example: [2nd] [APPS] (ANGLE B) displays the ANGLE menu.

The alpha function of each key is printed in green above the key. When you press the green [ALPHA] key, the alpha character printed in green above the other keys becomes active for the next keystroke.

For example: [ALPHA] [APPS] (ANGLE B) enters the letter B on your screen.

HOME SCREEN

The home screen is the primary screen. Use this screen to enter instructions and expressions you want to evaluate. The answer is displayed on the same screen.

To return to the home screen from any other screen, press [2nd] [MODE] (QUIT).

ENTERING AN EQUATION

Press [Y=]. The **Y=** editor screen is where you define functions for tables and graphing.

A highlighted = sign indicates that a function is selected. Use [CLEAR] and [▲], [▼], [◄], and [►] to clear any unwanted equations.

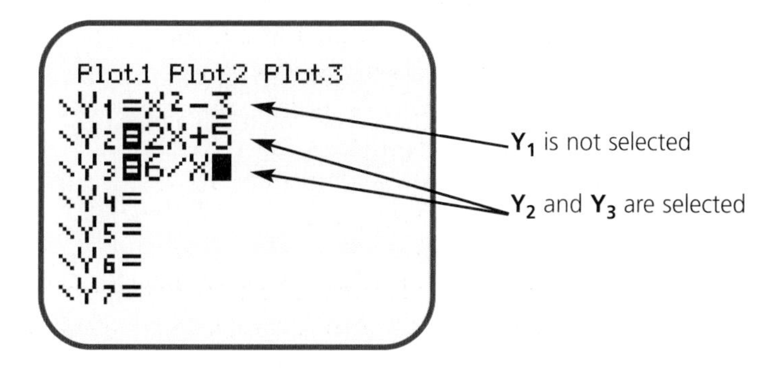

If any of **Plot 1, Plot 2,** or **Plot 3** at the top of the screen are highlighted, press [▲] and [►] to place the cursor on **Plot 1, Plot 2,** or **Plot 3** and then press [ENTER] to change the on/off status of the stat plot.

If any of **Plot 1, Plot 2,** or **Plot 3** at the top of the screen are highlighted, press [▲] and [▶] to place the cursor on **Plot 1, Plot 2,** or **Plot 3** and then press [ENTER] to change the on/off status of the stat plot.

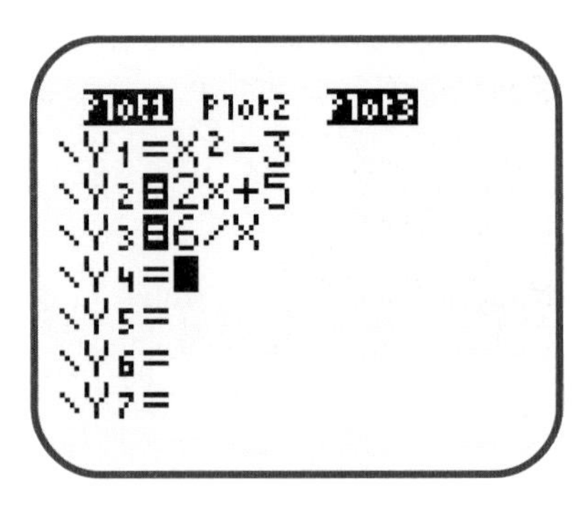

Plot 1 and **Plot 3** are highlighted. **Plot 2** is not highlighted.

Place the cursor beside $\mathbf{Y_1}$=. Enter the equation using [X.T.A.*n*] to enter the variable, [×] for multiplication, [÷] for division, and [^] to indicate an exponent. Remember to use [(-)] to enter a negative sign. The [-] key is used for the operation of subtraction.

If you wish to enter more than one equation, move the cursor to $\mathbf{Y_2}$= and repeat the procedure. The calculator stores up to ten functions in the **Y=** editor to the variables $\mathbf{Y_1}$ through $\mathbf{Y_9}$ and $\mathbf{Y_0}$.

CHANGING THE VIEWING WINDOW

Press [WINDOW] to display the window editor, where you can view and edit the values of the window variables.

```
WINDOW
 Xmin=-10
 Xmax=10
 Xscl=1
 Ymin=-10
 Ymax=10
 Yscl=1
 Xres=1
```

Xmin, Xmax, Ymin, and **Ymax** define the boundaries of the display.

Xscl and **Yscl** define the distance between tick marks on the *x*- and *y*-axes. To turn off tick marks, set **Xscl** = 0 and **Yscl** = 0.

Xres sets the pixel resolution (1 through 8) for function graphs only. The default value is 1. At **Xres** = 1, functions are evaluated and graphed at each pixel on the *x*-axis. At **Xres** = 8, functions are evaluated at every eighth pixel along the *x*-axis. Small **Xres** values improve graph resolution but may cause the calculator to draw graphs more slowly.

DISPLAYING THE FORMAT SETTINGS

To display the format settings, press [2nd] [ZOOM] (FORMAT). The default settings are highlighted in the screen below.

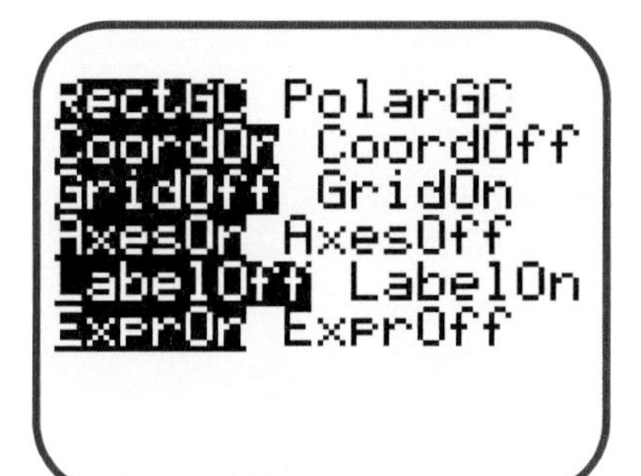

Sets cursor coordinates as rectangular or polar.
Sets coordinates display on or off.
Sets grid off or on.
Sets axes on or off.
Sets axes labels off or on.
Sets expression display on or off.

Use [◄], [►], [▲], [▼], and [ENTER] to change the highlighted settings.

CHANGING THE NUMBER OF DECIMAL PLACES DISPLAYED

Press [MODE]. The screen displays the current mode settings. **Float** (Floating) decimal mode displays up to ten digits plus a sign and decimal point.

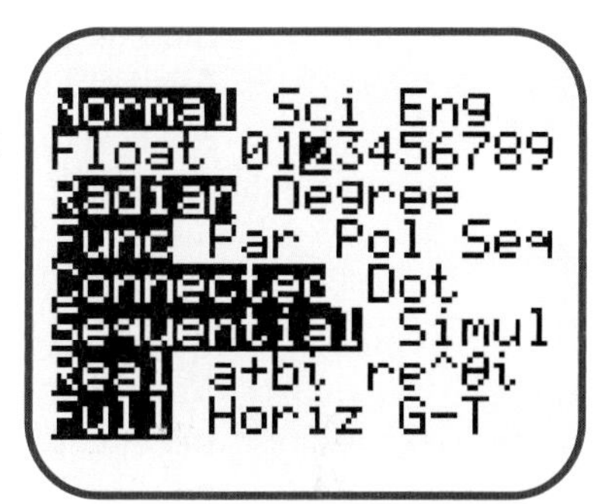

Press [▼] to move the cursor to **Float.**

Use [►] to move the cursor to the number of digits (0 through 9) to be displayed to the right of the decimal place. Press [ENTER].

PLOTTING THE FUNCTION

Press [Y=] to display the **Y=** editor. A function is selected if the = sign is highlighted.

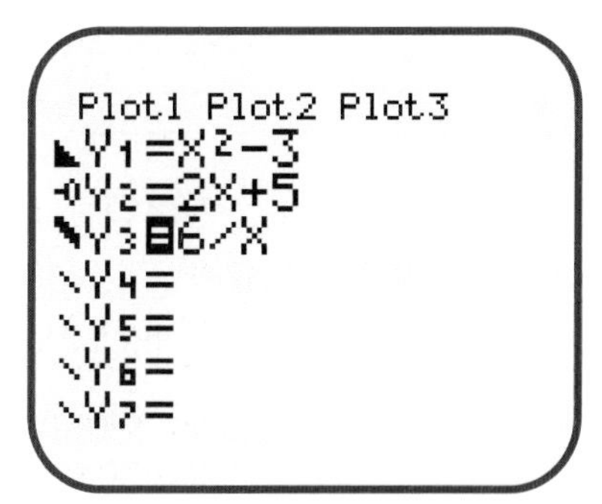

To select or deselect a function in the **Y=** editor, press [▼] or [▲] to move the cursor to the function you want to select or deselect.

Press [◄] to place the cursor on the function's = sign. Press [ENTER] to change the selection status.

Press [GRAPH]. The graph of the function will now appear.

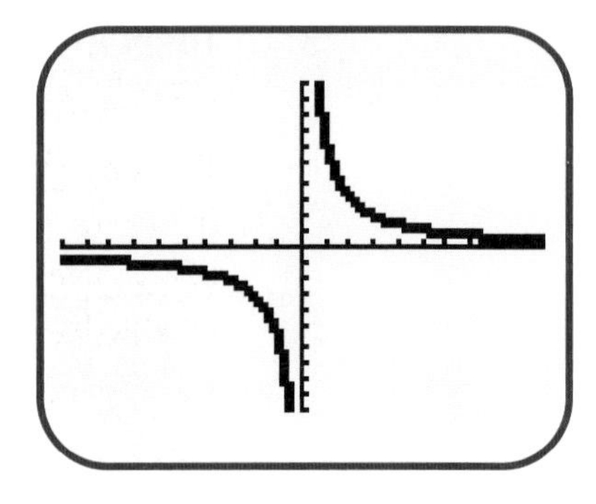

You may wish to change the viewing window. See "Changing the Viewing Window" or "Zoom."

FREE-MOVING CURSOR

When a graph is first displayed, no cursor is visible. Pressing [▲], [▼], [◄], or [►] causes the cursor to move from the centre of the viewing window.

Pressing [▲], [▼], [◄], or [►] will move the cursor around the window. The coordinate values of the cursor location are displayed at the bottom of the screen if the **CoordOn** format is selected. The **Float/Fix** decimal mode setting determines the number of decimal digits displayed for the coordinate value.

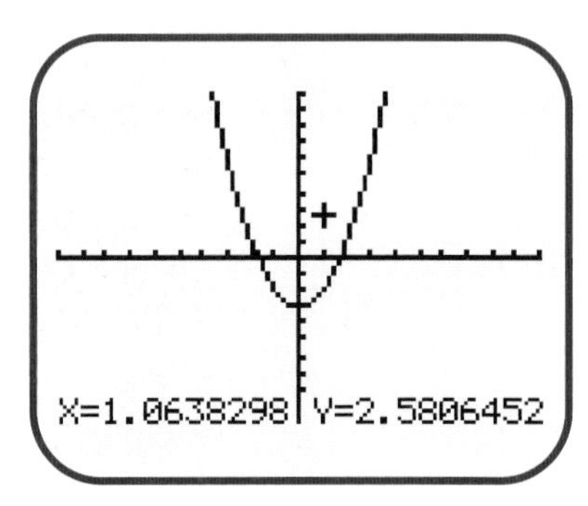

The free moving cursor moves from pixel to pixel on the screen. You can move the cursor so that it appears to be on the function, but the cursor may be on a pixel that is near the function, yet not actually on the function. The coordinate value displayed at the bottom of the screen may not be a point on the function. To move the cursor along a function, use [TRACE].

To display the graph with no cursor and no coordinate value, press [CLEAR] or [ENTER].

TRACE

Use the TRACE function to move the cursor from one plotted point to another along a function.

To begin TRACE, press [TRACE]. A flashing trace cursor appears on the first selected function in the **Y=** editor at the middle x value on the screen. The x- and y-coordinates of this point on the curve appear at the bottom of your screen if the **CoordOn** format is selected. The equation of the function is displayed in the top-left corner of the screen if the **ExprOn** format is selected. To display the coordinates, press [2nd] [ZOOM] (FORMAT) and select **CoordOn.**

Pressing [▶] or [◀] moves the cursor along the curve. As the cursor moves, the x- and y-coordinates at the bottom of the window change to the corresponding values.

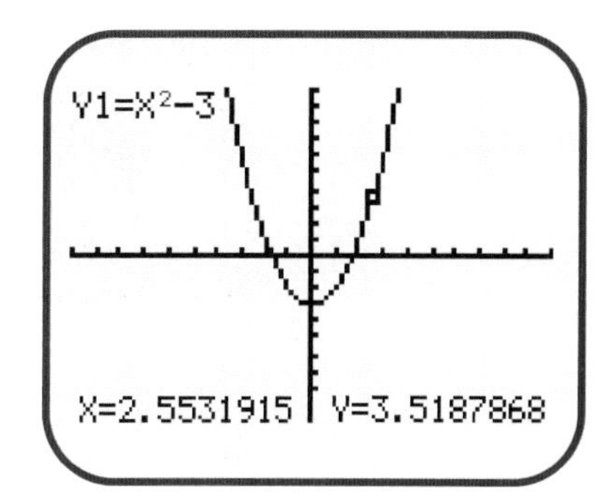

To move the trace cursor to any valid x-value on the current function, enter the value and then press [ENTER]. This feature is particularly useful when you are looking for the maximum or minimum values of a function or the zeros of a function.

To move the trace cursor from function to function, press [▲] or [▼]. The cursor follows the order of the selected functions in the **Y**= editor.

If you move the trace cursor beyond the top or bottom of the screen, the coordinate values at the bottom of the screen continue to change. The plot function must be deselected to scroll beyond the screen.

If you move the trace cursor beyond the left or right side of the screen, the viewing window automatically passes to the left or right. **Xmin** and **Xmax** are updated to correspond to the new viewing window. The plot function must be deselected to scroll beyond the screen.

While tracing, you can press [ENTER] to adjust the viewing window so that the cursor location becomes the centre of a new viewing window, even if the cursor is above or below the display.

ZOOM

To help you find maximum, minimum, roots, and intersections of functions, you can magnify the viewing window at a specific location using the ZOOM menu.

To display the ZOOM menu, press [ZOOM]. You can adjust the viewing window in several ways.

Zbox allows you to define a box on your graphing screen that will become the new enlarged window.

Select **1:Zbox** from the ZOOM menu. The zoom cursor is displayed at the centre of your screen. Move the cursor to the upper left corner of your desired box. Press [ENTER].

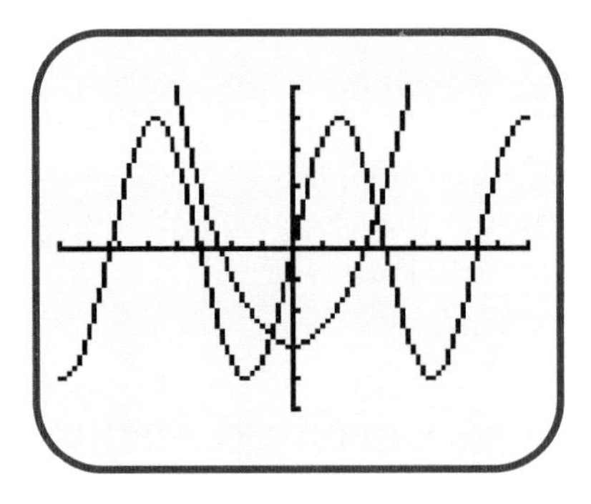

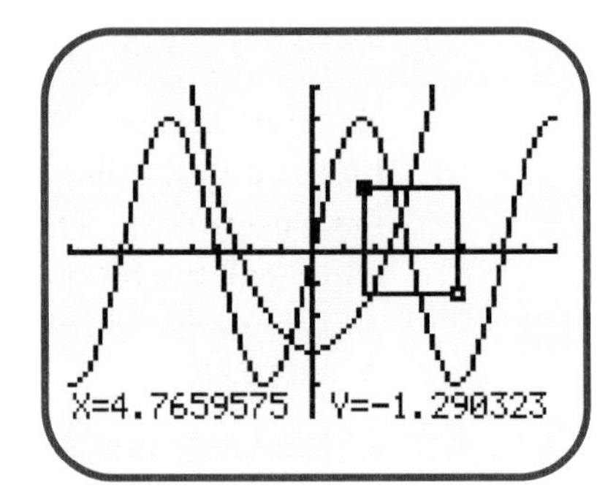

Use [▶] and [▼] to move the cursor to the lower right corner of your desired box. You will see the box growing on the screen.

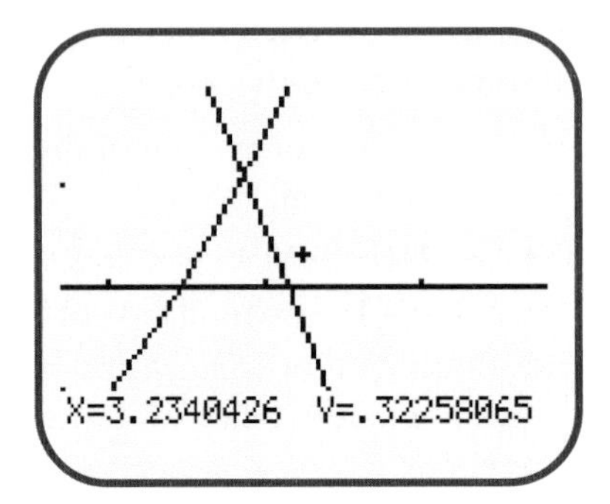

Press [ENTER] to replot the graph. The zoom cursor is still active, so you can draw a new box within this window and zoom again.

To cancel **Zbox**, press [CLEAR].

Zoom In, Zoom Out

Zoom In magnifies the part of the graph that surrounds the cursor location. **Zoom Out** displays a greater portion of the graph, centred on the cursor location. Select **Zoom In** or **Zoom Out** from the ZOOM menu. Move the zoom cursor to the desired location in the window and press [ENTER]. The functions are replotted centred on the cursor location.

ZDecimal

ZDecimal updates the window variables to the preset values shown below.

Xmin = −4.7	Ymin = −3.1
Xmax = 4.7	Ymax = 3.1
Xscl = 1	Yscl = 1

These values set $\Delta\mathbf{X}$ and $\Delta\mathbf{Y}$ each equal to 0.1. The **X**- and **Y**-value of each pixel is one decimal place. The graph is redrawn immediately with the new window variables. You now have pixels centred at −4.7, −4.6, . . . , 4.7. This is useful if you want to place the cursor at any of these specific *x*-values.

ZSquare

ZSquare changes the viewing window so that **ΔX** = ΔY, which makes the graph of a circle look like a circle. **ZSquare** adjusts only one direction. The midpoint of the current graph is the midpoint of the new graph. The graph is redrawn immediately with the new window variables.

ZStandard

ZStandard updates the window variables to the preset values shown below.

Xmin = 10	Ymin = −10
Xmax = 10	Ymax = 10
Xsci = 1	Ysci = 1

This allows you to return quickly to a standard grid setting. The graph is redrawn immediately with the new window variables.

ZTrig

ZTrig updates the window variables to preset values that are appropriate for plotting trig functions. These values are shown below in radian mode.

Xmin = −6.152285	Ymin = −4
Xmax = 6.152285	Ymax = 4
Xsci = 1.5707963	Ysci = 1

The graph is redrawn immediately with the new window variables.

ZInteger

ZInteger sets the distance between the centre of adjacent pixels at 1. To use **ZInteger,** move the cursor to the point that you want to be the centre of the new window and press [ENTER]. **ZInteger** updates the window variables to the preset values shown below.

ΔX = 1	ΔY = 1
Xsci = 10	Ysci = 10

The graph is redrawn immediately with the new window variables.

ZoomFit

ZoomFit recalculates **Ymax** and **Ymin** to include the maximum and minimum Y-values of the selected functions between the current **Xmin** and **Xmax**. The graph is redrawn immediately with the new window variables. Look at the following screens to see how **ZoomFit** works.

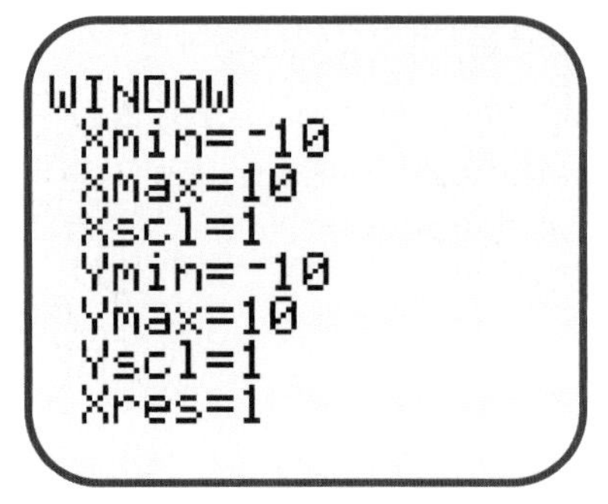

Here are the window variables.

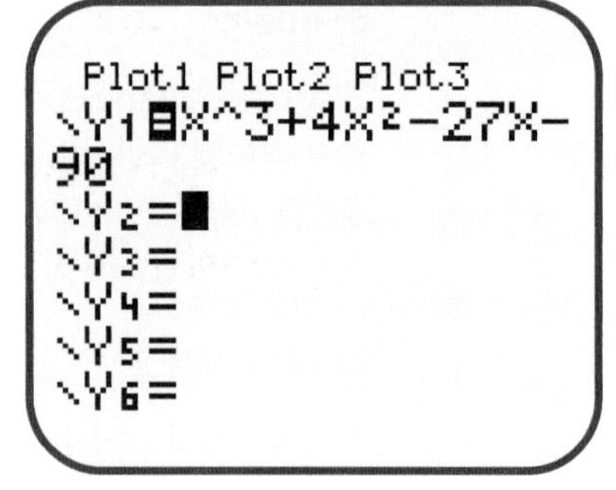

This is the function we are graphing.

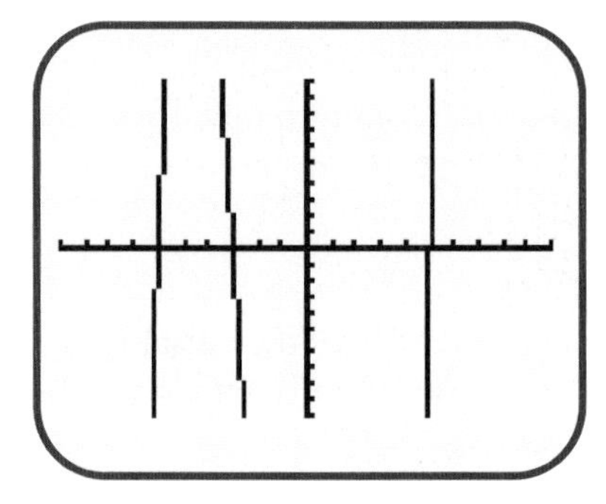
Here is the graph. We cannot see the maximum or minimum values of the function.

Press [ZOOM] and select **ZoomFit.** A new graph is drawn immediately.

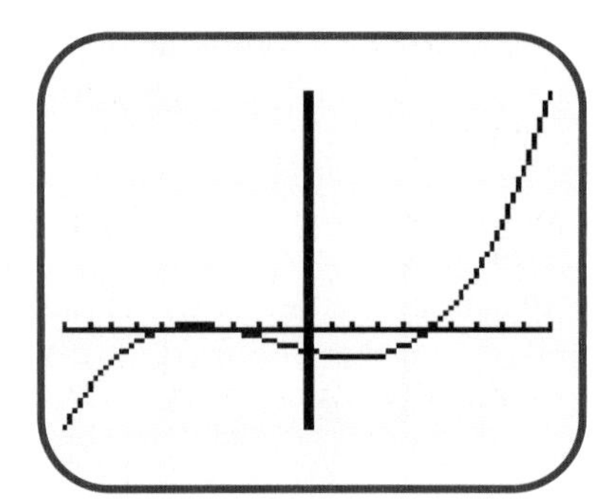
You can now see the maximum and minimum values of the function.

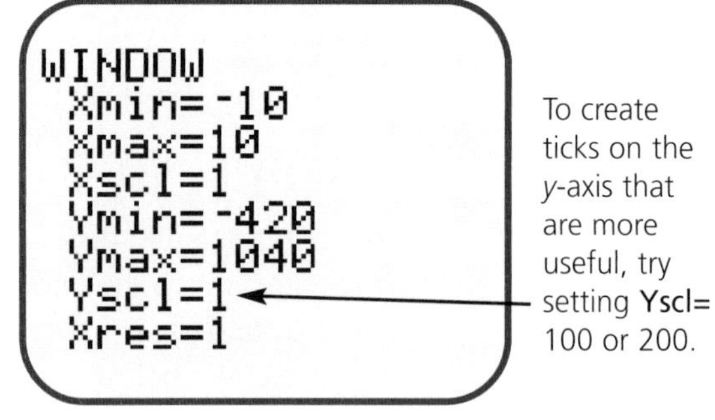

The window variables are updated.

SPLIT SCREENS

You can split the screen horizontally to display both a graph and its table or the **Y=** editor screen.

You can split the screen vertically to display a graph and its table simultaneously.

To split a screen, press MODE. Move the cursor to the bottom line of the mode screen.

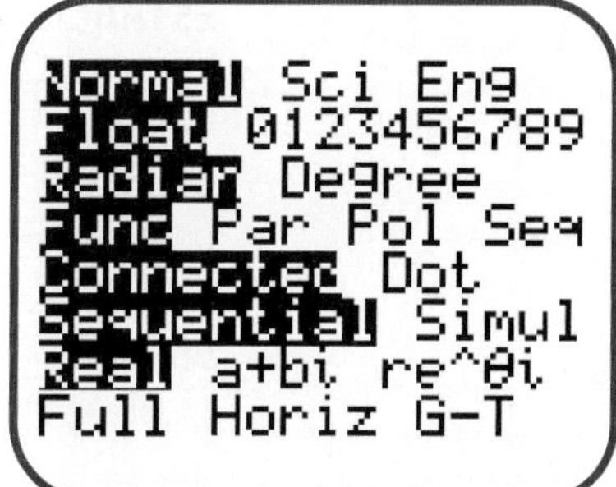

Full screen mode uses the entire screen to display a graph or edit screen. Each split screen mode displays two screens simultaneously.

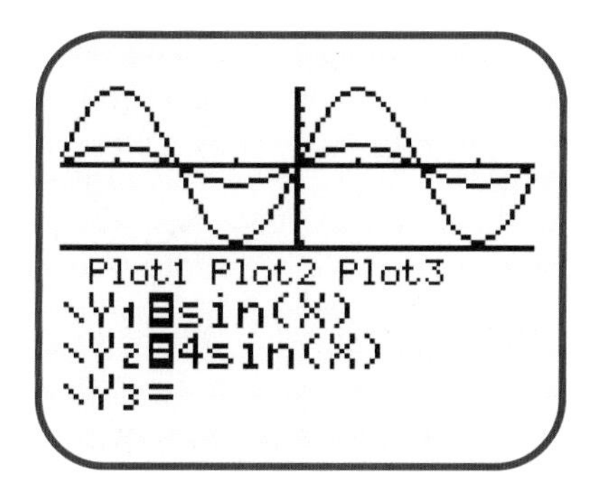

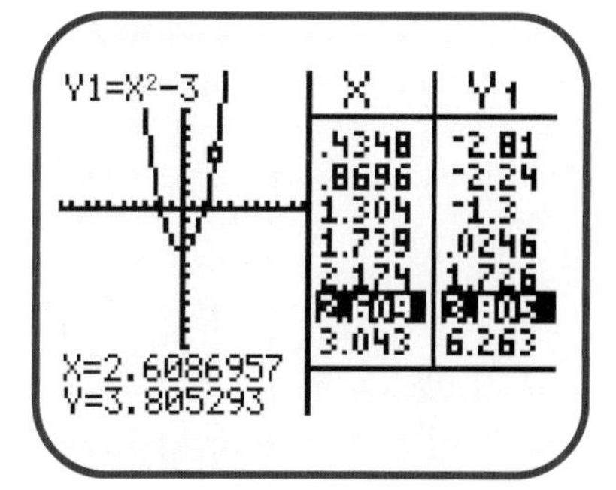

GRAPHING A FAMILY OF CURVES

If you enter a list as an element of an expression, the calculator plots the function for each value on the list.

$\{1, 2, 3\} \sin x$ graphs three functions:

$\sin x$

$2 \sin x$

$3 \sin x$

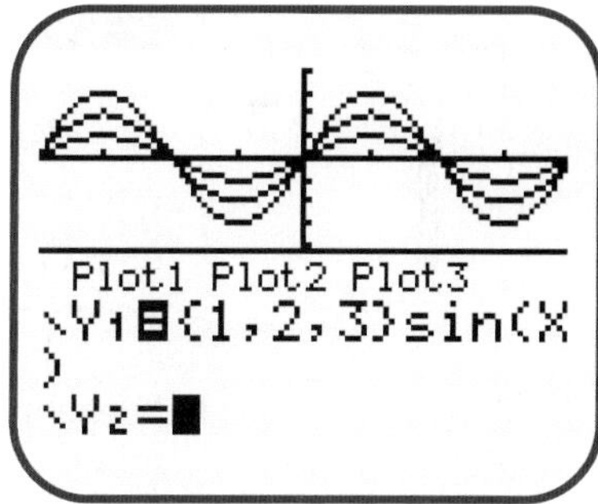

Make sure you use the correct style of brackets.

$(x - \{0,2,4\})^2$ graphs three functions:

x^2

$(x - 2)^2$

$(x - 4)^2$

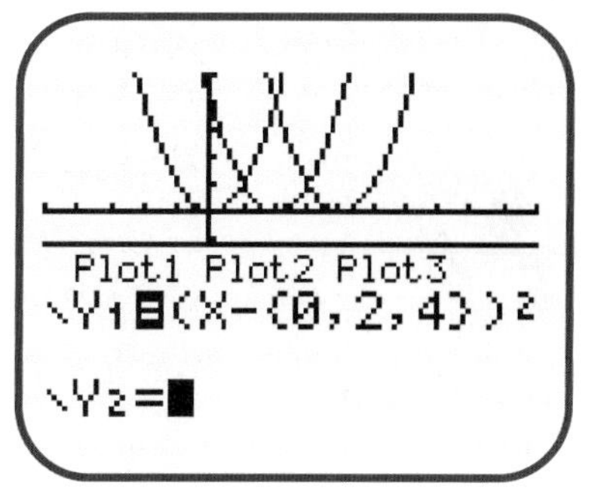

ESTABLISHING A TABLE OF VALUES FOR A FUNCTION

Press [Y=]. The **Y=** editor screen is where you define functions for tables and graphing.

Enter and/or highlight the function for which you wish a table of values.

Press [2nd] [WINDOW] (TBLSET) for TABLE SETUP. In the TABLE SETUP window, enter the starting value for the x-coordinate (**TblStart=**) and the increments by which the x-coordinate is to increase (**ΔTbl=**). Be sure that **Auto** is highlighted in the last two lines.

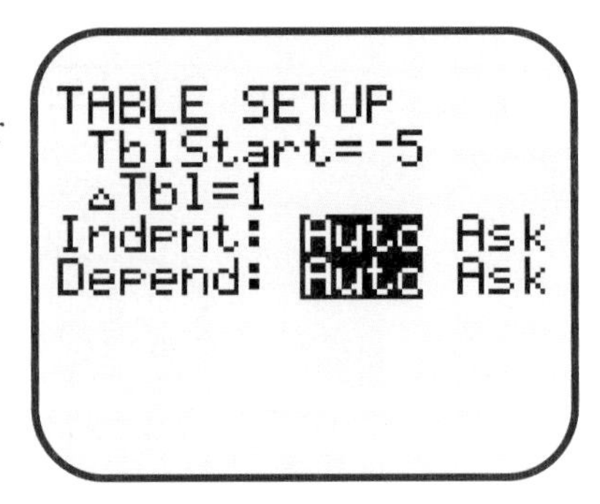

Press [2nd] [GRAPH] (TABLE) for TABLE. The table of values will appear. You can use [▲] and [▼] to scroll up and down the table.

If more than one function is selected in the **Y=** editor, there will be a list of y-values in the table for each selected function.

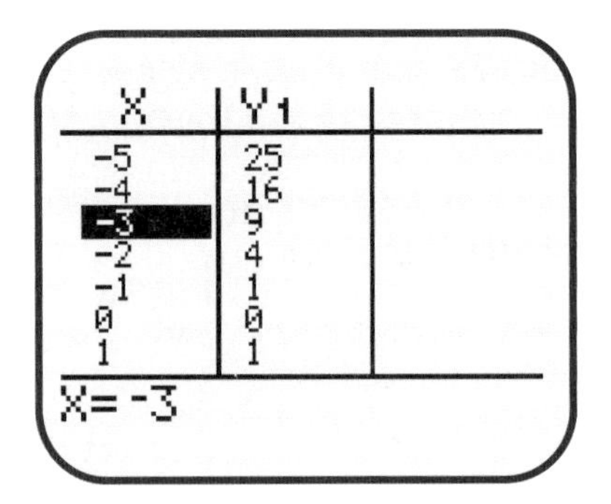

X	Y1	
-5	25	
-4	16	
-3	9	
-2	4	
-1	1	
0	0	
1	1	

X= -3

X	Y1	Y2
-5	25	-125
-4	16	-64
-3	9	-27
-2	4	-8
-1	1	-1
0	0	0
1	1	1

X= -5

Here we have the table for $Y_3 = \frac{1}{x}$. The table abbreviates the values if necessary.

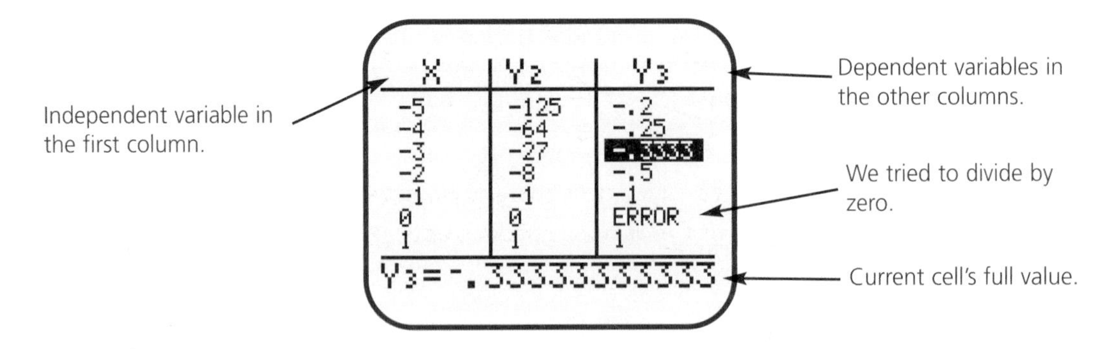

X	Y2	Y3
-5	-125	-.2
-4	-64	-.25
-3	-27	-.3333
-2	-8	-.5
-1	-1	-1
0	0	ERROR
1	1	1

Y3=-.3333333333

CALCULATING ROOTS AND ZEROS OF A FUNCTION

Functions can have more than one zero or x-intercept. The operation **zero** finds the x-intercept closest to your guess. The more accurate your guess, the less time the calculation takes.

Press [2nd] [TRACE] (CALC) and select **2:zero.** The current graph is displayed with **Left Bound?** in the lower corner. Use [▲] or [▼] to move the cursor onto the function for which you are seeking a zero. Use [►] or [◄] to select the left bound of the interval. Press [ENTER].

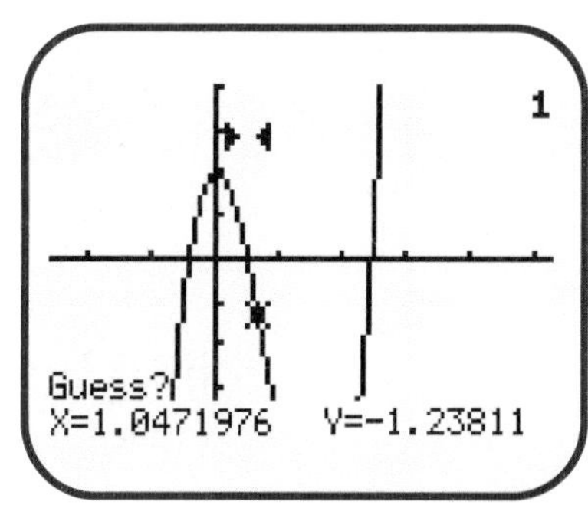

In the same way, select the x-value of the right bound. Indicators on the screen show the interval you have selected. Use [►] or [◄] or enter a value for the x-value of your guess in the selected interval. Press [ENTER].

The coordinates of the zero are displayed and the cursor is on the zero.

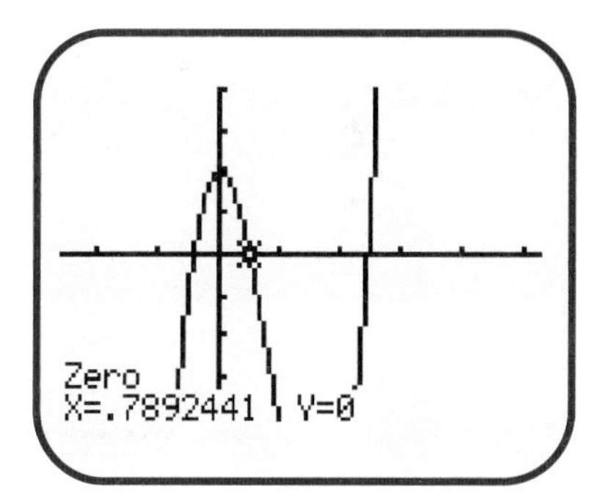

FINDING THE INTERSECTION OF FUNCTIONS

The **intersect** calculation finds the coordinates of a point where two or more functions intersect. The intersection point must appear on the calculator display.

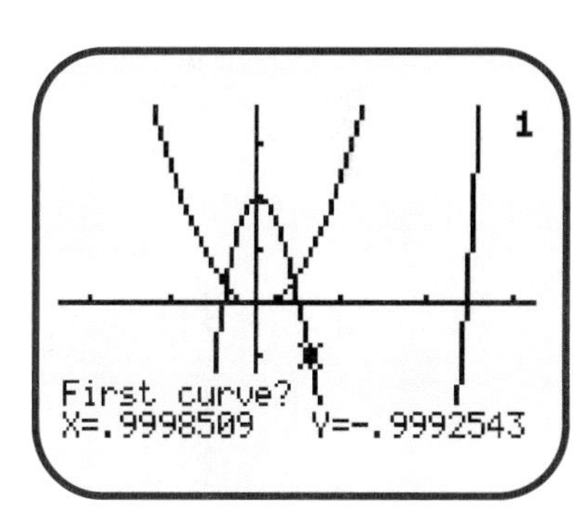

Press [2nd] [TRACE] (CALC) and select **5:intersect.** The current graph is displayed with **First curve?** in the lower corner. Use [▲] or [▼] to move the cursor onto the first function. Press [ENTER].

In the same way, select the second function. Use [►] or [◄] to move the cursor to your guess. Press [ENTER].

The coordinates of the intersection point are displayed and the cursor is on the intersection point.

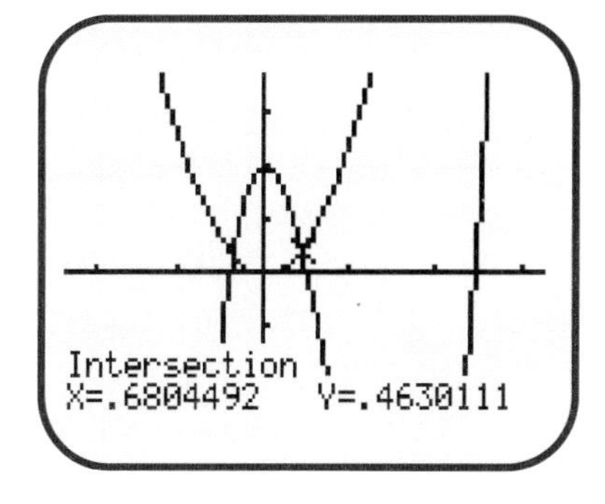

EXPLORING FUNCTION TRANSFORMATIONS

Transformations on functions can be investigated by graphing a family of curves (see previous section).

The DRAW menu can also be used to investigate transformations. The DRAW instructions draw on top of the graph. Drawings are not interactive. Changing the mode, format, or window variables and editing or deselecting functions will remove drawing from the screen.

To display the DRAW menu, press [2nd] [PRGM] (DRAW) and select **6:DrawF.** The home screen appears. Here you enter an expression for the transformed function.

DrawF ■

To select the function, press [VARS]. Move the cursor to Y-VARS. Press [ENTER].

Select the required function and press [ENTER]. The home screen appears. Complete the expression for the transformation. Press [ENTER]. The graph of the original function and its transformed image appear on the screen.

VARS Y-VARS
1:Function...
2:Parametric...
3:Polar...
4:On/Off...

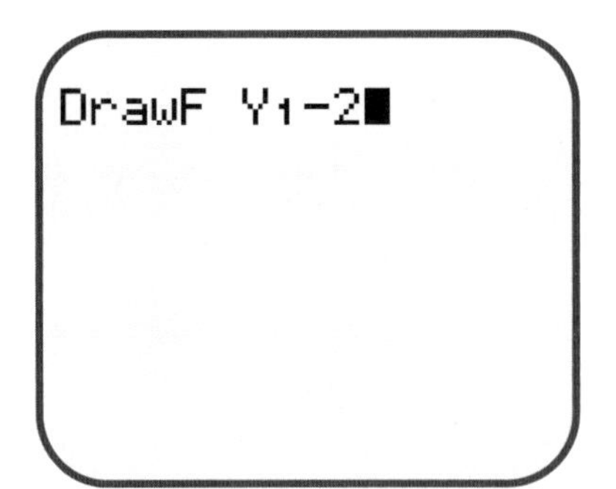

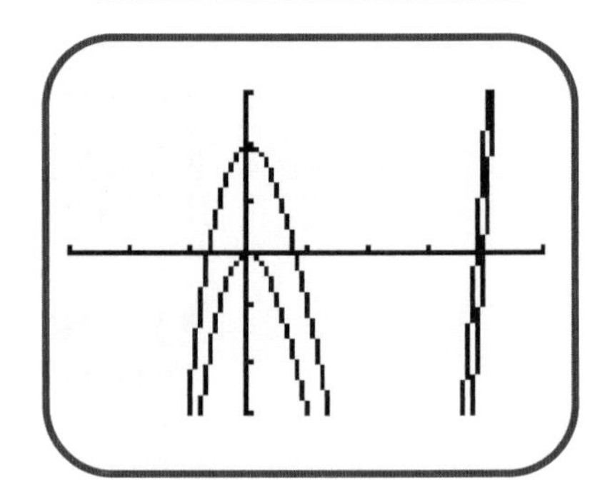

By repeating the process, additional transformations can be added to the graph. To remove the drawn curves, press [2nd] [PRGM] (DRAW) and select **1:ClrDraw.**

GRAPHING FUNCTIONS AND INVERSES

The DRAW menu can be used to draw the inverse of a function. The inverse is not interactive.

To display the DRAW menu, press [2nd] [PRGM] (DRAW) and select **8:DrawInv.**
The home screen appears. Here you enter the name of the original function.

To select the function, press [VARS].
Move the cursor to Y-VARS. Press [ENTER].

Select the required function and press [ENTER].
The home screen appears. Press [ENTER].
The graph of the original function and its inverse appear on the screen.

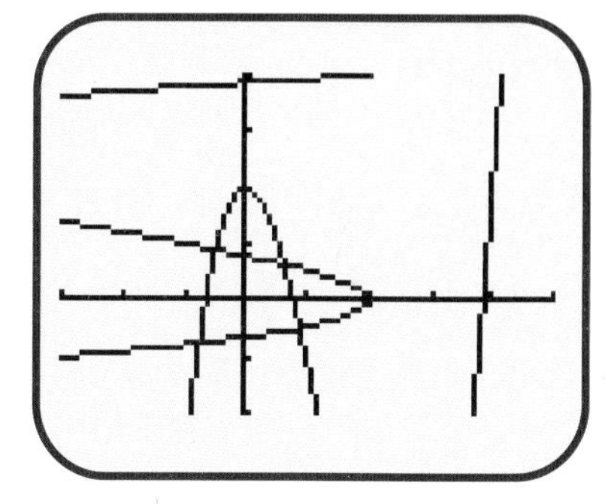

To remove the drawn curves, press [2nd] [PRGM] (DRAW) and select **1:ClrDraw.**

GRAPHING INEQUALITIES

Inequalities can be graphed using the **Shade(** operation on the DRAW menu. This operation shades the area between a lower function and an upper function.

Shade(lowerfunc, upperfunc)

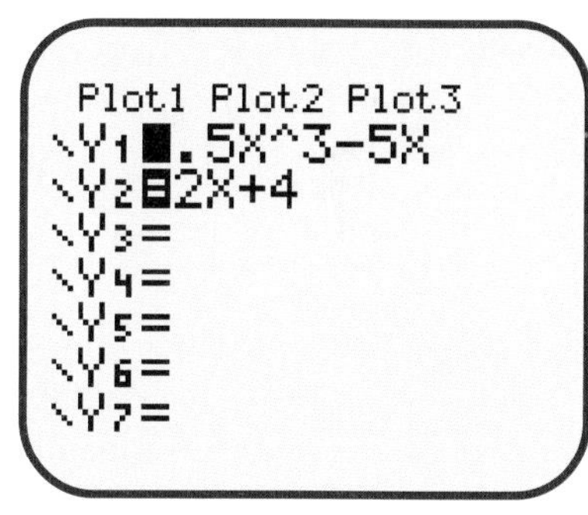

For example, to graph the inequality $0.5x^3 - 5x < 2x + 4$, enter the smaller side of the inequality as $\mathbf{Y_1}$ and the larger side of the inequality as $\mathbf{Y_2}$.

Adjust the window so that all intersection points are shown. If the coordinates of the intersection points are required, see "Finding the Intersection of Functions " in a previous section.

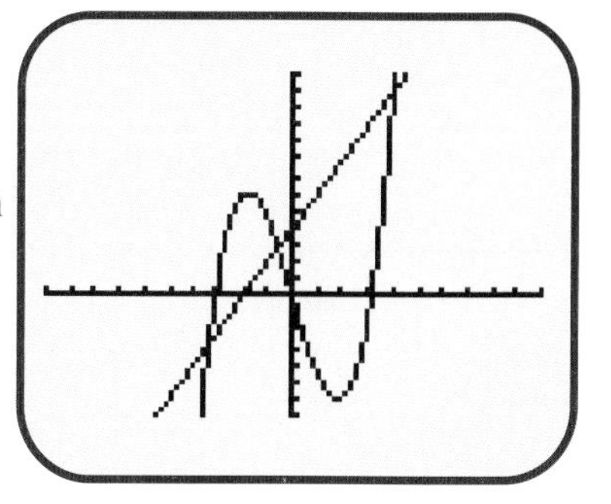

To display the DRAW menu, press [2nd] [PRGM] (DRAW) and select **7:Shade(.** The home screen appears. Here you enter the name of the smaller side of the inequality first.

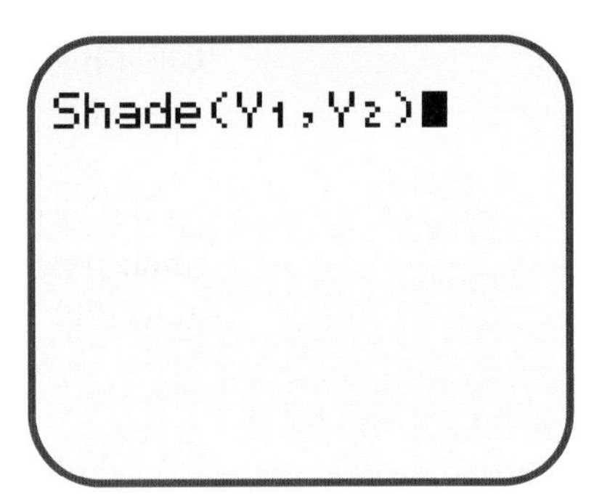

To select the function, press [VARS]. Move the cursor to Y-VARS. Press [ENTER]. Select the required function and press [ENTER]. The home screen appears.

Repeat the process to select the name of the larger side of the inequality. The home screen appears. Press [ENTER]. The region satisfying the inequality is shaded on the screen.

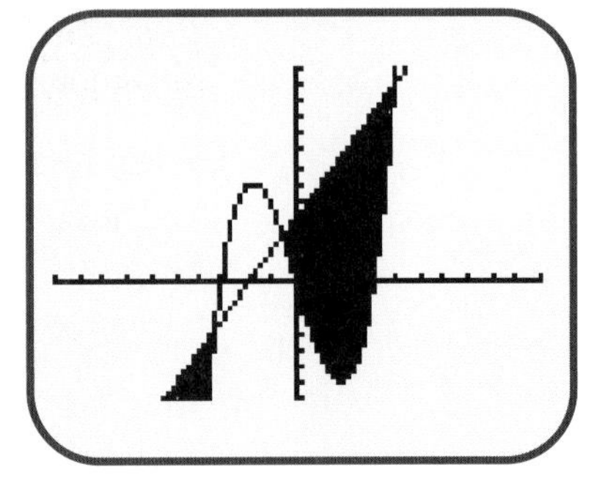

To remove the drawn curves, press [2nd] [PRGM] (DRAW) and select **1:ClrDraw.**

GRAPHING PIECEWISE FUNCTIONS AND EXPLORING CONTINUITY

A piecewise function is graphed using dots, not connected line segments.

To illustrate the procedure we will graph

$$y = \begin{cases} 5 & x \leq 3 \\ x + 4 & 3 < x \leq 6 \\ x - 3 & x > 6 \end{cases}$$

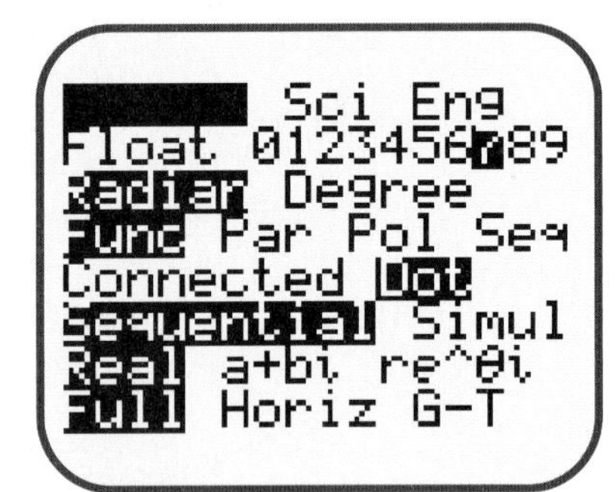

Press [MODE] and select **Func,** then **Dot** and the default settings. Press [Y=] and turn off all functions and stat plots.

Enter the expression for the function in $\mathbf{Y_1}$ as shown on the screen, using [2nd] [MATH] (TEST) menu operations to enter the inequality signs.

Plot1 Plot2 Plot3
\Y1=(5)(X≤3)+(X+4)(3<X)(X≤6)+(X-3)(6<X)
\Y2=
\Y3=
\Y4=
\Y5=

To set the graph style for the function, press [◄] to move the cursor left, past the = sign, to the graph style icon in the first column. Press [ENTER] repeatedly to rotate through the seven graph styles. When you have selected the dotted style, move the cursor back to the equal sign.

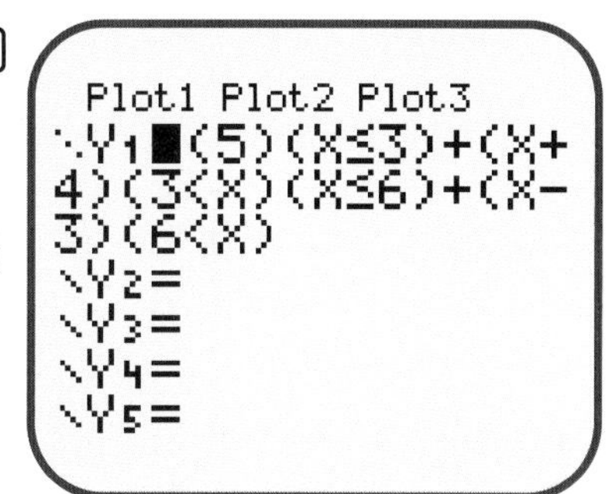

Press [GRAPH]. You may wish to adjust the viewing window.

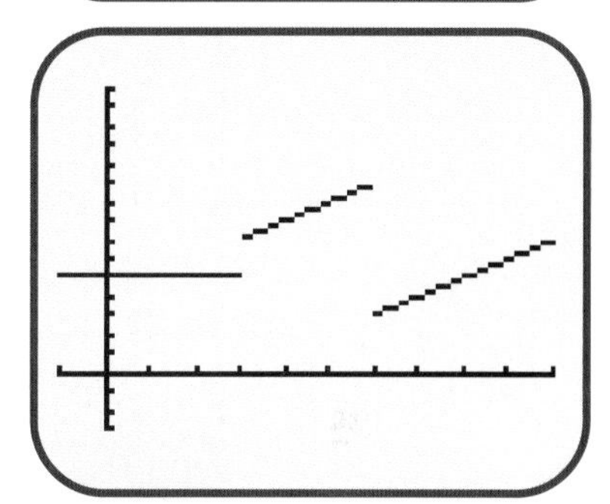

To explore the continuity of the function, we can use the TRACE operation.

Press [2nd] [ZOOM] (FORMAT) and turn on **CoordOn.**

Press [ZOOM] and select **2:Zoom In.** Move the cursor into the centre of the region where you wish to investigate the continuity of the function. Press [ENTER]. The graph is redrawn with the cursor in the centre of the screen.

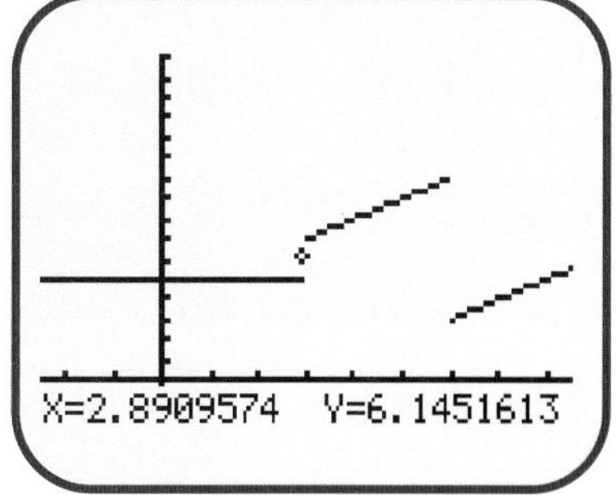

Press [TRACE]. Move the cursor along the curve, observing the value of the coordinates as you approach the point of discontinuity.

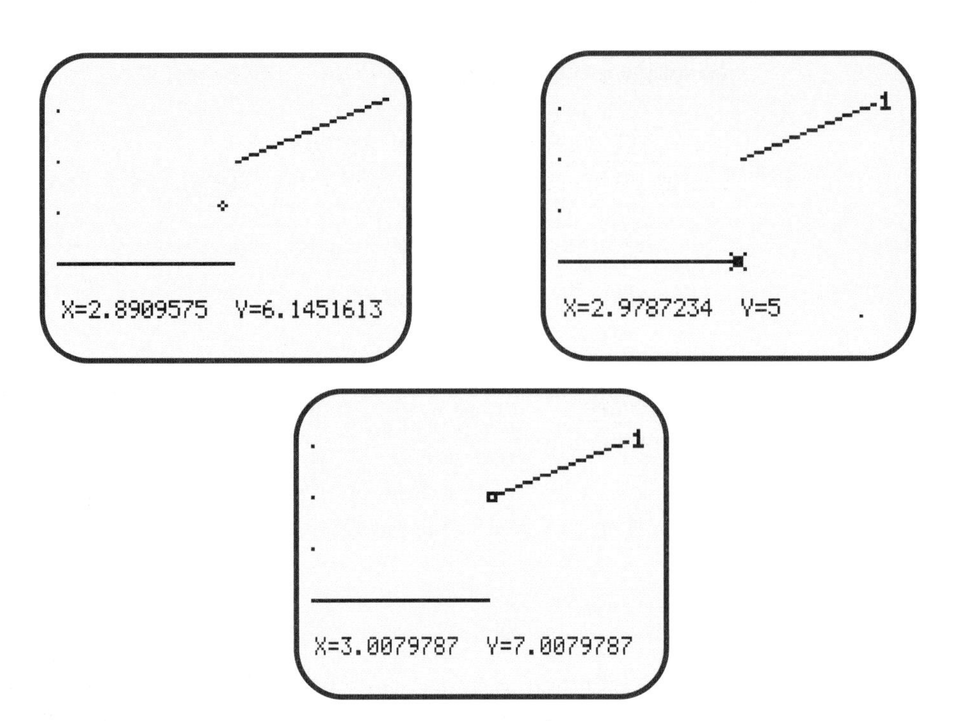

You can also use a table of values to explore the continuity of the function. See "Using a Table of Values to Explore Limits of Functions," in a following section.

DRAWING LINE SEGMENTS

Line segments can be drawn in two ways, using the DRAW menu. The DRAW instructions draw on top of the graph. Drawings are not interactive. Changing the mode, format, or window variables and editing or deselecting functions will remove drawing from the screen.

To remove a DRAW object from the screen, press [2nd] [PRGM] (DRAW) and select **1:ClrDraw.**

Drawing a line segment when a graph is displayed

Press [2nd] [PRGM] (DRAW) and select **2:Line**. Place the cursor on the point where you want the line segment to begin and press [ENTER].

Move the cursor to the point where you want the line segment to end and press [ENTER].

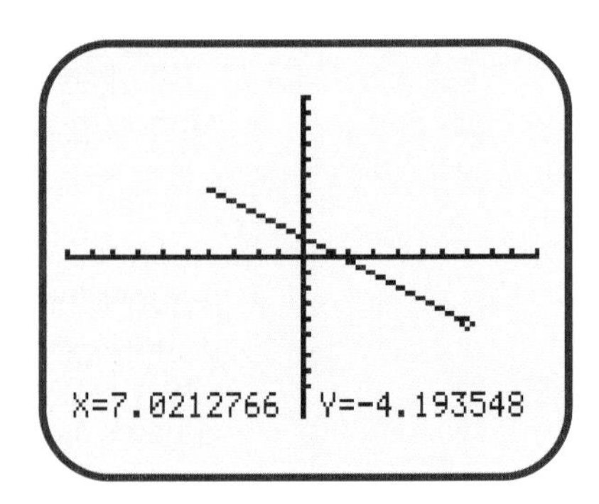

Drawing a line segment from the home screen

DRAW

Press [2nd] [PRGM] and select **2:Line.** Enter the coordinates of the beginning and ending points of the line segment. Press [ENTER].

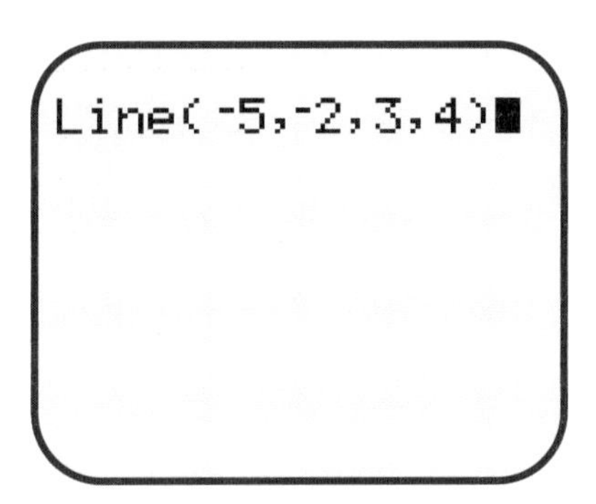

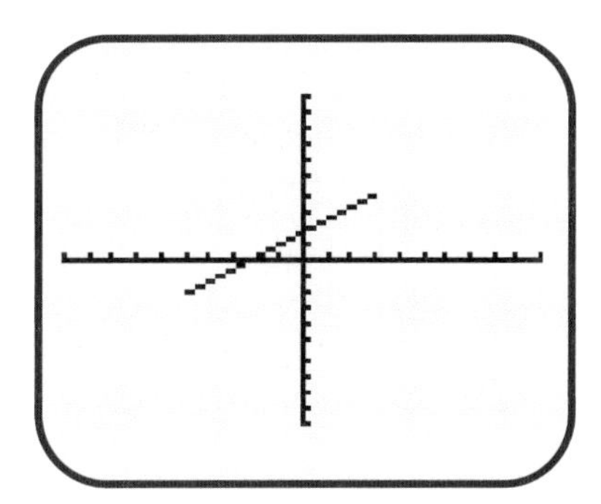

DRAWING TANGENTS

Tangents can be drawn in two ways, using the DRAW menu. The DRAW instructions draw on top of the graph. Drawings are not interactive. Changing the mode, format, or window variables and editing or deselecting functions will remove drawing from the screen.

DRAW

To remove a DRAW object from the screen, press [2nd] [PRGM] and select **1:ClrDraw.**

Drawing a tangent when a graph is displayed

DRAW

Press [2nd] [PRGM] and select **5:Tangent.**

Use [▼] or [▲] to move the cursor to the function for which you want to draw the tangent. Use [◄] or [►] or enter a number to move the cursor to the point on the function at which you want to draw the tangent.

Press [ENTER].

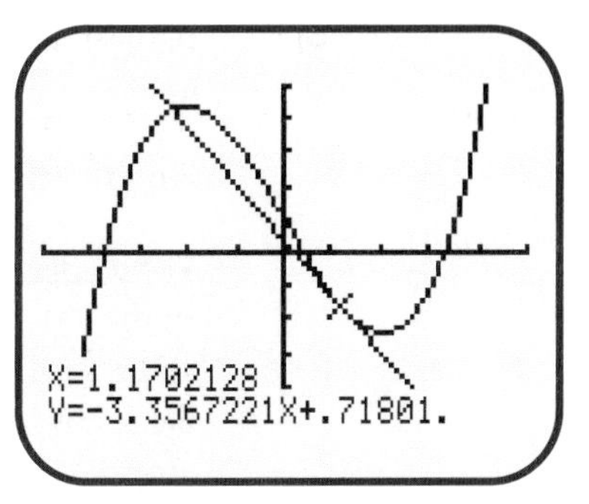

In **Func** mode, the *x*-coordinate at which the tangent was drawn is shown, along with the equation of the tangent. In all other modes, the value of **dy/dx** is shown. Changing the fixed decimal setting on the mode screen will reduce the number of decimals shown in the tangent equation.

Drawing a tangent when the home screen is displayed

Press [2nd] [PRGM] (DRAW) and select **5:Tangent.** To select the function, press [VARS]. Move the cursor to Y-VARS. Press [ENTER]. Select the required function and press [ENTER]. The home screen appears. Enter the x-coordinate at which you wish to draw the tangent. Press [ENTER].

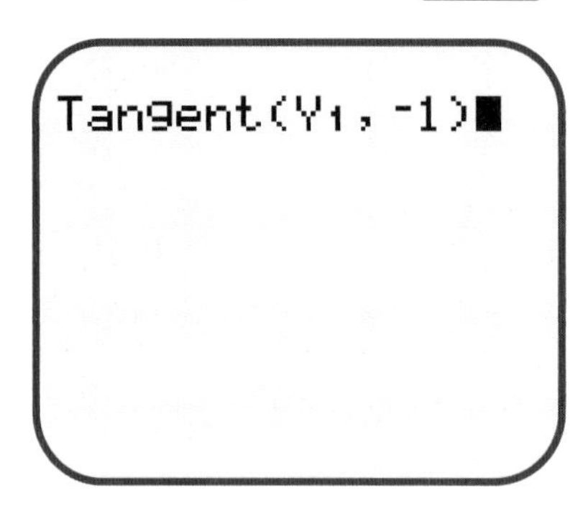

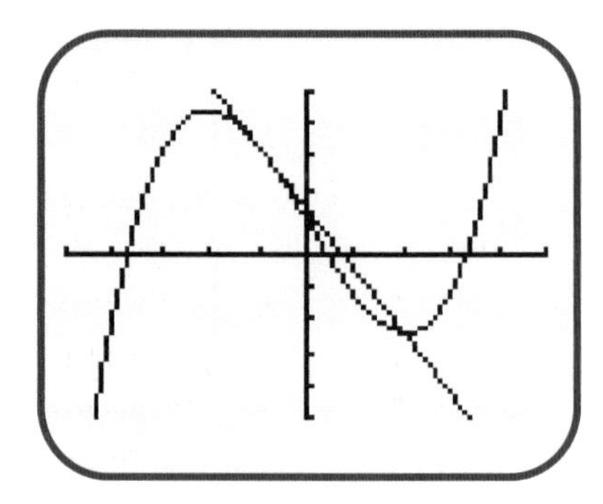

USING A TABLE OF VALUES TO EXPLORE LIMITS OF FUNCTIONS

To illustrate exploring limits using a graphing calculator, we will investigate the function $y = \frac{x^2 - 25}{x - 5}$.

In the ZOOM menu, choose **8:ZInteger.** Points are plotted for integral values of x. Notice the hole in the graph at $x = 5$.

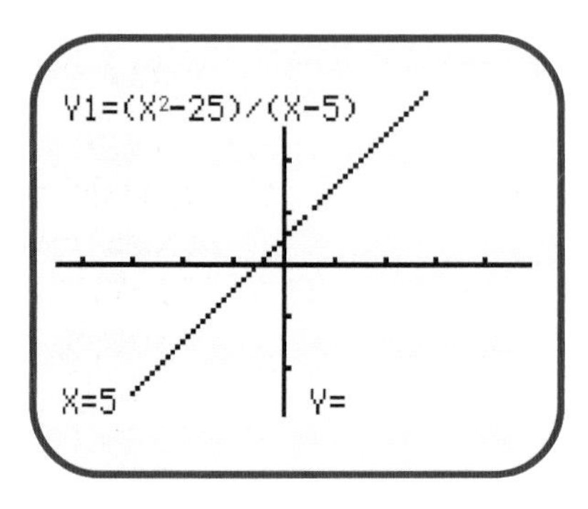

We can explore the limits of this function from the left and from the right, as x approaches 5, using a table of values.

Highlight the function for which you wish to create a table of values.

Press [2nd] [WINDOW] (TBLSET) for TABLE SETUP.

In the TABLE SETUP window, enter the starting value for the x-coordinate (**TblStart**=) and the increments by which the x-coordinate is to increase (**ΔTbl**=).

Choose a starting value that is very close to the point at which you wish to investigate the limit. In this case, we have a value to the left of 5, but close to 5. Be sure that **Auto** is highlighted in the last two lines.

Press [2nd] [GRAPH] (TABLE) for TABLE. The table of values will appear. You can use [▲] and [▼] to scroll up and down the table. As you scroll down the table, the value of x approaches 5, the value at which we are investigating a limit. Observe the corresponding y-values as x approaches 5.

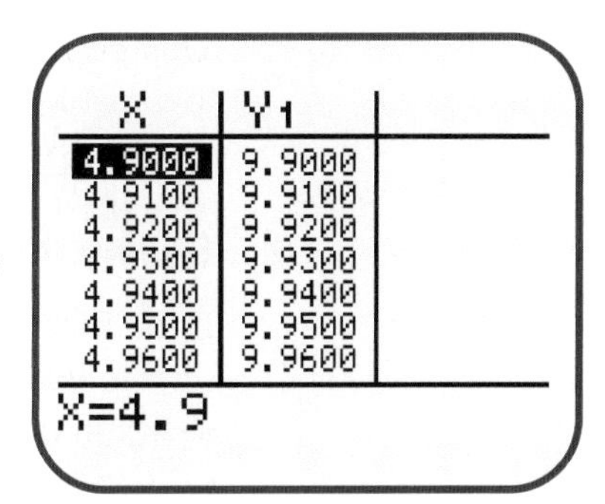

To investigate the limit from the right as x approaches 5, choose a value for **TlbStart,** in the TABLE SETUP window, that is close to the point at which we are investigating the limit and to the right of that point. Scroll up the table and observe the values of y as x approaches 5.

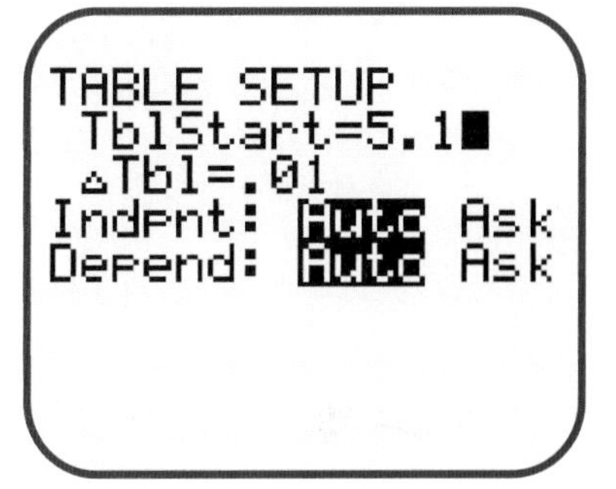

Using a split screen, you can see the graph and the table of values simultaneously.

To split a screen vertically, press [MODE]. Move the cursor to the bottom line of the mode screen and select **G-T** (graph-table mode). Use the TABLE SETUP window to define the starting point and increment for the table. To move from the graph to the table on the split screen, press [2nd] [GRAPH] (TABLE).

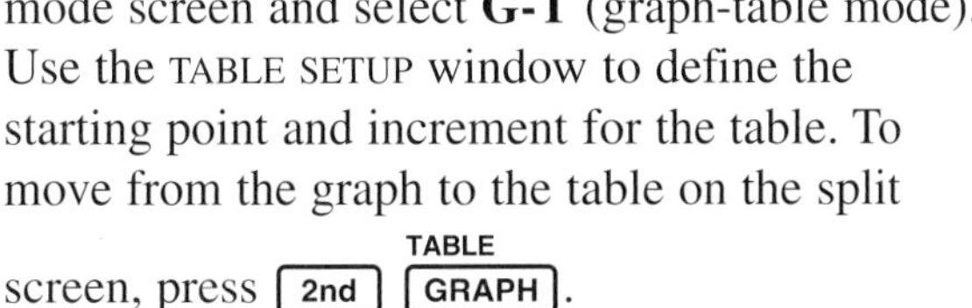

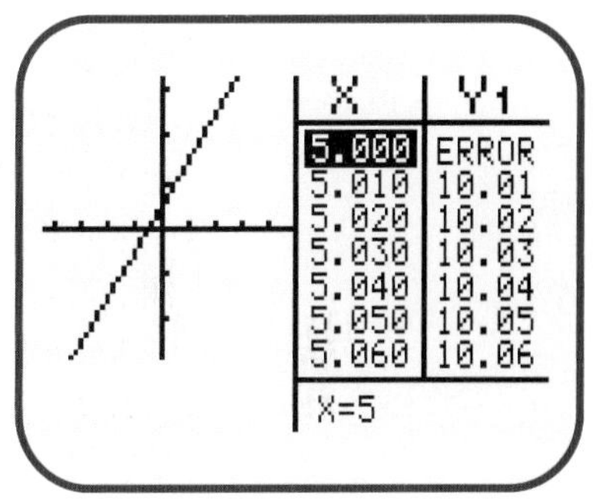

As you scroll up the table, notice that if $x = 5$, there is an error for y. To get closer to an x value of 5, choose a smaller increment in the TABLE SETUP window.

FINDING THE NUMERICAL DERIVATIVE AT A GIVEN POINT

The numerical derivative at a given point can be calculated in two ways.

Finding the numerical derivative of an expression

Press [MATH] and select **8:nDeriv(.**

nDeriv(expression, variable, value)

nDeriv(X²-2,X,-4)

This gives an approximate value of the derivative of the expression, with respect to variable, at a given value of the variable.
Press [ENTER] and the value of the derivative is displayed.

Finding the numerical derivative of a function

If the function is entered in the **Y=** editor screen, it may be easier to use the operation **dy/dx** in the CALCULATE menu to find the numerical derivative (slope) of a function at a point.

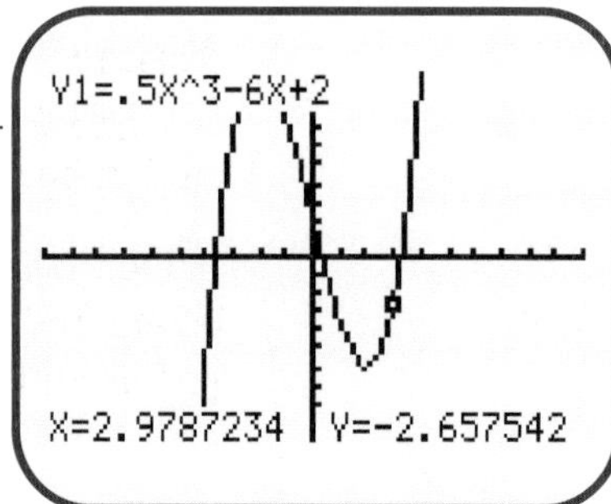

Press [2nd] [TRACE] (CALC) and select **6:dy/dx.** The graphing window is displayed.

Use [▲] or [▼] to move the cursor to the function for which you want to find the numerical derivative.

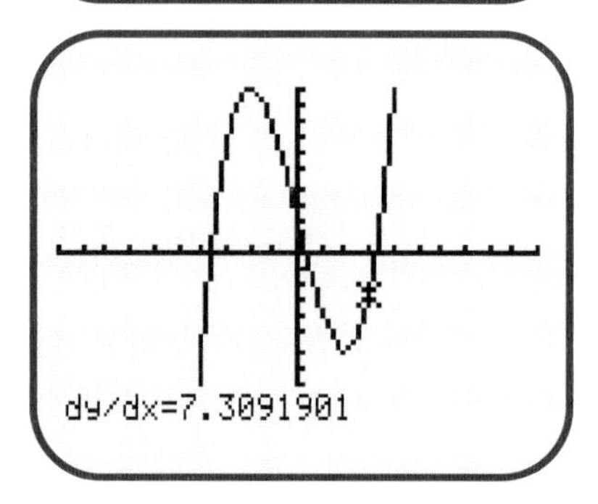

Use [▶] or [◀] or enter a number to select the point at which the derivative is to be calculated. Press [ENTER]. An approximate value of the numerical derivative, calculated at that point, is displayed.

CALCULATING MAX/MIN VALUES

The max/min value can be calculated in two ways.

Finding the max/min value of an expression

Press [MATH] and select **6:fMin(** or **7:fMax(**:

fMin(expression, variable, lower, upper)

fMax(expression, variable, lower, upper)

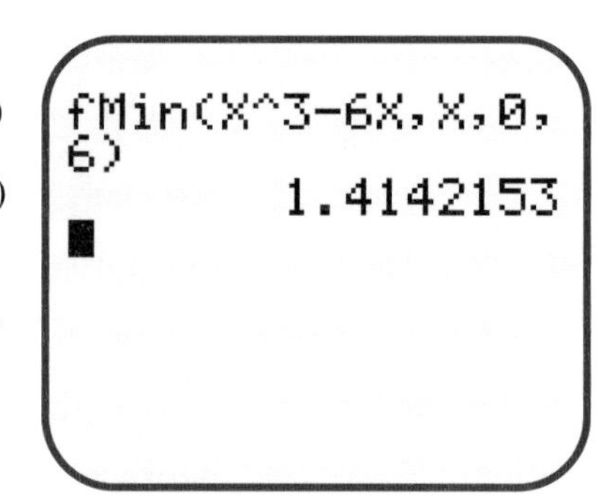

This gives an approximate value at which the minimum or maximum value of the expression, with respect to variable, occurs between the lower and upper values of the variable.
Press [ENTER] and the value of the variable is displayed.

Finding the max/min value of a function

If the function is entered in the **Y=** editor screen, or if you do not know appropriate values for the lower and upper values of the variable, it may be easier to use the operation **maximum** or **minimum** in the CALCULATE menu. The operation finds the maximum or minimum closest to your guess. The more accurate your guess, the less time the calculation takes.

Press [2nd] [TRACE] (CALC) and select **3:minimum** or **4:maximum.** The graphing window is displayed with **Left Bound?** in the lower corner. Use [▶] or [◀] or enter a value to select the left bound of the interval. Press [ENTER].

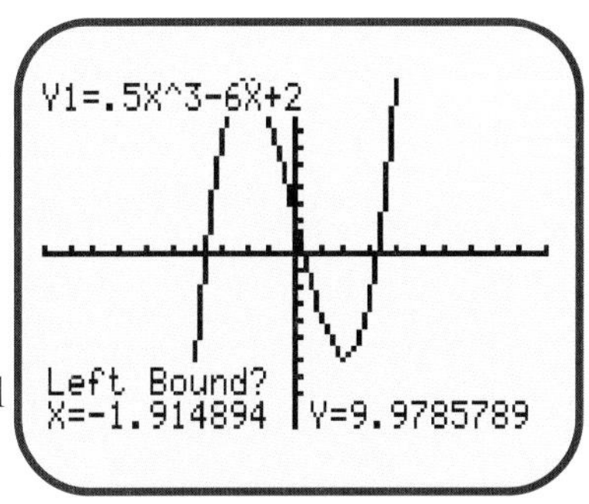

In the same way, select the *x*-value of the right bound. Indicators on the screen show the interval you have selected.

Use [▶] or [◀], or enter a value for the *x*-value of your guess in the selected interval. Press [ENTER].

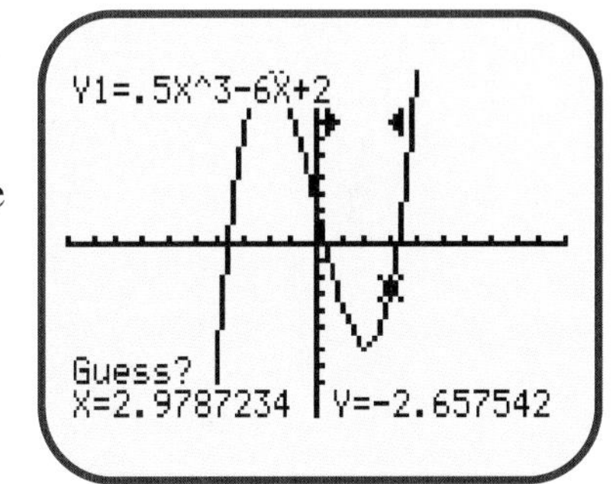

The coordinates of the maximum or minimum are displayed, and the cursor is on the maximum or minimum point.

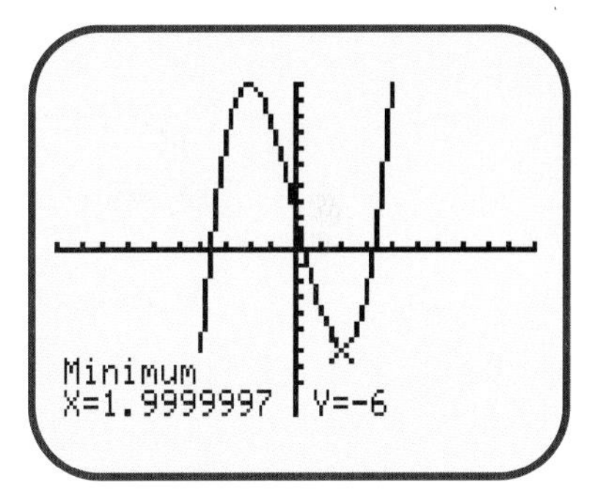

INSTRUCTIONS FOR ZAP-A-GRAPH

Zap-a-Graph is an easy to use graphing computer program.

Simultaneously graphing *f*, *f* ', *f* "

Click on **Define** and select the type and form of function *f*. Enter the coordinates and click on **Plot.** If **Show Equation** is selected in the OPTIONS menu, the equation is displayed at the bottom of the screen.

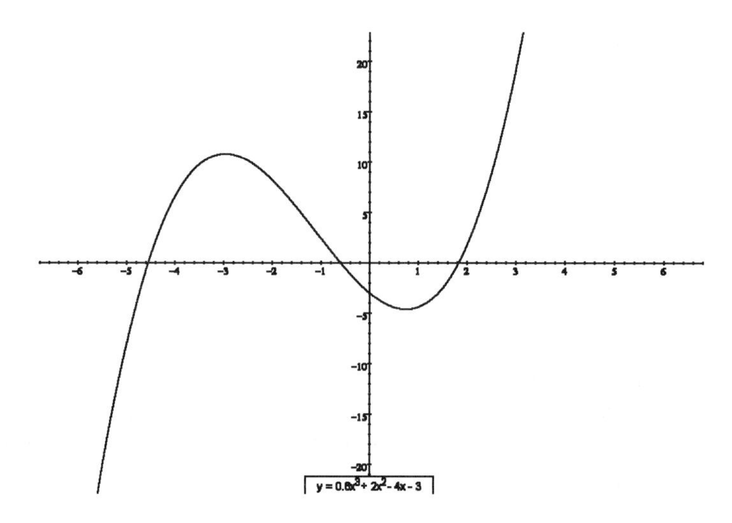

To graph f', click on the OPTIONS menu and select **Derivative.** If **Show Equation** is selected, the equation of f' is displayed.

To graph f'', repeat the process.

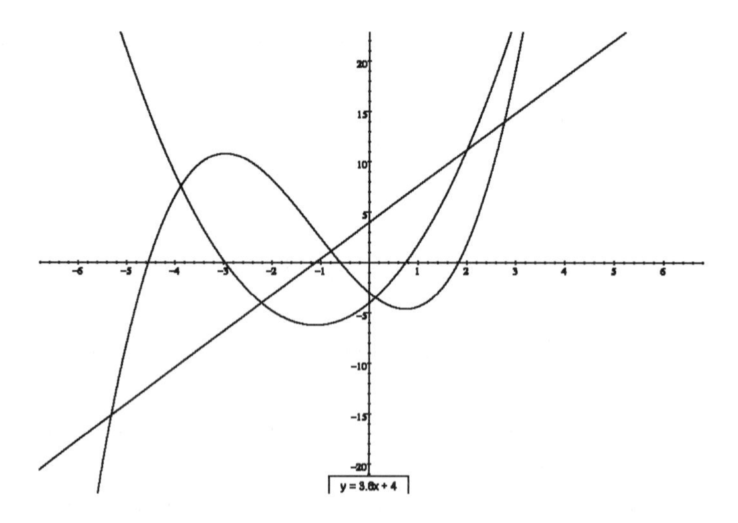

Calculating approximate area under a curve using rectangles

Click on **Define** and select the type and form of function *f*.
Enter the coordinates and click on **Plot.** Click on **Options** and select **Area.**

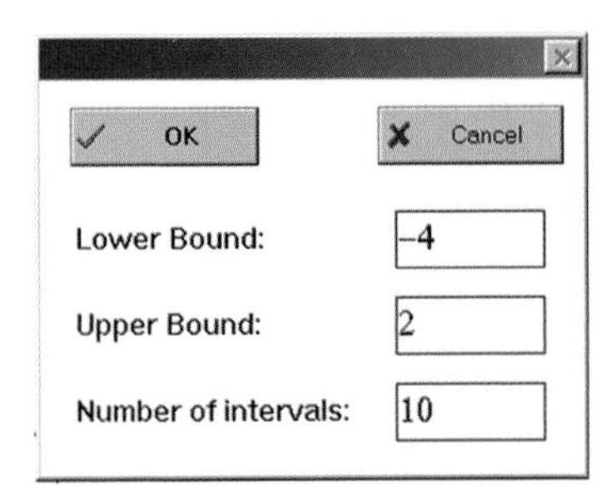

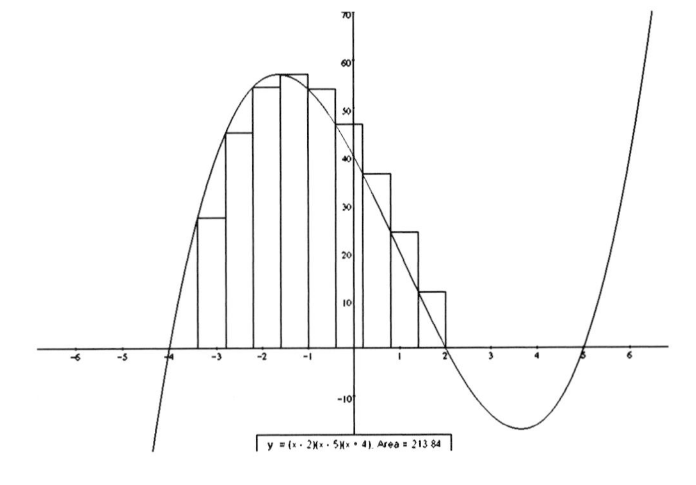

Enter lower bound, upper bound, and the number of intervals. Click on **OK.**
The approximate area under the curve is displayed.
By increasing the number of intervalsc you can obtain a better approximation of the area.

TECHNOLOGY EXTENSION FOR SECTION 8.1—DERIVATIVES OF EXPONENTIAL FUNCTIONS

Using a spreadsheet option

Try the following spreadsheet option for the Investigation on page 300 in Chapter 8.

INVESTIGATION

1. Set up a spreadsheet as shown.
In cell **C2**, enter the formula =(A2^B2-1)/B2.

C2 = =(A2^B2-1)/B2

	A	B	C	D
1	b	h	(b^h-1)/h	
2	1	0.0001	0.000000000000	
3				
4				

2. Using the FORMAT menu, set the number of decimal places displayed in column C to 10.

3. In cell **A3**, enter the formula =A2+1. In cell B3, enter the formula =B2.
Fill columns A, B, and C down to row 7.

4. Clear entries in column A. Enter 2.5 in cell **A2** and the formula =A2+0.1 in cell **A3.** Fill down.

5. Clear entries in column A. Enter 2.700 in cell **A2** and the formula =A2+0.001 in cell **A3.** Fill down.

Appendix D

PERFORMANCE ASSESSMENT AND CAREER LINK LETTERHEAD TASKS

Advanced Functions and Introductory Calculus Student Rubric End of Chapter Task Generic Rubric

This student rubric may assist you in understanding general assessment criteria and desired levels of performance related to Career Link Wrap-Up tasks and other mathematics assignments. You may wish to use this general rubric to

- identify what to pay attention to;
- outline the criteria clearly;
- help spot and solve weaknesses in your own work and in the work of others; and
- develop more informative feedback about strengths and areas that need improvement.

However, it is important to note the generic nature of this rubric. You can work with your teachers to develop more specific coaching or scoring criteria. Helpful rubrics are clear rubrics and therefore may involve many decisions, including defining quality, determining criteria, weighing criteria, setting a standard, determining levels, developing descriptors, and translating levels to marks or grades.

Assessment Category	LEVEL 1	LEVEL 2	LEVEL 3	LEVEL 4
Knowledge/ Understanding	• A mathematical model is generated with significant errors • Demonstrates, through algorithmic work, a limited understanding of concepts	• A mathematical model is generated with minor errors • Demonstrates, through algorithmic work, some understanding of concepts	• A correct mathematical model is generated • Demonstrates, through algorithmic work, a considerable understanding of concepts	• A correct mathematical model is generated *and verified* • Demonstrates, through algorithmic work, a thorough understanding of concepts
Thinking/Inquiry/ Problem Solving	• Limited mathematical reasoning • Sequences and selects tools with limited effectiveness	• Some mathematical reasoning • Sequences and selects tools with some effectiveness	• Considerable mathematical reasoning • Sequences and selects tools with considerable effectiveness	• Thorough mathematical reasoning extended to the general case • Sequences and selects tools efficiently and effectively
Communication	• Explanations and justifications have limited detail and lack clarity • Infrequently uses mathematical symbols, terminology, and conventions correctly	• Explanations and justifications are partially understandable, with some detail • Uses mathematical symbols, terminology, and conventions correctly some of the time	• Explanations and justifications are clear and understandable • Uses mathematical symbols, terminology, and conventions correctly most of the time	• Explanations and justifications are particularly clear and thoroughly detailed • Consistently and meticulously uses mathematical symbols, terminology, and conventions correctly
Application	• Applies concepts and procedures in an unfamiliar setting correctly only with significant assistance	• Applies concepts and procedures in an unfamiliar setting correctly with some assistance	• Independently applies concepts and procedures correctly in an unfamiliar setting	• Independently applies concepts and procedures in an unfamiliar setting using new or modified strategies

Letterhead Problem One for Chapter 4—Derivatives: Polynomials and Differentiation Rules

HealthLink
Health-Care Consultants
322 Transdermal Drive
Ste. 405
Sudbury, ON
P3C IA7

Re: *Ontario Health-Care Expenditure Mathematical Modelling Project*

Dear Advanced Functions and Introductory Calculus Student:

As you may be aware, Ontario faced unparalleled growth in health-care costs in the late 1990s. As a health-care consultant, I require accurate population projections and projected health-care expenditures in order to make recommendations on how we can make our health-care system viable and sustainable over the long term. I need your help, as an expert in advanced functions and differential calculus, to prepare mathematical models for population, health-care expenditures, and per-capita health-care costs. I will also need to know how quickly health-care expenses are growing per capita. These projections will help me to prepare public education materials on the use and abuse of the health-care system.

Please prepare a report that explains all your work in completing the following tasks:

1. Mathematical model for population as a function of time and predicted populations on January 1, 2001 and January 1, 2002;
2. Mathematical model for total health-care expenditures as a function of time and predicted expenditures in 2000/2001 and 2001/2002;
3. Mathematical model for per-capita health-care expenditures as a function of time and predicted per-capita expenditures in 2000/2001 and 2001/2002;
4. Mathematical model for the rate of change of per-capita health-care expenditures as a function of time and the rate of change on January 1, 2001 and January 1, 2002.

1

I have collected the information in the tables below to assist in developing the models:

Annual Ontario Population
(as of July 1 each year)

Year	Ontario Population (in thousands)
1990	10 299.6
1991	10 427.6
1992	10 570.5
1993	10 690.4
1994	10 827.5
1995	10 964.9
1996	11 100.9
1997	11 249.5
1998	11 384.4
1999	11 513.8

Source: Statistics Canada, *Canada Year Book 2001*, page 93

Annual Ontario Health-Care Costs
(assume a July 1 to June 30 budget year)

Year	Ontario Health-Care Expenditures (in thousands)
1989/90	15 442.8
1990/91	16 423.9
1991/92	18 418.6
1992/93	18 894.1
1993/94	18 472.1
1994/95	18 787.2
1995/96	18 419.4
1996/97	18 736.7
1997/98	19 111.3
1998/99	20 403.9
1999/00$_f$	21 823.7

f = forecast
Source: Canadian Institute for Health Information, Table C6.1 (www.cihi.ca)

Good luck and thank you in advance for all your work.

Yours truly,

Jeannine Truscott

Jeannine Truscott
President

2

In your report clearly explain
- the model development process (e.g., how you manipulated the data before performing regressions);
- your reasons for selecting your models (e.g., why you think a quadratic model is appropriate); and
- how the degree of the polynomial in your model affects the shape of the function and, consequently, the predictions of population and health-care costs.

Letterhead Problem Two for Chapter 8—Derivatives of Exponential and Logarithmic Functions: Exponential and Logarithmic Problem

Ivan K. Fedoruk, P. Eng.
1106 Valency Court
Chatham, NB
E1N 3V7

Re: *Electrical Engineering Research Project*

Dear Advanced Functions and Introductory Calculus Student:

I am a retired engineer with a strange hobby. In response to increased oil and electricity costs and environmental concerns, I spend each day in my workshop trying to develop a highly energy-efficient light bulb. I have a promising prototype, but in 100 trials, it has burnt out 95 times. I know that if the power consumed by the bulb exceeds 60 watts (W) or if the power increases at a rate of more than 0.3 watts per millisecond (W/ms) at the instant the switch is turned on, the bulb burns out. Please help me to determine why the bulb is burning out by using your knowledge of advanced functions and calculus.

I have data on current (I) and resistance (R) in the bulb, and I know that power (P) is related to current and voltage (V) by the equation $P = VI$. In addition, voltage, current, and resistance are related through ohms law ($V = IR$). I recall that current and time are related in a "bounded exponential decay" relationship, with an initial current of 3.0 A that quickly declines towards the steady-state (minimum) current of 1.5 A. I have measured the current at 2.052 A after 200 ms. From my old notes, I have an equation for "bounded exponential decay":

$$y(t) = y_{\min} + (y_{\max} - y_{\min})e^{-kt}$$

Resistance and time are related in a "bounded exponential growth" relationship, with an initial resistance of 5 ohms that quickly grows towards the steady-state (maximum) resistance of 20 ohms. I have measured the resistance at 13.260 ohms after 200 ms. The equation for "bounded exponential growth" from my notes is:

$$y(t) = y_{\text{max}} - (y_{\text{max}} - y_{\text{min}})e^{-kt}$$

Please prepare a report that explains all your work in completing the following tasks:

1. Determine mathematical models for predicting $I(t)$, $R(t)$ and $P(t)$.
2. Explain the concept of "bounded growth and decay" through the equations and graphs of $I(t)$ and $R(t)$.
3. Determine why the light bulb is burning out.

Good luck and thank you in advance for all your effort.

Yours truly,

Ivan Fedoruk, P. Eng.

In your report clearly explain

- the model development process (e.g., how you verified your models were correct);
- the constants and variables in the bounded growth and decay equations and how they affect the shape of the graph;
- the role calculus plays in this problem; and
- how you used technology in this problem.

Letterhead Problem Three for Chapter 5—Applications of Derivatives: Optimization

1594 Burton St.
Edmonton, AB
T0G 1M0

Re: *Optimal Production Levels for CD-ROM Games*

Dear Advanced Functions and Introductory Calculus Student:

I am the president of a discount computer game company. Our sales have been suffering for the last year because our average production cost has risen to $9.60 per game, exceeding our sales price of $9.40 each. We currently sell 1000 units per day. In addition to losing money, we are in some other serious trouble because our financial controller took a job with a competitor, and subsequently all of our cost-accounting records mysteriously disappeared.

About a month before the controller left, he proposed that we could get "out of the red" by dropping our price to $7.90 per game. He indicated that by dropping our price, we would be able to secure additional customers that would result in sales increasing to 2000 units per day. In turn, he said, we would start garnering profits of $200 per day at the 2000-unit sales level. Of course I immediately dismissed his idea because the $7.90 price is $1.70 less than our average cost. To me it seemed obvious that this price decrease would only exacerbate our losses. In hindsight, however, I am wondering if maybe our controller was right after all. That is why I am bringing you into the picture.

1

I need your expertise in advanced functions and calculus to determine, first, if we can make the $200 profit per day with a $7.90 price and sales of 2000 units per day and, second, what the optimum production level would be at the $7.90 price. The only cost-accounting information that I can share with you is that our variable costs depend solely on the square of the number of games made. I do not know what our fixed costs are. I would appreciate it if all of your calculations for cost, revenue, and profit were kept on a per-day basis as that is what I am used to working with.

Please prepare a report that explains all your work as you:

a. determine the cost structure (fixed and variable costs) for manufacturing the games;
b. confirm or deny that it is possible to have a profit of $200 per day at the $7.90 price and 2000-unit sales level;
c. determine the optimum level of production/sales at the $7.90 price; and
d. describe how it is possible that dropping the price below the current average price can increase the profits of my company.

Good luck and thank you in advance for all your work.

Yours truly,

T. B. LaRivière

Thomas B. LaRivière

President and CEO

2

In your report clearly explain

- how you determined the relationship between total, fixed and variable costs; and
- why calculus is relevant in this problem (e.g., comparing average versus marginal cost)

Glossary

Absolute Value the positive value for a real number, disregarding the sign. Written $|x|$. For example, $|3| = 3$, $|-4| = 4$, and $|0| = 0$.

Absolute Value Function a function consisting of terms that are expressed as absolute values. Example: $f(x) = |x|$.

Absolute Zero -273.15, the approximate number of degrees on the Celsius scale of absolute zero. On the Kelvin scale, 0 degrees K.

Acceleration the rate of change of velocity with respect to time $\left(\frac{dv}{dt}\right)$ or the second derivative of displacement with respect to time $\left(\frac{d^2s}{dt^2}\right)$.

Accuracy the number of significant digits given in a number.

Acute Angle an angle whose measure is less than 90°.

Algebraic Equation a statement that two expressions are equal; for example, $3x + y = 8$.

Algebraic Function a relation that assigns each element in the domain exactly one element in the range.

Algorithm derived from the name of a Persian author, Abu Ja'far Mohammed ibn al Khowarizmi (c. 825). A step-by-step description of a solution to a problem.

Amplitude the maximum displacement of a periodic wave.

Analog a descriptive term for a device that uses physical quantities rather than digits for storing and processing information.

Angle given two intersecting lines or line segments, the amount of rotation about the point of intersection (the vertex) required to bring one into correspondence with the other.

Angle of Depression the angle between the horizontal and the line of sight to an object below the horizontal.

Angle of Elevation the angle between the horizontal and the line of sight to an object above the horizontal.

Arithmetic Progression (Sequence) an ordering of numbers or terms where the difference between consecutive terms is a constant.

Arithmetic Series the sum of the terms of an arithmetic sequence.

Assumption a statement that is to be accepted as true for a particular argument or discussion.

Asymptote a line having the property that the distance from a point P on a curve to the line approaches zero as the distance from P to the origin increases indefinitely. The line and the curve get closer and closer but never touch. See **Horizontal**, **Vertical**, and **Slant Asymptote**.

Average Rate of Change given by the difference quotient $\frac{\Delta y}{\Delta x} = \frac{f(a + h) - f(a)}{h}$. The average rate of change of the function $f(x)$ over the interval $x = a$ to $x = a + h$.

Axiom a statement assumed to be true without formal proof. Axioms are the basis from which other theorems and statements are deduced through proof.

Axis of Symmetry a line that passes through a figure in such a way that the part of the figure on one side of the line is a mirror reflection of the part on the other side; an exact correspondence of form or shape on opposite sides of the line.

Base in the exponential expression b^p, b is called the base and p is the exponent.

Calculus a branch of mathematics, discovered independently by Sir Isaac Newton and Gottfried Wilhelm von Leibniz, that deals with the instantaneous rate of change of a function (Differential Calculus) and the area under a function (Integral Calculus).

Cardioid a plane curve traced by a point on a circle rolling on the outside of a circle of equal radius.

Cartesian Coordinate System a reference system in 2-space, consisting of two axes at right angles, or 3-space (three axes) in which any point in the plane is located by its displacements from these fixed lines (axes). The origin is the common point from which each displacement is measured. In 2-space, a set of two numbers or coordinates is required to uniquely define a position; in 3-space, three coordinates are required.

Catenary the curve a hanging flexible wire or chain assumes when supported at its ends and acted upon by a uniform gravitational force. A curve whose equation is of the form $y = \frac{a}{2}\left(e^{\frac{x}{a}} + e^{-\frac{x}{a}}\right)$.

Chain Rule if $f(x)$ and $g(x)$ are continuous and differentiable functions, then the composite function $h(x) = f[g(x)]$ has a derivative given by $h'(x) = f'[g(x)]g'(x)$. In Leibniz notation, if $y = f(u)$ where $u = g(x)$, then y is a composite function and $\frac{dy}{dx} = \frac{dy}{du}\frac{du}{dx}$.

Characteristic the integral part of the representation of a logarithm. For example, in the expression $\log_{10}643 = 2.808$, the characteristic is 2. The characteristic can have positive and negative values, as well as zero. See **Mantissa**.

Charles' Law discovered by Jacques Charles (1746–1823). A volume of gas at a constant pressure varies linearly with the temperature of the gas: $V \propto T$ where V is measured in litres and T is measured in degrees Celsius.

Circle the set of all points in the plane that are equidistant from a fixed point. The circumference of a circle is $2\pi r$ and the area is πr^2.

Common Difference the difference between any two consecutive terms in an arithmetic sequence. For example, in the sequence 5, 9, 13, 17, …, the common difference is 4.

Common Ratio the ratio of consecutive terms in a geometric sequence. For example, in the sequence 3, 12, 48, 192, …, the common ratio is 4.

Complementary Angle two angles are called complementary if the two angles add up to a right angle.

Complex Number a number of the form $z = a + bi$ where a and b are real numbers and $i = \sqrt{-1}$.

Composite Function given two functions, $f(x)$ and $g(x)$, the composite function $f \circ g = f[g(x)]$. $g(x)$ is called the inner function and $f(x)$ is the outer function.

Composition the process of combining functions.

Concave the shape of a curve or curved surface as seen from the inside; a surface curving toward the viewer. The reverse of convex. See **Concave Up/Down** and **Convex.**

Concave Up/Down $f(x)$ is concave up at x_0 if and only if $f'(x)$ is increasing at x_0. $f(x)$ is concave down at x_0 if and only if $f'(x)$ is decreasing at x_0. If $f''(x)$ exists at x_0 and is positive, then $f(x)$ is concave up at x_0. If $f''(x)$ exists and is negative, then $f(x)$ is concave down at x_0. If $f''(x)$ does not exist or is zero, then the test fails.

Cone a pyramid with a circular cross-section. A right cone is a cone with its vertex above the centre of its base. The volume of a right circular cone with height h and radius r is $\frac{1}{3}\pi r^2 h$.

Constant Multiple Rule if $f(x) = kg(x)$ where k is a constant, then $f'(x) = kg'(x)$. In Leibniz notation: $\frac{df}{dx} = k\frac{dg}{dx}$.

Continuity the condition of being uninterrupted, without break or irregularity.

Continuous Function a function $f(x)$ is continuous at a particular point $x = a$, if $f(a)$ is defined and if $\lim_{x \to a} f(x) = f(a)$. If this property is true for all points in the domain of the function, then the function is said to be continuous over the domain.

Convex the shape of a curve or curved surface seen from the outside; a surface curving away from the viewer. See **Concave**.

Coordinates a set of numbers that uniquely define the position of a point with respect to a frame of reference. Two coordinates are required in 2-space; three in 3-space.

Cosine Law a formula relating the lengths of the three sides of a triangle and the cosine of any angle in the triangle. If a, b, and c are the lengths of the sides and A is the magnitude of the angle opposite a, then $a^2 = b^2 + c^2 - 2bc \cos A$. Two other symmetrical formulas exist involving expressions for the other two sides.

Critical Points (of a Function) a critical point on $f(x)$ occurs at x_0 if and only if either $f'(x_0) = 0$ or the derivative doesn't exist.

Cubes, Sum and Difference of the sum and difference of the cubes of two quantities: $x^3 \pm y^3 = (x \pm y)(x^2 \pm xy + y^2)$.

Cubic Function a function that is a 3rd degree polynomial.

Cusp a type of double point. A cusp is a point on a continuous curve where the tangent line reverses sign.

Cylinder a three-dimensional solid of circular cross section in which the centres of the circles all lie on a single line of symmetry. For a right-circular cylinder of radius r and height h, the surface area is $2\pi rh + 2\pi r^2$ and the volume is $r\pi^2 h$.

Decibel Scale see **Loudness**.

Decreasing Function a function $f(x)$ is decreasing at a point x_0 if and only if there exists some interval I containing x_0 such that $f(x_0) < f(x)$ for all x in I to the left of x_0 and $f(x_0) > f(x)$ for all x in I to the right of x_0.

Degree the unit of angle measure defined such that an entire rotation is 360°. The degree likely arises from the Babylonian year, which was composed of 360 days (12 months of 30 days each). The degree is subdivided into 60 minutes per degree and 60 seconds per minute since the Babylonians used a base 60 number system.

Delta the fourth letter of the Greek alphabet: lower case [δ]; upper case [Δ].

Dependent Variable in a relation, the variable whose value depends upon the value of the independent variable. On a coordinate grid, the values of the independent variable are usually plotted on the horizontal axis, and the values of the dependent variable on the vertical axis.

Derivative the instantaneous rate of change of a function with respect to the variable. The derivative at a particular point is equal to the slope of the tangent line drawn to the curve at that point. The derivative of $f(x)$ at the point $x = a : f'(a) = \lim_{x \to a} \frac{f(x) - f(a)}{x - a}$ provided the limit exists.

Difference of Squares the difference of the squares of two quantities. The algebraic identity: $a^2 - b^2 = (a + b)(a - b)$.

Difference Quotient the slope of the secant drawn to a curve $f(x)$ between the points on the curve $(a, f(a))$ and $(a + h, f(a + h))$: $\frac{\Delta y}{\Delta x} = \frac{f(a + h) - f(a)}{h}$.

Difference Rule if functions $p(x)$ and $q(x)$ are differentiable and $f(x) = p(x) - q(x)$, then $f'(x) = p'(x) - q'(x)$. In Leibniz notation: $\frac{df}{dx} = \frac{dp}{dx} - \frac{dq}{dx}$.

Differentiability a real function is said to be differentiable at a point if its derivative exists at that point.

Differential Calculus that portion of calculus dealing with derivatives.

Dilatation a transformation that changes the size of an object.

Direct Proportion two quantities x and y are said to be in direct proportion if $y = kx$ where k is a constant. This relationship is commonly written as $y \alpha x$.

Discontinuity an interrupted or broken connection. A value for x, on an x–y grid, for which a value for y is not defined. A formal mathematical definition: a function $f(x)$ is discontinuous at a particular point $x = a$ if $f(a)$ is not defined and/or if $\lim_{x \to a} f(x) \neq f(a)$.

Discriminant in the quadratic formula, the value under the square root sign: $b^2 - 4ac$. It is used to determine the nature of the roots of an equation.

Displacement a translation from one position to another, without consideration of any intervening positions. The minimal distance between two points.

Distance the separation of two points measured in units of length, or the length of the path taken between two points, not necessarily the minimal distance (displacement).

Domain the set of values of the independent variable for which a function is defined. See **Range**.

e the base of the natural logarithm, whose symbol "e" honours Euler. It can be defined as the $\lim_{x \to \infty}\left(1 + \frac{1}{x}\right)^x$ and is equal to 2.7182818286......... (a non-repeating, infinite decimal).

Epsilon the fifth letter of the Greek alphabet: lower case (ϵ); upper case (E).

Equation a statement that two mathematical objects, for example, algebraic expressions, are equal under certain conditions.

Equation of a Circle the standard form of the equation in Cartesian coordinates is $(x - a)^2 + (y - b)^2 = r^2$, where the centre of the circle is (a, b) and the radius is r.

Equation of a Hyperbola the standard form of the equation in Cartesian coordinates is $\frac{x^2}{a^2} - \frac{y^2}{b^2} = 1$. a and b are the lengths of the semi-transverse and semi-conjugate axes respectively.

Equation of an Ellipse the standard form of the equation in Cartesian coordinates is $\frac{x^2}{a^2} + \frac{y^2}{b^2} = 1$. a and b are the lengths of the semi-major and semi-minor axes respectively.

Equation of a Parabola the standard form of a parabola in Cartesian coordinates is $y = ax^2 + bx + c$.

Equivalent equal in value or measure.

Even Function if $f(x) = f(-x)$ for all x, then $y = f(x)$ is symmetric under reflection in the y-axis and is called an even function. See **Odd Function**.

Explicit precisely and clearly expressed or readily observable; leaving nothing to guesswork.

Exponent the notation b^p means the product of p factors of b, where b is the base and p the exponent of the power b^p.

Exponential Decay occurs when quantities decrease at a rate proportional to the size of the original quantity present.

Exponential Function a function of the form $y = b^x$, $b > 0$. The most fundamental exponential function is $y = e^x$, where e is the base of the natural logarithm. See **e**.

Exponential Growth occurs when quantities increase at a rate proportional to the size of the original quantity present.

Exponential Series a series of the form $1 + x + \frac{x^2}{2!} + \frac{x^3}{3!} + ...$ Each term in the series is of the form $\frac{x^n}{n!}$.

Exponent Laws

Action	Result
$a^m \times a^n$	a^{m+n}
$\frac{a^m}{a^n}$	a^{m-n}
$(a^m)^n$	$a^{m \times n}$
$(ab)^m$	$a^m b^m$
$\left(\frac{a}{b}\right)^m, b \neq 0$	$\frac{a^m}{b^m}$

Action	Result
a^0	1
a^{-n}	$\frac{1}{a^n}$
$\left(\frac{a}{b}\right)^{-n}$	$\frac{b^n}{a^n}$
$a^{\frac{p}{q}}$	$(\sqrt[q]{a})^p$ or $\sqrt[q]{a^p}$

Extended Power Rule a symmetric expression that extends the Power Rule for the product of two functions to three functions and beyond. For example, if $f'(x) = g(x)h(x)k(x)$, then $f'(x) = g'(x)h(x)k(x) + g(x)h'(x)k(x) + g(x)h(x)k'(x)$. Note the symmetry.

Extreme Values (of a Function) the maximum and minimum values of a function over a particular interval of values (domain).

Factor one of two or more expressions that are multiplied together to produce a product.

Factorial for any positive integer n, the product of all the positive integers less than or equal to n. Factorial n is denoted by $n!$ and $n! = n(n-1)(n-2) \ldots 3.2.1.0!$ is defined as 1.

Factor Theorem $(x - p)$ is a factor of $f(x)$ if and only if $f(p) = 0$.

Finite bounded or limited in magnitude or spatial or temporal extent.

Formula a mathematical equation relating two or more quantities.

Fraction the quotient of two integers where the denominator does not equal zero.

Frequency the number of occurrences within a given time period (usually 1 s) *or* the ratio of the number of observations in a statistical category to the total number of observations.

Function a mapping of one set to another set so that each element in the first set (the domain) corresponds to only one element in the second set (the range).

Graph a diagram or visual representation designed to show the relation between two or more quantities.

Gravity the force of attraction exerted by one object on another. Specifically, on earth, the force of attraction between the earth and any body in close proximity to it.

Greatest Common Factor the largest number that divides two or more numbers evenly.

Half-life the time in years required for a radioactive substance to decay to one-half of its original size or weight.

Horizontal Asymptote the line $y = y_0$ is a horizontal asymptote of $f(x)$ if and only if $f(x)$ approaches y_0 as $x \to \pm\infty$.

Hyperbolic Functions the hyperbolic functions sinh, cosh, tanh, csch, sech, coth (hyperbolic sine, hyperbolic cosine, etc.) share many properties with the corresponding circular functions. For example, $\cosh x = \frac{1}{2}(e^x + e^{-x})$.

Hypothesis a concept that is not yet verified but, if true, would explain certain facts or phenomena.

Identity a mathematical statement of equality that is true for all values of the variables. For example, $\sin^2\theta + \cos^2\theta = 1$ is an identity, true for all values of the variable.

Implicit implied though not directly expressed.

Implicit Differentiation a method for differentiating an implicit function, utilizing the Chain Rule and ultimately solving for the derivative desired $\left(\frac{dy}{dx}\right)$.

Implicit Function a function in which the dependent variable is not directly stated as a function of the independent variable.

Increasing Function a function $f(x)$ is increasing at a point x_0 if and only if there exists some interval I containing x_0 such that $f(x_0) > f(x)$ for all x in I to the left of x_0 and $f(x_0) < f(x)$ for all x in I to the right of x_0.

Independent Variable in a relation, the variable whose value determines the value of the dependent variable. See **Dependent Variable**.

Indeterminate Form a quotient $\lim_{x \to a} \frac{f(x)}{g(x)}$ where $f(x)$ and $g(x)$ both approach 0 or $\pm \infty$ as x approaches a is an indeterminate form: $\frac{0}{0}$ *or* $\frac{\infty}{\infty}$.

Inequality a statement that one quantity is not equal to another.

Inequation a statement of inequality involving an unknown for which values can be calculated. In place of an equal sign, the signs $>$, $<$, $\leq$, or $\geq$ may be used.

Infinity something that is not finite, that is, countable or measurable.

Inflection Point an inflection point occurs on $f(x)$ at x_0 if and only if $f(x)$ has a tangent line at x_0 and there exists an interval I containing x_0 such that $f(x)$ is concave up on one side of x_0 and concave down on the other side.

Instantaneous Rate of Change the rate of change of $y = f(x)$ at a particular point $x = a$ is given by $\lim_{h \to 0} \frac{\Delta y}{\Delta x} = \lim_{h \to 0} \frac{f(a+h) - f(a)}{h}$ provided the limit exists.

Integer any of the numbers .... $-4, -3, -2, -1, 0, 1, 2, 3, 4, \ldots$. The positive integers or natural numbers are $1, 2, 3, 4, \ldots$. The negative integers are $-1, -2, -3, -4, \ldots$.

Integral Calculus that portion of calculus dealing with integrals, enabling applications to find areas and volumes of curves.

Intercept the directed distance from the origin to the point on one of the axes of a graph of a figure where the graph cuts the axis.

Irrational Number a real number that cannot be expressed as the ratio of two integers.

Isosceles Triangle a triangle that has two sides of equal length.

Iteration a method of evaluating a function, where an initial value is calculated, and each subsequent term is determined based on the value of the previous term.

Leibniz Notation for example, $\frac{dy}{dx}$ is Leibniz notation for the derivative of y with respect to x. The notation we use in everyday calculus is attributable primarily to Leibniz.

Limit (of a Function) the notation $\lim_{x \to a} f(x) = L$ implies that as x approaches closer and closer to the value a, the value of the function approaches a limiting value of L.

Linear Equation an equation where the highest degree term is that of the first degree, for example, $3x + 4 = 0$.

Linear Relation (Function) a relation between two variables that, when graphed on a Cartesian coordinate system, results in a straight line.

Local Maximum a function $f(x)$ has a local maximum at x_0 if and only if there exists some interval I containing x_0 such that $f(x_0) \geq f(x)$ for all x in I.

Local Minimum a function $f(x)$ has a local minimum at x_0 if and only if there exists some interval I containing x_0 such that $f(x_0) \leq f(x)$ for all x in I.

Logarithm the exponent to which a base must be raised to get the number.

Logarithm (Common) logarithms of numbers using a base of 10. Usually written as $\log_{10}x$.

Logarithm (Natural) logarithms of numbers using a base of e. Usually written as $\ln x$. The relationship between natural and common logarithms is given by $\ln x = \frac{\log_{10}x}{\log_{10}e}$.

Logarithmic Function the inverse of the exponential function. If $y = b^x$ represents the exponential function, then $x = \log_b y$ is the logarithmic function. Usually written as $y = \log_b x$.

Logistic Model a mathematical model that describes a population that grows exponentially at the beginning and then levels off to a limiting value. There are several different forms of equations representing this model.

Loudness (of Sound) the loudness of any sound is measured relative to the loudness of sound at the threshold of hearing (the softest that can be heard). The loudness (L) in decibels is given by the formula $L = 10\log\left(\frac{I}{I_0}\right)$ where I_0 is the intensity of a sound at the threshold of hearing. At the threshold of hearing, $L = 0$ dB.

Mantissa the positive fractional part of the representation of a logarithm; in the expression $\log_{10} 643 = 2.808$, the mantissa is .808. See **Characteristic**.

Mapping a rule that assigns to every element of one set a unique element of another set. For example, a function has a 1 for 1 mapping between its domain and range. See **Relation**.

Maximum the largest value of a function on a given interval of values.

Minimum the smallest value of a function on a given interval of values.

Monic Polynomial a polynomial in one variable.

Normal Line the line drawn at a point on a graph of $f(x)$, perpendicular to the tangent line drawn at that point.

Oblique (Slant) Asymptote the line $y = ax + b$ is a slant or oblique asymptote of $f(x)$ if and only if $\lim_{x \to \pm\infty} f(x) = ax + b$.

Odd Function if $f(-x) = -f(x)$ for all x, then $y = f(x)$ is symmetric under reflection through the origin. See **Even Function**.

Optimization a procedure to determine the best possible outcome of a situation. If the situation can be modelled as a function, it may involve finding either the maximum or minimum value of the function over a set of values (domain).

Order of Magnitude one order of magnitude means 10 times larger, two orders of magnitude 100 times larger, three orders 1000 times larger, and so on. Expressed as an exponent: 1, 2, 3 … is also known as the logarithm of the pattern.

Parameter a variable that permits the description of a relation among other variables (two or more) to be expressed in an indirect manner using that variable.

Perimeter the distance around the outside of a plane figure.

Perpendicular at right angles to a figure; a straight line at right angles to another line.

pH Scale the measurement of the acidity of a liquid determined from the concentration of hydrogen ions (H^+) in the liquid. $pH = -\log(H^+)$, where (H^+) is the concentration of hydrogen ions in moles per litre. A liquid with a pH lower than 7 is called an acid; higher than 7, a base.

Point of Inflection See **Inflection Point**.

Polynomial an algebraic expression consisting of one or more terms with each term being the product of a constant and a non-zero power of a variable.

Polynomial Equation an equation obtained by setting a polynomial equal to a real number.

Polynomial Function a function, $f(x)$, consisting of one or more terms, with a variable or unknown raised to non-negative integral powers only.

Polynomial Inequality a polynomial equation where the equal sign is replaced by any one of the signs $>$, $<$, $\geq$, or $\leq$. The resulting solution of such inequalities is usually a range of values.

Power Function a function of the form $f(x) = x^n$, where n is a real number.

Power of a Function Rule if u is a function of x and n is a positive integer, then in Leibniz notation $\frac{d}{dx}(u^n) = nu^{n-1}\frac{du}{dx}$. Also, in function notation, if $f(x) = [g(x)]^n$, then $f'(x) = n[g(x)]^{n-1}g(x)$.

Power Rule if $f(x) = x^n$, where n is a real number, then $f'(x) = nx^{n-1}$.

Product Rule if $h(x) = f(x)g(x)$, then $h'(x) = f'(x)g(x) + f(x)g'(x)$. See **Extended Power Rule**.

Quadratic Formula a formula giving the roots of a quadratic function. The formula giving the two roots of $f(x) = ax^2 + bx + c$, $a \neq 0$, is $x = \frac{-b \pm \sqrt{b^2 - 4ac}}{2a}$.

Quadratic Function a polynomial function of degree 2. The general formula is $f(x) = ax^2 + bx + c$, $a \neq 0$. When plotted on a Cartesian coordinate system grid, the result is a geometric figure called a parabola.

Quartic Function a polynomial function of the 4th degree.

Quotient the ratio of the dividend over the divisor. The result of dividing the dividend by the divisor.

Quotient Rule if $h(x) = \frac{f(x)}{g(x)}$, then

$$h(x) = \frac{g(x)f'(x) - f(x)g'(x)}{[g(x)]^2},\ g(x) \neq 0.$$

Radian the unit of plane angle adopted under the Système international d'unités; equal to the angle at the centre of a circle subtended by an arc equal in length to the radius (approximately 57.295°). Also π radians = 180°.

Range (of a Relation) the set of second coordinates of the order pairs of the relation. See **Domain**.

Ratio a number or quantity compared with another. It is usually written as a fraction or with the symbol ":".

Rational Number a number that can be expressed as an integer or as a quotient of integers (a fraction).

Real Number any rational or irrational number.

Reflection a transformation of a point, line, or figure that results in a mirror image of the original.

Relation a mapping of one set to another set so that each element in the first set (the domain) corresponds to one or more elements in the second set (the range). When the correspondence between domain and range is 1 to 1, the mapping is defined as a function.

Remainder Theorem if $f(x)$ is divided by $(x - p)$, giving a quotient $q(x)$ and a remainder r, then the remainder is given by $r = f(p)$.

Richter Scale a method of comparing the intensities of earthquakes. The formula used is $M = \log\left(\frac{I}{I_0}\right)$, where I is the intensity of the earthquake being measured and I_0 is the intensity of a reference earthquake.

Root a value that satisfies an equation $f(x) = 0$. Also known as the solution to the equation.

Secant a line segment that cuts through a circle or other figure. In a circle, the portion of the secant inside the circle is called a chord.

Similarity two plane figures are similar if the angles of one, taken in order, are respectively equal to the angles of the other, in the same order, and the corresponding sides are proportional.

Sine Law the theorem that relates the lengths of sides of a triangle to the sines of the angles opposite those sides. In a triangle, with sides of lengths a, b, and c and angles opposite those sides A, B, and C, then $\frac{a}{\sin A} = \frac{b}{\sin B} = \frac{c}{\sin C}$.

Slant (Oblique) Asymptote the line $y = ax + b$ is a slant or oblique asymptote of $f(x)$ if and only if $\lim_{x\to\pm\infty} f(x) = ax + b$.

Slope the steepness of a line or curve. In the plane, the slope is equal to the tan θ where θ is the angle of inclination.

Slope of Tangent the slope of the tangent to the function $y = f(x)$ at the point $(a, f(a))$ on the curve is given by $\lim_{h\to 0}\frac{\Delta y}{\Delta x} = \lim_{h\to 0}\frac{f(a + h) - f(a)}{h}$.

Speed distance travelled per unit time. The absolute value of velocity.

Sum Rule if functions $p(x)$ and $q(x)$ are differentiable and $f(x) = p(x) + q(x)$, then $f'(x) = p'(x) + q'(x)$. In Leibniz notation: $\frac{df}{dx} = \frac{dp}{dx} + \frac{dq}{dx}$.

Tangent a line segment drawn to a figure that touches that figure at one and only one point.

Theorem a statement that has been proved and for which there is general agreement that it is useful.

Transcendental Number a number that is not the root of any polynomial equation with integer coefficients. For example, e and π are transcendental.

Translation a transformation that changes *only* the position of a figure. A transformation that maps each point (x, y) on the figure to a new point $(x + a, y + b)$ where a and b are components of the translation vector $\overrightarrow{(a, b)}$.

Trigonometric Functions the sine (sin), cosine (cos), tangent (tan), and their inverses, cosecant (csc), secant (sec), and cotangent (cot). Also called circular functions.

Trigonometry the study of the properties of trigonometric functions and their applications to various mathematical problems.

Variable a quantity, represented by an algebraic symbol, that can take on any one of a set of values.

Velocity the rate of change of displacement with respect to time: $\left(\frac{ds}{dt}\right)$.

Vertical Asymptote the line $x = x_0$ is a vertical asymptote of $f(x)$ if and only if $f(x) \to \pm\infty$ as $x \to x_0$ from the left or from the right.

Zero the absence of any magnitude. On the number line, zero stands between the positive and the negative numbers.

Zero of a Function the value(s) of x for which the function $f(x) = 0$. A polynomial of the nth degree has n or fewer zeros.

Answers

CHAPTER 1 POLYNOMIAL FUNCTIONS

Review of Prerequisite Skills

1. a. $(P + r)^2$ **b.** $(4n + 1)^2$ **c.** $(3u + 5)^2$ **d.** $(v + 3)(v + 1)$
e. $(2w + 1)(w + 1)$ **f.** $(3k + 1)(k + 2)$ **g.** $(7y + 1)(y + 2)$
h. $(5x - 1)(x - 3)$ **i.** $(3v - 5)(v - 2)$

2. a. $(5x - y)(5x + y)$ **b.** $(m - p)(m + p)$ **c.** $(1 - 4r)(1 + 4r)$
d. $(7m - 8)(7m + 8)$ **e.** $(pr - 10x)(pr + 10x)$
f. $3(1 - 4y)(1 + 4y)$ **g.** $(x + n + 3)(x + n - 3)$
h. $(7u + x - y)(7u - x + y)$ **i.** $(x^2 + 4)(x + 2)(x - 2)$

3. a. $(k + p)(x - y)$ **b.** $(f + g)(x - y)$ **c.** $(h + 1)(h^2 + 1)$
d. $(x - d)(1 + x - d)$ **e.** $(2y + z - 1)(2y + z + 1)$
f. $(x - z - y)(x - z + y)$

4. a. $2(2x + 3)(x - 1)$ **b.** $4(7s - 5t)(s + t)$
c. $(y + r - n)(y - r + n)$ **d.** $8(1 + 5m)(1 - 2m)$
e. $(3x - 2)(2x - 3)$ **f.** $(y + 1)(y^2 - 5)$ **g.** $10(3y + 4)(2y - 3)$
h. $2(5x^2 + 19x + 10)$ **i.** $3(3x - 4)(3x + 4)$

5. a. $(12x + 4y - 5u)(12x - 16y + 5u)$ **b.** $g(1 - x)(1 + x)$
c. $(y - 1)(y^4 + y^2 + 1)$ **d.** $(n^2 + w^2)^2$
e. $(-x + 14y - z)(7x - 2y + 7z)$ **f.** $(u + 1)(4u + 3)(2u - 1)$
g. $(p - 1 + y + z)(p - 1 - y - z)$ **h.** $(3y^2 + 2)^2$
i. $(ax + m)(bx + n)$ **j.** $\left(x + \frac{1}{x}\right)^2$

Exercise 1.2

1. $f(x) = x^2 - 5x + 4$
2. $f(x) = 3x - 4$
3. $f(x) = 2x^2 + 5x - 3$
4. $f(x) = 2x^2 - 7x - 4$
5. $f(x) = 2x^3 - 5x^2 - 21x + 36$
6. $f(x) = x^3 - 15x - 20$
7. $f(x) = x^3 - x^2 - 14x + 24$
8. $f(x) = 2x^3 + x^2 - 13x + 6$
9. $f(x) = x^4 - 10x^3 + 35x^2 - 52x + 24$
10. $f(x) = 2^{x-1}$
11. a. $V = -0.0374t^3 + 0.1522t^2 + 0.1729t$
b. maximum volume of 0.8863 L at 3.2 s
12. a. $f(t) = t^3 - 27t^2 + 3t + 403t$ **b.** 1999 **c.** 57 000

Exercise 1.3

1. a. $17 = 5(3) + 2$ **b.** $42 = 7(6) + 0$ **c.** $73 = 12(6) + 1$
d. $90 = 6(15) + 0$ **e.** $103 = 10(10) + 3$ **f.** $75 = 15(5) + 0$

2. a. The remainder is not zero. **b.** The remainder is zero.
c. possible solution from Question 1: **1.d.** 15; **1.f.** 5
d. 15 **f.** 5

3. The dividend equals the product of the divisor and the quotient added to the remainder of the division.

4. a. $x - 2$ **b.** $x^2 + 3x - 2$ **c.** 5 **d.** $x^3 + x^2 - 8x + 9$
5. $f(x) = 3x^2 - 8x^2 + 8x + 26$
6. $f(x) = x^4 + x^2$
7. a. $x^3 - 3x^2 + x + 2 = (x + 2)(x^2 - 5x + 11) - 20$
b. $x^3 + 4x^2 - 3x - 2 = (x - 1)(x^2 + 5x + 2)$
c. $2x^3 - 4x^2 - 3x + 5 = (x - 3)(2x^2 + 2x + 3) + 14$
d. $3x^3 + x^2 - x - 6 = (x + 1)(3x^2 - 2x + 1) - 7$
e. $3x^3 - 4 = (x - 4)(3x + 12) + 44$
f. $x^3 - 2x - 4 = (x - 2)(x^2 + 2x + 2)$
g. $4x^3 + 6x^2 - 6x - 9 = (2x + 3)(2x^2 - 3)$
h. $3x^3 - 11x^2 + 21x - 7 = (3x - 2)(x^2 - 3x + 5) + 3$
i. $(3x - 2)(2x^2 - 1) + 7$
j. $3x^3 + 7x^2 + 5x + 1 = (3x + 1)(x^2 + 2x + 1)$

8. a. No. **b.** Yes. **c.** No. **d.** No. **e.** Yes. **f.** Yes. **g.** Yes. **h.** No.
i. No. **j.** Yes. The degree of the remainder is less.

9. a. $x^3 + 3x^2 + 14x + 53, R = 220$
b. $2x^3 - 2x^2 - x + 1$ **c.** $4x^2 - 8x + 16$
d. $x^4 + x^3 + x^2 + x + 1$
10. $x + 6, x - 1$
11. $x^2 - x - 1$ with $R = -5$
12. $x^2 - x$
13. $x^2 + 3x + 2$
14. $r(x) = 0$
15. 0, 1
16. a. $r = 0$ **b.** 1, 2, 3, 4; 1, 2, 3, 4, 5, 6; 1, 2, 3, ..., $n - 1$
17. a. $x^3 + 4x^2 - 5x - 9 = (x - 2)(xv + 6x + 7) + 5$
$x^2 + 6x + 7 = (x + 1)(x + 5) + 2$ **b.** Yes.
c. $r = r_1 + (x - 2)r_2$ or $r_2x + (r_1 - 2r_2)$

Exercise 1.4

1. Find $f(1)$.
2. a. -10 **b.** -13 **c.** $-\frac{47}{8}$ or 5.875 **d.** $\frac{-171}{8}$ or -21.375
3. a. 12 **b.** 3 **c.** -25 **d.** 1 **e.** 17 **f.** -16
4. a. -2 **b.** 58 **c.** 13 **d.** 0 **e.** 11 **f.** -5 **g.** 1 **h.** 3
5. a. 4 **b.** 2 **c.** 5
6. $m = 2, g = 1$
7. $m = -\frac{4}{9}, g = \frac{13}{9}$
8. $24x + 73$
9. $42x - 39$
10. a. 4 **b.** 3 **c.** 2 **d.** -1 **e.** 9
11. $f(x) + 2$
12. a. $(x^2 + x + 3)(x^2 - x + 3)$ **b.** $(3y^2 + 2y + 2)(3y^2 - 2y + 2)$
c. $(x^2 + 2x + 5)(x^2 - 2x + 5)$
d. $(2x^2 + 2x + 3)(2x^2 - 2x + 3)$

Review Exercise

1. a. **b.**

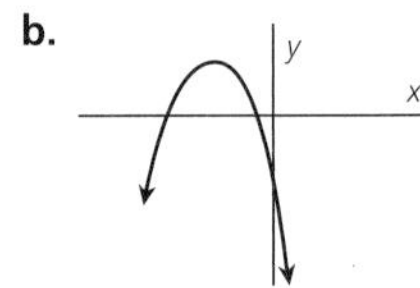

c. **d.**

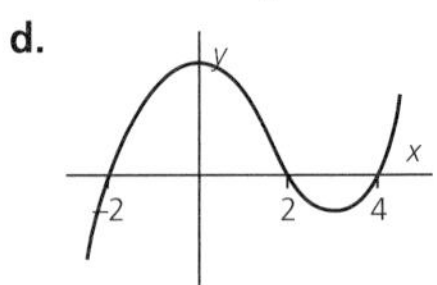

e.

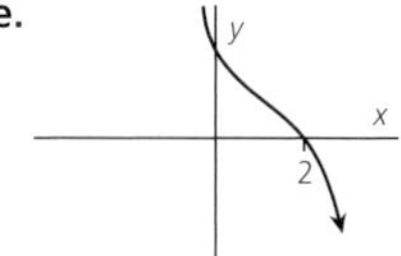

f.

g.

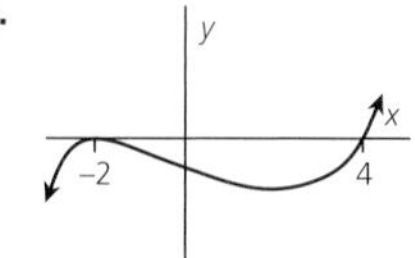

h.

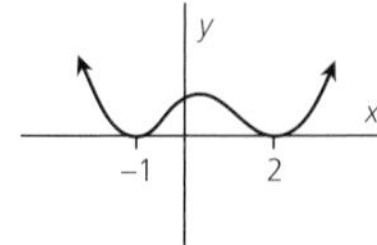

i.

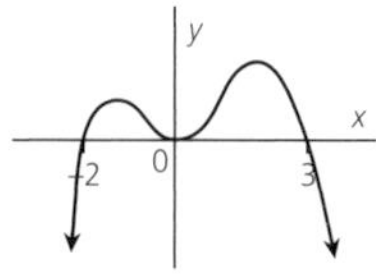

j.

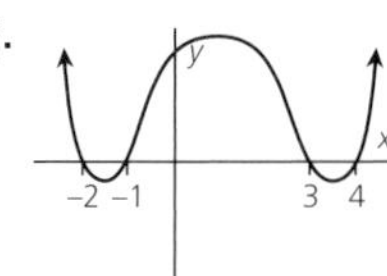

k.

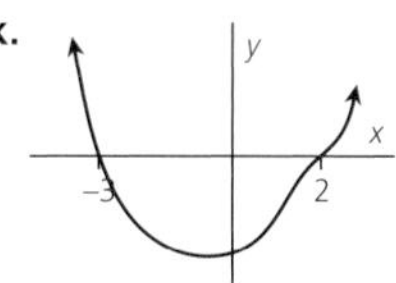

l.

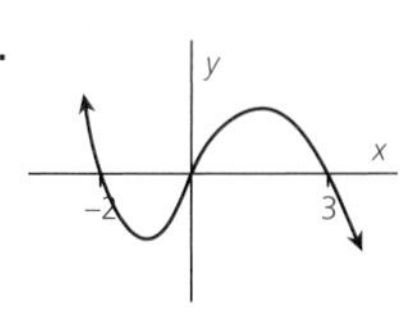

2. a. $f(x) = x^3 - 5x^2 + 10x - 11$
b. $f(x) = 2x^3 - 3x^2 + 12x + 4$
c. $f(x) = x^4 - 14x^2 + 5x - 1$
d. not enough information given
e. not enough information given

3. a. $x^3 - 2x^2 + 3x - 1 = (x - 3)(x^2 + x + 6) + 17$
b. $2x^3 + 5x + 4 = (x + 2)(2x^2 - 4x + 13) - 22$
c. $4x^3 + 8x^2 - x + 1 = (2x + 1)(2x^2 + 3x - 2) + 3$
d. $x^4 - 4x^3 + 3x^2 - 3 = (x^2 + x - 2)(x^2 - 5x + 10) - 20x + 17$

4. a. 3 **b.** 1 **c.** −33 **d.** −1 **e.** $\frac{22}{9}$

5. a. $x^3 + 2x^2 - x + 2 = (x - 1)(x + 1)(x + 2)$
b. $x^3 - 3x^2 - x + 3 = (x - 3)(x - 1)(x + 1)$
c. $6x^3 + 31x^2 + 25x - 12 = (2x + 3)(3x - 1)(x + 4)$

6. a. $k = \frac{1}{2}$ **b.** $r = 2, g = 5$

Chapter 1 Test

1. a. $2(3x - 56)(3x + 56)$ **b.** $(pm + 1)(m^2 + 1)$
c. $2(3x - 2)(2x - 3)$ **d.** $(x + y - 3)(x - y + 3)$

2. a.

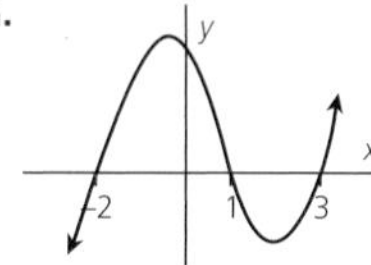

b.

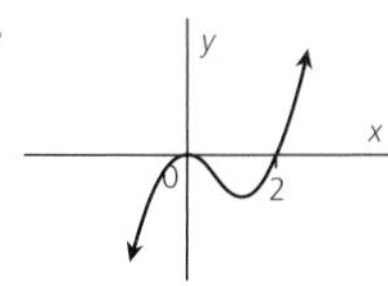

3. a. $q(x) = x^2 - 7x + 20$ $r(x) = -44$
b. $q(x) = x^2 + 3x + 3$ $r(x) = 11$

4. Yes.

5. −40

6. $k = 3$

7. a. Yes. **b.** $f(x) = 2x^3 - 3x^2 + 5x - 8$

8. $c = \frac{-14}{3}, d = -\frac{5}{3}$

9. $(x - 3)(x + 3)$

CHAPTER 2 POLYNOMIAL EQUATIONS AND INEQUALITIES

Review of Prerequisite Skills

1. a. −3 **b.** no solution **c.** $\frac{11}{4}$ or 2.75 **d.** 1

2. a. $x > 7$

b. $x \leq 6$

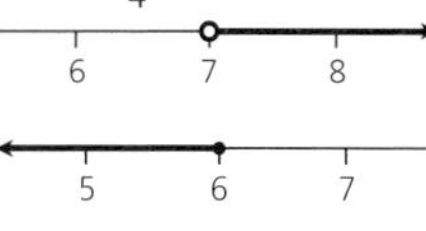

c. $x \leq -4.5$

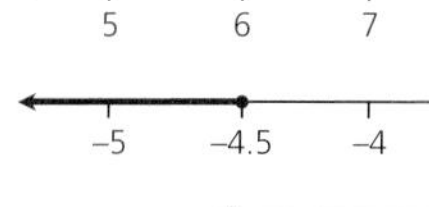

d. $x > -2$

3. a. 0 **b.** 15 **c.** 10 **d.** 0

4. a. −2 **b.** 13 **c.** −52 **d.** $\frac{53}{8}$

5. a. $(x - 6)(x - 8)$ **b.** $(y - 2)(y - 1)$ **c.** $(3x - 7)(x - 1)$
d. $3(x - 5)(x + 5)$ **e.** $(3x - 1)(2x + 3)$ **f.** $x(x + 8)(x - 7)$
g. $4x(x + 5)$ **h.** $3x(x - 2)(x + 2)$ **i.** $2(3x + 2)(x - 3)$

6. a. 0, 4 **b.** 3, −2 **c.** −3, −2 **d.** −6, −3 **e.** 5, −3 **f.** $-1, \frac{4}{7}$
g. $1, \frac{7}{3}$ **h.** −3, 0, 3 **i.** $\frac{1}{3}$, 4

7. a. 1.5, −5.5 **b.** 2.3, −0.6 **c.** $\frac{-1 \pm i\sqrt{35}}{6}$ **d.** 5.7, −0.7
e. 3, −0.5 **f.** 1.5, −0.7 **g.** $\frac{3 \pm i\sqrt{31}}{4}$ **h.** −6, 1 **i.** 8.3, 0.7

Exercise 2.1

1. 0

2. a. $(x - 5)$ **b.** Divide.

3. $(x + 1), (x - 2), (x + 3)$

4. a. Yes. **b.** No. **c.** Yes. **d.** No. **e.** No. **f.** Yes.

5. b. $x - 3$ **c.** $x^2 + x + 1$

6. b. $x + 2$ **c.** $x^2 - 4x + 3$

7. a. $(x - 1)(x^2 + x - 3)$ **b.** $(x + 2)(x - 1)(x + 1)$
c. $(y - 1)(y^2 + 20y + 1)$ **d.** $(x + 1)(x^2 + x + 4)$
e. $(y - 2)(y^2 + y + 1)$ **f.** $(x - 4)(x^2 - 5x + 2)$
g. $(x + 2)(x - 3)(x^2 - 7x + 2)$ **h.** $(x + 2)(x - 8)(x^2 + 1)$

8. 2.5

9. 1.5

10. a. $(x - 3)(x^2 + 3x + 9)$ **b.** $(y + 2)(y^2 - 2y + 4)$
c. $(5u - 4r)(25u^2 + 20ur + 16r^2)$
d. $2(10w + y)(100w - 10wy + y^2)$
e. $(x + y - uz)(x^2 + 2xy + y^2 + xuz + yuz + u^2z^2)$
f. $(5)(u - 4x - 2y)(u^2 + 4ux + 2uy + 16x^2 + 16xy + 4y^2)$

12. b. $x^3 + x^2y + xy^2 + y^3$ **c.** $(x - 3)(x^3 + 3x^2 + 9x + 27)$

13. b. $x^4 + x^3y + x^2y^2 + xy^3 + y^4$
c. $(x - 2)(x^4 - 2x^3 + 4x^2 - 8x + 16)$

14. b. $x^{n-1} + x^{n-2}y + x^{n-3}y^2 + ... + y^{n-1}$

17. If n is odd.

18. $(x + y)(x^4 - x^3y + x^2y^2 - xy^3 + y^4)$

19. No.

Exercise 2.2

1. a. $\pm\frac{1}{2}, \pm\frac{5}{2}, \pm 1, \pm 5$ **b.** $-\frac{1}{3}, \frac{2}{3}$ **c.** $\pm 1, \pm 2, \pm\frac{1}{2}, \pm\frac{1}{4}$
d. $\pm 1, \pm 2, \pm 4, \pm\frac{1}{2}, \pm\frac{1}{4}, \pm\frac{1}{8}$ **e.** $\pm 1, \pm 3, \pm\frac{1}{2}, \pm\frac{3}{2}, \pm\frac{1}{3}, \pm\frac{1}{6}$ **f.** $\pm 1, \pm 2, \pm 3, \pm 6, \pm\frac{1}{2}, \pm\frac{3}{2}$

2. $5(2x - 3)(x - 2)$

3. $-2(x - 3)(4x + 3)(x + 2)$

4. a. $(2x-1)(x^2+x+1)$ **b.** $(x+2)(x-1)(5x-2)$
c. $(x-2)(2x-1)(3x-1)$ **d.** $(x+3)(2x-5)(3x-1)$
e. $(x+2)(x-2)(5x^2+x-2)$ **f.** $(3x+1)(2x-1)(3x-2)$
g. $(x-2)(3x-2)(x^2+x+1)$ **h.** $(x-4)(4x-3)(x^2+1)$
5. a. $(x+2)(px^2-(p+q)\times 7q)$ **b.** $(x-1)(ax-2)(bx+1)$

Exercise 2.3

1. the factors of 8
2. $(x-1)(x+2)(x-4)=0$
3. a. $f(x)=kx(x-2)(x+3)$ **b.** $f(x)=2x(x-2)(x+3)$
4. a. $f(x)=k(x-1)(x+1)(x+2)$
b. $f(x)=-\frac{1}{2}(x-1)(x+1)(x+2)$
5. a. $f(x)=k(x+2)(x+1)(x-1)(x-3)$
b. $f(x)=\frac{1}{2}(x+2)(x+1)(x-1)(x-3)$
6. $(x-1)(x-2)(5x-3)=0$
7. 2
8. a. $-4, 5$ **b.** $-1\pm 3i$ **c.** $0, 2, -5$ **d.** $0, 2, -2$ **e.** $-1, 0, 1$
f. $\pm i, \pm 1$ **g.** $-1, 0, 4$ **h.** $\frac{3}{2}, \frac{-3\pm 3i\sqrt{3}}{4}$ **i.** $-2, 3, 3$
j. $2, 3, 4$ **k.** $-1, -1, 2$ **l.** $3, 3, -4$ **m.** $5, 1\pm\sqrt{3}$
n. $2, \frac{1\pm\sqrt{33}}{2}$
9. a. $1, \frac{-7\pm\sqrt{17}}{4}$ **b.** $-4, -1, \frac{1}{4}$ **c.** $-2, 3\,\frac{3}{5}$ **d.** $0, \frac{1}{2}, \pm 2$
e. $\pm 3, \pm 2$ **f.** $\pm i, \pm 7$ **g.** $-2, \frac{-1\pm\sqrt{3}i}{2}$ **h.** $-2, \frac{-7\pm\sqrt{13}}{2}$
10. a. $\pm 1, \pm i, \pm\sqrt{3}, \pm i\sqrt{3}$ **b.** $2, -1, -1\pm 3i, \frac{1\pm 2\sqrt{3}}{2}$
c. $-2, -1, 2, 3$ **d.** $-\frac{1}{3}, -\frac{1}{4}, 3, 4$ **e.** $\frac{-1\pm\sqrt{34}}{3}, \frac{-1\pm\sqrt{2}}{3}$
f. $-8, 2, -3\pm i\sqrt{21}$
11. 5 cm
12. a. $-7.140, 0.140$ **b.** $-2.714, 1.483, 3.231$ **c.** $1, -0.732, 2732$
d. $-2.278, -1.215, 1.215, 2.278$
13. 3 cm, 4 cm, 5 cm
14. 6.64 m
15. 3.1 s

Exercise 2.4

1. a. $-5, 11$ **b.** $\frac{5}{2}, \frac{9}{2}$ **c.** $\frac{7}{3}, \frac{-8}{3}$
2. a. $x^2-3x+7=0$ **b.** $x^2+6x+4=0$ **c.** $25x^2-5x-2=0$
d. $12x^2+13x+3=0$ **e.** $3x^2+33x-2=0$
3. a. $x^2-10x+21=0$ **b.** $x^2-3x-40=0$
c. $3x^2-10x+3=0$ **d.** $8x^2-10x+3=0$
e. $125x^2+85x-12=0$ **f.** $x^2-4x+5=0$
4. -6
5. $6, k=21$
6. $x^2-4x-13=0$
7. $2x^2-37x+137=0$
8. $x^2+7x+9=0$
9. $16x^2-97x+4=0$
10. $x^2+10x+5=0$
11. $4x^2-40x+1=0$
12. $8x^2+40x+1=0$
13. $x_1+x_2+x_3=\frac{-b}{a}, x_1x_2+x_1x_3+x_2x_3=\frac{c}{a}, x_1x_2x_3=-\frac{d}{a}$
14. $2x^3-13x^2+22x-8=0$
15. $x^3-10x^2+31x-32=0$
16. $x_1+x_2+x_3+x_4=-\frac{b}{a}$,
$x_1x_2+x_1x_3+x_1x_4+x_2x_3+x_2x_4+x_3x_4=\frac{c}{a}$,
$x_1x_2x_3+x_1x_2x_4+x_1x_3x_4+x_2x_3x_4=-\frac{d}{a}, x_1x_2x_3x_4=\frac{e}{a}$

Exercise 2.5

1. a. $f(x)>0$ for $x<-3, 0<x<4$ $f(x)<0$ for $-3<x<0$, $x>4$ **b.** $f(x)>0$ for $-2<x<1, x>4$ $f(x)<0$ for $x<-2, 1<x<4$ **c.** $f(x)>0$ for $x<-3, 0<x<2$ $f(x)<0$ for $-3<x<0$
2. a. $0<x<2$ **b.** $-3\le x\le 1$ **c.** $2\le x\le 5$
d. $x<-3$ or $x>0.5$ **e.** $x=2$ **f.** $x\le -3, 0\le x\le 3$
g. $x<-1, 1<x<5$ **h.** $x\le -2, 0.5\le x\le 1$
i. $-3.1\le x\le -.2$ or $x\ge 3.3$ **j.** R
3. a.
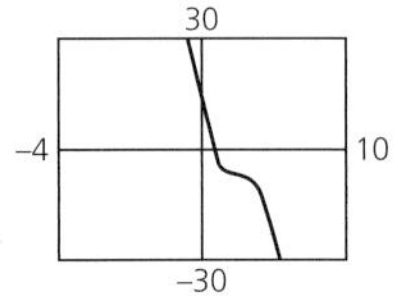

b. $t<59.15$ °C **c.** $t>270.50$ °C
4. between 1.96 and 4.16 s
5. $3.27<w<3.30$ in cm

Exercise 2.6

1. a. 10 **b.** 19 **c.** 4 **d.** 6
2. a.
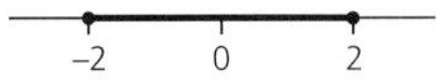

$-2\le x\le 2$
b.
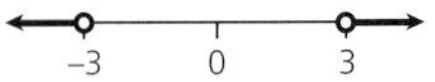

$x>3$ or $x<-3$
c.
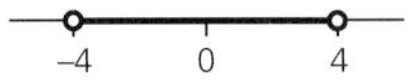

$-4<x<4$
d.
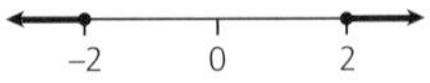

$x\ge 2$ or $x\le -2$
3. a.
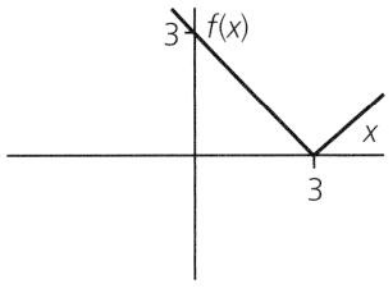

b.
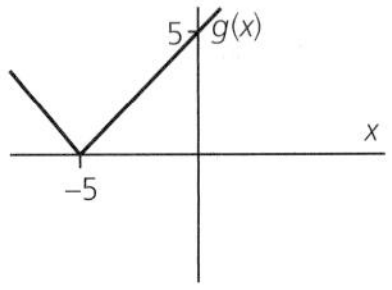

c.
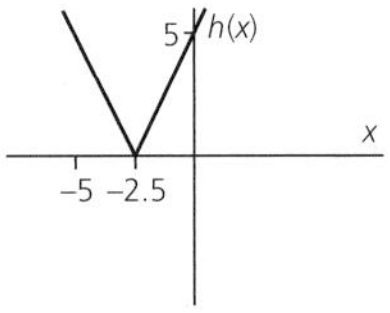

d.
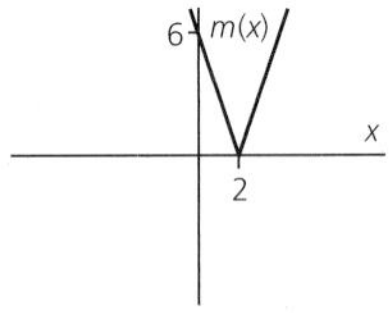

e.
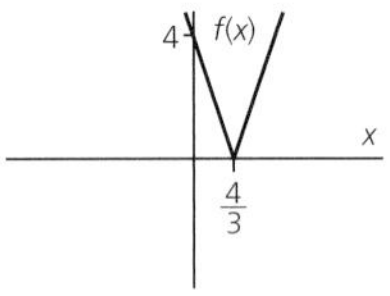

f.
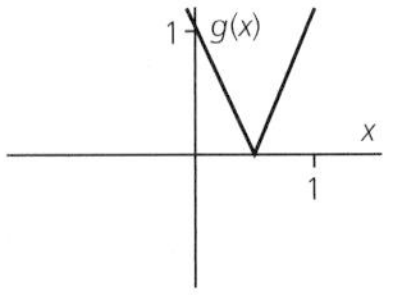

4. a.
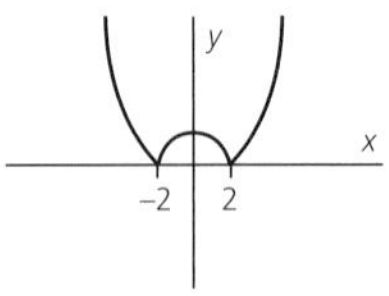

b.
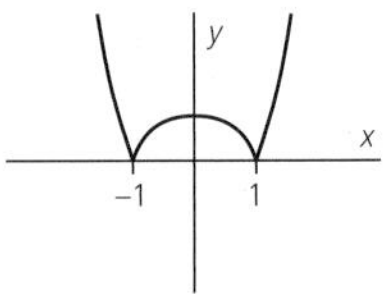

c.
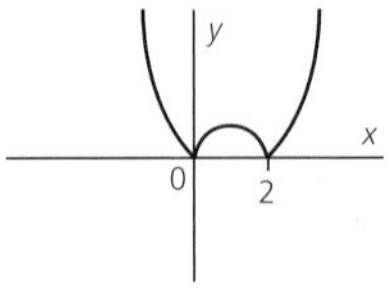

d.
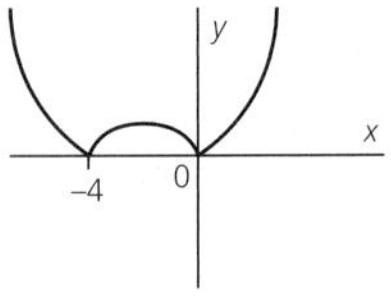

e.

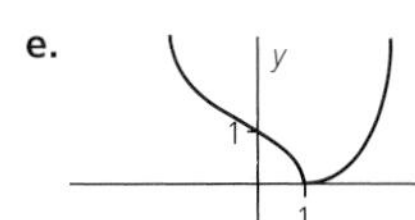

f.

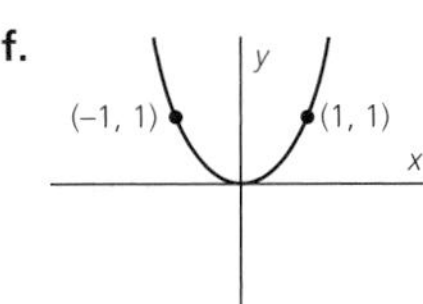

6. a.

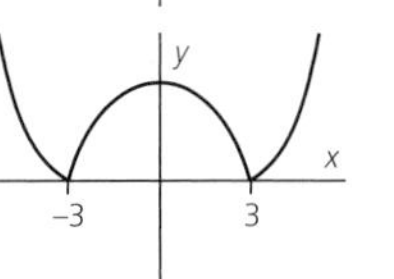

b.

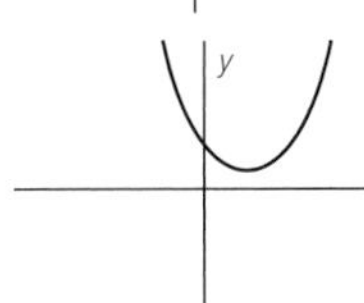

c.

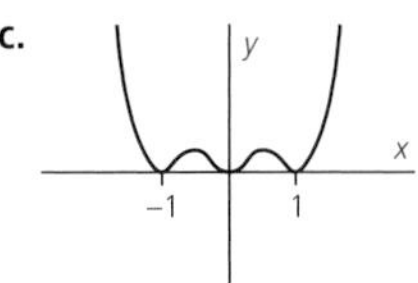

7. **a.** $x = 4, -3$ **b.** $x = \frac{4}{3}, \frac{-8}{3}$ **c.** $-6 \le x \le 12$
d. $x \ge 1$ or $x \le -9$ **e.** $-\frac{1}{2} < x < \frac{7}{2}$ **f.** no solution
8. **a.** -1 **b.** 0.8 **c.** $4, \frac{4}{3}$ **d.** $x > \frac{1}{2}$ **e.** $x < \frac{2}{5}$
f. $x \le -1$ or $x \ge \frac{5}{3}$ **g.** $-2, 4$ **h.** 0
9. none
10.

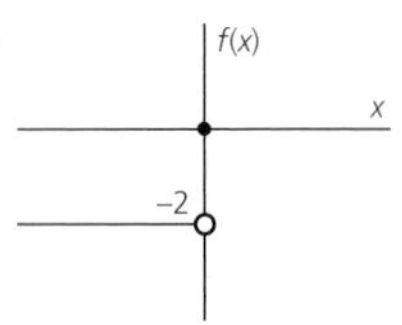

Review Exercise

1. **a.** $(x + 3)$ **b.** $(3x - 2)$
2. **a.** $y = a(x - 4)(x - 1)(x + 2)$ **b.** $y = -(x - 4)(x - 1)(x + 2)$
3. **a.** No. **b.** Yes.
4. $(x - 5)(x^2 - x + 1)$
5. **a.** $\frac{3}{4}$ **b.** $\frac{35}{33}$
6. **a.** $(x - 1)(x^2 - x + 1)$
b. $(x - 1)(x - 2)(x - 3)$ **c.** $(2x - 3y)(4x^2 + 6xy + 9y^2)$
d. $3(x + 2x - pr)(x^2 + 4xw + 4w^2 + prx + 2wpr + p^2r^2)$
8. **a.** $(2x + 3)(x^2 + x + 1)$ **b.** $(x - 1)(3x + 5)(3x - 1)$
9. **a.** No **b.** Yes
10. **a.** $(3x - 1)(x^2 - x + 1)$ **b.** $(2x - 5)(x^2 + 3x + 1)$
c. $(5x - 1)(3x - 1)(2x - 1)$
11. **a.** $-2, 5$ **b.** $0, -5, 5$ **c.** $-2, 1 \pm i\sqrt{3}$ **d.** $1, 3, -3$
e. $-4, 4, \pm 2i$ **f.** $1, \frac{3 \pm \sqrt{21}}{2}$ **g.** $2, \frac{1 \pm i\sqrt{3}}{2}$
h. $-1, 3, \frac{-3 \pm 3i\sqrt{3}}{2}, \frac{1 \pm i\sqrt{3}}{2}$ **i.** $-1 \pm \sqrt{5}, -1 \pm i\sqrt{2}$
12. **a.** $x \doteq \pm 1.414$ **b.** $x \doteq -10.196, 0.196$
c. $x \doteq -1.377, -0.274, 2.651$ **d.** $x \doteq -1.197$
e. $x \doteq \pm 2.857, \pm 1.356$ **f.** $x \doteq -5.67$
13. $x_2 = 3$ and $k = -1$
14. $x^2 + 5x + 2 = 0$
15. **a.** $x_1 + x_2 = \frac{1}{2}, x_1x_2 = 2$ **b.** $15x^2 - x - 2 = 0$
c. $x^2 - 6x + 13 = 0$ **d.** $x_2 = -\frac{2}{3}, k = -1$
e. $x^2 + x - 4 = 0$ **f.** $4x^2 - x - 2 = 0$
16. **a.** $-4 < x < 2$ **b.** $x \le -2$ or $x \ge 1$ **c.** $x \le 0$
d. $-1 < x < 1$ or $x > 2$ **e.** $x = 0$ **f.** R
g. $-2.8 < x < -.72$ or $.72 < x < 2.8$
h. $-1.44 < x < 1$ or $x > 1.38$
17. **a.** $\frac{-10}{3}, 4$ **b.** $-4 < x < 2$ **c.** $x \le -1$ or $x \ge 4$
18. 5 cm

Chapter 2 Test

1. No.
2. **a.** $(x - 1)(x^2 + 4x + 2)$ **b.** $(x + 1)(2x - 3)(x - 3)$
c. $(x + 1)(x - 1)^3$
3. $(3x - 2)(x^2 + 2x + 2)$
4. **a.** $3, \frac{-3 \pm 3i\sqrt{3}}{2}$ **b.** $1, \frac{3 \pm i\sqrt{3}}{2}$ **c.** $0, \frac{1}{2}, 3$ **d.** $\pm 2, \pm 1$
5. $x^2 - 8x + 20 = 0$
6. Yes.
7. **a.** $-2 < x < 3$ or $x < -2$ **b.** $-2 \le x \le 0$ or $x \ge 2$
c. $x < -7$ or $x > 2$
8. **a.** 3 zeros, positive, cubic (3rd)
b. 2 zeros, positive, quartic (4th)
c. 3 zeros, negative, cubic (3rd)
9. **a.** 173.9 cm **b.** 6.52 kg

CHAPTER 3 INTRODUCTION TO CALCULUS

Review of Prerequisite Skills

1. **a.** -3 **b.** -2 **c.** 12 **d.** -1 **e.** $\frac{-2}{3}$ **f.** $\frac{-2}{3}$ **g.** 4 **h.** -4 **i.** $\frac{-5}{6}$
j. -1 **k.** $-\frac{41}{10}$ **l.** -1
2. **a.** $y = 4x - 2$ **b.** $y = -2x + 5$
c. $y + 5 = 0$ **d.** $2x - 3y + 12 = 0$ **e.** $6x - 5y + 36 = 0$
f. $x + y - 2 = 0$ **g.** $6x - y + 2 = 0$ **h.** $4x - y = 0$
i. $7x - y - 27 = 0$ **j.** $3x + y - 6 = 0$ **k.** $x + 3 = 0$
l. $y - 5 = 0$
3. **a.** $\frac{-5}{52}$ **b.** $\frac{-3}{13}$ **c.** 0 **d.** $\frac{5}{52}$
4. **a.** 6 **b.** $\sqrt{3}$ **c.** 9
5. **a.** $\frac{-1}{2}$ **b.** -1 **c.** 5 **d.** 1 **e.** 10^6
6. **a.** $\frac{5\sqrt{2}}{2}$ **b.** $\frac{6\sqrt{3} + \sqrt{6}}{3}$ **c.** $\frac{6 + 4\sqrt{3}}{3}$ **d.** $\frac{3 - \sqrt{3}}{6}$
e. $\frac{-5\sqrt{7} - 20}{9}$ **f.** $-6 - 4\sqrt{3}$ **g.** $\frac{-15 + 10\sqrt{3}}{2}$
h. $\frac{-6\sqrt{6} - 15\sqrt{2}}{13}$ **i.** $\frac{20 + 2\sqrt{5}}{19}$
7. **a.** $\frac{2}{5\sqrt{2}}$ **b.** $\frac{3}{6\sqrt{3} + \sqrt{6}}$ **c.** $\frac{-9}{5\sqrt{7} + 4}$ **d.** $\frac{-13}{6\sqrt{6} + 15\sqrt{2}}$
e. $\frac{-1}{\sqrt{3} + \sqrt{7}}$ **f.** $\frac{1}{2\sqrt{3} - 7}$
8. **a.** $(x - 2)(x + 2)$ **b.** $x(x - 1)(x + 1)$ **c.** $(x + 3)(x - 2)$
d. $(2x - 3)(x - 2)$ **e.** $x(x + 1)(x + 1)$ **f.** $(x + 2)(x^2 - 2x + 4)$
g. $(3x - 4)(9x^2 + 12x + 16)$ **h.** $(x - 2)(x^2 + 3)$
i. $(x - 1)(x + 2)(2x - 3)$
9. **a.** $x \in R$ **b.** $x \in R$ **c.** $x \ge -5, x \in R$ **d.** $x \in R$
e. $x \ne 1, x \in R$ **f.** $x \in R$ **g.** $x \ge 9, x \in R$ **h.** $x \ne 0, x \in R$
i. $x \ne 5, x \in R$ **j.** $x \ne 4, -1, -5, x \in R$ **k.** $x \ne 3, \frac{1}{2}, x \in R$
l. $x \ne -2, 1, -5, x \in R$

Exercise 3.1

1. **a.** 3 **b.** $\frac{-5}{3}$ **c.** $\frac{-1}{3}$
2. **a.** $\frac{-1}{3}$ **b.** $\frac{-7}{13}$

3. a. $x - y = 0$ **b.** $y = 8x + 6$ **c.** $3x - 5y - 15 = 0$
d. $x - 5 = 0$

4. a. $4 + h$ **b.** $75 + 15h + h^2$ **c.** $108 + 54h + 12h^2 + h^3$
d. $\frac{-1}{1+h}$ **e.** $6 + 3h$ **f.** $12 + 6h + h^2$ **g.** $\frac{-3}{4(4+h)}$ **h.** $\frac{1}{4+2h}$

5. a. $\frac{1}{\sqrt{16+h}+4}$ **b.** $\frac{h+5}{\sqrt{h^2+5h+4}+2}$ **c.** $\frac{1}{\sqrt{5+h}+\sqrt{5}}$

6. a. $6 + 3h$ **b.** $3 + 3h + h^2$ **c.** $\frac{1}{\sqrt{9+h}+3}$

7. a. $P(2, 8)$

Q	Slope of PQ
(3, 27)	19
(2.5, 15.625)	15.25
(2.1, 9.261)	12.61
(2.01, 8.120601)	12.0601
(1, 1)	7
(1.5, 3.375)	9.25
(1.9, 6.859)	11.41
(1.99, 7.880599)	11.9401

b. 12 **c.** $12 + 6h + h^2$ **d.** 12

8. a. -12 **b.** 5 **c.** 12

9. a. $\frac{1}{2}$ **b.** $\frac{1}{4}$ **c.** $\frac{5}{6}$

10. a. -2 **b.** $\frac{-1}{2}$ **c.** $\frac{-1}{25}$

11. a. 1 **b.** -1 **c.** 9 **d.** $\frac{1}{4}$ **e.** $\frac{-1}{10}$ **f.** $\frac{-3}{4}$ **g.** $\frac{-1}{6}$ **h.** $\frac{-1}{16}$

16. $\frac{-5}{4}$

17. 1600 papers/month

18. (2, 4)

19. $\left(-2, \frac{28}{3}\right), \left(-1, \frac{26}{3}\right), \left(1, \frac{-26}{3}\right), \left(2, \frac{-28}{3}\right)$

Exercise 3.2

1. 0 s and 4 s

2. a. slope of the secant between two points $(2, s(2))$ and $(9, s(9))$
b. slope of the tangent at $(6, s(6))$

3. slope of the tangent to $y = \sqrt{x}$ at (4, 2)

4. a. between A and B **b.** greater

7. a. 5 m/s, 25 m/s, 75 m/s **b.** 55 m/s **c.** 20 m/s

8. a. i) 72 km/h **ii)** 64.8 km/h **iii)** 64.08 km/h **c.** 64 km/h

9. a. 15 terms **b.** 16 terms/h

10. a. $-\frac{1}{3}$ mg/h

11. $\frac{1}{50}$ s/m

12. $-\frac{12}{5}$°C/km

13. 2 s, 0 m/s

14. a. \$4800 **b.** \$80/ball **c.** $0 < x < 8$

15. a. 6 **b.** -1 **c.** $\frac{1}{10}$

18. 200π m²/m

Exercise 3.3

1. a. $\frac{8}{11}$ **b.** π

4. a. -5 **b.** 10 **c.** 100 **d.** -8 **e.** 4 **f.** 8

5. 1

6. a. 0 **b.** 2 **c.** -1 **d.** 2

7. a. 2 **b.** 1 **c.** does not exist

8. a. 8 **b.** 2 **c.** 2

9. 5

10. a. 0 **b.** 0 **c.** 5 **d.** $\frac{-1}{2}$ **e.** $\frac{1}{5}$ **f.** does not exist

11. a. does not exist **b.** 2 **c.** 2 **d.** does not exist

13. $m = -3, b = 1$

14. $a = 3, b = 2, c = 0$

15. b. 6, 4 **c.** 2000 **d.** $2\frac{1}{2}$ years after the spill, or $8\frac{1}{2}$ years in total.

Exercise 3.4

4. a. 1 **b.** 1 **c.** $\frac{100}{9}$ **d.** $5\pi^3$ **e.** 2 **f.** $\sqrt{3}$

5. a. 2 **b.** $\sqrt{2}$

7. a. 4 **b.** 4 **c.** 7 **d.** 1 **e.** $\frac{-7}{3}$ **f.** 27 **g.** 0 **h.** $\frac{7}{2}$ **i.** $\frac{1}{2}$ **j.** $-\frac{1}{4}$ **k.** $\frac{1}{4}$
l. $-\frac{1}{\sqrt{7}}$ **m.** $\frac{-1}{2}$ **n.** $\frac{3}{4}$ **o.** 1

8. a. $\frac{1}{12}$ **b.** -27 **c.** $\frac{1}{6}$ **d.** $\frac{1}{2}$ **e.** $\frac{1}{12}$ **f.** $\frac{1}{12}$

9. a. 0 **b.** 0 **c.** 4 **d.** -1 **e.** 0 **f.** $\frac{2}{3}$ **g.** -16 **h.** $\frac{1}{4}$ **i.** $\frac{-3}{2}$ **j.** $\frac{1}{2}$
k. $2x$ **l.** $\frac{1}{32}$

10. a. does not exist **b.** does not exist **c.** does not exist **d.** 0

11. b. $V = 0.08213T + 22.4334$ **c.** $T = \frac{V - 22.4334}{0.08213}$

13. a. 27 **b.** -1 **c.** 1

14. a. 0 **b.** 0

15. a. 0 **b.** 0 **c.** $\frac{1}{2}$

16. 2

17. No.

18. $b = 2$

19. $m = 6, b = 9$

Exercise 3.5

4. a. 3 **b.** 0 **c.** 0 **d.** ± 3 **e.** $-3, 2$ **f.** 3

5. a. $x \in R$ **b.** $x \in R$ **c.** $x < 0, 0 < x < 5, x > 5, x \in R$
d. $x \geq -2, x \in R$ **e.** $x \in R$ **f.** $x \in R$

7. continuous everywhere

8. No.

9. 0, 100, 200, and 500

10. Yes.

11. discontinuous at $x = 2$

12. $k = 16$

13. $a = -1, b = 6$

14. a. 1, -1, does not exist **b.** discontinuous at $x = 1$

Review Exercise

1. a. -3 **b.** 7 **c.** $2x - y - 5 = 0$

2. a. $-\frac{1}{3}$ **b.** $\frac{1}{2}$ **c.** $\frac{-1}{27}$ **d.** $\frac{-5}{4}$

3. a. 2 **b.** 2

4. a. -5 m/s; -15 m/s **b.** -40 m/s **c.** -60 m/s

5. a. 0.0601 g **b.** 6.01 g/min **c.** 6 g/min

6. a. 7×10^5 tonnes **b.** 1.8×10^5 tonnes/year
c. 1.5×10^5 tonnes/year **d.** 7.5 years

7. a. 10 **b.** 7, 0 **c.** $t = 3, t = 4$

9. a. $x = -1, x = 1$ **b.** do not exist

10. not continuous at $x = 3$

11. a. $x = 1, x = -2$ **b.** $\lim_{x\to 1} f(x) = \frac{2}{3}$, $\lim_{x\to -2} f(x)$ does not existt

12.a. does not exist **b.** 0 **c.** $\frac{37}{7}$, does not exist

13. $\frac{1}{3}$

x	f(x)
1.9	0.34483
1.99	0.33445
1.999	0.33344
2.001	0.33322
2.01	0.33223
2.1	0.32258

b. $\frac{1}{2}$

x	f(x)
0.9	0.52632
0.99	0.50251
0.999	0.50025
1.001	0.49975
1.01	0.49751
1.1	0.47619

14.

x	f(x)
−0.1	0.29112
−0.01	0.28892
−0.001	0.2887
0.001	0.28865
0.01	0.28843
0.1	0.28631

15. a.

x	f(x)
2.1	0.24846
2.01	0.24984
2.001	0.24998
2.0001	0.25

c. $\frac{1}{4}$

16. a. 10, slope of the tangent to $y = x^2$ at $x = 5$

b. $\frac{1}{4}$, slope of the tangent to $y = \sqrt{x}$ at $x = 4$

c. $\frac{-1}{16}$, slope of the tangent to $y = \frac{1}{x}$ at $x = 4$

d. $\frac{1}{147}$, slope of the tangent to $y = \sqrt[3]{x}$ at $x = 343$

17. a. $\frac{-3}{2}$ **b.** $5a^2 - 3a + 7$ **c.** does not exist **d.** 1 **e.** -12 **f.** 4

g. $\frac{1}{3}$ **h.** $10a$ **i.** $\frac{-3}{7}$ **j.** $\frac{3}{5}$ **k.** 1 **l.** -1 **m.** $\frac{3}{2}$ **n.** $\frac{\sqrt{3} - 2}{2}$

o. $\frac{1}{\sqrt{5}}$ **p.** -3 **q.** 0 **r.** 16 **s.** 48 **t.** $-\frac{1}{4}$ **u.** 2

Chapter 3 Test

5. -13

6. $\frac{-4}{3}$

7. 2

8. $x + y + 2 = 0$

9. a. does not exist **b.** 1 **c.** 1 **d.** 1, 2

10. a. 1.8×10^5 **b.** 4000 people/year

11. a. 1 km/h **b.** 2 km/h

12. $\frac{\sqrt{16 + h} - 4}{h}$

13. -31

14. a. 12 **b.** $\frac{7}{5}$ **c.** 4 **d.** $\frac{-3}{4}$ **e.** $\frac{1}{6}$ **f.** $\frac{1}{12}$

15. $a = 1, b = \frac{-18}{5}$

17. $k = 8$

CHAPTER 4 DERIVATIVES

Review of Prerequisite Skills

1. a. 5^{11} **b.** a^8 **c.** 4^{18} **d.** $-8a^6$ **e.** $6m^{13}$ **f.** $2p$ **g.** $\frac{1}{a^2b^7}$ **h.** $48e^{18}$

i. $-\frac{b}{2a^6}$

2. a. $x^{\frac{7}{6}}$ **b.** $4x^4$ **c.** $a^{\frac{2}{3}}$

3. a. $\frac{-3}{2}$ **b.** 2 **c.** $\frac{-3}{5}$ **d.** 1

4. a. $x + 2y - 5 = 0$ **b.** $3x - 2y + 16 = 0$ **c.** $4x + 3y - 7 = 0$

5. a. $2x^2 - 5xy - 3y^2$ **b.** $x^3 - 5x^2 + 10x - 8$

c. $12x^2 + 36x - 21$ **d.** $-13x + 42y$ **e.** $29x^2 - 2xy + 10y^2$

f. $-13x^3 - 12x^2y + 4xy^2$

6. a. $\frac{15x}{2}, x \neq -2, 0$ **b.** $\frac{y - 5}{4y^2(y + 2)}, y \neq 5$ **c.** $\frac{8}{9}, h \neq -k$

d. $\frac{2}{(x + y)^2}, x \neq y$ **e.** $\frac{11x^2 - 8x + 7}{2x(x - 1)}$ **f.** $\frac{4x + 7}{(x - 2)(x + 3)}$

7. a. $2a(5a - 3)$ **b.** $(2k - 3)(2k + 3)$ **c.** $(x + 4)(x - 8)$

d. $(y - 14)(y + 3)$ **e.** $(3a - 7)(a + 1)$ **f.** $(6x + 5)(x + 2)$

g. $(x - 1)(x + 1)(x^2 + 1)$ **h.** $(x - y)(x^2 + xy + y^2)$

i. $(r - 1)(r + 1)(r - 2)(r + 2)$

8. a. $(a - b)(a^2 + ab + b^2)$

b. $(a - b)(a^4 + a^3b + a^2b^2 + ab^3 + b^4)$

c. $(a - b)(a^6 + a^5b + a^4b^2 + a^3b^3 + a^2b^4 + ab^5 + b^6)$

d. $(a - b)(a^{n-1} + a^{n-2}b + a^{n-3}b^2 + ... + ab^{n-2} + b^{n-1})$

9. a. $\frac{3\sqrt{2}}{2}$ **b.** $\frac{4\sqrt{3} - \sqrt{6}}{3}$ **c.** $-\frac{30 + 17\sqrt{2}}{23}$ **d.** $-\frac{11 - 4\sqrt{6}}{5}$

Exercise 4.1

1. a. $x \in R, x \neq -2$ **b.** $x \in R, x \neq 2$ **c.** $x \in R$ **d.** $x \in R, x \neq 1$

e. $x \in R$ **f.** $x > 2, x \in R$

4. a. 2 **b.** 9 **c.** $\frac{1}{2}$

5. a. $2x + 3$ **b.** $\frac{-3}{(x + 2)^2}$ **c.** $\frac{3}{2\sqrt{3x + 2}}$ **d.** $\frac{-2}{x^3}$

6. a. -7 **b.** $\frac{-2}{(x - 1)^2}$ **c.** $6x$

7. $-4, 0, 4$

8. 8 m/s, 0 m/s, -4 m/s

9. $x - 6y + 10 = 0$

10. a. 0 **b.** 1 **c.** m **d.** $2ax + b$

12. a and e, b and f, c and d

13. -1

14. $f'(0) = 0$

15. 3

16. $f(x) = (x - 3)^{\frac{1}{3}}$, answers will vary

Exercise 4.2

2. a. 4 **b.** 0 **c.** $4x + 1$ **d.** $\frac{1}{2\sqrt{x}}$ **e.** $12x^2$ **f.** $3x^2 - 2x$ **g.** $-2x + 5$

h. $\frac{1}{3\sqrt[3]{x^2}}$ **i.** x^3 **j.** $18x$ **k.** $\frac{x^3}{4}$ **l.** $-3x^{-4}$

3. a. $\frac{dy}{dx} = 2x - 3$ **b.** $f'(x) = 6x^2 + 10x - 4$

c. $v'(t) = 18t^2 - 20t^4$ **d.** $s'(t) = \frac{-2}{t^3}, t > 0$ **e.** $f'(x) = 6x^5$

f. $h'(x) = 4x + 11$ **g.** $\frac{ds}{dt} = 4t^3 - 6t^2$ **h.** $g'(x) = 20x^4$

i. $\frac{dy}{dx} = x^4 + x^2 - x$ **j.** $g'(x) = 40x^7$ **k.** $s'(t) = 2t^3 - \frac{3}{2}$

l. $g'(x) = 7f'(x)$ **m.** $h'(x) = \frac{21}{x^8}$ **n.** $\frac{dy}{dx} = m$

4. a. $2x^{\frac{-4}{5}}$ **b.** $5x^{\frac{2}{3}}$ **c.** $-9x^{\frac{-5}{2}}$ **d.** $8x^7 + 8x^{-9}$

e. $2x^{\frac{-1}{3}} - 2x^{\frac{-2}{3}} - \frac{1}{3}x^{\frac{-4}{3}}$ **f.** $2x^{\frac{-3}{2}} + 6x^{-2}$ **g.** $-18x^{-4} - 4x^{-3}$

h. $-18x^{-3} + \frac{3}{2}x^{\frac{-1}{2}}$ **i.** $100x^4 + x^{\frac{-2}{3}}$ **j.** $\frac{1}{2}x^{\frac{-1}{2}} + 9x^{\frac{1}{2}}$

k. $1.5x^{0.5} + 3x^{-1.25}$ **l.** $-x^{-2} - \frac{1}{2}x^{\frac{-3}{2}}$

5. a. $-4t + 7$ **b.** $5 - t^2$ **c.** $2t - 6$

6. a. $\frac{191}{4}$ **b.** $\frac{11}{24}$

7. a. 12 **b.** 5 **c.** $-\frac{1}{2}$ **d.** 12

8. a. 9 **b.** $\frac{1}{2}$ **c.** 4 **d.** -7

9. a. $6x - y - 4 = 0$ **b.** $18x - y + 25 = 0$ **c.** $9x - 2y - 9 = 0$
d. $x + y - 3 = 0$ **e.** $7x - 2y - 28 = 0$ **f.** $5x - 6y - 11 = 0$

10. $x + 18y - 125 = 0$

11. 8 or -8

12. No

14. $(-1, 0)$

15. $(2, 10), (-2, -6)$

17. a. $y - 3 = 0, 16x - y - 29 = 0$;
b. $20x - y - 47 = 0, 4x + y - 1 = 0$

18. 7

19. a. 50 km **b.** 0.12 km/m

20. 0.29 min, 1.71 min

21. -20 m/s

22. $(1, -3), (-1, -3)$

23. $(0, 0)$

25. $1 - \frac{1}{n}$, approaches 1

26. a. $f'(x) = \begin{cases} 2x, x < 3 \\ 1, x > 3 \end{cases}$

$f'(x)$ does not exist at $(3, 9)$.

b. $f'(x) = \begin{cases} 6x, x < -\sqrt{2} \\ -6x, -\sqrt{2} < x < \sqrt{2} \\ 6x, x > \sqrt{2} \end{cases}$

$f'(x)$ does not exist at $(-\sqrt{2}, 0), (\sqrt{2}, 0)$.

c. $f'(x) = \begin{cases} -1, x < -1 \\ 1, -1 < x < 0 \\ -1, 0 < x < 1 \\ 1, x > 0 \end{cases}$

$f'(x)$ does not exist at $(-1, 0), (0, 1), (1, 0)$.

Exercise 4.3

1. a. $2x - 4$ **b.** $6x^2 - 2x$ **c.** $12x - 17$ **d.** $-8x + 26$
e. $45x^8 - 80x^7 + 2x - 2$ **f.** $-8t^3 + 2t$

2. a. $15(5x + 1)^2(x - 4) + (5x + 1)^3$
b. $6x(3 + x^3)^5 + 15x^2(3x^2 + 4)(3 + x^3)^4$
c. $-8x(1 - x^2)^3(2x + 6)^3 + 6(1 - x^2)^4(2x + 6)^2$

4. a. 9 **b.** -4 **c.** -9 **d.** 6 **e.** -36 **f.** 22 **g.** 671 **h.** -12

5. $10x + y - 8 = 0$

6. a. $(14, -450)$ **b.** $(-1, 0)$

7. a. $3(x + 1)^2(x + 4)(x - 3)^2 + (x + 1)^3(x - 3)^2 +$
$2(x + 1)^3(x + 4)(x - 3)$
b. $2x(3x^2 + 4)^2(3 - x^3)^4 + 12x^3(3x^2 + 4)(3 - x^3)^4 -$
$12x^4(3x^2 + 4)^2(3 - x^3)^3$

8. -30

9. a. $f'(x) = g'(x)g_2(x) \ldots g_{11}(x) + g_1(x)\, g'_2(x)\, g'_3(x) \ldots g_{11}(x)$
$+ g_1(x)\, g_2(x)\, g'_3(x) \ldots g_{11}(x) + \ldots$
$+ g_1(x)\, g_2(x) \ldots g_{x-1}(x)\, g'_{11}(x)$ **b.** $\frac{n(n + 1)}{2}$

10. $f(x) = 3x^2 + 6x - 5$

11. a. ± 1 **b.** $f'(x) = 2x, x < -1$ or $x > 1$;
$f'(x) = -2x, -1 < x < 7$ **c.** $-4, 0, 6$

Exercise 4.4

2. $f'(x) = 1, g'(x) = 2x^{\frac{-1}{3}}, h'(x) = \frac{-1}{2x^6}, \frac{dy}{dx} = 8x, \frac{ds}{dt} = 1$

4. a. $\frac{1}{(x + 1)^2}$ **b.** $\frac{x^2 + 2x}{(x + 1)^2}$ **c.** $\frac{13}{(t + 5)^2}$ **d.** $\frac{7}{(x + 3)^2}$ **e.** $\frac{2x^4 - 3x^2}{(2x^2 - 1)^2}$
f. $\frac{-2x}{(x^2 + 3)^2}$ **g.** $\frac{5x^2 + 6x + 5}{(1 - x^2)^2}$ **h.** $\frac{x^2 + 4x - 3}{(x^2 + 3)^2}$ **i.** $\frac{x^2 + 6x + 1}{(3x^2 + x)^2}$

5. a. $\frac{13}{4}$ **b.** $\frac{7}{25}$ **c.** $\frac{200}{841}$ **d.** $\frac{-7}{3}$

6. -9

7. $\left(9, \frac{27}{5}\right), \left(-1, \frac{3}{5}\right)$

9. a. $(0, 0), (8, 32)$ **b.** $(1, 0)$

10. $p'(1) \cong 75.36, p'(2) \cong 63.10$

11. $5x - 12y - 4 = 0$

12. a. 20 m **b.** -1.1 m/s

13. $ad - bc > 0$

Exercise 4.5

1. a. 0 **b.** 0 **c.** -1 **d.** $\sqrt{15}$ **e.** $\sqrt{x^2 - 1}$ **f.** $x - 1$

2. a. $f(g(x)) = x, x \geq 0$; $g(f(x)) = |x|, x \in R$; $f \circ g \neq g \circ f$
b. $f(g(x)) = \frac{1}{x^2 + 1}, x \in R$; $g(f(x)) = \frac{1}{x^2} + 1, x \neq 0$; $f \circ g \neq g \circ f$
c. $f(g(x)) = \frac{1}{\sqrt{x + 2}}, x > -2$; $g(f(x)) = \sqrt{\frac{1 + 2x}{x}}, x < -\frac{1}{2}$ or
$x > 0$; $f \circ g \neq g \circ f$

3. a. $3\sqrt{x} + 1$ **b.** $\frac{1}{\sqrt{x + 1}}$ **c.** $(3x + 1)^3$
d. $\sqrt{x^3}$ **e.** $\frac{1}{\sqrt{x} + 1}$ **f.** $3x^3 + 1$ **g.** $\frac{1}{3\sqrt{x} + 2}$ **h.** $3x\sqrt{x} + 1$
i. $\frac{1}{(\sqrt{x} + 1)^3}$

4. a. $f(x) = x^4, g(x) = 2x^2 - 1$ **b.** $f(x) = \sqrt{x}, g(x) = 5x - 1$
c. $f(x) = \frac{1}{x}, g(x) = x - 4$ **d.** $f(x) = x^{\frac{5}{2}}, g(x) = 2 - 3x$
e. $f(x) = x(x + 1), g(x) = x^2 + 2$
f. $f(x) = x^2 - 9x, g(x) = x + 1$

5. $g(x) = x^3$

6. $f(x) = (x + 7)^2$

7. $f(x) = (x + 3)^2$

8. $g(x) = x + 4$ or $g(x) = -x - 4$

9. $u(x) = 2x$ or $u(x) = -2x + 4$

10. a. $\frac{x}{x - 1}$ **b.** $\frac{1}{x}$ **11.** $-2, -3$ **12. a.** x

Exercise 4.6

2. a. $8(2x + 3)^2$ **b.** $-6(5 - x)^5$ **c.** $6x(x^2 - 4)^2$ **d.** $-15x^2(7 - x^3)^4$
e. $4(4x + 3)(2x^2 + 3x - 5)^3$ **f.** $5(5x - x^2)^4(5 - 2x)$
g. $-6x(\pi^2 - x^2)^2$ **h.** $4(-1 + 2x - 3x^2)(1 - x + x^2 - x^3)^3$
i. $-12(2 - x)^3[(2 - x)^4 + 16]^2$ **j.** $\frac{2}{\sqrt{4x + 1}}$ **k.** $\frac{5}{2\sqrt{5x + 7}}$
l. $\frac{x}{\sqrt{x^2 - 3}}$ **m.** $\frac{-10x}{(x^2 - 16)^6}$ **n.** $\frac{-x}{\sqrt{x^2 + 4^3}}$ **o.** $\frac{-1}{2\sqrt{x}(\sqrt{x} + 1)^2}$
p. $\frac{2(1 + u^{\frac{1}{3}})^5}{\sqrt[3]{u^2}}$ **q.** $3\sqrt{2x - 5}$ **r.** $\frac{2(x + 2)^2(x - 1)}{x^2}$

3. a. $\frac{-6}{x^3}$ **b.** $\frac{6}{x^4}$ **c.** $\frac{-1}{(x + 1)^2}$ **d.** $\frac{-2x}{(x^2 - 4)^2}$ **e.** $\frac{-8}{x^3}$ **f.** $\frac{6x}{(9 - x^2)^2}$
g. $\frac{-10x - 1}{(5x^2 + x)^2}$ **h.** $\frac{-4(2x + 1)}{(x^2 + x + 1)^5}$ **i.** $\frac{(1 + \sqrt{x})^2(\sqrt{x} - 2)}{x^3}$

4. a. $3(3x + 5)(x + 4)^2(x - 3)^5$ **b.** $\frac{(3x + 1)(x + 3)}{(1 - x^2)^2}$
c. $4(2x - 1)^3(2 - 3x)^3(7 - 12x)$
d. $\frac{-2(x^2 - 3x - 1)}{(x^2 + 1)^2}$ **e.** $3x^2(3x - 5)(4x - 5)$

f. $\frac{-(2x-1)(2x+5)}{(x-2)^4}$ **g.** $4x^3(1-4x^2)^2(1-10x^2)$

h. $\frac{48x(x^2-3)^3}{(x^2+3)^5}$ **i.** $6x(2x^3+3x+3)(x^2+3)^2(x^3+3)$

j. $\frac{1}{(1+x^2)^{\frac{3}{2}}}$ **k.** $12(4-3t^3)^3(1-2t)^5(9t^3-3t^2-4)$

l. $\frac{1}{(1-x)\sqrt{1-x^2}}$

5. a. $\frac{91}{36}$ **b.** $\frac{7}{48\pi}$

6. $x = 0, x = 1$

7. $\frac{-1}{4}$

8. $60x - y - 119 = 0$

9. a. 52 **b.** 78 **c.** 54 **d.** 320 **e.** $\frac{9728}{27}$ **f.** $\frac{-1}{8}$ **g.** -48608

10. 10

11. $\frac{-42}{25}$

12. -6

13. a. $h'(x) = p'(x)g(x)r(x) + p(x)q'(x)r(x) + p(x)q(x)r'(x)$
b. -344

15. $\frac{-2x(x^2+3x-1)(1-x)^2}{(1+x)^4}$

17. $(a-1)d = (c-1)b$

Technology Extension

b. i) 6 **ii)** 3 **iii)** 32 **iv)** 6 **v)** $\frac{-3}{4}$ **vi)** -4 **vii)** 6 **viii)** -1

Review Exercise

2. a. $4x - 5$ **b.** $\frac{1}{2\sqrt{x-6}}$ **c.** $\frac{4}{(4-x)^2}$

3. a. $2x - 5$ **b.** $-3x^2$ **c.** $\frac{3}{4}x^{\frac{-1}{4}}$ **d.** $20x^{-5}$ **e.** $\frac{-28}{3x^5}$ **f.** $\frac{-1}{(x-3)^2}$

g. $\frac{-2x}{(x^2+5)^2}$ **h.** $\frac{12x}{(3-x^2)^3}$ **i.** $\frac{-1}{2\sqrt{2-x}}$ **j.** $\frac{7x+2}{\sqrt{7x^2+4x+1}}$

k. $60x^3(5x^4+\pi)^2$ **l.** $\frac{-4}{x^5} - \frac{6x^2}{5(x^3-4)^{\frac{7}{5}}}$

4. a. $\frac{2x^3+2}{x^3}$ **b.** $\frac{\sqrt{x}}{2}(7x^2-3)$ **c.** $\frac{-4}{x^2\sqrt{x}}$ **d.** $\frac{-3x+2}{x^3}$ **e.** $\frac{-5}{(3x-5)^2}$

f. $\frac{3x-1}{2\sqrt{x-1}}$ **g.** $\frac{-1}{3\sqrt{x}\sqrt[3]{(\sqrt{x}+2)^5}}$ **h.** $\frac{x}{\sqrt{x^2-9}}$ **i.** $1, x \neq -4$

j. $2x + 6$

5. a. $20x^3(x-1)(2x-6)^5$ **b.** $\frac{2x^2+1}{\sqrt{x^2+1}}$ **c.** $\frac{(2x-5)^3(2x+23)}{(x+1)^4}$

d. $\frac{x^2+15}{3(x^2+5)^{\frac{4}{3}}}$ **e.** $\frac{318(10x-1)^5}{(3x+5)^7}$ **f.** $\frac{12x(x^2-1)^2}{(x^2+1)^4}$ **g.** $\frac{-1}{(x^2-1)^{\frac{3}{2}}}$

h. $(x-2)^2(x^2+9)^3(11x^2-16x+27)$

i. $-6(1-x^2)^2(6+2x)^{-4}(3x^2+6x-1)$

j. $\frac{(3x^2-2)(15x^2-62)}{\sqrt{x^2-5}}$

6. a. $g'(x) = f(x^2) \bullet 2x$ **b.** $h'(x) = 2f(x) + 2xf'(x)$

7. a. $\frac{92}{9}$ **b.** $\frac{25}{289}$ **c.** $\frac{-8}{5}$

8. $\frac{-2}{3}$

9. $2 \pm 2\sqrt{3}, 5, -1$

10. a. i. $\pm 2, 0$ **ii.** $0, \pm 1, \pm \frac{\sqrt{3}}{3}$

11. a. $160x - y + 16 = 0$ **b.** $60x + y - 61 = 0$

12. $5x - y - 7 = 0$

13. $(2, 8), b = -8$

14. c. $(0, 0), \left(3\sqrt{2}, \frac{9\sqrt{2}}{2}\right), \left(-3\sqrt{2}, \frac{-9\sqrt{2}}{2}\right)$ **d.** -14

15. a. $\sqrt[3]{50} \doteq 3.68$ **b.** 1

16. a. 9, 19 **b.** 1.7 words/min, 2.3 words/min

17. a. $\frac{30t}{(\sqrt{9+t^2})^3}$ **b.** Yes. The limit of $N(t)$ as $t \to 0$ is 0.

18. a. $x^2 + 40$ **b.** 6 gloves/week

19. a. $750 - \frac{x}{3} - 2x^2$ **b.** \$546.67

20. $\frac{-5}{4}$

Chapter 4 Test

3. $f'(x) = 1 - 2x$

4. a. $x^2 + 15x^{-6}$ **b.** $60(2x-9)^4$ **c.** $\frac{1}{\sqrt{3}} - \frac{1}{\sqrt{x^3}} - \frac{2}{\sqrt[3]{x^2}}$

d. $\frac{5(x^2+6)^4(3x^2+8x-18)}{(3x+4)^6}$ **e.** $\frac{16x^3-14x}{\sqrt[3]{6x^2-7^2}}$ **f.** $\frac{4x^5-18x+8}{x^5}$

5. 14

6. $\frac{-40}{3}$

7. $60x + y - 61 = 0$

8. $\frac{75}{32}$ p.p.m./year

9. $\left(-\frac{1}{4}, \frac{1}{256}\right)$

10. $(1, 0), \left(-\frac{1}{3}, \frac{32}{27}\right)$

11. $a = 1, b = -1$

Cumulative Review Chapters 1–4

1.

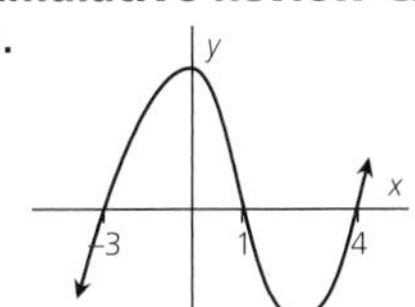

2.

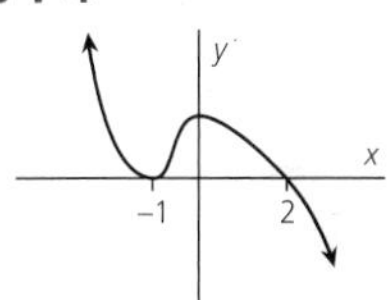

3. $y = 2x^3 - 3x^2 - 24$

4. a. $x^2 - x - 2$ **b.** $3x^2 - 13x + 50, R: -153$
c. $x^2 + x - 5, R: -5x + 4$

5. 27

6. 6

7. -3

8. $(x - 2)$ is a factor.

9. $(x - 3)$ and $(x - 1)$

10. a. $(x-4)(x+2)(x+5)$ **b.** $(x-2)(x+2)(x+5)$
c. $(2x+1)(x-2)(x+2)$ **d.** $(5x-2)(x^2+2x+5)$

11. a. $1, -2, -2$ **b.** $2, -2, 3i, -3i$ **c.** $1, -2, -3$ **d.** $1, -1, \frac{1}{2}$
e. $1, 1, -3$ **f.** $\frac{1}{3}, \frac{1 \pm 3i}{2}$

12. $-4, \frac{5}{2}$

13. $x^2 - 77x + 4 = 0$

14. a. $-2 < x < 3$ **b.** $-2 \leq x \leq 1, x \geq 3$

15. a. $-3 < x < 7$
b. $-1 \leq x \leq 4$ **c.** $x > 5$ or $x < -\frac{17}{3}$

16. a. 13 m/s **b.** 15 m/s

17. 5

18. a. 3 **b.** 1 **c.** 3 **d.** 2 **e.** No.

19. Answers will vary.

20. at $x = 2$

21. 2

22. x^3

23. a. $-\frac{1}{5}$ **b.** does not exist **c.** $-\frac{1}{9}$ **d.** 2 **e.** $\frac{1}{12}$ **f.** $\frac{1}{4}$
24. a. $6x + 1$ **b.** $-x^{-2}$
25. a. $-8x + 5$ **b.** $3x^2(2x^3 + 1)^{-\frac{1}{2}}$ **c.** $6(x + 3)^{-2}$
d. $4x(x^2 + 3)(4x^5 + 5x + 1) + (20x^4 + 5)(x^2 + 3)^2$
e. $\frac{(4x^2 + 1)^4(84x^2 - 80x - 9)}{(3x - 2)^4}$
f. $5[x^2 + (2x + 1)^3]^4[2x + 6(2x + 1)^2]$
26. $4x + 36 = 10$
27. $8x - 16y - 65 = 0$
28. $\left[\frac{18}{(x^3 + 2)^2} + \frac{4}{(x^3 + 2)} + 5\right] \bullet \frac{-3x^2}{(x^3 + 2)^2}$
29. 3
30. a. $4t + 6$ **b.** 46 people/year **c.** 2002

CHAPTER 5 APPLICATIONS OF DERIVATIVES

Review of Prerequisite Skills

5. a. $\frac{14}{5}$ **b.** -13 **c.** 3, 1 **d.** $-\frac{1}{2}$, 3 **e.** 2, 6 **f.** -3, 0, 1 **g.** 0, 4
h. $-\frac{1}{2}, \frac{1}{2}$, 3 **i.** $\pm\frac{9}{2}$, ± 1
6. a. $x > 3$ **b.** $x < 0$ or $x > 3$ **c.** $0 < x < 4$
7. a. 25 cm^2 **b.** 48 cm^2 **c.** 49π cm^2 **d.** 36π cm^2
8. a. $S = 56\pi$ cm^2, $V = 48\pi$ cm^3 **b.** $h = 6$ cm, $S = 80\pi$ cm^2
c. $r = 6$ cm, $S = 144\pi$ cm^2 **d.** $h = 7$ cm, $V = 175\pi$ cm^3
9. a. $V = 972\pi$ cm^3, $S = 324\pi$ cm^2
b. $V = 36\pi$ cm^3, $S = 36\pi$ cm^2 **c.** $r = 3$, $S = 36\pi$ cm^2
d. $r = 5\sqrt{10}$ cm, $V = \frac{5000\sqrt{10}}{3}\pi$ cm^3
10. a. 16π cm^3 **b.** 9 cm **c.** $\frac{9}{2}$ cm
11. a. $S = 54$ cm^2, $V = 27$ cm^3 **b.** $S = 30$ cm^2, $V = 5\sqrt{5}$ cm^3
c. $S = 72$ cm^2, $V = 24\sqrt{3}$ cm^3 **d.** $S = 24k^2$ cm^2, $V = 8k^3$ cm^3

Exercise 5.1

2. a. $-\frac{x}{y}$ **b.** $\frac{x}{y}$ **c.** $\frac{x^2}{5y}$ **d.** $-\frac{y}{2xy + y^2}$, $y \neq 0$ **e.** $\frac{3x^2}{20y^3}$ **f.** $\frac{9x}{16y}$
g. $-\frac{13x}{48y}$ **h.** $-\frac{3x + 2y^3}{6xy^2}$ **i.** $-\frac{2x}{2y + 5}$ **j.** $\frac{2y - x^2}{y^2 - 2x}$ **k.** $-\frac{y}{x}$, $y \neq 0$
l. $\frac{1}{1 + 5y^4}$ **m.** $\frac{3x^2y - y^3}{3y^2 - x^3}$ **n.** $-\frac{\sqrt{y}}{\sqrt{x}}$ **o.** $-\frac{y}{x}$
3. a. $2x - 3y - 13 = 0$ **b.** $2x - 3y + 25 = 0$
c. $3\sqrt{3}x + 5y + 15 = 0$ **d.** $11x - 10y + 81 = 0$
4. (0, 1)
5. a. 1 **b.** $\left(\frac{3\sqrt{5}}{5}, \sqrt{5}\right), \left(-\frac{3\sqrt{5}}{5}, -\sqrt{5}\right)$
6. -10
7. $7x - y - 11 = 0$
8. $x - 2y - 3 = 0$
9. a. $\frac{3x^2 - 8xy}{4x^2 - 3}$
10. a. 1 **b.** 1 **c.** 1 **d.** 2
12. $x - 4 = 0$, $2x - 3y + 10 = 0$
15. $x^2 + y^2 - 8x + 2y - 1 = 0$, $x^2 + y^2 + 4x - 10y + 11 = 0$

Exercise 5.2

2. a. $90x^8 + 90x^4$ **b.** $-\frac{1}{4}x^{-\frac{3}{2}}$ **c.** 2
3. a. $v(t) = 10t - 3$, $a(t) = 10$ **b.** $v(t) = 6t^2 + 3b$, $a(t) = 12t$
c. $v(t) = 1 - 6t^{-2}$, $a(t) = 12t^{-3}$ **d.** $v(t) = 2t - 6$, $a(t) = 2$
e. $v(t) = \frac{1}{2}(t + 1)^{-\frac{1}{2}}$, $a(t) = -\frac{1}{4}(t + 1)^{-\frac{3}{2}}$
f. $v(t) = \frac{27}{(t + 3)^2}$, $a(t) = -\frac{54}{(t + 3)^3}$
4. a. i) $t = 3$ **ii)** $1 < t < 3$ **iii)** $3 < t < 5$ **b. i)** $t = 3$, $t = 7$
ii) $1 < t < 3$, $7 < t < 9$ **iii)** $3 < t < 7$
5. $v(t) = t^2 - 4t + 3$, $a(t) = 2t - 4$, direction changes at $t = 3$ and $t = 1$ returns to original position at $t = 3$
6. a. positive at $t = 1$, negative at $t = 4$
b. neither at $t = 1$, positive at $t = 4$
c. negative at $t = 1$, positive at $t = 4$
7. a. $2t - 6$ **b.** 3 s
8. a. $t = 4$ **b.** 80 m
9. a. 3 m/s **b.** 2 m/s^2
10. a. $v(t) = \frac{35}{2}t^{\frac{3}{2}} - \frac{7}{2}t^{\frac{5}{2}}$, $a(t) = \frac{105}{4}t^{\frac{1}{2}} - \frac{35}{4}t^{\frac{3}{2}}$ **b.** $t = 5$ **c.** $t = 5$
d. $0 < t < 3$ **e.** $t = 7$
11. a. 25 m/s **b.** 31.25 m **c.** $t = 5$, 25 m/s
12. a. Velocity is 98 m/s, acceleration is 12 m/s^2. **b.** 38 m/s
13. a. $v(t) = 6 - 2t$, $a(t) = -2$, 19 m **b.** $v(t) = 3t^2 - 12$, $a(t) = 6t$, -25 m
14. 1 s, away
15. b. $v(0) = 5 - 3k$, $s(t - 3k) = -9k^3 + 30k^2 - 23k$
16. No.
17. b. $v(t) = 1$, $a(t) = 0$

Exercise 5.3

1. a. $\frac{dA}{dt} = 4$ m^2/s **b.** $\frac{dS}{dt} = -3$m^2/min **c.** $\frac{ds}{dt} = 70$ km/h, $t = .25$
d. $\frac{dx}{dt} = \frac{dy}{dt}$ **e.** $\frac{d\theta}{dt} = \frac{\pi}{10}$ rad/s
2. a. decreasing at 5.9ºC/s **b.** 0.577 m c. let $T''(x) = 0$.
3. 100 cm^2/s, 20 cm/s
4. a. 100 cm^3/s **b.** 336 cm^2/s
5. 40 cm^2/s
6. a. $\frac{5}{6\pi}$ m/s **b.** $\frac{5}{3\pi}$ m/s
7. $\frac{1}{\pi}$ km/h
8. $\frac{4}{9}$ m/s
9. 8 m/min
10. 214 m/s
11. $5\sqrt{13}$ km/h
12. a. $\frac{1}{72\pi}$ cm/s **b.** 0.01 cm/s **c.** 0.04 cm/s
13. $\frac{1}{2\pi}$ m/min, 94 min
15. 0.46 m^3/a
16. $\frac{2}{\pi}$ cm/min
17. $V = \frac{5\sqrt{3}}{2}s^2$ (s-side of triangle)
18. $\frac{\sqrt{3}}{4}$ m/min
19. 144 m/min
20. 62.83 km/h
21. $\frac{4}{5\pi}$ cm/s, $\frac{8}{25\pi}$ cm/s
22. $x^2 + y^2 = \frac{l^2}{4}, \frac{x^2}{k^2} + \frac{y^2}{(l - k)^2} = 1$
23. 96 m/s

Exercise 5.4

1. a. Yes. The function is continuous.
b. No. There is a discontinuity at $x = 2$.
c. No. The left side of the domain is not defined.
d. Yes. The function is continuous on the domain given.
2.

	Absolute Maximum	Absolute Minimum
a.	+8	−12
b.	+30	−5

c.	$+100$	-100
d.	30	-20

3. a. maximum 3 at $x = 0$, minimum -1 at $x = 2$
b. maximum 4 at $x = 0$, minimum 0 at $x = 2$
c. maximum 0 at $x = 0, 3$, minimum -4 at $x = -1, 2$
d. maximum 0 at $x = 0$, minimum -20 at $x = -2$
e. maximum 8 at $x = -1$, minimum -3 at $x = -2$
f. maximum $\frac{16}{3}$ at $x = 4$, minimum 0 at $x = 0$

4. a. maximum $\frac{52}{5}$ at $x = 10$, minimum $+4$ at $x = 2$
b. maximum 4 at $x = 4$, minimum 3 at $x = 9$
c. maximum 1 at $x = 1$, minimum $\frac{1}{2}$ at $x = 0$
d. maximum 47 at $x = -3$, minimum -169 at $x = 3$
e. maximum 2 at $x = 1$, minimum -2 at $x = -1$
f. maximum $\frac{8}{5}$ at $x = 2$, minimum $\frac{16}{17}$ at $x = 4$

5. a. minimum velocity $\frac{4}{5}$ m/s, maximum velocity $\frac{4}{3}$ m/s
b. minimum velocity of 4 as $t \to \infty$

6. 20
7. a. 80 km/h **b.** 50 km/h
8. maximum 0.0083, minimum 0.00625
9. 0.049 years
10. 70 km/h, \$31.50
11. 245
12. 300

Exercise 5.5

1. $L = W = 25$ cm
2. If the perimeter is fixed, then the figure will be a square.
3. 300 m × 150 m
4. $L = 82.4$ cm, $W = 22.4$ cm, $h = 8.8$ cm
5. 10 cm × 10 cm × 10 cm
6. 100 units^2
7. a. $r = 5.4$ cm, $h = 10.8$ cm **b.** $h{:}d = 1{:}1$
8. a. 15 cm^2 **b.** 30 cm^2 **c.** The largest area occurs when the length and width are each equal to one-half of the sides adjacent to the right angle.
9. a. $AB = 20$ cm, $BC = AD = 20$ cm **b.** $15\sqrt{3} \times 10^4$ cm^3
10. a. $h = 1.085$ m, equal sides $= 0.957$ m **b.** Yes. All the wood would be used for the outer frame.
11. $t = 0.36$ h
14. a. $r = \frac{50}{\pi}$ cm and no square **b.** $r = 7$ cm, $w = 14$ cm
15. $\sqrt{17}$
16. Both slopes $= \frac{2}{a + b}$.
17. $\frac{25}{2}$
18. $\frac{4\sqrt{3}k^3}{9}$

Exercise 5.6

1. a. \$1.80/L **b.** \$1.07/L **c.** 5625 L
2. a. 15 terms **b.** 16 term/h **c.** 20 terms/h
3. a. $t = 1$ min **b.** 1.5 **d.** maximum **e.** decreasing
4. $h = 15\ 000$ m, $C = \$6000$/h
5. 375 m × 250 m
6. $W = 24.0$ m, $L = 40.8$ m, $h = 20.4$ m
7. $r = 43$ mm, $h = 172$ mm
8. 10 586 m south of the power plant
9. \$22.50
10. 6 nautical miles/h
11. 139 km/h
12. a. \$15 **b.** \$12.50, \$825
14. $r = 2.285$ m, $h = 9.146$ m or 915 cm
15. 5.91 m from stronger light
16. $r = \frac{2}{3}r_0$, velocity $= \frac{4}{27}r_0^3A$

Review Exercise

1. a. $-\frac{3x^2}{5y^4}$ **b.** $-\frac{y^3}{x^3}$ **c.** $\frac{2}{3y^2(x + 1)^2}$ **d.** $\frac{2xy}{3x^2 + y^4}$
e. $\frac{14x^6y}{7y^2 - 10x^7}, y \neq 0$ **f.** $\frac{y^{\frac{2}{5}}\left(5x^{\frac{3}{5}} - 2\right)}{3x^{\frac{3}{5}}}$
2. a. $\frac{5}{4}$ **b.** 0
3. $\frac{4}{5}, -\frac{4}{5}$
4. $f'(x) = 4x^3 + 4x^{-5}$, $f''(x) = 12x^2 - 20x^{-6}$
5. $72x^7 - 42x$
7. $v(t) = 2t + \frac{1}{\sqrt{2t - 3}}$, $a(t) = 2 - \frac{1}{\sqrt{(2t - 3)^3}}$
8. $v(t) = 1 - \frac{5}{t^2}$, $a(t) = \frac{10}{t^3}$
9. $v(t) > 0$ for $0 \leq t \leq \frac{9}{2}$, $v\left(\frac{9}{2}\right) = 0$, $v(t) < 0$ for $t > \frac{9}{2}$
10. a. maximum 0, minimum -52 **b.** maximum 16, minimum -65 **c.** maximum 20, minimum 12
11. a. 62 m **b.** yes, 2 m beyond the stop sign
12. $x - y - 3 = 0$
13. maximum velocity $2 + 3\sqrt{3}$ at $t = \frac{\sqrt{3}}{3}$, minimum velocity 2 at $t = 0$
14. 250
15. a. i) \$2200 **ii)** \$5.50 **iii)** \$3.00, \$3.00 **b. i)** \$24 640 **ii)** \$61.60 **iii)** 43.21, \$43.21 **c. i)** \$5020 **ii)** \$12.55 **iii)** \$0.025, \$0.024 98 **d. i)** \$2705 **ii)** \$6.762 5 **iii)** \$4.993 75, \$4.993 76
16. 2000
17. a. Object is moving away from its starting position.
b. Object is moving towards its starting position.
18. a. $\frac{1}{4\pi}$ m/h **b.** $\frac{3}{50\pi}$ m/h
19. 2 cm^2/s
20. $2\sqrt{10}$ cm^3/s
21. $\frac{8\sqrt{5\pi}}{5}$
22. decreasing; -3.75 m/s
23. a. $t = \frac{2}{3}$ s **b.** maximum **c.** $a > 0$, accelerating
24. 27.14 cm × 27.14 cm × 13.57 cm
25. large: 189.9 m × 63.2 m; small 37.98 m × 63.2 m
26. base is 11.6 d × 31.6 d, $h = 4.2\ d$
27. $r = 4.3$ cm, $h = 8.6$ cm
28. Run the pipe 7199 m along the river from A, then cross to R.
29. 10:35
30. either \$204 or \$206
31. Run the pipe from P to a point 5669 m along the shore from A in the direction of the refinery. Then run the pipe along the shore.

Chapter 5 Test

1. $\frac{x + 2y}{y - 2x}$
2. $3x - 4y + 7 = 0$

3. a. 4 m/s **b.** 2 s, 4 s **c.** 12 m/s^2 **d.** towards
4. 240π m^2/s
5. a. 512 m^3/min
b. Rate of change in volume depends on both $\frac{dr}{dt}$ and the radius. The larger the radius, the larger $\frac{dv}{dt}$ will be.
6. 1.6 cm^2/min
7. $\frac{9}{20\pi}$ m/min
8. minimum is -0.536, maximum is 1.6
9. 7.1 m/s
10. 250 m $\times$ 166.7 m
11. 162 mm $\times$ 324 m $\times$ 190 m

CHAPTER 6 THE EXPONENTIAL FUNCTION

Review of Prerequisite Skills

1. a. 64 **b.** 9 **c.** -27 **d.** $\frac{9}{16}$
2. a. $\frac{1}{x^7}$ **b.** $\frac{5}{m^2}$ **c.** $\frac{1}{27b^3}$ **d.** w^5 **e.** $\frac{9}{4}$
3. a. $\frac{1}{25}$ **b.** $\frac{3}{2}$ **c.** $\frac{64}{27}$ **d.** $\frac{9}{4}$
4. a. 2 **b.** 3 **c.** $\frac{1}{2}$
5. a.

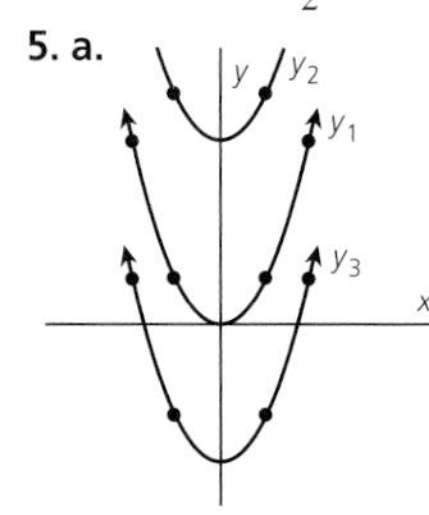

5. b. i) vertical shift of 4 units
ii) vertical shift of -3 units
c. vertical shift upwards of 4 units
d. A positive constant shifts graph upwards. A negative constant shifts graph downwards.

6. a.

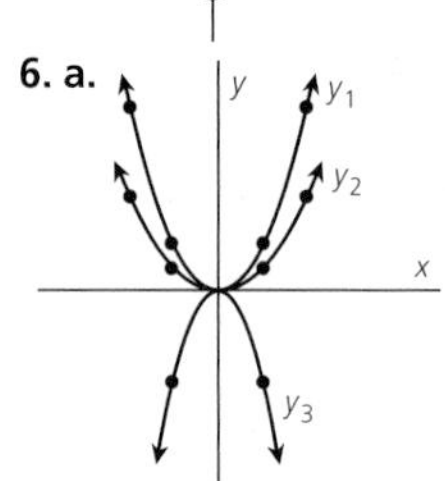

6. b. i) compressed by $\frac{1}{2}$
ii) stretched by a factor of 2
c. vertical stretch by factor of 3 and shifted upwards 25 units
d. $c < 0$, a reflection in the x-axis
$0 < c < 1$, a compression of a factor of c
$c > 1$, a stretch of a factor of c

7. a.

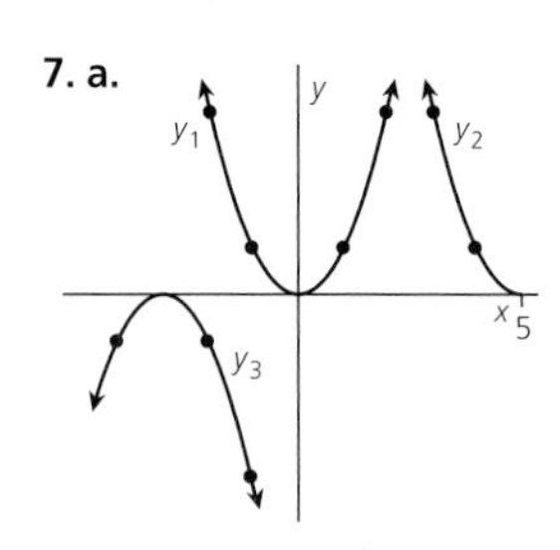

7. b. i) shift 5 units to the right
ii) shift 3 units left and reflected in the x-axis
c. shift 6 units to the left and 7 units down
d. A positive constant causes a shift to the left. A negative constant causes a shift to the right.

Exercise 6.1

1. a. 49 **b.** 0.16 **c.** 81 **d.** 125 **e.** 4 **f.** 64 **g.** $\frac{-1}{16}$ **h.** 1 **i.** $\frac{100}{9}$
j. 1 **k.** 6561 **l.** $\frac{1}{3}$ **m.** $-\frac{1}{2}$ **n.** $2^{-10} = \frac{1}{1024}$ **o.** 729
2. a. $\frac{x^2}{y^2}$ **b.** x^4y^4 **c.** $\frac{9a}{b^4}$ **d.** $\frac{8}{gh^2}$ **e.** x^3y^6 **f.** $\frac{b}{c}$ **g.** $\frac{5x^5}{2y^6}$ **h.** $\frac{\pi x}{4y^2}$
i. $\frac{1}{25x^4y^2}$ **j.** $\frac{a^6b^3}{c^3}$ **k.** $\frac{b^3}{a^6}$ **l.** b^8
3. a. $\frac{x^2}{3y^3}$ **b.** $\frac{\sqrt[3]{b^2}}{\sqrt{a}}$ **c.** x^4 **d.** $x^{\frac{2}{3}}y^{\frac{1}{12}}$ **e.** $\frac{2}{3a^3b}$ **f** $\frac{25}{x^7\sqrt{y}}$
4. a. $8x^2$ **b.** 8 **c.** 81 **d.** $8a^{\frac{5}{4}}$ **e.** $3p^2$ **f.** $2a^2$ **g.** a^6 **h.** $5^{\frac{-7}{12}}$ **i.** $t^{\frac{19}{6}}$
5. a. 12 **b.** $a + b$ **c.** $\frac{(p + q^2)^3}{q}$ **d.** $\frac{x - 1}{2x^4}$ **e.** $\frac{3t^2 - 2}{t^4}$ **f.** $\frac{3p^5 - 1}{p^7}$
6. a. $x^2 - x - x^{-\frac{1}{2}}$ **b.** $\frac{4\sqrt{x} - x}{x^2}$ **c.** $\sqrt{x} + 3$ **d.** $-\frac{\sqrt{x} + 1}{\sqrt{x}}$
7. By the law of exponents, $(a^m)^n = a^{mn}$, so $64^{\frac{1}{6}} = (8^2)^{\frac{1}{6}} = 8^{\frac{1}{3}}$.

Exercise 6.2

1.

	i)	ii)	iii)	iv)	v)
a.	1	decreasing	$0 < b < 1$	$x = 1, y = \frac{1}{2}$ $x = -1, y = 2$	$y = \left(\frac{1}{2}\right)^x$
b.	1	increasing	$b > 1$	$x = 1, y = 4$ $x = -1, y = \frac{1}{4}$	$y = 4^x$
c.	1	decreasing	$0 < b < 1$	$x = 1, y = \frac{1}{3}$ $x = -1, y = 3$	$y = \left(\frac{1}{3}\right)^x$
d.	1	increasing	$b > 1$	$x = 1, y = 8$ $x = -1, y = \frac{1}{8}$	$y = 8^x$

2. a. positive **b.** always increases **c.** 1
3. a. positive **b.** always decreases **c.** 1
4. Find b in the point $(1, b)$ on the graph

Exercise 6.3

1.

	Equation of Asymptote	Function Is	y-intercept
a.	$y = -5$	increasing	-4
b.	$y = 4$	increasing	5
c.	$y = 0$	decreasing	4
d.	$y = 2$	decreasing	3
e.	$y = -1$	increasing	1
f.	$y = 1$	decreasing	6s

2. a. i) $y = 5$ **ii)** 8 **iii)** increasing **iv)** domain: $x \in R$, range: $y > 5, y \in R$
3. a. i) $y = -4$ **ii)** -2 **iii)** decreasing **iv)** domain: $x \in R$, range: $y > -4$ $y \in R$
4. The graph of $y = ab^x + c$ can be sketched with asymptote $y = c$ and y-intercept $y = a + c$, and if $b > 1$, it always increases or if $0 < b < 1$, it always decreases.

Exercise 6.4

1. 948 000
2. \$21 600
3. a. $P = 5000(1.07)^5$ **b. i)** 6125 **ii)** 13 800 **c.** $10\frac{1}{4}$ years
4. \$221 000
5. \$9500
6. \$0.65
7. 0.22 g
8. a. 20 days **b.** 5 days ago **c.** 10 days ago **d.** 25 days ago
9. a. \$4.14 **b. i)** 8 years **ii)** 35 years ago
10. a. 28 g **b.** 2 g **c.** 7 h
11. a. 15 h **b.** $A = 160\left(\frac{1}{2}\right)^{\frac{t}{15}}$ **c.** 174 mg **d.** 11.5 mg

12. 5 h **b.** 320
14. a. 783 000 **b.** 2032
15. \$1075
16. B

Exercise 6.5

1. b. $y = 996.987(1.143)^x$ **c.** 3794 **d.** 17 h 15 min
2. a. $y = 0.660(1.462)^x$ **b.** 6.45 billion **c.** 2061
3. a. $y = 283.843(1.032)^x$ **b.** 317 348 **c.** 2062
4. a. $y = 9.277(2.539)^x$ **b.** 105 **c.** 1977
5. Answers will vary.
6. graphing, finite differences

Review Exercise

1. a. $\frac{72}{17}$ **b.** $\frac{1}{6}$ **c.** 27 **d.** 400
2. a. $\frac{1}{8}$ **b.** $\frac{9}{25}$ **c.** $\frac{1}{2}$ **d.** $\frac{25}{8}$
3. a. a^{2q^2} **b.** $x^{\frac{1}{18}}$ **c.** x^{-b^2} **d.** 2^{7p+q}
4. a. $\left(1 + \frac{5}{x}\right)\left(1 + \frac{3}{x}\right)$ or $x^{-2}(x + 5)(x + 3)$ **b.** $x^{\frac{1}{2}}(1 - x)(1 + x)$
c. $x^{-3}(x + 4)(x - 3)$ or $\frac{1}{x}\left(1 + \frac{4}{x}\right)\left(1 - \frac{3}{x}\right)$ **d.** $x^{-\frac{1}{2}}(x + 5)(x - 5)$
5. a. $y = 8^x$ **b.** $y = \left(\frac{1}{3}\right)^x$
6. a. i) $y = -6$ **ii)** -4 **iii)** increasing **iv)** $x \in R$, $y > -6$, $y \in R$
b.

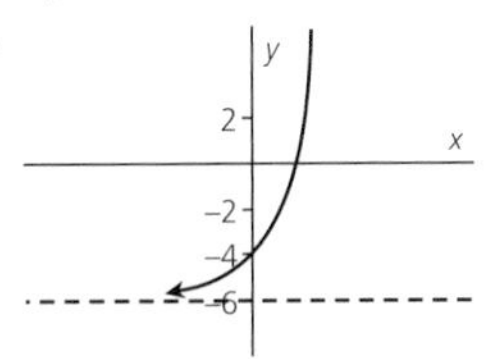

7. a. i) $y = 3$ **ii)** 8 **iii)** decreasing **iv)** domain: $x \in R$,
range $y > 3$, $y \in R$
b.

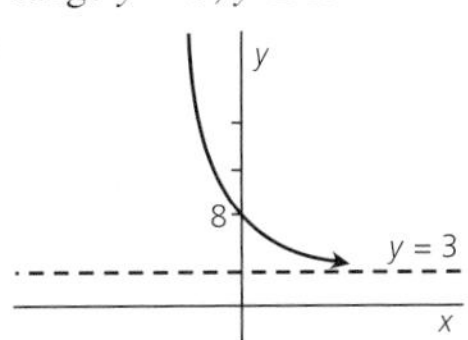

8. 1 638 400
9. 8 days
10. a. $y = 29040.595(1.0108)^x$ **b.** 34 487
c. 2011 **11. a. i)** 0.8 million/year **ii)** 3.79 million/year
iii) fivefold increase **b. i)** 0.38 million/year
ii) 2.77 million/year **iii)** sevenfold increase

Chapter 6 Test

1. a. 8 **b.** 25 **c.** $-\frac{5}{8}$ **d.** 16 **e.** 6 **f.** $-\frac{1}{5}$
2. a. a^3 **b.** $9x^4y^2$ **c.** x^6y^{-7} **d.** x^{2a} **e.** $x^{p^2-q^2-p-q}$ **f.** $x^{\frac{11}{12}}$
3. $x^{\frac{1}{2}} + 4$
4. positive, $b > 1$, increases; $0 < b < 1$, decreases; $b = 1$, constant
5. a. i) $y = -5$ **ii)** -3 **iii)** decreasing **iv)** domain: $x \in R$,
range: $y > -5$, $y \in R$
b.

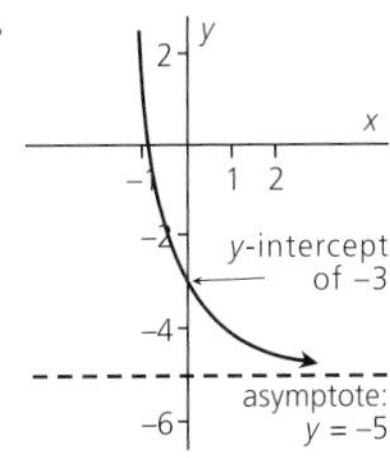

6. \$10 330
7. 2729
8. 3.5 min
9. a. $y = .660(1.462)^x$ **b.** 43 billion **c.** 4.65 m²/person
d. Answers will vary.
10. a. $f(x) = 2^x + 3$

CHAPTER 7 THE LOGARITHMIC FUNCTION AND LOGARITHMS

Review of Prerequisite Skills

2. a. positive **b.** increasing **c.** 1
3. a. positive **b.** decreasing **c.** 1
4. approximately 7700
5. 32 h
6. a. 6.59 g **b.** 520 years

Exercise 7.1

1. a. $\log_3 9 = 2$ **b.** $\log_9 1 = 0$ **c.** $\log_{\frac{1}{2}} \frac{1}{4} = 2$ **d.** $\log_{36} 5 = \frac{1}{2}$
e. $\log_{27} 9 = \frac{2}{3}$ **f.** $\log_2 \frac{1}{8} = -3$
2. a. $5^3 = 125$ **b.** $7^0 = 1$ **c.** $5^{-2} = \frac{1}{25}$ **d.** $7^{-1} = \frac{1}{7}$ **e.** $\left(\frac{1}{3}\right)^{-2} = 9$
f. $9^{\frac{3}{2}} = 27$
3. a. 1.5682 **b.** -0.6198 **c.** 3 **d.** 1.7160 **e.** 0.1303 **f.** 4.7214
4.

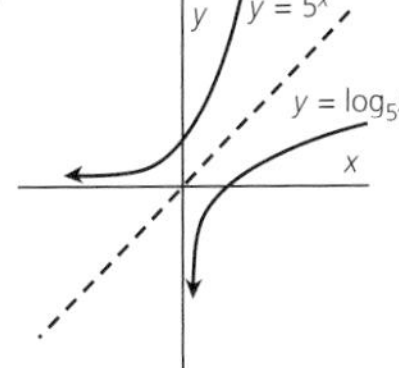

5.

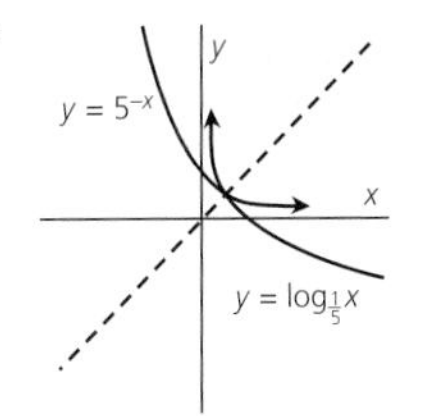

6. a. 3 **b.** 2 **c.** 4 **d.** 2 **e.** -3 **f.** -3 **g.** $\frac{1}{2}$ **h.** 4 **i.** $\frac{5}{4}$
7. a. 0 **b.** $-\frac{5}{2}$ **c.** $\frac{1}{2}$ **d.** $\frac{3}{4}$ **e.** $\frac{12}{5}$ **f.** $\frac{4}{3}$
8. a. 125 **b.** 16 **c.** 3 **d.** -3 **e.** $\frac{1}{3}$ **f.** 16
10.

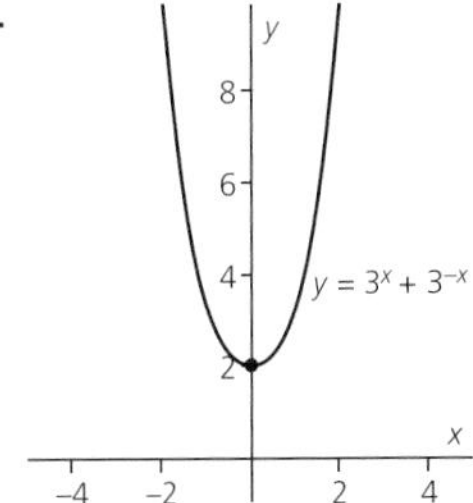

11. 23

Exercise 7.2

1. a. $\log_a x + \log_a y$ **b.** $\log_m p + \log_m q$
2. a. $\log_a(xw)$ **b.** $\log_a(sr)$
3. a. $\log_b x - \log_b y$ **b.** $\log_a r - \log_a s$
4. a. $4\log_6 13$ **b.** $-2\log_5 1.3$ **c.** $\frac{1}{3}\log_7 x$ **d.** $-\frac{3}{4}\log_a 6$
5. a. $\log_b x + \log_b y - \log_b z$ **b.** $\log_a x - \log_a y - \log_a z$
6.

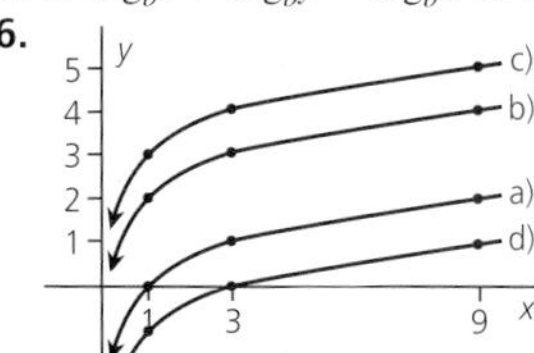

7.

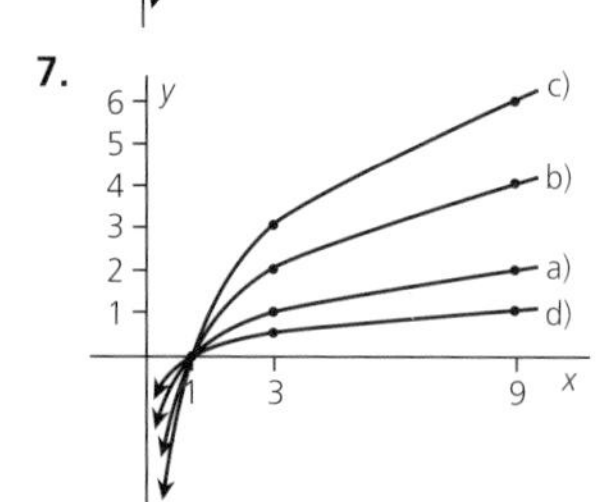

8. a. 3 **b.** 5 **c.** 2 **d.** 2 **e.** 5 **f.** 3
9. a. 1 **b.** 3 **c.** 2 **d.** 3 **e.** 4 **f.** 7 **g.** 3 **h.** 2 **i.** 3
10. a. $\frac{2}{3}\log_a x + \frac{4}{3}\log_a y$ **b.** $\frac{3}{2}\log_a x + \log_a y - \frac{1}{2}\log_a w$
c. $\frac{23}{8}\log_a x + \frac{11}{3}\log_a y$ **d.** $\frac{5}{4}\log_a x - \frac{3}{4}\log_a y$
11. a. 1.347 **b.** -0.1084 **c.** -1.4978 **d.** 1.8376 **e.** 0.1513
f. 2.0614
12. a. 2.5 **b.** -6.93 **c.** $-\frac{2}{3}$ **d.** 0.4889 **e.** -2.6178 **f.** -0.5831
13. a. -2.45 **b.** -0.83 **c.** 0.09 **d.** 0.59 **e.** 5.5 **f.** 2.4 **g.** 1.93
h. 0.64
14. a. $\log_a[\frac{\sqrt[3]{x}\sqrt[4]{y}}{\sqrt[5]{w^2}}]$ **b.** $\log_5\left(\frac{x^4}{y^2}\right) \div \log_5 w^3$
15. a. vertical translation of 1 unit up
b. vertical stretch of a factor of 2, vertical translation of 3 upwards **c.** vertical stretch of a factor of 3, upward vertical translation of 3 units
16. a. $\frac{77}{12}$ **b.** $\frac{23}{12}$
17. a. i) increases by 3 log2 or 0.9 **ii)** decreases by 3log2 or 0.9
b. i) increases by 5log4 or 3.01 **ii)** decreases by 5log5 or about 3.5

Exercise 7.3

1. a. 16 **b.** 81 **c.** 6 **d.** 49
2. a. 1.46 **b.** 1.11 **c.** 2.32 **d.** 1.16
3. a. 72 **b.** $\frac{4}{3}$ **c.** ± 4 **d.** $\frac{1}{81}$ **e.** 64 **f.** $\frac{1 + \sqrt{61}}{2}$
4. a. 1 **b.** 5 **c.** 2 **d.** 2 **e.** 3
5. $y = \log_a x$ is defined only if $x > 0$ and $a > 0$.
6. 4 years, 3 months
7. 2400 years
8. 6 years
9. 1450; no.
10. 81
11. 2.23×10^{11}

Exercise 7.4

2. 10 times
3. 60 dB
4. 5.06
5. 100 times
6. 40 000 times
7. a. 5 times
8. 5 times
9. 32 000 times
10. 10 000
11. 10 000
12. 13
13. 3.2×10^{-7} mol/L
14. 3.2×10^{-7} mol/L

Exercise 7.5

1. a. 1.892 **b.** 2.477 **c.** 0.656 **d.** 1.116
3. a.

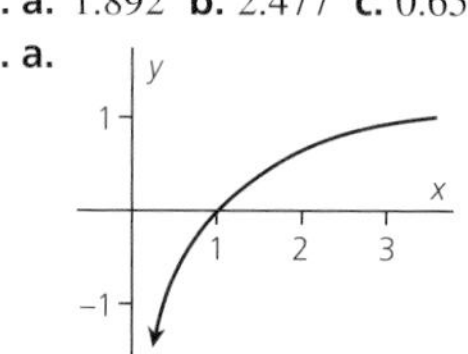

b.

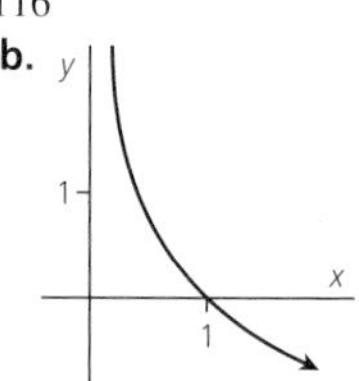

c.

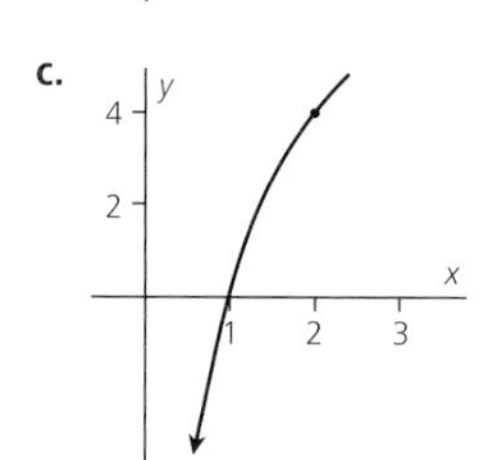

d.

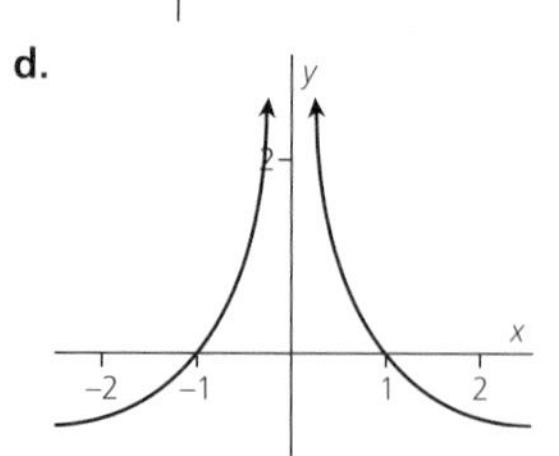

4. Graph is reflected in y-axis.

Review Exercise

1. a. 3 **b.** -3 **c.** 2.5 **d.** $\frac{2}{3}$
2. a. 2 **b.** 6 **c.** $-\frac{1}{3}$ **d.** 5
3. a. $\frac{1}{8}$ **b.** 2 **c.** $\frac{11}{8}$ **d.** 3 or 2
4. twice as intense
5. 100 000 times
6. 2.4×10^{-6} mol/L
7. vertical stretch by a factor 2, translated 2 units up
8. a. 1.894 **b.** 2.202

Chapter 7 Test

1. a. 3 **b.** 3 **c.** -4 **d.** $\frac{1}{4}$ **e.** t **f.** $\frac{2}{3}$
2. a. 4 **b.** 2
3. vertically stretch by factor 2, translated 2 units up
4. a. 8 **b.** 4 **c.** 2 **d.** 3
5. Log of a negative number does not exist.
6. 16.87 h
7. 6.3 times
8. 1000 times
9. 4.90×10^{-9} mol/L

Cumulative Review—Chapters 5–7

1. a. $-\frac{x}{y}$ **b.** $\frac{x}{4y}$ **c.** $\frac{5 - 2x}{32y - 4}$ **d.** $\frac{4x - y}{x - 2}$ **e.** $-\frac{y^2}{x^2}$ **f.** $-\frac{2}{3}$
2. a. $2x - 3y + 13 = 0$ **b.** $27x + 11y - 59 = 0$

c. $x + y - 2 = 0$ **d.** $25x + 6y - 37 = 0$

3. a. $5x^4 - 15x^2 + 1$; $20x^3 - 30x$ **b.** $\frac{4}{x^3}$; $-\frac{12}{x^4}$

c. $-2x^{-\frac{3}{2}}$; $3x^{-\frac{5}{2}}$ **d.** $4x^3 + 4x^{-5}$; $12x^2 - 20x^{-6}$

4. a. $20x^3 - 60x^2 + 42x - 6$ **b.** $-60x^3 - 72x + 2$

5. a. $s(t) = 3t^3 - 40.5t^2 + 162t$; $v(t) = 9t^2 - 81t + 162$; $a(t) = 18t - 81$ **b.** stationary 3, 6; advancing $0 \leq t < 3$, $6 < t \leq 8$; retreating $3 < t < 6$ **c.** 4.5 **d.** $0 \leq t < 4.5$ **e.** $4.5 < t \leq 8$

6. a. $v(t) = 6t^2 + 6t - 36$ **b.** $a(t) = 12t + 6$ **c.** 61

7. i) a. \$4600 **b.** \$5.11 **c.** \$5.00 **ii) a.** \$8030 **b.** \$8.92 **c.** \$0.02

8. a. \$26, \$25, \$25.60, \$27

9. a. $-\frac{4}{\sqrt{3}}, \frac{4}{\sqrt{3}}$ **b.** 1000

10. a. 0.2 p.p.m./year **b.** 0.15 p.p.m.

11. Radius is decreasing at $\frac{5}{64\pi}$ cm/min and surface area is decreasing at 2.5cm^2/min.

12. $\frac{1}{10\pi}$ m/h

14. a. 1 **b.** 2^{x+1} **c.** 1 **d.** 243 **e.** e^{3-x} **f.** e^{12x}

15. a. -3 **b.** 1, 3 **c.** 9 **d.** 2, 3 **e.** 0 **f.** 0

16. a. 19 940 **b.** 80 000

17. 26

18. a. $C(t) = P(1.05)^t, 0 \leq t \leq 10$ **b.** \$65.07 **c.** \$24.95

19. a. $V(t) = 30\,000(0.75)^t, t \geq 0$ **b.** \$16 875 **c.** 8 years

20. $y = 1200(0.6)^t, 0 \leq t \leq 4$

22. a. 2 **b.** 4 **c.** 5 **d.** -3 **e.** $\frac{1}{3}$ **f.** $-\frac{3}{2}$ **g.** 1 **h.** 0.342 **i.** -2 **j.** 7 **k.** $\frac{1}{3^{10}}$ **l.** a^4

23. a. $\log 2 - \log 3$ **b.** $\log x + \log y - \log z$ **c.** $-\log 5$ **d.** $\frac{1}{2}\log(x + 1) - \frac{1}{2}\log(x - 1)$ **e.** $4[\log(x^2 - 4) - 5\log x]$ **f.** $\log_a 4 + 5$

24. a. $\log\frac{x - 4}{3 - x}$ **b.** $\log_2\frac{x^3y^2}{z^4}$ **c.** $\log\frac{9}{\sqrt{x^2 + 1}}$ **d.** $\log\frac{x\sqrt{x + 1}}{x - 5}$

25. a. 3.58 **b.** -0.63 **c.** 1.89 **d.** $0.\dot{6}$ **e.** 1.29 **f.** -3.91

26. a. 3 **b.** 2 **c.** 51 **d.** 10 **e.** 2 **f.** $\frac{24}{11}$ **g.** 2.8 **h.** -1 **i.** 14 **j.** 10^{-5}, 10^2

27. a. 74 dB **b.** Yes. **c.** 1.0×10^7 W/m^2 **d.** 0.1 W/m^2

CHAPTER 8 DERIVATIVES OF EXPONENTIAL AND LOGARITHMIC FUNCTIONS

Review of Prerequisite Skills

1. a. $\frac{1}{9}$ **b.** 4 **c.** $\frac{1}{9}$ **d.** $\frac{9}{4}$.

2. a. $\log_5 625 = 4$ **b.** $\log_4\left(\frac{1}{16}\right) = -2$ **c.** $\log_x 3 = 3$ **d.** $\log_{10} 450 = W$ **e.** $\log_3 z = 8$ **f.** $\log_a T = b$

3. a. $11^2 = 121$ **b.** $125^{\frac{1}{3}} = x$ **c.** $a^4 = 1296$ **d.** $b^w = A$

4. a. 5 **b.** -4 **c.** 2 **d.** 2 **e.** 25 **f.** -6

5. a. 6.322 **b.** 2.397

Exercise 8.1

1. The graphs are identical.

2. The Power Rule is valid only when the function has the variable x in the base and a constant for the exponent.

3. a. $y' = 3e^{3x}$ **b.** $s' = 3e^{3t-5}$ **c.** $y' = 20e^{10t}$ **d.** $y' = -3e^{-3x}$ **e.** $y' = (2x - 6)e^{5-6x+x^2}$ **f.** $y' = \frac{1}{2}e^{\sqrt{x}}x^{-\frac{1}{2}}$

4. a. $y' = 6x^2e^{x^3}$ **b.** $y' = e^{3x}(1 + 3x)$ **c.** $f'(x) = x^{-1}e^{-x^3}(-3x^2 - x^{-1})$ **d.** $s' = 2e^{3t^2}\left(\frac{3t^2 - 1}{t^3}\right)$ **e.** $f'(x) = e^x\left[\frac{2x + 1}{2\sqrt{x}}\right]$ **f.** $h'(t) = 2te^{t^2} - 3e^{-t}$ **g.** $p' = (1 + e^w)e^{w+e^w}$ **h.** $g'(t) = \frac{2e^{2t}}{(1 + e^{2t})^2}$

5. a. $p'(1) = e^3 - e^{-3}$ **b.** $f'(0) = \frac{1}{e}$ **c.** $h'(-1) = -(2 + 3e)$

6. a. $x - 2y + 2 = 0$ **b.** $y = 0.499999958335x + 1$ **c.** Clearly the calculator is giving a 12 decimal place approximation to slope $\frac{1}{2}$, which is very awkward to use.

7. $x - 3y + (1 + \ln 3) = 0$

8. $y - e^{-1} = 0$

9. (0, 0) and $(2, 4e^{-2})$

11. a. $-3e^{-3x}, 9e^{-3x}, -27e^{-3x}$ **b.** $\frac{d^ny}{dx^n} = (-1)^n3^ne^{-3x}$

12. a. $x - y + 1 = 0$ **b.** $2x + y - 2 = 0$ **c.** In order to use the calculator, the equations must be reorganized to define y as a function of x. This is not easy to do with the relations given in this question.

13. a. 31 000 **b.** $\frac{dN}{dt} = -\frac{10^2}{3}e^{-\frac{t}{30}}$ **c.** decreasing at 17 per hour **d.** 31 000

14. a. $v = 40\left(1 - e^{-\frac{t}{4}}\right)$ **c.** 40 m/s **d.** $t = 4\ln 20$, $s = 160(\ln 20 - 0.95)$

15. a. 1 **b.** e^2

16. $m = 2$ or -3

Exercise 8.2

1. A natural logarithm has base e; a common logarithm has base 10.

2.

n	100	10 000	100 000	10^9
$\left(n + \frac{1}{n}\right)^n$	2.70481	2.71815	2.71827	2.7182818

3. a. $\frac{5}{5x + 8}$ **b.** $\frac{2x}{x^2 + 1}$ **c.** $\frac{15}{t}$ **d.** $\frac{1}{2(x + 1)}$ **e.** $\frac{3t^2 - 4t}{t^3 - 2t^2 + 5}$ **f.** $\frac{2z + 3}{2(z^2 + 3z)}$

4. a. $1 + \ln x$ **b.** $\frac{1 - 2\ln x}{x^3}$ **c.** 1 **d.** $\frac{3(\ln x)^2}{x}$ **e.** $e^t\left[\frac{1}{t} + \ln t\right]$ **f.** $\frac{-ze^{-z}}{e^{-z} + ze^{-z}}$ **g.** $\frac{e^t(t\ln t - 1)}{t(\ln t)^2}$ **h.** $\frac{e^{\sqrt{u}}}{2}\left(\frac{1}{u} + \frac{\ln\sqrt{u}}{\sqrt{u}}\right)$ **i.** $\frac{x^2 - 2x - 1}{(x^2 + 1)(x - 1)}$

5. a. $g'(1) = 2e$ **b.** $f'(5) = \frac{1}{10}$ **c.** $g'(1) = 2e \doteq 5.436563657$. The CALC button produces a value $g'(1) = 5.43657$, which is accurate to only 4 decimal places. For $f'(5)$, the CALC button produces in the first approximation $x = 5.042553$ and $f'(x) = 0.0983198$. The theoretical result is 0.1. The ZOOM must be used to improve the accuracy.

6. a. 0 **b.** no solution **c.** $0, \pm\sqrt{e - 1}$

7. a. $x - 3y - 1 = 0$ **c.** The first approximation answer on a window with domain $-1 \leq x \leq 4$ is $y \doteq 0.31286x - 0.31286$. This can be improved by using the ZOOM feature. Notice the equation is not as easy to use as the theoretical result.

8. $x - 2y + (2\ln 2 - 4) = 0$

9. a. (1, 0), (e^{-1}, e^{-2}) **c.** The theoretical approach gives more accurate values in less time.

10. $x + 2y - 2\ln 2 = 0$

11. a. 90 km/h **b.** $-\frac{90}{3t + 1}$ **c.** $\frac{-90}{7}$ km/h/s **d.** 6.36 s

12. a. 4.2 **b.** 1.16

14. a. $-\frac{(2 + \ln 2)}{2}$ **b.** -9

15. $\frac{1}{2}$

16. b. $S_3 = 2.5, S_4 = 2.\dot{6}, S_5 = 2.708\dot{3}, S_6 = 2.71\dot{6}, S_7 = 2.7180\dot{5}$

17. a. $\frac{1}{x}$ b. $\frac{2}{2x+1}$ c. $2x \ln |x| + x$

Exercise 8.3

1. a. $3 \ln 2(2^{3x})$ b. $\ln 3.1(3.1^x) + 3x^2$ c. $3 \ln 10(10^{3t-5})$
   d. $\ln 10(2n-6)(10^{5-6n+n^2})$ e. $\frac{3x^2-4x}{\ln 5(x^3-2x^2+10)}$
   f. $\frac{2}{\ln 10(1-x^2)}$ g. $2(\ln 7)t(7^{t^2})$ h. $\frac{2t+3}{2\ln 2(t^2+3t)}$
   i. $2(\ln 3)x(3^{x^2+3})$
2. a. $\frac{2^t(\ln 2t - 1)}{t^2}$ b. $\frac{2^{x+2}}{x \ln 2}[x\log_2 x(\ln 2)^2 + 1]$ c. $\frac{2\ln 5 - \ln 4}{\ln 3}$
   d. $2t \log_{10}(1-t) - \frac{t^2}{(1-t)\ln 10}x$ e. $\frac{3^{\frac{x}{2}}[x \ln 3 - 4]}{2x^3}$
   f. $\left[\frac{2\sqrt{x+1}}{x \ln 5} - \frac{\log(3x^2)}{2\sqrt{x+1}}\right](x+1)^{-1}$
3. a. $\frac{5}{52 \ln 2}$ b. $\frac{1}{24 \ln 2 \ln 3}$
4. $\frac{-3\ln 10}{4}$
5. a. $y = \left(20 \ln 10 + \frac{7}{\ln 10}\right)x + 10 - 5\left(20 \ln 10 + \frac{7}{\ln 10}\right)$
   c. A first approximation, using the DRAW tool, gives $y = 53.05x - 255.3$. The theoretical calculation for the slope is $\left(20 \ln 10 + \frac{7}{\ln 10}\right) \doteq 49.091\,763$. To guarantee that the calculator is accurate to 3 decimal places, the ZOOM must be used until the x-coordinate value is accurate to 5 ± 0.0005.
6. $\sqrt{10} \ln 10x - 5y + 10\sqrt{10} = 0$
7. a. $x > 1$ b. At $x = 2, f'(2) = \frac{1}{2(\ln 2)^2}$. c. The calculator does not do base 2 logarithmic calculations. In this case, a double conversion will be required to convert the given function to base e.
8. a. 3.45 cm/m b. 10 min
9. a. As a ratio, $\frac{\text{Rate in 1978}}{\text{Rate in 1968}} = \frac{7.4}{1}$. b. The rate of increase for 1998 is 7.4 times larger than that for 1988.
10. b. 1.24 units/s
11. b. Rewrite 7^x as $e^{x \ln 7}$. c. The graph of $y = e^x$ is stretched vertically by a factor of ln 7.
12. c. The factor $\frac{1}{\ln 5}$ causes a vertical compression of the function $y = \ln x$.

Exercise 8.4

1. Calculator first approximations are

	Absolute Maximum	Absolute Minimum
a.	0.384 90	0
b.	46702.77	2.718 28
c.	10.043	−5961.9
d.	13.8355	2.804 40

2.

	Absolute Maximum	Absolute Minimum
a.	$\frac{2}{3\sqrt{3}} \doteq 0.3849$	0
b.	$\frac{e^{12}}{1+\ln 12}$	e
c.	$\frac{e^3}{2}$	$-2e^8$
d.	$6 \ln 10 + \ln 101 - \ln 99$	2.810 08

3. a. 5 b. 20 c. (54.9, 10) e. P grows exponentially to point I, then the growth rate decreases and the curve becomes concave down.
4. a. 1001 b. 500
5. five hundred units
6. 0.61
7. at $t = \frac{3}{4}h$
8. 47.25% when $t = 0.46h$
9. b. Growth rate in 1967 = 4.511 times growth rate in 1947.
   c. Growth rate in 1967 is 7.5% of total invested.
   d. total = \$59.537 billion, growth rate = 4.4849 billion per annum. e. \$62.5 billion, error was 3.5% f. Total = \$570.48959 billion and the rate of growth will be \$42.97498 billion.
10. $t = \frac{(\ln b - \ln a)}{(b-a)}$
11. a. 478 158 at $t = 38.2$ min b. 42.7 min
12. for course one, 10 h; for course two, 20 h
13. for course one, 8.2 h; for course two, 16.8 h
14. a. Graph $P = \frac{10000}{1+99e^{-t}}$. b. 4.595 days, $P = 5000$
    c. At $t = 3$, growth rate is 1402 cells per day; at $t = 8$, the growth rate has slowed down to 311 cells per day.

Exercise 8.5

1. a. $\sqrt{10}x^{(\sqrt{10}-1)}$ b. $15\sqrt{2}x^{(3\sqrt{2}-1)}$ c. $\pi t^{(\pi-1)}$
   d. $ex^{(e-1)} + e^x$
2. a. $\left(\frac{2\ln x}{x}\right)x^{\ln x}$ b. $\frac{(x+1)(x-3)^2}{(x+2)^3}\left[\frac{1}{x+1} + \frac{2}{x-3} - \frac{3}{x+2}\right]$
   c. $x^{\sqrt{x}}\left[\frac{\sqrt{x}}{x} + \frac{\ln x}{2\sqrt{x}}\right]$ d. $\frac{1}{t^t}(-1 - \ln t)$
3. a. $2e^e$ b. $e(e + 2^{e-1})$ c. $-\frac{4}{27}$
4. $32(1 + 2\ln 2)x - y - 16(3 + 8\ln 2) = 0$
5. $-\frac{11}{36}$
6. $(e, e^{\frac{1}{e}})$
7. (1, 1) and (2, 4 + 4 ln 2)
8. $\frac{32(1+\ln 4)^2}{(2+\ln 4)}$
9. a. $v = \frac{t^{\frac{1}{t}}(1-\ln t)}{t^2}$ $a = \frac{t^{\frac{1}{t}}}{t^4}(1-\ln t)\left(1 - \ln t - 2t - \frac{t}{1-\ln t}\right)$
   b. $t = e$ and $a = -e^{\frac{1}{e}-3})$
10. $e^{\pi} > \pi^e$

Review Exercise

1. a. $2e^{2x+3}$ b. $\frac{3t^2}{t^3+1}$ c. $\frac{3x^2-6x+6}{x^3-3x^2+6x}$ d. $(5-6x)e^{-3x^2+5x}$
   e. $\frac{e^x - e^{-x}}{e^x + e^{-x}}$ f. $(\ln 2)e^x \times 2^{e^x}$
2. a. $e^x(x+1)$ b. $\frac{x \ln x}{e^x}\left(\frac{1}{x} + \frac{1}{x \ln x} - 1\right)$ c. $\frac{\sqrt{2+t^4}}{t} + \frac{2t^3\ln(3t)}{\sqrt{2+t^4}}$
   d. $\frac{(x+2)(x-4)^5}{(2x^3-1)^2}\left[\frac{1}{x+2} + \frac{5}{x-4} - \frac{12x^2}{2x^3-1}\right]$ e. $\frac{2e^t}{(e^t+1)^2}$
   f. $e^x\left(\sqrt{x^2+3}\right)^{e^x}\left[\frac{x}{x^2+3} + \ln\sqrt{x^2+3}\right]$
   g. $\left(\frac{30}{x}\right)^{2x}(2\ln 30 - 2 - 2\ln x)$ h. $\frac{[1 - y(x+y)e^{xy}]}{[x(x+y)e^{xy} - 1]}$
3. a. 1 b. $\frac{3+2\sqrt{3}}{3}, \frac{3-2\sqrt{3}}{3}$
4. a. $\left[\frac{1+10(\ln 10)^2}{\ln 10}\right] \times 10^9$ b. 0
5. a. $\frac{1}{t}$ b. $10e^{10x}(10x+2)$
6. $(1 - \ln 4)x - 8y + (8\ln 4 - 4) = 0$

8. a. 7 **b.** 4, −4 **c.** −3, 0, 4

9. $3x - y + (2 \ln 2 - 2) = 0$

10. $x = 1$

11. a. day 20 **b.** 42

12. 2.718 h

13. highest at 4 years, lowest at 0.368 years

14. a. c_2 **b.** c_1

15. a. $T'(x) = 10(0.9^{-x})\left(0.10536 + \frac{0.10536}{x} - \frac{1}{x^2}\right)$ **b.** 2.62

16. a. $\frac{\ln 2}{2}$ **b.** $2\ln 2 - 1$

17. a. 0 **b.** $C'(t) = k(5e^{-5t} - 2e^{-2t})$ **c.** 7.32 days

Chapter 8 Test

1. a. $-4xe^{-2x^2}$ **b.** $\frac{2x}{x^2 - 6}$ **c.** $(3^{x^2+3x})(\ln 3)(2x + 3)$
d. $\frac{1}{2}(3e^{3x} - 3e^{-3x})$ **e.** $\frac{8x^3 - 2x}{(2x - 1)\ln 10} + (12x^2 - 1)\log_{10}(2x - 1)$
f. $\frac{\frac{x}{x+4} - 3\ln(x + 4)}{x^4}$

2. $\frac{13}{14}$

3. 2

4. $\frac{2xy + 1 + \ln x}{3 - x^2}$

5. 1

6. −2, −1

7. $x + (1 + 28 \ln 3)y - (4 + 84 \ln 3) = 0$

8. b. 10 cm/s **c.** $t = \frac{\ln 2}{k}$, $a = -5k$ cm/s^2

9. a. \$87.70 **b.** \$9426.76

CHAPTER 9 CURVE SKETCHING

Review of Prerequisite Skills

1. a. $-\frac{3}{2}$, 1 **b.** −2, 7 **c.** $-\frac{5}{2}, -\frac{5}{2}$ **d.** −2, −3 + 1

2. a. $x < -\frac{7}{3}$ **b.** $x \le 2$ **c.** $-1 < t < 3$ **d.** $x < -4$ or $x > 1$

4. a. 0 **c.** 0 **d.** 0

5. a. $x^3 + 6x^2 + x^{-2}$ **b.** $-\frac{(x^2 + 2x + 3)}{(x^2 - 3)^2}$ **c.** $-2xe^{-x^2}$
d. $x^4(5\ln x + 1)$

6. a. $x - 8 + \frac{28}{x + 3}$ **b.** $x + 7 - \frac{2}{x - 1}$

Exercise 9.1

1. a. (0, 1), (−4, 33) **b.** (0, 2) **c.** $\left(\frac{1}{2}, 0\right)$, (−2, −125), $\left(\frac{9}{4}, -48.2\right)$
d. (1, −3)

2. Function is increasing when $f'(x) > 0$, whereas it is decreasing when $f'(x) < 0$.

3. a. rises up into quadrant I **b.** rises up into quadrant I
c. drops down into quadrant IV **d.** rises up into quadrant I

4.

	Increasing	Decreasing	Horizontal
a.	OK	OK	(−1, 4), (2, −1)
b.			(−1, 2), (1, 4)
c.			none
d.			(2, 3)

5.

	Increasing	Decreasing
a.	$x < -2$ or $x > 0$	$-2 < x < 0$
b.	$x < 0$ or $x > 4$	$0 < x < 4$
c.	$x < -1$ or $x > +1$	$-1 < x < 0$ or $0 < x < 1$
d.	$-1 < x < 3$	$x < -1$ or $x > 3$
e.	$x > \frac{1}{e}$	$0 < x < \frac{1}{e}$
f.	$x < 1$	$x > 1$

6. The function is increasing when $x < -3$ or $-2 < x < 1$ or $x > 1$. The function is decreasing when $-3 < x < -2$.

7. The function is increasing when $\frac{1}{2} < x < \frac{2}{3}$ or $x > 1$.
The function is decreasing when $x < \frac{1}{2}$ or $\frac{2}{3} < x < 1$.

9. $f(x) = x^3 + 3x^2 - 9x - 9$

11. a. $f(x)$ increases on $x < 4$, decreases for $x > 4$, $x = 4$
b. $f(x)$ increases when $-1 < x < 1$, $x = -1$ and 1
c. $f(x)$ decreases when $-2 < x < 3$, $x = -2$ and 3

14. strictly decreasing

Exercise 9.2

2. b. (0, 0), (4, −32)

3. a. (−2, −16) is local minimum (10, 0) is a local maximum, (2, −16) is a local minimum
b. $\left(-3, -\frac{1}{3}\right)$ is local minimum, $\left(3, \frac{1}{3}\right)$ is local maximum
c. $\left(\frac{1}{4}, \frac{1}{4}e\right)$ is local maximum **d.** $\left(\frac{3}{2}, \ln\left(\frac{7}{4}\right)\right)$ is local minimum

4.

	x-Intercept	y-Intercept
a.	$-2\sqrt{2}, 2\sqrt{2}, 0$	0
b.	0	0
c.	0	0
d.	none	ln 4

5. a. (0, 3) is a local minimum, tangent parallel to x-axis; (2, 27) is a local maximum, tangent parallel to x-axis
b. (0, 0) is a local maximum, tangent parallel to t-axis; $\left(\frac{2}{3}, -\frac{4}{9e^2}\right)$ is a local minimum, tangent parallel to t-axis
c. (5, 0) is neither **d.** (0, −1) is a local minimum, tangent parallel to x-axis; (−1, 0) has tangent parallel to y-axis (1, 0) has tangent parallel to y-axis **e.** (0, 0) is neither, tangent parallel **f.** (0, 0) has tangent parallel to y-axis; (1.516, −11.5) has tangent parallel to x-axis at a local minimum

7. a. (2, 21) is a relative maximum
b. (−3, 20) is a local maximum, (3, −16) is a local minimum
c. (−2, −4) is a local maximum, (−1, −5) is a local minimum
d. no critical points **e.** (1, 1) is a local minimum
f. (0, 0) is neither, (1, −1) is a local minimum
g. (0, 1) is local maximum **h.** $\left(e^{-\frac{1}{2}}, -0.184\right)$ is local minimum

8. At $x = -6$, there is a local minimum. At $x = 2$, there is a local minimum. At $x = -1$ there is a local maximum.

10. $y = -\frac{11}{9}x^2 + \frac{22}{3}x + 1$

12. a. $y = 3x^4 - 4x^3 - 36x^2 - 9$ **b.** (3, −198) **c.** local minima at (−2, −73), (3, −198); local maxima at (0, −9)

13. a. local maximum at (0, 4)
b. local maximum at $(-\sqrt{2}, 28\sqrt{2})$; local minimum at $(\sqrt{2}, -28\sqrt{2})$

Exercise 9.3

1. a. vertical asymptotes $x = -2$, $x = 2$; horizontal asymptote $y = 1$ **b.** vertical asymptote $x = 0$; horizontal asymptote $y = 0$

3. a. 2 **b.** 5 **c.** $-\frac{5}{2}$ **d.** $\pm\infty$

4.	Discontinuities	Vertical Asymptotes
a.	$x = -5$	$x = -5$
b.	$x = 2$	$x = 2$
c.	$t = 3$	$t = 3$
d.	$x = 3$	none
e.	$x = \ln 2$	$x = \ln 2$
f.	$x \leq 0$	no asymptotes

5. a. $y = 1$ from below as $x \to \infty$, from above as $x \to -\infty$
b. $y = 0$ from above as $x \to \infty$, from below as $x \to -\infty$
c. $y = 3$ from above as $t \to \infty$, from below as $t \to -\infty$
d. no horizontal asymptote
7. a. $y = 3x + 7$ **b.** $y = x + 3$ **c.** $y = x - 2$ **d.** $y = x + 3$
8. a. As $x \to \infty$ $f(x)$ is above the line.
b. As $x \to -\infty$ $f(x)$ is below the line.
10. a. $y = \frac{a}{c}$ **b.** $x = -\frac{d}{c}$, $c \neq 0$ and $ax + b \neq k(cx + d)$
11. $a = \frac{9}{5}$ $b = \frac{3}{5}$
12. b. -2
14. $y = x + 1$

Exercise 9.4

1.	Point A	Point B	Point C	Point D
a.	negative	negative	positive	positive
b.	negative	negative	positive	negative
c.	negative	zero	negative	positive
d.	negative	zero	negative	positive

2. a. $(-1, 18)$ is a local maximum, $(5, -90)$ is a local minimum
b. $\left(0, \frac{25}{48}\right)$ is a local maximum
c. $(-1, -2)$ is a local maximum, $(1, 2)$ is a local minimum
d. neither
3. a. $(2, -36)$ **b.** $\left(-4, \frac{25}{64}\right), \left(4, \frac{25}{64}\right)$ **c.** no points **d.** $(3, 8)$
4. a. 24, curve is above **b.** 4, curve is above **c.** e, curve is above **d.** $-\frac{9\sqrt{10}}{1000}$, curve is below
5. b. i) 1 **ii)** 0, 2
6. For any $y = f(x)$
(1) evaluate $y = f'(x)$ and solve $f'(x) = 0$ to get at least one solution, x_1.
(2) evaluate $y = f''(x)$ and calculate $f''(x_1)$.
(3) if $f''(x_1) < 0$, then curve is concave down; if $f''(x_1) > 0$ then curve is concave up.
7. Step 4: Determine the type of critical point by using either the first derivative test or the second derivative test.
8. a. i) $(-2, -16)$, $(0, 0)$ **b. i)** none **c. i)** none
d. i) $\left(\frac{-3}{\sqrt{2}}, \frac{-8\sqrt{2}}{9}\right), \left(\frac{3}{\sqrt{2}}, \frac{8\sqrt{2}}{9}\right)$
10. $f(x) = -3x^3 + 9x^2 - 1$
11. $\frac{27}{64}$
12. inflection points are $(0, 0)$, $\left(-\frac{b}{2a}, -\frac{b^4}{16a^3}\right)$

Exercise 9.5

2. $y = -\frac{1}{4}x^3 + 3x$
7. a. $y = 1$ as $x \to \infty$, $y = -1$ as $x \to -\infty$
b. $y = \frac{3}{2}$ as $x \to \infty$, $y = \frac{-3}{2}$ as $x \to -\infty$

Review Exercise

1. a. $y' = ne^{nx}$, $y'' = n^2e^{nx}$ **b.** $f'(x) = \frac{1}{2(x + 4)}$, $f''(x) = -\frac{1}{2(x + 4)^2}$ **c.** $s' = \frac{2e^t}{(e^t + 1)^2}$, $s'' = \frac{d^2S}{dt^2} = \frac{2e^t(1 - e^t)}{(e^t + 1)^3}$
d. $g'(t) = \frac{1}{\sqrt{1 + t^2}}$, $g''(t) = \frac{-t}{(1 + t^2)^{\frac{3}{2}}}$

2.	Increasing	Decreasing	Derivative = 0
a.	$x < 1$	$x > 1$	$x = 1$
b.	$x < -3$ or $x > 7$ or $-3 < x < 1$	$1 < x < 3$ or $3 < x < 7$	$x = 1, x = 7$

4. a. $(0, 20)$, is a local minimum; tangent is parallel to x-axis. $(3, 47)$ is a local maximum; tangent is parallel to x-axis.
b. $(-1, e^2)$ is a local minimum; tangent is parallel to x-axis.
c. $\left(-1, -\frac{1}{2}\right)$ is a local minimum; tangent is parallel to x-axis. $\left(7, \frac{1}{14}\right)$ is a local maximum; tangent is parallel to x-axis.
d. $(-1, \ln 5)$ is a local maximum; tangent is parallel to x-axis.
5. a. $a < x < b$ or $x > e$ **b.** $b < x < c$ **c.** $x < a$ or $d < x < e$
d. $c < x < d$

6.	Discontinuity	Asymptote	Left Side	Right Side
a.	at $x = 3$	$x = 3$	$y \to -\infty$	$y \to +\infty$
b.	at $x = -5$	$x = -5$	$g(x) \to +\infty$	$g(x) \to -\infty$
c.	at $x = \ln 4$	$x = \ln 4$	$s \to -\infty$	$s \to +\infty$
d.	at $x = -3$	none	$f(x) \to -8$	$f(x) \to -8$

7. a. $-e^{\frac{3}{2}}, -\frac{3}{e^{\frac{3}{2}}}$ **b.** $(-2, -2e^{-2})$
9. a. i) Concave up on $-1 < x < 3$, concave down on $x < -1$ or $x > 3$. **b.** Points of inflection when $x = -1$ or $x = 3$.
ii) a. Concave up on $-5 < x < 1$ or $x > 5$, concave down on $x < -5$ or $1 < x < 5$. **b.** Points of inflection when $x = -5, x = 1, x = 5$.
10. a. $a = 1, b = 0$
11. a. $y = x - 3$
b. $y = 4x + 11$ **13. a.** 18 994 when $t = 5$ **b.** when $t > 0$
15. a. $|k| \leq 2$ and $x \neq \pm k$

Chapter 9 Test

1. a. $x < -9$ or $-6 < x < -3$ or $0 < x < 4$ or $x > 8$
b. $-9 < x < -6$ or $-3 < x < 0$ or $4 < x < 8$
c. $(-9, 1), (-6, -2), (0, 1), (8, -2)$ **d.** $x = -3, x = 4$
e. $f''(x) > 0$ **f.** $-3 < x < 0$ or $4 < x < 8$ **g.** $(-8, 0), (10, -3)$
2. a. critical points: $\left(\frac{1}{2}, \frac{15}{8}\right), \left(-\frac{1}{2}, -\frac{17}{8}\right), (3, -45)$ **b.** $\left(\frac{1}{2}, \frac{15}{8}\right)$ is a local maximum; $\left(-\frac{1}{2}, -\frac{17}{8}\right)$ is a local minimum; $(3, -45)$ is a local minimum
4. discontinuities at $x = -2, x = 3$; vertical asymptote is $x = 3$; hole in the curve is at $\left(-2, -\frac{3}{5}\right)$
5. local minimum at $(1, -e^2)$, local maximum at $(-2, 2e^{-4})$
7. $k = \frac{11}{4}$
8. a. $f(x) = x^3 + 3x^2 + 2$
10. $k = -3$

Cumulative Review Chapters 3–9

1. a. $2 - \frac{1}{5}, 2 - \frac{1}{5^2}, 2 - \frac{1}{5^3}, 2 - \frac{1}{5^4}, \ldots 2$ **b.** $\frac{1}{2}, \frac{1}{6}, \frac{1}{12}, \frac{1}{20}; 0$
2. a. $\frac{2}{3}$ **b.** $\frac{1}{2}$ **c.** 12 **d.** $-\frac{2}{5}$ **e.** 0 **f.** $\frac{1}{4}$ **g.** $-\frac{1}{3}$ **h.** $\frac{1}{2\sqrt{x}}$ **i.** $\frac{x}{2}$
3. $3x^2 - 10x + 10$
4. a. $2t + 10$ **b.** $\frac{x - 4}{x^3}$

5. a. $25t^4 - 100t^3 - 6t^2 + 34t - 35$
b. $\frac{x^4 + 4x^3 + 18x^2 - 15}{(x^2 + 2x + 5)^2}$ **c.** $e^w(2 + w)$ **d.** $\frac{4}{(e^t + e^{-t})^2}$
e. $e^x\left(\ln x + \frac{1}{x}\right)$ **f.** $(1 + \ln t) + e^t(1 + t)$

6. a. $(2t - 5)e^{(t^2 - 5t)}$ **b.** $\frac{2x + 1}{x^2 + x + 1}$ **c.** $\frac{3x^2 - 1}{2x^{\frac{3}{2}}\sqrt{3x^2 + 1}}$
d. $3\left(2 + \frac{1}{t}\right)e^{(2t + \ln t)}$ **e.** $\frac{1}{r \ln a} + \frac{3}{r}$ **f.** $\frac{y - e^{x+y}}{e^{x+y} - x}$
g. $x(a^2 - x^2)^{-\frac{3}{2}}$ **h.** $\frac{2y}{2xy - x}$

7. $-\frac{3}{4}$

8. a. $2^r(1 + r \ln 2) - 2e^{2r}(r^2 + r)$ **b.** $\frac{2a + 3bw}{2\sqrt{a + bw}}$
c. $\frac{18}{(2 + 3t)^{\frac{1}{2}}(2 - 3t)^{\frac{3}{2}}}$ **d.** $e^x + 2e^{-x}$ **e.** $-\frac{b^2x}{a^2y}$
f. $-\frac{x(x + 2y)}{(x^2 + y^2)}$

9. $e^{\pi^2}(1 + 2\pi^2)x - y - 2\pi^3e^{\pi^2} = 0$

10. a. 1, 2 **b.** 1, 2, −2

11. $\frac{10(y^2 - 6xy - x^2)}{(y - 3x)^3}$

12. e

13. $x - y - 12 = 0$ or $x - y + 12 = 0$

14. $10x - y - 32 = 0$ and $2x - y - 8 = 0$

15. $6x - 2y - (2 \ln 2 + 2) = 0$

16. a. 7 m **b.** 8.5 m/s, 9.3 m/s **c.** 1.5 m/s^2, 0.4 m/s^2 **d.** 10 m/s

17. a. −1 mm/s **b.** 0 **c.** 2 mm/s^2

18. a. 112π mm^2/s **b.** 56π mm/s^2

19. $\frac{3\sqrt{3}}{2}$ m/s

20. a. $\frac{dv}{dt}$ is rate of increase of volume; $\frac{dr}{dt}$ is rate of increase of radius; $\frac{dh}{dt}$ is rate of increase of height **b.** $V = \frac{5\pi r^3}{12}$
c. $\frac{1}{9\pi}$ cm/min

21. $a = \frac{1}{k(1 + 2\ln v)}$

22. 14:13

23. a. $(-3, 91), (2, -34); \left(-\frac{1}{2}, 28\frac{1}{2}\right)$ **b.** $(0, 3.6); \left(-\frac{5}{\sqrt{3}}, 1\right)$, $\left(\frac{5}{\sqrt{3}}, 1\right)$ **c.** $\left(\frac{1}{\sqrt{e}}, -\frac{1}{2e}\right)\left(e^{-\frac{3}{2}}, -\frac{3e^{-3}}{2}\right)$ **d.** $\left(\frac{3}{2}, \frac{27e^{-3}}{8}\right)$; $(0, 0)$,
$\left(\frac{3 + \sqrt{3}}{2}, \frac{(3 + \sqrt{3})^3}{8}e^{-(3 + \sqrt{3})}\right)$,
$\left(\frac{3 - \sqrt{3}}{2}, \frac{(3\ 3\ \sqrt{3})^3}{8}e^{\ \sqrt{3} - 1}\right)$
e. $\left(-\sqrt{2}, -5\sqrt{2}e^{-\frac{1}{2}}\right), (\sqrt{2}, t\sqrt{2}e^{\frac{1}{2}}), (0, 0), \left(-\sqrt{6}, -5\sqrt{6}e^{-\frac{3}{2}}\right)$, $\left(\sqrt{6}, 5\sqrt{6}e^{-\frac{3}{2}}\right)$ **f.** $(1, 10e^{-1} + 2); (2, 20e^{-2} + 2)$

24. a. $x = -3, x = 3, y = 0; \left(0, -\frac{8}{9}\right)$ **b.** $x = -1, x = +1, y = 4x$; $(0, 0), (-\sqrt{3}, -6\sqrt{3}), (\sqrt{3}, 6\sqrt{3})$

26. 14 062.5 m^2

27. $r = 4.3$ cm, $h = 8.6$ cm

28. $r = 6.8$ cm, $h = 27.5$ cm

29. a. $h = 140 - 2x$ **b.** $V = 101\ 629.5$ cm^3; $x = 46.7$ cm, $h = 46.6$ cm

30. $x \doteq 4.1$

31. a. 4000 **b.** 8 **d.** 6

32. $f(x) = 2x^3 - 12x^2 + 18x - 15$

34.

	Absolute Maximum	Absolute Minimum
a.	82	2
b.	$9\frac{1}{3}$	2
c.	$\frac{e^4}{1 + e^4}$	$\frac{1}{2}$
d.	6.61	1

35. \$1140

36. $8x + y + 38 = 0$, $8x + 7y - 38 = 0$

38. −901 800 m^3/week

39. $f(x) = \frac{2}{9}x^3 + \frac{1}{3}x^2 - \frac{4}{3}x + \frac{7}{9}$

40. a. $x - 1\ 440\ 000 + 4y + 9 = 0$ **b.** $32x + 6y - 143 = 0$

APPENDIX A DERIVATIVES OF TRIGONOMETRIC FUNCTIONS

Review Exercise

1. a. $\frac{y}{r}$ **b.** $\frac{x}{r}$ **c.** $\frac{y}{x}$

2. a. 2π **b.** $\frac{\pi}{4}$ **c.** $-\frac{\pi}{2}$ **d.** $\frac{\pi}{6}$ **e.** $\frac{3\pi}{2}$ **f.** $-\frac{2\pi}{3}$ **g.** $\frac{5\pi}{4}$ **h.** $\frac{11\pi}{6}$

3. a. b **b.** $\frac{\text{b}}{\text{a}}$ **c.** a **d.** a **e.** b **f.** −b

4. a. $\cos\theta = -\frac{12}{13}$, $\tan\theta = -\frac{5}{12}$
b. $\sin\theta = -\frac{\sqrt{5}}{3}$, $\tan\theta = \frac{\sqrt{5}}{2}$
c. $\sin\theta = -\frac{2}{\sqrt{5}}$, $\cos\theta = \frac{1}{\sqrt{5}}$
d. $\cos\theta = 0$, $\tan\theta$ is undefined

5. a. per: π, amp: 1 **b.** per: 4π, amp: 2
c. per: 2, amp: 3 **d.** per: $\frac{\pi}{6}$, amp: $\frac{2}{7}$
e. per: 2π, amp: 5 **f.** per: π, amp: $\frac{3}{2}$

8. a. $\frac{\pi}{6}$ or $\frac{5\pi}{6}$ **b.** 0 or $\frac{\pi}{2}$ or $\frac{3\pi}{2}$ or 2π
c. 0 or $\frac{\pi}{2}$ or π or $\frac{3\pi}{2}$ or 2π **d.** $\frac{\pi}{2}$ or $\frac{7\pi}{6}$ or $\frac{11\pi}{6}$
e. $\frac{2\pi}{3}$ or $\frac{5\pi}{3}$ **f.** $\frac{\pi}{3}$ or $\frac{5\pi}{3}$

Exercise A1

2. a. $-\sin R$

3. a. $\frac{56}{65}$

5. c. $1 - 2\sin^2 A$

7. a. $\frac{\sqrt{3} - 1}{2\sqrt{2}}$ **b.** $\frac{\sqrt{3} - 1}{2\sqrt{2}}$ **c.** $\frac{1 - \sqrt{3}}{2\sqrt{2}}$ **d.** $\frac{-\sqrt{3} - 1}{2\sqrt{2}}$

8. a. $\frac{\sqrt{3}\cos x + \sin x}{2}$ **b.** $\frac{-\cos x - \sin x}{\sqrt{2}}$ **c.** $\frac{\cos x + \sin x}{\sqrt{2}}$
d. $-\sin x$

9. a. $\frac{-\sqrt{15} - 2\sqrt{2}}{12}$ **b.** $\frac{-2\sqrt{30} + 1}{12}$ **c.** $-\frac{7}{9}$ **d.** $\frac{-\sqrt{15}}{8}$

10. a. $\frac{3}{5}$ **b.** $\frac{4}{5}$

12. 2

13. 2

14. 2.65° and 5.2°

16. c. $\frac{2\tan A}{1 - \tan^2 A}$

Exercise A2

1. a. $2\cos 2x$ **b.** $2x - \sin x$ **c.** $-2\cos x \sin x$
d. $(3x^2 - 2)\cos(x^3 - 2x + 4)$ **e.** $8\sin(-4x)$ **f.** $\cos x - x\sin x$
g. $3\sec^2 3x$ **h.** $9\cos(3x + 2\pi)$ **i.** 0 **j.** $\frac{-1}{x^2}\cos\frac{1}{x}$
k. $-\frac{1}{2\sqrt{x}}\sin\sqrt{x}$ **l.** $6x^2\sin x + 2x^3\cos x - 3\cos x + 3x\sin x$
m. $2\cos 2x$ **n.** $\frac{-2x\sin 2x - \cos 2x}{x^2}$ **o.** $-2\cos 2x\sin(\sin 2x)$

p. $\frac{\cos x}{(1 + \cos x)^2}$ **q.** $6x^2 \sec^2 x^3 \tan x^3$ **r.** $2e^x \cos x$

2. a. $y - \frac{\sqrt{3}}{2} = \frac{1}{2}\left(x - \frac{\pi}{3}\right)$ **b.** $y - 1 = 2\left(x - \frac{\pi}{4}\right)$ **c.** $y = 2x$

d. $y = -3\left(x - \frac{\pi}{2}\right)$ **e.** $y + \frac{\sqrt{3}}{2} = -\left(x - \frac{\pi}{4}\right)$

3. a. $\frac{1}{\cos y}$ **b.** -1 **c.** $\frac{-2\sec^2 2x}{3 \sin 3y}$ **d.** $\frac{-y \sin(xy)}{1 + x \sin(xy)}$

e. $-\frac{\sin y + \sin(x + y)}{x \cos y + \sin(x + y)}$

5. $-\csc x \cot x$; $\sec x \tan x$; $-\csc^2 x$

6. a. $\lim_{x \to 0} \frac{\sin x}{x} = \frac{\pi}{180}$ **b.** $\frac{d}{dx} \sin x = \frac{\pi}{180} \cos x$

$\frac{d \cos x}{dx} = \frac{-\pi}{180} \sin x$

Exercise A3

1. $y = -\left(x - \frac{\pi}{2}\right)$

2. $y - \frac{5\pi}{6} = -\left(x - \frac{\pi}{3}\right)$

3. a. maximum $\sqrt{2}$; minimum $-\sqrt{2}$ **b.** maximum 2.26; minimum -5.14

4. $v = 80\pi \cos(10\pi t)$; $a = -800\pi^2 \sin(10\pi t)$

5. 5, 10, 20

6. $\frac{\pi}{3}$ rad

7. 4.5 m

8. $\frac{10\pi}{3}$ km/min

9. $\frac{3\sqrt{3}}{4}R^2$

10. 0.32 rad/s

11. 2.5 m

12. $\frac{\pi}{6}$ rad

APPENDIX B ANTIDERIVATIVES

Exercise B1

1. a. $2x + c$ **b.** $\frac{3}{2}x^2 - 4x + c$ **c.** $x^4 + \frac{1}{3}x^3 + c$ **d.** $2\ln x + c$

e. $\frac{3}{2}x^4 - \frac{2}{3}x^{\frac{3}{2}} + c$ **f.** $-\frac{1}{x} + \frac{1}{2x^2} - \frac{1}{3x^3} + c$ **g.** $-\cos 2x + c$

h. $\frac{1}{2}e^{x^2} + c$ **i.** $\frac{2}{9}(x^3 + 1)^{\frac{3}{2}} + c$ **j.** $\ln(\sin x) + c$

2. a. $4x^3 - 12x^2 + x + 5$ **b.** $2x^{\frac{3}{2}} + \cos x - 1$ **c.** $4x - \frac{3}{4}x^{\frac{4}{3}} - 8$

d. $\frac{1}{3}e^{3x} - \frac{1}{2}\ln x + \frac{2}{3}e^3$ **e.** $\frac{2}{3}\sqrt{x^3 + 1} + \frac{10}{3}$ **f.** $\frac{\sin^5 x}{5} - 1$

3. 10 051

4. 200 min

5. a. $10e^{-0.002t} - 9$ cm **b.** 0.94 cm **c.** 52.7 years

6. 8.75 m

Exercise B2

1. a. $\frac{8}{3}t^{\frac{3}{2}} + 4$ **b.** $3e^t - \ln(t + 1) - 1$ **c.** $2\left(t + \frac{1}{t + 1}\right) - 2$

d. $\frac{3}{\pi}\sin(\pi t) - 1$

2. a. $-2t + 10$, $-t^2 + 10t$

b. $\frac{2}{9}(3t + 1)^{\frac{3}{2}} - \frac{2}{9}$, $\frac{4}{135}(3t + 1)^{\frac{5}{2}} - \frac{2}{9}t - \frac{4}{135}$

c. $\sin t - \cos t + 4$, $-\cos t - \sin t + 4t + 1$

d. $-\frac{2}{1 + 2t} + 2$, $-\ln(1 + 2t) + 2t + 8$

3. a. $-4.905t^2 + 450$ **b.** 9.58 s **c.** -94 m/s

4. a. $-4.905t^2 - 10t + 450$ **b.** 8.6 s **c.** -94.4 m/s

5. a. $-4.905t^2 + 10t + 450$ **b.** 10.7 s **c.** -95 m/s

6. 1.3 m/s^2

7. 1.1 m/s^2

8. 32 m/s

9. 127 m

Exercise B3

1. a. $200e^{2 \cdot 2t}$ **b.** 416 **c.** 1.8 h

2. a. $150\,000e^{0.026t}$ **b.** 327 221

3. a. $200e^{-0.005t}$ **b.** 156 mg **c.** 738 days

4. 20 years

5. 14 296

6. $\frac{25000}{1 + 0.25e^{\frac{1}{3}\ln\left(\frac{6}{11}\right)t}}$

7. 9.5 min

8. 8 min

Index